HISTORY OF MANKIND
CULTURAL AND SCIENTIFIC DEVELOPMENT

VOLUME IV

THE FOUNDATIONS OF THE MODERN WORLD
1300–1775

PART TWO

LITERARY COMMUNICATION AND BELLES-LETTRES;
THE VISUAL ARTS AND MUSIC; SCIENCE AND TECH-
NOLOGY; TECHNOLOGY AND SOCIETY; EDUCATION

PUBLISHED FOR THE
INTERNATIONAL COMMISSION FOR A HISTORY OF THE
SCIENTIFIC AND CULTURAL DEVELOPMENT
OF MANKIND

BY

GEORGE ALLEN AND UNWIN LIMITED
LONDON

HISTORY OF MANKIND

CULTURAL AND SCIENTIFIC DEVELOPMENT

VOLUME IV

By **LOUIS GOTTSCHALK**
LOREN C. MacKINNEY and **EARL H. PRITCHARD**

THE FOUNDATIONS OF THE MODERN WORLD

PART TWO

LITERARY COMMUNICATION AND BELLES-LETTRES;
THE VISUAL ARTS AND MUSIC; SCIENCE AND TECHNOLOGY;
TECHNOLOGY AND SOCIETY; EDUCATION

FIRST PUBLISHED IN 1969

© UNESCO 1969

SBN 04 900009 8

---

*Prepared under the auspices and
with Financial Assistance of the
United Nations Educational, Scientific and
Cultural Organization*

Editorial Consultants

Professor Roland Mousnier (Sorbonne), with the collaboration
of Professors Georges Canguilhem (Sorbonne), André Chastel
(Sorbonne), Alphonse Dupront (Sorbonne), Olivier Lacombe
(Sorbonne), Pierre Le Gentil (Sorbonne), Raymond Picard
(Sorbonne), Raymond Polin (Sorbonne) and Bertrand Gille
(University of Clermont-Ferrand).

PRINTED IN GREAT BRITAIN
in 11-pt. Plantin type
BY UNWIN BROTHERS LIMITED
WOKING AND LONDON

CONTENTS

PART TWO

ILLUSTRATIONS

All illustrations are grouped together at the end of the book, following page 1136

Sculpture in Europe

Architecture in Europe

ILLUSTRATIONS IN LINE

All line drawings were executed especially for this work by Stella Robinson in collaboration with R. G. Hadlow.

MAP

ACKNOWLEDGEMENTS

Alinari, Florence
Archaeological Survey of India A S I
Archives de l'Assistance publique, Paris
Bayerisches Nationalmuseum Munich B N M
Berlin Staatlichen Museen B S M
Bibliothèque Nationale, Paris B N
Bildarchiv Foto-Marburg B F M
Central Office of Information in London B I
Cincinnati Art Museum, Cincinnati (Ohio)
Commission of the French Republic for Education, Science and
   Culture C E S C
Editions Robert Laffont, Paris
Freer Gallery of Art, Smithsonian Institution, Washington D.C.
Vladimir Fyman
Giraudon, Paris
Honolulu Academy of Arts, Honolulu, Hawaii
Indian National Commission for Cooperation with Unesco
Institute of History, Moscow
Instituto Nacional de Antropolgia e Historia, Mexico I N A H
Japanese National Commission for Unesco J C U
Paolo Koch
Guy S. Métraux G S M
Mexican Embassy, Paris M E P
Musée d'Art et d'Histoire, Geneva M A G
Musée du Louvre, Paris LOUVRE
Museum of the History of Science, Oxford
Museum für Kunsthandwerk, Frankfurt a.M. M K F
Museum für Völkerkunde und Vorgeschichte, Hamburg
National Gallery, London N G
National Palace Museum, Taipei, Taiwan
Oeffentliche Kunstsammlung Basel Ö K B
Josephine Powell
Roger-Viollet
Royal Museum of the History of Science, Leiden
   (Courtesy of Dr Maria Rooseboom)
Science Museum, London S M L
Seattle Museum, Seattle (Wash.)
Service de Documentation Photographique des Musées Nationaux
   S M N
Spanish National Commission for Unesco S C U
Swedish National Commission for Unesco
University of Minnesota Library, James Ford Bell Collection
   (Minn.)
Yale University Library, Map Collection, New Haven (Conn.)
   YALE

CHAPTER X

LITERARY COMMUNICATION AND BELLES-LETTRES (1300–1500)

MANUSCRIPTS, BOOKS, AND PRINTING

IN the period 1300–1775 literacy and literature, without becoming common possessions, became less exclusively than before the marks of upper-class status. The rise in the rate of book-collection helped to bring on this popularization of literature. The early libraries, to be sure, were generally restricted to clerical, royal, aristocratic, or university establishments. Yet the idea that reading matter should be easily accessible spread, particularly after printing made books cheaper. The growth of literature in the vernacular also increased the number who could and wished to read and therefore often influenced the choice of subject-matter of what was written.

The long-established techniques of producing books by script made great strides in Europe during the fourteenth and fifteenth centuries. Manuscript books were copied in small factories, as well as in monasteries, with improved materials (e.g. bleached and polished parchment and paper), more beautiful and compact (though somewhat less legible) scripts, elaborate coloured illustrations, and ornate bindings. More than one copy could be made by dictation from the manuscript to several scribes at once. Paper, made in Europe in the twelfth century, was common for literary purposes in the fifteenth.

Book collecting and library building gained impetus from the revival of interest in Classical manuscripts. Petrarch's description of his own inspired copying of a Cicero manuscript illustrates the personal zeal of an amateur bibliophile. Half a century later Niccolo de' Niccoli, no less zealous as a bibliophile and perhaps more effective as a collector, bankrupted himself by purchases of manuscripts in centres as far distant as Lübeck and Constantinople. More efficient collecting was carried on by rulers such as Cosimo de' Medici, who could make use of agents to arrange for purchases at home and abroad.[1]

Thus, one of the most famous libraries in the world came into being at Florence. Cosimo de' Medici took over the eight-hundred-volume library of the bankrupt Niccolo de' Niccoli and expanded it through additions by copying and purchase. Cosimo's forty-five professional copyists duplicated two hundred manuscripts in a period of less than two years. Lorenzo de' Medici added to the collection, sometimes giving to other collectors the privilege of copying in his library in return for the privilege of copying in theirs. He also purchased finished works through agents whom he sent far and wide. The Greek scholar Joannes Lascaris acquired for him two hundred such works from one of the monasteries at Mount Athos in Greece. Before Lorenzo died, he had collected well over a thousand books, almost half of them in Greek. Eventually housed in a splendid building planned by Michaelangelo, it now, with later accretions, constitutes the famous Laurentian Library, second only to the Vatican Library in the number and value of its manuscript treasures.

The Vatican Library itself had a similar history. Pope Nicholas V was its founder; Pope Sixtus IV enlarged it, increasing the collection from about a thousand to almost four thousand manuscript volumes. He also opened it to scholars for research. The Medici pope, Leo X, further augmented its holdings. These popes sent clerical agents throughout Europe to search for manuscripts. Church councils sometimes facilitated the task of manuscript collection. Poggio Bracciolini, a papal secretary at the Council of Constance, as a supplementary activity explored monastic libraries at St Gall, Fulda, and Cluny, uncovering neglected treatises of Cicero, Quintilian, Lucretius, and other Latin authors.

The excitement that such finds roused among humanists was equalled in the fifteenth-century quest for Greek manuscripts. Although many Greek manuscripts had been carried from Constantinople to Italy by plunderers during the Crusades, Greek literature received little attention from Italians until late in the fourteenth century. The teaching of Greek in Florence and other Italian centres by the Byzantine émigré Chrysoloras (d. 1415) inspired a revival of interest in Hellenic letters. The great flight of manuscripts from Constantinople to the West began almost a half century before the fall of that city to the Turks. Guarino da Verona stayed in Constantinople for five years (1403–09), returning to Italy with over fifty manuscripts, both Greek and Latin. More profitable still were the trips of Giovanni Aurispa (1413–23), who acquired about two hundred and fifty manuscripts, most of them Greek classics. The Council of Florence (1439) brought five hundred Greeks to Italy, where they charmed western scholars with their Classical knowledge. Plethon and Bessarion (see Chapter VI) contributed to the zeal of western collectors; Bessarion willed his own collection of some five hundred manuscripts in Greek and half as many in Latin to the Republic of Venice, where it now comprises an important section of the Library of San Marco. The conquering Turks continued to sell Greek manuscripts to westerners, although in dwindling quantity and importance.

These collectors and libraries were but outstanding examples of a widespread vogue in the fourteenth and fifteenth centuries. Princes such as Galeazzo Visconti and Federigo of Urbino, scholars such as Petrarch, Salutati, and Bembo, and businessmen such as Vespasiano and Chigi were assiduous collectors; and some of their libraries, now incorporated in larger ones, still carry their names (e.g. the Urbino and Chigi collections at the

Vatican). The private collection of Federigo of Urbino is especially note-worthy for the beauty of its manuscripts, their miniatures, and their bindings, since its owner, scorning the new-fangled technique of making books by machinery (i.e. the printing press), lavished money and learning on his beloved hand-made manuscripts. Before 1500 great manuscript collections were to be found (in addition to those in the monasteries) also in the collegiate libraries of Oxford University and the library (some fifty thousand titles) of King Matthias Corvinus of Hungary.

Impressive libraries, monastic, royal, and private, grew up in other advanced civilizations. In India, the Delhi sultans possessed large libraries, and so did the rulers of the Islamic and Hindu states. Many of the Indian monastic foundations assembled palm leaf manuscripts, and wealthy Brahman families made their own collections of manuscripts, sacred and profane. The rulers of south-east Asia also maintained libraries, and the monasteries of Tibet housed considerable numbers of books. In China the great imperial collections of the Ming dynasty included, in addition to printed books and rare manuscripts, immense files of historical records. The Imperial Library catalogue of 1441 listed 7,350 titles of 42,600 volumes (*ts'e*); the great manu-script Yung-lo encyclopedia alone consisted of 11,095 volumes. One author described 14,907 volumes that he considered to be the most important works produced during the Ming period. Among the most famous private libraries before 1500 was the Wan-chüan-lou of the Fang family. Korean kings and monasteries, too, brought together large libraries, and in Japan the Ashikaga College, near Kamakura, and the Kanazawa, patronized by the Hōjō family, reached sizeable proportions.

The 'Burgherization' of Learning in Europe

The uneven history of printing in the Far East will be sketched below in connection with Far Eastern belles-lettres. An ancient technique in China, printing became known also in the West, though only for pictorial block-prints, long before it triumphed over the handicraft of book making. The 'invention' of printing in the West required more than the use of movable type. For the human scribe to be replaced by a machine other factors were needed as well, such as better ink (since scribal ink was not satisfactory for mechanical purposes) and a durable but cheap substitute for parchment. These needs were slowly satisfied during the first half of the fifteenth century. An early result was an increase in the number of picture books with block prints, on which a few words of explanatory text were carved. Efforts were doubtless made to substitute movable for carved type in the texts of these block prints, perhaps in order that the same picture might be used to illus-trate several texts. Experiments with movable type and one-sheet prints seem to have been tried some time before Johann Gutenberg. Finally, about mid-century the thirty-six and forty-two line Bibles of Gutenberg and Schöffer-Fust were produced.

The new technique was developed by Gutenberg and others in the vicinity of Mainz and was so successful that it spread rapidly. German artisans introduced it into neighbouring countries, and within the half-century that constitutes the 'cradle' (*incunabula*) era of the industry (1450–1500) presses were set up throughout western Europe. Several were established in Italy— at Subiaco in 1465, at Rome in 1467, at Venice in 1469, and at Florence in 1471. Printed books appeared in Bohemia in 1468, in Switzerland probably the same year, in France in 1470, in Spain in 1475, and in Poland about the same time. William Caxton, having learned to print in Cologne and having already printed some books at Bruges, founded a press at Westminster in 1476. Sweden and Portugal put up their first presses during the last two decades of the century. The famous printer Aldus Manutius was a late comer, starting his 'Aldine' press in Venice around 1495 (see Chapter XI).

'Democratization' of learning was not the immediate effect of printing, for illiteracy continued unabated and printed books were not cheap. The effect was, rather, the 'burgherization' of learning, especially humanistic learning. Greek and Latin classics, as well as theological works, turned out in numerous large editions, became widely procurable—particularly in Italy— at much lower prices than manuscript versions of the same works. Since the number of schools was increasing concomitantly (see Chapter XVI), the number of laymen with a fair store of Classical books and knowledge multiplied. The domination by universities over learning was lessened, because the scholarly world was no longer dependent upon the authority of the institution or the professor who commanded the only accessible copy of a text. As philological studies improved (see Chapter IX), printing made available a number of identical copies of the same collated and approved texts in different places at the same time.

With the introduction of printing the manufacture of books ceased to be exclusively a learned profession of writers and scribes for learned readers alone. The technical skill of the artisans who perfected and operated the printing press was now also necessary for the spread of scholarly and literary works. In the sixteenth century one of the printing centres was Switzerland, which Erasmus and the printers of Basel made for a time Europe's headquarters for scholarly publication. The leading printer of Basel was Joannes Froben, who not only published in numerous copies the books that Erasmus wrote or edited but also employed Hans Holbein to make them and other books more attractive by illustrating them. With the rise of Protestantism, printing was brought still more prominently into the service of literary communication. Not only did Protestant scholars, continuing the work of Gerson, Cusa, Valla, Reuchlin, Erasmus, Ximines, and other Catholic scholars, openly challenge the manuscript tradition of medieval theological scholarship but also public propaganda, whether Protestant or Catholic, became more effective with the printed word. The genteel humanist of the fifteenth century (like Federigo of Urbino) who lamented the passing of

Classical texts into vulgar hands was replaced both by the scholarly editor (like Erasmus) of printed texts for the amateur reader and by the zealous preacher (like Luther) of popular causes through broadsides and pamphlets.

Despite the nascent secular and middle-class attitudes and the new techniques, the clergy and religious preoccupation continued to dominate European literature for a long time. Theological and philosophical discussions persisted among university faculties both orally and in print, and authors produced literature of devotion in increasing amounts, especially in the north of Europe. As the theocratic unity of Christendom broke down, religious writings in the vernacular also increased. The statistics of the first half-century of printing bear convincing evidence of the strength of religion in the fifteenth century. Before the technique of movable type was developed, a majority of the books of block prints were illustrated religious books. About forty-five per cent of the known *incunabula* are also religious books. Even in Italy, where the brilliance of Renaissance heterodoxy tends to blind one's eyes to the fundamental strength of orthodox religion, almost half of the printed books were orthodox. The Bible led the list, but sermon literature, *exempla* (moral anecdotes such as those in the *Gesta Romanorum*), and other, less intellectual types of religious writing were also prevalent. Theology in a sense was still queen of the sciences even if her power was being challenged.

With the expansion of the media of communication, conservative elements, and especially the church, began to feel the need of controls. A formal censorship of printed matter did not come, however, until the Catholic Counter-Reformation set up an *Index Librorum Prohibitorum* (see Chapter IV), which was later supplemented by civil censorship. The early history of printing will be treated in the next chapter. Printing, to be sure, had little direct effect on the illiterate, but its influence seeped down at second hand by means of sermons, lawsuits, meetings, plays, conversations, and other oral media. The height of its influence, however, was far in the future. Before 1500 it was the upper middle-class, the scholars, and the aristocracy who chiefly profited from—or were led astray by—the printed book. The clergy, too, profited but perhaps not enough to compensate for the advantage afforded to the reformers of the sixteenth century by the printed word as a propaganda weapon.

THE DEVELOPMENT OF VERNACULAR LANGUAGES

In many parts of the world during the fourteenth and fifteenth centuries the languages of the common people were slowly replacing the languages of the learned in literary usage. Centuries before 1300 Latin, for example, had ceased to be the common language of western Europe, but it continued to be the language of religion, learning, and literature. Therefore scholars often were bilingual. In England, in fact, they might well be tri-lingual, since Norman–French as the court language had been added to Latin and Anglo–

Saxon after the Norman Conquest. Medieval Latin was an artificial medium laboriously acquired by a minority of the population. Whatever its advantages in the world of scholarship, it well might have been a hindrance to creative writing. Although in western Europe Latin continued for centuries as the medium for the formal exposition of theology, philosophy, law, science, and other branches of learning (considered in other parts of this volume), the greatest creations of poetry, drama, and fiction were in the vernaculars, i.e. English, French, German, Italian, Spanish, etc. Only toward the end of the seventeenth century did the respective vernaculars distinctly begin to displace Latin as the medium for learned works.

In Europe literary creativity in the vernacular tongues synchronized with the emergence of nationalism. With some exceptions such as chronicles or translations from the Latin, no great literature was written down in the vernacular before the twelfth and thirteen centuries, when *chansons de geste*, Icelandic sagas, folklore, and several other kinds of oral literature were put into writing. Some of the most notable of these early written vernacular creations were poetical—e.g. the *Chanson de Roland*, the *Poema del Cid*, and the *Roman de la Rose*.[2] By 1300 the merit and popularity of these works seemed to hold the promise of a vigorous future for the folk languages of several regions.

Before 1300 the vernaculars had developed upon a local rather than a national scale. In the nation that we now think of as France, the *langue d'oil* prevailed in the north, and the *langue d'oc* (a form of Provençal) in the south. In some parts of Spain, Catalan was spoken, in others Castilian, and in still others Portuguese. In the Italies, Lombard Italian, Tuscan Italian, and Sicilian Provençal dominated literary work in north, centre, and south respectively. Different kinds of German were spoken in various parts of central Europe, and different kinds of Russian in various parts of what is now Russia.

Standardization along modern national lines came by various means, largely of a political nature. The north French language expanded during the Crusading era, and the Albigensian Crusade of the thirteenth century paved the way for its triumph over the *langue d'oc*. In England the dialect of London eventually became literary English, thanks to the prestige of the metropolis and of Chaucer, who spoke of the English king as 'lord of this language'. In France, England, Spain, and Russia political centralization helped to bring ultimate victory to the dialect of the ruling dynasties, and London English, Parisian French, Castilian Spanish, and Muscovite Russian became the national tongues. The failure of the German-speaking peoples to form an effective union helps to account for the survival of several different kinds of spoken German to this day—*Plattdeutsch*, Swiss, Austrian, and Alsatian, for example—along with *Hochdeutsch*.

Although Italy was no less disunited than Germany, Tuscan Italian became standard through other than political pressures alone. In the thirteenth century at the Sicilian court of Emperor Frederick II, an Italianized Provençal poetry flourished, but its influence was superseded by the Tuscan dialect of Dante and his contemporaries. Dante not only argued the merits of vernacular Italian in his *De Vulgari Eloquentia* (written in Latin for scholars to read); he also proved its worth in his own poems, notably the *Divina Commedia*. Petrarch's and Boccaccio's earlier writings gave additional prestige to the *stil nuovo*, but by their enthusiasm for classical Latin they unwittingly contributed to a century-long eclipse of the vernacular. Late in the fifteenth century Lorenzo de Medici's Florentine court reversed the trend by a revival of the neglected Italian vernacular, and Tuscan Italian became the language of Tasso, Ariosto, and other great poets of the sixteenth century. The triumph of Dante's dialect was not solely attributable, however, to politics, or to the influence of the Medici court. It achieved world fame because of its own intrinsic musicality also and the preference it won in consequence from several literary geniuses.

The triumphant European languages of modern times have taken over elements of the submerged dialects and have absorbed elements of more distant languages as well. English, basically Germanic, is larded with Latin, Greek, Hebrew, Arabic, and Norman French elements, to say nothing of English dialectal curiosities. Russian, basically Old Bulgarian, adapted many words from Greek, Tatar, Germanic, and western European languages. On the other hand, some ancient languages refused to die. Nourished by church ritual, they remained a subject of study and a part of the living tradition. Old Church Slavonic has persisted in Orthodox Russian liturgy. 'Pure' Greek (*koine*) survived in the churches of the Greek Orthodox, Hebrew in the synagogues, Czech and Gaelic in their respective minority religions and traditions—all to become in later centuries a factor in the national revival of the people who spoke or once had spoken them. Medieval Latin persisted in Catholic church services, learned discourse, and official documents, adopting and Latinizing vernacular expressions wherever desirable.

The fifteenth and sixteenth centuries nevertheless saw the gradual decline of medieval Latin as a literary medium. Though scholars continued to use it for their learned works, creative works in Latin were rarely comparable to the great Latin hymns, poems, or prose of the earlier centuries. The national vernaculars and humanistic classicism combined with the declining prestige of the universal church to diminish the importance of medieval Latin as the *langue de culture* of Europe. Philological studies, inspired by the revival of classical Greek and Latin, were presented in classical rather than medieval Latin. The linguistic diatribes of Petrarch, Valla, and Erasmus suggest something of the prevailing scholarly antipathy to medieval church Latin.

The most general characteristic of the European languages during the formative centuries under consideration was an increasing consciousness of the vernacular tongues as media of communication. With varying degrees of intensity language became a subject of scholarly study and rational or aesthetic concern. Scholars became increasingly aware of the nature of speech, the regularities among languages, and the peculiarities within them. For a variety of reasons, the separate tongues were unified and standardized. Models arose everywhere by which to judge and evaluate usage. Among the literate irregular and arbitrary uses of words, phrases, spelling, and syntax were reduced, and many linguistic areas were subjected to more systematic, often more rational, and in any case more accepted standards. Dialects and local linguistic idiosyncracies began to give way to the standardized languages, though provincial differences persisted and still persist, particularly in spoken usage. Dictionaries and grammars—the Castilian grammar, dictionary, and orthography of Antonio de Lebrija (better known as Antonius Nebrissensis, 1444–1522) are perhaps the earliest examples—made feasible communication by the educated in a more uniform style. In a few instances a specific authority was set up and formally approved as the arbiter of correct forms of oral expression (see below). Scholars began to discover relationships among groups of languages and were able to relate the peculiarities of a people's language to their general culture. Towards the end of our period various thinkers, such as Vico and Herder, came to consider a people's language as a product and an expression of their collective soul.

Conscious reflection upon language and its manipulation was furthered by a number of factors. Political centralization tended to reinforce standardization. Growing nationalist sentiment (in part itself an outgrowth of greater awareness of the separateness of national languages) helped to focus attention upon the desirability of a common means of expression for those who shared one national feeling over against those who shared another. Intensified contacts with strange peoples and different cultures led to increasing reflection about the resemblances and analogies as well as the contrasts in their languages. In Europe, concern with language, already fashionable among the humanists with their love for 'more humane letters' and graceful communication, was to grow as the religious conflicts of the sixteenth and seventeenth centuries made polemic eloquence and style desirable for mass persuasion.

The force with which the vernacular languages asserted themselves in the West helped to augment the rate of breakdown in the ideal of a great united Christian empire. As the dream of universal empire and church faded and the realities of dynastic statism grew more vivid, the need for common media of communication within local groups became more distinctly felt than the need for a universal language, and languages began to become national. Religious reformers preferred to cultivate the means of communication by which a smaller group might reach all its own members rather than the *langue de culture* of a far-reaching church. Certain serious, though limited, efforts were made to preserve the two leading church languages of Europe, but the general emphasis was not reversed. In western Europe only a decreasing, if still large, minority of intellectuals, clerics, officials, and international-minded aristocrats consciously cultivated Latin. In the east European lands, though Church Slavonic prevailed for a long time as the cultured form of expression, in Russia, the 'third Rome', language reform led to an attack upon it and was finally successful during the late-seventeenth and eighteenth centuries.

However divided it might be into religious sects, Europe from the Russian steppes to the Atlantic shores remained mostly Christian, and the basic book of Christianity continued to be of key importance in its literary development. The Bible probably was the most commonly read (and therefore translated) book even before the outbreak of the Protestant revolt. When Anne, the daughter of Emperor Charles IV, went to England to become King Richard's queen (1383), she took with her a Bible translated into Bohemian and German as well as Latin. Religious protest groups such as the Lollards and the Hussites held the heretic view that the Bible should be accessible in the ordinary language to the ordinary believer without the mediating influence of the clergy. At approximately the same time, the humanists, in their desire to go back to the earliest sources, rendered the attack on the revered Vulgate easier by drawing attention to the Greek and Hebrew originals, as well as to Jerome's mistranslations. Religious and scholarly considerations thus reinforced the rising tide of nationalism in prompting the translation of the Bible into the vernacular tongues.

As Queen Anne's Bible showed, translations appeared even before the Reformation in the areas where these movements were strong. Manuscript versions existed or had existed not only in German and Czech but also in English, Dutch, French, and Spanish, and printed translations were published in German as early as 1466, Italian in 1471, Spanish in 1478, French in 1487, and Bohemian in 1488. The English, one of the first of the great nations of the West to become a nation-state and to begin a national literature, were one of the first to translate the Bible into their vernacular, although they were one of the last to print it. Late in the fourteenth century Wycliffe—or his followers or, possibly, some predecessor—translated the Bible into English, but Tyndall's printed edition did not appear for a century and a half (1526). Translations of the Bible helped to assure the victory of Europe's vernaculars over the international languages preferred by the churches (see Chapter XI).

The Standard Languages of Asia and Africa

The Islamic cultural life of the time can be divided between two geographical zones. The first was the one in which Arabic continued to predominate as the literary tongue; it extended from Iraq and Arabia west to the Atlantic and kept penetrating ever farther south into Africa. The second, and perhaps more populous, zone was the one in which Persian had become the predominant Muslim literary language; it extended from the Balkans east to Turkestan and China and south to southern India. In so far as the Islamic world had a common language, it was Arabic, but Persian was culturally more important in a large area.

In the zone where Arabic was predominant the most productive intellectual centres from the fourteenth to the eighteenth centuries were in Syria and Egypt, but all the other areas took some part in intellectual activity. Among these areas now came to be included the countries of the western Sudan, under Maghribī influence. The learned Sudanese generally used Arabic, and their histories were composed on the model of earlier Arabic works. Gradually Hausa, which they learned to write with Arabic characters, came to be a popular vehicle of Islam in the Sudan. Another area of Arabic influence was Muslim east Africa, which was linked to southern Arabia and western India. Since in both southern Arabia and western India different Shī'ite and other sects maintained a communal importance scarcely known elsewhere, Muslim east Africa became a mosaic of mutually exclusive sectarian groupings. Eventually Swahili (essentially a Bantu language with Arabic admixtures) became a vehicle for carrying the Islamic outlook widely in these parts.

The zone in which the Persian language had become the main vehicle of culture showed far more cultural vitality than the Arabic zone. By the end of the Mongol period, Persian was dominant not only in Iran and Turkestan but also in all those lands to the east and west into which the Turks had brought Islam by conquest. Gradually the areas that did not speak Persian began to develop their own literary languages, based on Persian literary and cultural ideals but with national differentiations—among others, western or Ottoman Turkish, Turki of Turkestan, (somewhat later) the highly cultivated Urdu in India, and finally Malay. For a long time, however, the Persian literature of Iran continued to serve as their literary model, even when Persian itself was not written. Persian religious and philological scholarship, meanwhile, proceeded in a lively manner.

In India, although Sanskrit remained the dominant language of learning, its great days were over, especially in the fields of belles lettres and devotional literature. Its position had never been firmly established in the south, where Tamil and other Dravidian tongues had long produced eminent literature and Sanskrit had always been regarded as an intruder confined to the learned. In the north, where Sanskrit and the vernaculars were more closely related because both had a common ancestor in Indo–Aryan, its dominance as a court language was destroyed by the Islamic conquests, and Persian replaced it at the Muslim courts. Under Islamic rule, and often with the patronage of Muslim courts, many of the north Indian nationalities in this period began to develop their vernaculars as vehicles of an increasingly impressive literary output—usually deeply rooted, however, in the Sanskrit tradition.

In China the use of ideographic characters made it possible for the non-conversational literary language to serve as a type of *langue de culture*. Whether pronounced according to the Peking or the Canton dialect, the written characters had the same meaning and so provided a unified written medium. Among the spoken or colloquial languages that of north, west, and central China was by far predominant. It was spoken by most of the officials and was called Kuan-hua (Mandarin), the speech of officials. It was the basic medium of communication among the learned, and its Peking dialect became the standard. The other main spoken media were the Wu group of southern Kiangsu and Chekiang, Fukienese, and Cantonese. The spoken languages differed somewhat from the written language in vocabulary, idiom, and grammar, and the rise of colloquial literature during our period meant that authors were writing in the spoken idiom rather than in the compressed literary idiom, though their writings might be read with Pekingese, Wu, Fukienese, or Cantonese pronunciation. Because of its wider as well as official use, the Kuan-hua was made the national tongue (Kuo-yü) in the twentieth century and the standard for both written and spoken communication.

POETRY, DRAMA, AND STORY IN EUROPE

In western Europe's literary development the fourteenth and, still more, the fifteenth century are sometimes called (with perhaps too much emphasis) 'the Great Transition'. While medieval forms and subjects persisted and no writer departed completely from earlier models, the period marked the gradual dimming of Latin prosody, troubadour conventions, and courtly traditions in secular letters. As they faded, there grew in brilliance a less imitative style, which had its roots in humbler soil and newer themes that were more individualistic and real. Yet borrowings from the medieval romances, imitations of the *Roman de la Rose*, and other evidences of inspiration from older sources continued (nor have they ever vanished); not even the intensely personal poetry of François Villon (1431–63) was wholly free of medieval influences.[3] Moreover, with the partial eclipse of the learned languages came a more vital use of the vernaculars.

In Italian vernacular poetry, the troubadours' Provençal gave way to the *stil nuovo*. The greatest names in this movement were Dante and Petrarch. It would be tedious and should be unnecessary to list their numerous works (some of which, besides, are mentioned in other connections in this book) as testimony or illustration of contemporary developments. Although Dante's subject matter and spirit were still essentially medieval, his use of rhyme—*terza rima*, sonnets, and other newer rhythmic techniques—whether in the lyrics of the *Vita Nuova* or in the cantos of the *Divina Commedia*, constituted a signal milestone in the evolution of modern poetry. It is commonly agreed that no one ever has excelled Dante's skill with tercets, but his successor Petrarch, before turning his literary talents to the imitating of Cicero's style, perfected the sonnet, first used as a written device by Italian poets of the thirteenth century. The easy grace of Petrarch's verses concerning Laura reflected poetry's liberation from the formalism of the troubadours. With similar informality Boccaccio, before his conversion to Latin classicism, set new standards for Italian prose and poetry in his glorification of Fiammetta and profane love, and his *Filostrato*, a poem in *ottava rima*, tells the tale of

Cressida's infidelity to Troilus with a sensitivity that contrasts with the crassness in some of the prose tales in his fascinating *Decameron*.

No comparable contributions were made to Italian poetic style until the revival of the vernacular late in the fifteenth century. In northern Italy, Boiardo in *Orlando Innamorato* and Ariosto in *Orlando Furioso* reinterpreted the Roland epics in a new Charlemagne cycle suited to the sophisticated tastes of despot courts. Ariosto told how Roland, spurned by his beloved in favour of a pagan paladin, was driven mad by jealousy but recovered through the heroic efforts of his friend Astolpho. Although Ariosto's forty thousand lines of polished verse narrated fantastic adventures, they beautifully and understandingly depicted human frailties and feelings. While also a pastoral poet and a literary critic, Tasso (1544–95) is best known as the last of the brilliant epic poets of the period. His *Gerusalemme liberata* portrayed in Virgilian style the capture of Jerusalem from the Muslims in the First Crusade. Doubtless it was also a reminder of the imminent dangers of his own day, for, like the epic of Boiardo and of Ariosto, Tasso's did not hesitate to make bold allusions to contemporary affairs; against the double menace of Turkish infidels and Protestant heretics, the new Jerusalem needed a champion, and Tasso looked for one in a reformed Catholic Church.

Though no other countries of Europe during these two centuries were so often blessed with genius as Italy, the evolution of poetry in some of them did not lag far behind. In Spain the vernacular had acquired a literary respectability through the efforts of Alfonso X, the Wise, king of Castile and Leon (1252–84), who encouraged translations, compilations, and original composition in Castilian. The first significant Castilian poetry came, however, only in the next century—from the pen of Juan Ruiz. The candour and earthiness of his versified autobiography, *Libro de buen amor*, was nowise inhibited by the circumstance that he was the archpriest of Hita and, probably because of irregularities of thought or conduct, was in jail when he finished it (1343). Intending it to be recited by jongleurs rather than to be read, he borrowed from the *fabliaux*, Aesop, and other predecessors with deftness, painted original characters with vividness, and used metrical innovations with variety and skill.

In the next century or so, as the Moors receded and the Christians advanced and as Spain's cities became the foci of Spanish culture, the place once held by the courtly troubadours was taken by the popular *romanceros*, singers of *romances*—i.e. ballads about El Cid and other medieval heroes of war, love, and religion—in verses of eight trochaic feet chanted to instrumental accompaniment. Usually oral but sometimes contemporaneously written down, these lyric-epics were first collected by Martin Nuncio in 1550 in the *Cancionero de romances* and then in other anthologies (also called *romanceros*). They became veritable storehouses of lengthy epic ballads; some of the *romances* not only were later adapted for the Spanish stage but provided writers in other languages also with favourite themes. In the fifteenth century, too, more aristocratic Spanish poets, frequently under the influence of Dante, Petrarch, and other Italian models, wrote sedate, didactic, lengthy poems. Ausias March (1397–1459) broke with the troubadour tradition in his *Cants d'amor*, abandoning Provençal for Castilian and depicting women as real flesh-and-blood creatures. The *Coplas por la muerte de su padre* of Jorge Manrique (1440?–79), inspired by a genuine filial grief, added to Spanish letters enduring stanzas of elegiac melancholy and resignation that recall his contemporary Villon's best lines in a similar mood. The Marqués de Santillana (1398–1458) composed not only imitative sonnets but *canciones* (lyrics) of Spanish style and theme as well and speculated in prose on the nature of poetry.

In the north the older medieval trends, relatively undisturbed by Classical revivals, carried on through the fourteenth and fifteenth centuries. Perhaps the best-known English poems of the fourteenth century were *Piers Plowman* and *The Pearl*. Both were in alliterative verse; both were allegories; both used the convention of the dream or vision introduced a century earlier by the *Roman de la rose* as a literary device; both were anonymous, and their authorship has long been a matter of learned speculation. A background of orthodox Christian ideology softened their main themes (worldly injustice in the one and death in the other) by holding forth the promise of an ultimate reward in Heaven. In *The Pearl* the vision of Paradise is suggestive of that in the *Divine Comedy*. Several other poems are sometimes attributed to the author of *The Pearl*, among them *Sir Gawain and the Green Knight*, an especially eloquent version of a tale narrating the trial of one of King Arthur's knights for courage and integrity. Poems like these, along with numerous popular ballads and folksongs in the vernacular, evidenced the enlivening of the native English tongue as a literary medium. The lower levels of English society sought self-expression in ballads about Robin Hood, legends about King Arthur, and other folklore generally characterized by a marked persistence of medieval religious views and chivalric moral standards.

English vernacular poetry attained the high level of the better poems in the Romance languages through the genius of Geoffrey Chaucer (1340?–1400), but only late in the fourteenth century. Having travelled in France and Italy, he was influenced by French poets such as Guillaume de Machaut (c. 1300–77) and Italians such as Dante and Boccaccio. His borrowing from Boccaccio for his *Troilus and Criseyde* was easy to detect, but while Boccaccio was primarily concerned with narrative, Chaucer's longer poem portrayed character and emotion as well. Chaucer delineated his subjects as victims of war and of other trying circumstances rather than as the embodiments of good and evil that Shakespeare was later to make of them. In the *Canterbury Tales*, somewhat reminiscent of Boccaccio's prose stories, Chaucer produced a work of poetical brilliance, picturesque vigour, and psychological insight. Although he made a translation of Boethius' *De Consolatione Philosophiae*, his perceptive candour in dealing with contemporary events revealed that his humane spirit was not exclusively a product or a concomitant of his humanistic classicism. Without essential reliance upon Antiquity for theme or inspiration, he acquired and gave expression to an understanding of human behaviour and feelings that compares favourably with that of contemporary Italian men of letters. He used metrical forms like the heroic couplet and the rhyme-royal with previously unmatched skill.

The French poet Machaut, who had some influence upon Chaucer, was also a composer of music (see Chapter XII). He was one of a flourishing school of lyricists, among whom the chronicler Froissart and Eustache Deschamps were likewise outstanding members. These men and their confrères wrote literally thousands of lyrics, long and short, making the *ballade* a common form among French poetasters. They gave good standing as well to several other metrical designs; in fact Deschamps wrote an *ars poetica*, a manual for aspiring versifiers—*L'art de dictier et de fere chançons, balades, virelais et rondeaulx*—presenting poetry almost as a handmaiden to song.[4]

Charles d'Orléans (1391–1465) perhaps best marks the transition in France from the troubadours to Villon. It was no mere coincidence that this poet was a great noble, a duke, who was captured in the Battle of Agincourt, which revealed the obsolescence of the armoured knight, and spent many years in England as a prisoner of war. His poems are polished examples of the pure, precise, allegorical, and conventional style of the passing chivalric tradition. Nor was it mere coincidence that François Villon, hardly a chivalric figure, should have been one of his courtly circle at Blois.

Villon (1413–c. 1463) ranks with the greatest poetic geniuses of his day in Italy and England. He revealed, a half-century later than Chaucer, a compassion for human weakness somewhat like that of the English poet. The humane touch in Villon's poetry was apparently derived from the emotional impact of a none too wholesome career upon a sensitive mind rather than from imitation of earlier models. His known literary output was decidedly limited. It consisted of both ballads in underworld slang (known as *le jargon*) and some exquisitely polished lyrics. With tenderness alternating with irony, his poems depicted slices of his own life, the Parisian types he knew, and his preoccupation with death and the vanity of human existence.

German poetry was now also undergoing a transition from the troubadour tradition of courtly love. The German troubadours had been known as *Minnesingers*. With the decline of chivalry the *Minnesang* tended to speak less of love and more of politics and became the *Spruch*; and as the court gave way to the city, the *Spruchdichter* became the *Meistersinger*. Whereas the *Minnesinger* had generally been a lesser nobleman, the *Meistersinger* was usually a city artisan. Organized in clubs resembling guilds, the *Meistersinger* prepared his masterpiece somewhat as the candidate for a mastership in any other craft might prepare his. He went to school, entered competitions, and passed from rank to rank upon the approval of recognized judges, who judged not only the merit of his lyric but also that of the song he had composed to go with it. Naturally this sort of contest required rules, and the rules, set forth in a rules book called a *Tabulatur*, did not encourage originality. The Meistersingers made song-writing a common practice in cities where German was spoken. Their schools flourished not only in Germany (Mainz and Frankfurt, for instance) but also in Alsace (Strasbourg), Bohemia (Prague), and Switzerland (Zürich). The outstanding Meistersinger was a well beloved cobbler of Nuremberg, Hans Sachs (1494–1576), whose poems were numbered in the thousand, the best known one being in praise of Luther, *The Nightingale of Wittenberg*.

Among the more learned, German poetry, like German prose, tended toward the serious aspects of human experience, notably religion. Public stupidity and morals were the major theme of Sebastian Brant's satire, *Das Narrenschiff* (*Ship of Fools*) (*c.* 1500), in which various categories of fools sail under other fools to fools' land. In literary quality and in originality of thought, for all its popularity and its influence on future satires of fools, it was inferior to the best of contemporary poetry in other regions of western Europe; its illustrations made up for the humour it lacked.

Didactic poetry still flourished in Germany and other northern regions. It usually lacked lightness of touch, often making use, like the contemporary morality play, of allegory and the 'dream' technique for public moralizing. Such poems portrayed the tribulations of human existence, the injustices of society, and the struggles between 'Vice' and 'Virtue' in the spiritual life of the Christian pilgrim, sometimes in a heavy satirical vein. Chaucer once referred to his English friend John Gower, who wrote didactic poems of this sort in English, Norman French, and Latin, as 'the moral Gower'.

In Bohemia the use of the Czech vernacular was closely associated with the Hussite movement and its offshoot, the Union of the Bohemian Brethren. Huss preached to the people in a simple vernacular that set a standard for contemporary Czech prose, which Chelčický and the Brethren continued to cultivate. The hymns of the people were likewise in the vernacular. Some Czech scholars were, like Huss, fluent in both Latin and Czech. Latin survived, however, chiefly as the language of the oppressors—the aristocracy, the Roman clergy, and the imperial officialdom.

Russian literature did not prosper under the Tatar yoke, but the decline of the Golden Horde brought a new folk spirit. In the fourteenth century trained performers recited the *bylíni*, heroic tales, borrowed sometimes from eastern sources, usually about the largely legendary knights-errant who shared the adventures of the sainted Prince Vladimir of Kiev. Composed in a set literary form—unrhymed, intoned verse—the *bylíni* were not yet permanently recorded. In the fifteenth century, many poems celebrated Dimitri's victory on the plain of Kulikovo in 1380 (see Chapter I); the *Zadónshchina* by the priest Sophonia of Ryazan was the richest of them in poetic imagery.

Bulgarian and Serbian monks, fleeing from the conquering Turks, brought legends and other stories of great saints with them, and a fairy-tale fiction grew up about lay heroes' struggles against dragons, devils, and other forces of evil. In the *Legend of Prince Peter of Murom and the Maiden Fevronia*, the wise Fevronia, a peasant woman, is the heroine. These folk legends, though prose, often attained a lofty lyrical quality.

In short, Europe of the fourteenth and fifteenth centuries elaborated several forms of poetry (lyric, epic, narrative, didactic) in the vernacular or near-vernacular. Lyrics were perhaps the most popular in western Europe, for gentlemen composed ballades and sonnets on the spur of the moment; Meistersingers frequently and studiously composed *Bare*, or poems to be set to music; and the spirit, if not the quality, of the thirteenth-century Latin hymn continued in popular sacred songs in the vernacular. Epic ran lyric a close second in popularity by reason of the eminence of the Italian epicists. Ballads and other types of folk poems were still common but were yielding to the verse of the professed rhymster and lyricist.

In addition, the epigram, anthologized by the Greeks and, since Roman times, a medium of folk expression in pithy sayings on tombstones, became a formal poetic device. The Greek Anthology, a collection of short, printed poems of Hellenic origin, had been preserved (sometimes mutilated) by various collectors during the Middle Ages. The last such collection was that of Maximus Planudes in 1320. Joannes Lascaris published the Planudean Anthology in 1494, transforming the epigram, a succinct poem with a well-turned ending, into a respectable poetic form (see Chapter XI). In the fifteenth century, too, Santillana collected the proverbs (*refranes*) of the Spanish folk, and Erasmus's *Adagia* (first edited in 1500) culled thousands of quotable proverbs from Classical sources.

Since Goliards, Minnesingers, and troubadours had already shown the way, Western poetry's trend toward earthy and secular themes continued steady, especially in Italy, where the obvious contrast between Dante's *Divine Comedy* and Ariosto's *Orlando Furioso* provides a pat measure of the trend. Piety and chivalry gave way often to sensuous love and coarse adventure; the Christian legend yielded on occasion to pagan, historical, and contemporary themes; and allegory was sometimes fortified by introspection. In Italian poetry the influence of the despot's court was especially noticeable, not only in the sympathetic portrayal of aristocratic and romantic scenes but also in the generally sincere glorification of not always glorious rulers, sometimes accentuated by the revived interest of Italian intellectuals in Vergil, Horace, and other poets who had glorified the Roman emperors. For all this secular tide, however, the religious spirit of the age did not abate in its poetry, particularly in the north. Even in the sometimes far from pious stories of Chaucer's *Canterbury Tales*, contrasting markedly with the piety of *Piers Plowman* and *The Pearl*, the narrators were pilgrims to a martyr's shrine; and one of Villon's most beautiful poems—rowdy, thief, and murderer though he was—was his prayer to the Virgin 'composed on his mother's request'.

The Rise of Secular Drama

Drama, too, continued to be dominated by religion, though it had moved from the altar to the town square. The theatre had been one of the crowning achievements of Classical civilization, but the glamour of the stage had grown dim during the Middle Ages. It had not only run afoul of the general aversion to pagan thought but had in particular suffered from the incompatibility of some of the essential elements of Classical drama, such as the unmitigated tragedy of death and the inexorable decree of fate, with the Christian view of life. Popular church spectacles had taken the place of the theatre, having developed in connection with the celebration of holy days such as Christmas, Carnival, Passion Week, Easter, Corpus Christi, All Saints' Day, and All Souls' Day; and mystery or miracle plays (sometimes distinguished as dealing respectively with Biblical and post-Biblical subjects) had also become familiar. The Resurrection drama evolved from simple Eastertide dialogues at the altar in the ninth century into the action plays of the fourteenth: characters like the three Marys, the angels, the apostles, and Jesus (represented by the priest) moved down the nave of the church and about the chancel, using 'stage props' such as Mary's 'alabaster box of precious ointment'; they ended with a chorus chanting the *Te Deum*. In similar fashion the Nativity was dramatized at Christmastide with living shepherds, angels, and magi, a puppet Christ-child in a manger, and a guiding star pulled along a wire.

Gradually the religious drama moved outside the church edifice, and, as it did so, laymen took charge, the vernacular displaced Latin, and action became freer and more diversified. Mystery and miracle plays continued to portray Adam and Eve, the Last Judgment (with a 'horrid mouth of Hell'), episodes from the life of Jesus, and miracles of the saints, but under secular influences buffoonery and obscenity invaded the stage so that, as early as the thirteenth century, puritanical bishops forbade Christians to take part in or even to attend some performances. In England the 'Towneley Plays' (or 'the Wakefield Mysteries') reflected this trend toward humour and vivacity; in fact, their anonymous author was a virtual pioneer in the comic drama.[5]

Then came the morality plays, of which *Everyman* is the best-known example. *Everyman* probably was Dutch in origin, but it was widely adapted for other peoples. It portrays the death of Everyman, who, summoned before 'the Fader of Heven', finds that of all his earthly companions—Beauty, Knowledge, Goods, Good Deeds, Strength, Fellowship, Kindred, and similar abstractions—only Good Deeds will accompany him. Despite the secular trends of the day and despite the growing number of laity among playwrights and performers, until late in the fifteenth century religious subjects predominated in the drama, as in painting. They were presented, however, in an increasingly secular fashion.

The rise of secular drama can be traced most clearly in Italy. Travelling dramatic companies gradually developed the *commedia dell'arte all' improvviso*, the more or less improvised plays of the professional actors' guilds. These actors presented farcical scenarios of everyday life in a satirical vein, with stock characters like Harlequin, Scaramouch, and Pierrot in stock situations speaking usually stock speeches but adding impromptu lines *ad lib*. The *commedia dell'arte* was immensely popular until the eighteenth century and has left its imprint on ballet, circus, and drama. In similar fashion, public festivals, with elaborate processions and simple festival poems, evoked enthusiastic approval from all classes. The Italian cities of the Renaissance gave to the ancient Roman *panem et circenses* a new form—the public 'carnival' celebration. For the Florentine Mardi Gras a Lorenzo de' Medici might compose verses and a Leonardo da Vinci might prepare magnificent mechanical displays of floats. During the Renaissance the medieval tournament also took on a refined and expanded form, more or less resembling rehearsed drama. (Pl. 60a, b, c.)

If the tableaux and the *trionfi* of a carnival float were not true drama, a more truly dramatic effect was produced as a result of revived Classical influences. Politian, one of the most brilliant Classical scholars of his day (1454–94) was also a good dramatic stylist, and his *Tournament* (*Giostra*) dazzled the Medici with its descriptions of the mythological garden of love, of Venus rising from the foam, and of other scenes (subsequently painted by Botticelli) that seem to have been acted out on occasion. His *Orfeo*, retelling the myth of Orpheus and Eurydice, was actually intended as a play and, with a musical accompaniment, was presented on the stage in 1471. It marks the liberation of Italian drama from both medieval liturgy and Latin classicism.

Before 1500, even though Seneca's influence (see Chapter XI) was becoming more pronounced, Classical tragedy did not yet appeal to Italian tastes. The revived comedies of Terence and Plautus were more palatable, and thus more important in the evolution of Italian drama, especially when they were done in Italian translation. Machiavelli's humorously risqué *Mandragola* illustrates the type of theatre that won public acclaim from all classes. It tells the story of a young wife's seduction, in which her mother and her husband connive and which only the gullible wife resists, and she but half-heartedly. Completely secular, unburdened with formal classicism, it reflected the extreme of the Renaissance swing away from medievalism. Coming at a time when the moral tone among both aristocracy and populace was far from puritanical, it set for Italian dramatic subject-matter for a long time a hardly edifying standard.

In other regions of Europe the farcical and the burlesque were not considered the highest type of dramatic production. In the north, religious plays sometimes were humorous without losing their moral fervour. In Spain, Nativity, Passion, and Resurrection remained the dominant themes, whether performed under lay or ecclesiastical auspices. A conspicuous exception to the general rule came in the reign of Ferdinand and Isabella with the *Tragi-comedia de Calisto y Melibea*, generally known, after the old bawd who is one of its leading characters, as *La Celestina*. It is a dialogue in twenty-one acts, which tell a story of seduction somewhat like that of *Mandragola* and of frustrated young love somewhat like that of *Romeo and Juliet*. At least part of it was the work of a Spanish Jew named Fernando de Rojas. Although it was apparently never performed, its individualistic treatment of already typical roles had a decided influence on the subsequent development of secular drama and fiction not only in Spain but, translated into several other languages, elsewhere as well. On the whole, however, Europe's dramatic maturity still lay in the future.

The Rise of the Prose Narrative

Before 1300 story-tellers seldom told their stories in writing unless they wrote them in verse. Prose was usually devoted to learned purposes. It was little used as an art form for the expression of aesthetic impulses or as a medium of entertainment. Somewhere either at the end of the thirteenth century or, more likely, in the fourteenth appeared a collection in *media latinitas* of anecdotes and miscellaneous material inappropriately labelled *Gesta Romanorum*. Actually it was a sort of compilation (author unknown) intended to help preachers to point a moral or adorn a sermon. Since it borrowed widely, from outside as well as inside Christendom, it became a treasure house from which later authors were to borrow material for their works in the vernacular. Chaucer and Shakespeare were among these borrowers. The book was enormously popular and was issued in numerous editions, each somewhat revised by variant anecdotes.

One aspect of the development of Western prose, which we have already considered, presented a paradox. It was the humanistic effort to achieve stylistic perfection in the use of Latin by imitating the style of Classical antiquity. This earnest effort, perhaps worthy of success, was nonetheless doomed to failure. After a century of valiant and sometimes astonishingly good attempts, the effort to expound thought in a style and a language that were essentially foreign succumbed to the superior flexibility of the mother tongues as media of self-expression.

Vernacular prose reached a high level in the realm of fiction. A partly imaginative hero-literature survived from the Middle Ages in the *Acta Sanctorum*, which now, however, were more thoroughly authenticated and took on the qualities of biography (see Chapter IX). A more creative prose literature flourished in certain vernacular religious writings of the fourteenth and fifteenth centuries. *The Dance of Death* (*Danse Macabre*), originally a set of vividly imaginative dialogues in German[6] between Death and his retinue, gave rise to poems and plays (not to mention pictures) on an elevated as well as a popular level, particularly in the fourteenth century, when the Black Death made dying familiar.

Indicative of the rising tide of secularism was the *novella*, or prose story, often taken from medieval *fabliaux*. The medieval *fabliau* was generally a tale cut to the popular taste and told by strolling *jongleurs*, who entertained, wherever they could find an audience, with tricks and narratives, sometimes derived from Muslim and other Eastern sources. Good *jongleurs* flourished still in the fourteenth century. Their purpose was entertainment rather than edification. In the fifteenth century a collection of the French *jongleurs'* tales, nearly all distinguished by a certain boisterous humour, appeared under the title *Cent Nouvelles Nouvelles*, frequently attributed to a writer of *novella* named Antoine de La Sale. In his *Decameron*, Boccaccio re-clothed some of the *jongleurs' fabliaux* in vernacular prose. Chaucer preferred verse for his *Canterbury Tales*, but the work attributed to Marguerite d'Angoulême, the *Heptameron* (1558), was avowedly an imitation of Boccaccio's *Decameron* even in its title—seven days of story-telling in contrast to the ten of the *Decameron*, and hence 70 (actually 72) stories in contrast to 100. Fiction in prose comparable to Boccaccio's had to await the fuller development of the novel in the sixteenth century and after (see Chapter XI).[7]

Another distinguished prose work of this period is the full-length heroic tale, or 'romance'. In England Caxton published (1485) the *Morte d'Arthur*, a careful selection from the mass of romances in the Arthurian cycle, which he ascribed to Thomas Malory. Whether originally compiled or translated from the French by Malory, the book pieced together a running account of Arthur and the knights of the Round Table. Another full-length romance of the period was *Amadis de Gaula*. At least the final (fourth) book of this work is generally ascribed to the fifteenth-century Spanish writer Garcia Rodriguez de Montalvo. The work deals with the fantastic adventures of a legendary prince, who, though cast away at sea in his cradle, returned to rule in Gaul.

From such romances to the novel dealing at length with credible characters in a plausible setting was but a step—a step first taken in Spain in the fifteenth century in Jahanot Martorell's long, humorous, ribald adventure story entitled *Libre del valerós e estrenu cavaller Tirant lo Blanch* (Valencia, 1490). This work, pretending to be a translation from English but actually composed in Catalan, has been called 'the very first realistic novel', even though some of the hero's exploits may seem superhuman.[8]

Aristocrat, Bourgeois, and Commoner in Literature

Despite the decline of political, military, and economic feudalism, the literature of chivalry remained popular. Amadis of Gaul and Tirant lo Blanch enjoyed a vogue in Spain similar to that of Roland in Italy, and their adventures were among the stories of a dying chivalry that in the seventeenth century were to drive Don Quixote mad. French cycles of romances and epics were re-written and re-read through the West. The medieval *chansons de geste* were now matched by songs of valour, mixed with love and rollicking mischief—sometimes in a cynical, farcical, and humorous combination but not without appeal to the nobler aspects of the aristocratic tradition. In the realm of historiography (see Chapter VIII) heroic accounts were written, especially in France, for and sometimes by the nobility. Literacy was apparently increasing among the upper classes of the laity. In actual life and in the educational theories of Alberti, Castiglione, and other writers of the period (see Chapter XVI), women of the upper middle-class as well as of the aristocracy still enjoyed great consideration. Dante's Beatrice as the personification of theology in 1300 contrasts with Castiglione's spirited and knowledgeable lady of north-Italian court life two centuries later, but both ladies were gracious and respected ornaments of society. Chivalric gallantry was not yet dead.

In short, the literature dealing with the aristocracy changed in attitude only slowly. The slowness is all the more impressive in view of the increase in the number of works concerning the expanding urban life of the period. Villani's burgher approach to Italian history as contrasted with Froissart's aristocratic approach to French history reflects the priority of the emergence of urban interests in Italy. Soon etiquette books appeared, bearing witness to the social ambitions of the wealthy middle class nearly everywhere, and sober essays lectured the burghers on their civic responsibility. Alberti's *Trattato della cura della famiglia* (1431) is a revealing analysis of the social standards and domestic problems of the new rich in northern Italy, an eloquent plea for respect of parental authority combined with devotion to civic duty, but essayists elsewhere also emphasized civic virtue and social welfare (see Chapter XVI). In the Italian *scuola d'abaco* the techniques of business were the subject of specialized studies dealing with commercial arithmetic, money, and various other aspects of mercantile life. And the lighter but not necessarily carefree side of Italian town life among the privileged citizenry stood out vividly not only in Boccaccio's stories but also in the *Autobiography* of Benvenuto Cellini.

The literature of other countries likewise betrayed a mounting concern with the bourgeois virtues. In the north too the rising bourgeoisie showed awareness of the obligations that went with economic success. The papers published in part as *The Paston Letters*, recording the dealings of a pushing family of Norfolk landowners and lawyers in the troubled times of the War of the Roses, provide ample testimony of the middle-class Englishman's literacy, his litigious knowledge of the law, and his loyalty to family. A nascent bourgeois patriotism is manifest in the Tver merchant Nikitin's *Journey beyond the Three Seas* (see Chapter VIII). Though they did not always seem to realize it, the literature by and about townspeople of the fifteenth century shows them caught up in the incipient waves of the bourgeois future.

In this period workingmen were few in the towns, but in the country they were so many that everywhere they formed a vast majority of the total

v*

population. Yet they occupied a minor and passive place in literature. Being generally illiterate, the rural population rarely produced formal works of prose or poetry. In the things written by the clergy, theirs was the role of the humble workers who sweat to support the fighters and the prayers, their military and spiritual protectors. In aristocratic literature the peasant and the city worker alike usually were represented as, and may well have been in fact, stupid and beastly, despised and oppressed, fit only to serve their betters.

Yet occasionally in imaginative literature, though certainly less often than among the political writers (see Chapters VIII and IX), a voice was raised in favour of social justice for the peasant. A William Langland (if he was indeed the author of *Piers Plowman*) might now and then appear to express for them as well as for himself the indignation of the oppressed poor. And Piers Plowman's protests were unmistakable even if mild compared with the rebellious spirit of the Wycliffites. François Villon spoke, in a way, for the proletarian poor, but he was not only exceptional, he was suspect. The *jongleur* often constituted himself a friend of the poor, but he too was likely to be a scamp. True proletarian and peasant protests remained largely unwritten. Folk poetry and ballad, the dramas performed in churchyard and market place, and mouth-to-mouth protests were perhaps the truest sources and reflections of the thought of the common man, but of these we have only faint evidence and few survivals. While social injustice is often their theme (witness the Robin Hood ballads), they do not reveal a steady or strong consciousness of class.9

POETRY, STORY, AND FORMAL PROSE IN ISLAM

In Islam, as in Europe, one of the most important general literary developments of the period was the rise of vernacular literature. The development of the Islamic vernacular differed, however, in two regards from the European experience: the classical Islamic languages, Arabic and Persian, did not deteriorate, and Islam did not become more secular-minded as vernacularization went on.

Since Islamic cultural life had come by 1300 to be divided more or less sharply into two geographical zones, the intellectual and cultural life, and therefore the development of the languages, of the two zones can to a certain degree be characterized separately. In Arabia, the Fertile Crescent, Egypt, North Africa, and the Sudanese lands, Arabic continued to predominate as the literary tongue even where it was not the spoken language; Cairo was the intellectual capital of this zone, though there were lesser centres, as in south Arabia and in Spain. East of the Arabic zone, Persian became the standard literary language among Muslims, and with it went a whole tradition of literary and artistic taste; the seats of cultural life in this zone were legion, especially in Iran.

Nevertheless, the division between Iranic and Arabic civilization was never complete. For instance, it was a Persian of the fourteenth century, Fairūz-ābādī, who composed the nearly definitive Arabic dictionary, the Qāmūs. In an area like Malaysia, both Arabic and Persian influences were prevalent. Arabic was used for certain religious purposes throughout the Dār al-Islām, and in these matters the authors of one zone were read in the other; the Islamic world presented by the *Thousand and One Nights* is one world. At the same time, the Persian zone undoubtedly contained the larger number of Muslims, and the tendency of Persian ways to affect Iraq, Egypt, and the rest of the Arabic zone was very old. The Persian zone was also by and large the more culturally creative.

Many lines of activity, however, took the same turn in both zones. This period (the great controversies having subsided) produced definitive compendia and textbooks of orthodox religious and legal scholarship, which crystallized the points of view accepted by 1500 into statements at once unambiguous and easy of access. Various secondary problems were traced out in the same fields—problems which had escaped the attention of earlier scholars—either in the form of little monographs or of commentaries on earlier writings.

Poetry was the most distinguished medium of literary expression in the Islamic culture of the day. The Arabic zone fell completely behind in this field, for Arabic poetry, though abundant, failed to achieve much novelty or distinction, at least after the fourteenth century. Persian poetry, which had already seen a period of unsurpassed greatness, continued to flourish, and its tradition was now internationalized in many parts of far-flung Islam. To Arabic forms such as the *qaṣīda* (the desert-inspired panegyric ode) and the *ghazal* (love lyric) had been added such Persian forms as the *mathnawī* (historical or romantic epic). In Iran the fourteenth century is that of Ḥāfiz of Shīrāz, greatest of all Persian lyric poets. He combined musical grace and technical perfection with an unsurpassed subtlety of esthetic insight in his half-mystical, half-mundane *ghazals*. His nobility of mind was exceptional among the poets. Devoted to the town of Shīrāz, which his verses amply praised, he refused all temptations to seek preferment elsewhere. Contemporary with him was a numerous constellation of talented poets—satirists, lyricists, panegyrists, and mystics. Unlike Ḥāfiz they wandered among the many shifting courts of war-torn Iran, seeking princely favour, yet often remaining in relative obscurity in their own time. The practice of writing poetry in Persian was now established outside Iran also. An excellent exponent of this practice was Amīr Khusrav (d. 1324 or 1325) of Delhi, who was the fountainhead of a notable Indian school (see below).

Within Iran in this century the tendency became almost universal for a degree of mysticism to pervade every kind of poetry. Awḥadī inculcated a mystical morality, and Ibn-i Yamīn, using especially the form of *muqaṭṭa'āt* (fragments), produced ethico-philosophical verse also mystically tinged. With Khwājū, author of romantic-mystical *mathnawīs*, and Salmān of Sāwa, a panegyrist noted for subtle verbal conceits, the Persian poetic tradition became more delicately nuanced. Non-mystical attitudes were represented by the satirist 'Ubayd-i Zākānī, who could also write good eulogies, and the parodist Abū-Isḥāq, who sang of material things like foods. More typically, at the end of the fourteenth century Maghribī wrote pure praises of unity in the Divine, while Kātibī wrote panegyrics at mutually hostile courts till he eventually retired as a Ṣūfī.

The religious trend continued in the fifteenth century. Early in that century there flourished (among others) Ni'mat-Allāh, founder of an influential *ṭariqa*, who was famous for his apocalyptic prophecies, which he alternated with more conventional mystical verse, and Qāsim al-Anwār, who was associated with the Ṣafawiyya order. The foremost poet of the century was Jāmī (1414–92). He wrote not only fine *ghazals* but also a septet of speculative and allegorical *mathnawīs*, the most celebrated of which told the story of the love of Joseph and Zulaykhā (Potiphar's wife), a major theme of Muslim parable. He also wrote good prose, producing not only mystical treatises but serious studies in literary history. The mystical monism embodying a concept of divine unity contemporaneously held by one school of Persian thought (see Chapter VI) was most prominently presented in the works of Jāmī in Iran and several other poets of his persuasion. Jāmī set forth his commentaries on mystical texts in verse as well as in prose. Even 'Abd al-Karim al-Jīlī, who was the most systematic expositor of this persuasion, thought of himself also as a poet.

Appropriately enough, the internationalization of the Persian poetic tradition was carried out under the aegis of Ṣūfism, but poetry came to be an expression of the regional cultures at least as much as of international Ṣūfism. In Iran itself the golden age had ended. Though poets continued to produce sweet and stately poems in profusion, none could match the giants of the past; some of the greatest of contemporary Persian poets were more appreciated in India and Turkey than at home (and indeed many of them went to live at the Mogul court). In northern India the main vehicle of Islamic verse long continued to be Persian, but in the Deccan by the sixteenth century a Ṣūfī poetry thrived in Urdu, the common language of Muslims in northern and central India. (We shall deal with belles-lettres in India below and in Chapter XI.) In the Ottoman Empire Turkish was most cultivated, for there Arabic, though dialects of it were spoken in much of the empire, played a distinctly secondary role in cultivated life, being treated almost as a dead classical tongue.

Outside the great empires new Islamic literary languages also sprang up. On the east African coast Swahili, which had been developed as the language of the Muslim Bantu, came to possess a sophisticated poetic tradition which could rival Arabic within the region. At the other end of the Indian Ocean a Malay literature eventually grew up under the influence of Persian. It consisted in large part of renderings from Persian and Urdu, but it also took over much from the earlier Malaysian heritage, particularly in poetic forms, only partly Persianized. All of these regional literatures—Arabic, Persian, Turkish (in three forms), Urdu, Swahili, Malay—as well as some lesser Muslim languages which began to be cultivated in this period, used the Arabic alphabet, were infiltrated with Arabic and (in most cases) Persian words, and treated traditional Arabic and Persian themes in their poetry. But of the literature then being produced, Persian alone had an audience among most of the other Muslim language-groups, and even it was little read in the Arabic zone except so far as Turkish rule gave it currency.

Turkish poetry began to develop as early as the fourteenth century, but only in the fifteenth century did it attain mastery, although still essentially modelled on the Persian. Three forms of Turkish emerged—Chaghatai, Azerbaijan, and Ottoman Turkish. Newā'ī (c. 1440–1501), who also wrote and—having a high political position—richly patronized Persian poetry, made of the Chaghatai Turkish of Turkestan a standard language, which was to be used for poetry in the sixteenth century by many even in the Ottoman Empire as well as in Turkestan. Chaghatai Turkish was the vehicle of a prose masterpiece likewise—the memoirs of Bābur, ancestor of the Mogul rulers of India. On the other hand, Fuzūlī of Baghdad (see Chapter XI), who has been called the greatest Turkish poet of all time, was in the sixteenth century to do his best work in the Turkish of Azerbaijan. Moreover, many Ḥurūfī poets—followers of a mystical and esoteric Shī'ite sect of the fifteenth century, especially widespread in the Ottoman domains—used the western or Ottoman form of the language. Nesīmī, killed as a heretic at the beginning of that century, was the ablest of them. Shaykhī and other Persianizing poets of the fifteenth century firmly established this form of Turkish. Subsequently, in the sixteenth century (see Chapter XI), Ottoman Turkish literature was to become the most important of the three.

Arabic poetry, on the other hand, though abundant, failed to achieve much novelty or distinction after the fourteenth century. The old patterns of the qaṣīda and the verbally clever lyric or satire were still repeated, sometimes gracefully but usually with preciosity. As the quality of Arabic poetry declined, Persian poetry improved, although by the seventeenth century both had to yield precedence to Turkish poetry.

Prose as a Medium of Islamic Literature

In the Arab countries the telling or prose stories was a common practice. Story-tellers collected Greek, Indian, Persian, and Arabic tales, and several such collections, often in vernacularized Arabic, had been available in writing for many centuries. One of them, put in final form only around the fourteenth century in Egypt or Syria had a vogue also in the West. This was the *Thousand*

and One Nights, which in the eighteenth century became in translation, first in French and then in other languages, part of the Western literary heritage, too. The device used to effect unity is a single narrator who tells one story each night to her husband, the sultan, in order to keep him distracted from his vow to execute her at daybreak, until he eventually revokes his vow. European merchants and *jongleurs* brought back some of these tales from the Levant, and the oriental tales in Boccaccio and Chaucer probably are borrowed from them.[10] They also seem to have migrated eastward.

As in Europe, prose was not considered in the Muslim countries so appropriate a medium for creative imagination as poetry, and hence prose storytelling was not regarded as one of the major arts. Prose was reserved there, as in the West, rather for history, science, philosophy, and books of travel. Some of the most beautiful pieces of Islamic prose were in Persian, the products of the poet Jāmī. In the *Spring Garden* (1487), part of which was verse, he produced a book-size treatise on ethics illustrated with parables and fables.

In the fourteenth and fifteenth centuries the significant work done in systematizing the information and insight of the past on an encyclopedic level sometimes was in its own way seriously creative. The Egyptian Suyūṭī, in thus bringing together the religious and historical learning of Islam, imposed his own personality on the closely-knit result. Far more important than any other Arabic figure of all this period was Ibn-Khaldūn. In a long work that served as introduction to his historical studies, he made use of the encyclopedic approach—mobilizing the resources both of philosophy and of religious learning—to develop the trenchant analysis of the dynamics of history that we have already encountered (Chapter VIII) and will encounter again (Chapter XIII). He recognized his own time as a time of decline. His new departure was not followed up in the Arabic zone, and truly creative scholarship on a broad scale hardly existed there after Ibn-Khaldūn. A figure like Sha'rānī, a mystical thinker of the sixteenth century who brought a warm personal touch to the older patterns, was exceptional.

In the zone where Persian literary influence prevailed, prose became increasingly afflicted, from the end of Mongol times, with the cultivation of a resplendent but often inappropriate ornateness. Occasional writers preserved a simple style, as did the poet Jāmī in his biographies, but more often desire for an impressive form was allowed to outweigh the need for clarity of matter. This tendency was eventually carried even further perhaps in Turkish and Urdu than in the imitated Persian. In the field of history the masterful fair-mindedness and directness of speech of Rashīd al-Dīn Faḍl-Allāh (see Chapter VIII) set high standards in his vast world history but was less imitated than the elegance of his contemporary Waṣṣāf, who, though he gave much pertinent information, smothered it in skilfully florid verbiage. The many subsequent writers of history and biography in Iran rarely met the standards of either of these masters.

BELLES-LETTRES IN INDIA, SOUTHEAST ASIA, AND SOME NEIGHBOURING LANDS

Like several other regions considered above or below, during this period India and southeast Asia developed a vernacular literature. In India, various Dravidian and Indo-European tongues emerged to challenge the dominance of Sanskrit as the language of literature and learning. In Burma, Siam, Cambodia, Malaya, and Java the vernaculars had to contend with Pali as well as Sanskrit. In India and southeast Asia, palm leaf provided a cheap writing material, but no system of ready reproduction of the written word had yet come into general use.

Sanskrit had begun to lose its vitality even before the Islamic conquest, and the destruction of seats of learning and monastic centres by the conquerors dealt it a debilitating blow from which it never recovered. Little original and creative work was still being done in the field of *kāvya* literature —i.e. the artificial and ornate verse and prose of the Sanskrit masterpieces. Sanskrit remained dominant, however, in (1) Vedic commentary; (2) theology, philosophy, and *dharma*; (3) grammar, lexicography, and metrics; (4) poetics and literary criticism; (5) politics; and (6) technical or scientific subjects. The growing sectarian character of the literature was evident in the later *purānas* and *tantras* and other theological and philosophical writings (see Chapter VI). Among the eminent traditionalists of the mid-fourteenth century were Mādhava (Vidyāranya), author of the famous manual (see Chapter VI) on the Hindu system of thought, and his brother Sāyana, a notable commentator on the Vedas, both of whom promoted the founding of the Vijayanagar Empire.

In the field of poetics and literary criticism several of the works composed in Sanskrit were still of a high order. Among the books on dramaturgy was Vidyānātha's *Pratāparudra-yashobhūshana* (c. 1300); it included a play which celebrated the glory of the author's patron, the king of Warangal, and which was intended to illustrate the rules of drama. Vishvanātha (fl. in Orissa c. 1350) in his *Sāhityadarpana* covered the whole field of poetics. Bhānudatta (also fourteenth century) in his *Rasamañjarī* and *Rasatarañginī* emphasized the importance of emotion and atmosphere in literature.

Sanskrit poetry itself declined more patently. No great Sanskrit epic was produced after the Islamic conquest. The best Sanskrit poetic achievements of the period were anthologies, but they contained only little of the work of contemporary writers, and that little showed an increasing tendency toward pedantry. Among the anthologies were several collections of lyric poetry— for example, in the fourteenth century, Shāngadhara's *Paddhati* (1363) and Sūrya's *Sūktiratnākara* and, in the fifteenth century, Vallabhadeva's *Subhāshitāvalī* (citing over 350 authors) and Shrīvara's work by the same name (citing more than 380). There were also several collections of Sanskrit gnomic and didactic verse.

Sanskrit prose was not without distinction during the period. The didactic beast fable (usually partly in verse) was represented by a fresh version of the *Pañchatantra*, which in various forms was well known and influential in Europe by 1500. Romantic tales were popular; Vidyāpati's *Purusapariksā* was an early fifteenth-century collection of such tales, and several Jaina collections appeared in the fourteenth and fifteenth centuries. Of the full-scale prose romance, the *Vemabhūpāla-carita* of Vāmana Bhatta Bāna (fl. in south India *c*. 1400) was probably the outstanding example. Drama (combining poetry with prose) was best represented by Gangādhar's *Gangādāsa Pratāpa Vilāsa*, which celebrated the struggle of a prince of Chāmpāner against Muhammed II of Gujarat.

Perhaps the leading literary figure of the period was the early fourteenth-century writer Venkatanātha (or Vedānta Deshika). In addition to writing significantly on religious and philosophical subjects (see Chapters V and VI), he was a distinguished belletrist. Among his Sanskrit works were a lyric in imitation of the illustrious Kālidāsa, an elaborate devotional poem, many shorter devotional and ritualistic poems, a drama in ten acts, and the *Yādavābhyudaya*, an epic on the life of Krishna. He also wrote poems in Tamil. His valiant efforts did not check the decline of Sanskrit in the area of imaginative literature. Nor did the rising vernaculars wholly fill the resulting gap, since they tended to concentrate on religious and devotional, if at times erotic, poetry and disregarded other literary forms as well as secular subjects in general.

Persian and Arabic Letters in India

As Sanskrit drooped in India, one of the two great classical languages of contemporary Islam, Persian, blossomed along with the vernaculars. The rulers of the Muslim kingdoms in north India were for the most part patrons of learning and literature and attracted to their courts numerous Persian and even Arabic writers. Several cities in north India became centres of Persian learning and produced a considerable body of literature in Persian. As indicated above, the most famous Persian-writing literary figure in India of the early-fourteenth century was Amīr Khusrav, who was head of the Imperial Library of Delhi and court poet of Sultan 'Alā-ud-dīn Khaljī (d. 1316). He was prolific in both poetry (reputedly composing Hindi verse also) and prose, writing on music and other subjects. Delhi under 'Alā-ud-dīn was said to be the envy of Baghdad, the rival of Cairo, and the equal of Constantinople because of the scholars and literary figures who came there. Sultan Muḥammad ibn Tughluq (ruled 1325–51) was himself a learned man who wrote with skill in Persian and Arabic, but the leading literary figure of his reign was Maulāna Muaiyyan-ud-dīn-'Umrānī. The long sultanate of Fīrūz Shāh (1351–88) was graced by several memorable literary figures. Sultan Sikandar Lodi (1489–1517) was likewise a poet and patron of literature.

Literature in the Vernaculars of India

The contemporary religious and political situation contributed to the rise of India's vernaculars. For one thing, they were intimately associated with the growth of the theistic religious sects. A sect leader could easily recognize that the use of a newer language would distinguish his sect from the older religious groupings and at the same time make it more readily intelligible to the masses. The Vishnu, Shiva, and Shākta sects exploited this opportunity in whatever tongue seemed best and thus contributed to its development, but Tantric Buddhism also made a contribution to Bengali, and Jainism to Kanarese. The Islamic conquest contributed to the rise of the vernaculars, since it stimulated the religious nationalism of *bhaktism*, furthered the decline of the centres of Sanskrit learning, and weakened the ruling class that used it. Some local Islamic rulers patronized vernacular writers, especially those who used Urdu (or Hindustani), a Persianized form of western Hindi, largely Persian in vocabulary and Hindi in grammar.

Some Persian literary forms slipped into the vernaculars, but Sanskrit left a wide, indelible mark on all of them. They borrowed from it not only words and literary forms but concepts, grammatical structures, and types of meter as well. Moreover, most of the religious ideas in the vernacular literature came from Sanskrit sources, since early sect leaders usually were Brahmans or learned men who had done their own studies in Sanskrit. Many other themes too were drawn from the vast Sanskrit storehouse. Furthermore, and during this period in particular, a considerable portion of vernacular belles-lettres consisted of translations or adaptations of Sanskrit epics and religious works. Most of the early vernacular writings were epic or lyrical poems, largely religiously inspired and, therefore, devotional or didactic in nature, though in small part also historical. The Sanskrit religious and moralistic lyric provided perhaps their richest element, but they tended also to borrow inferior and decadent elements from both Sanskrit and Persian—for example, stereotyped modes and ideas, outworn clichés, minutiae of anatomy, and other forms of eroticism, whether allegorical or not.[11]

In the Dravidian south, Tamil remained the favoured tongue. The Vijay-anagar emperors used Sanskrit and Telugu, but they did not discourage Tamil, and in the far south the Pandya kings gave it deliberate encourage-ment. Tamil authors were numerous, and they lengthened a productive tradition with a large number of philosophical works, commentaries, *purānas*, and *prabandhas* (grand epics). The new literature was, however, largely imitative and critical rather than creative. A 'somewhat arid scholasticism' pervaded the *maths* (monastic schools) and, as their influence spread in learning and education, infected the entire educational system.[12]

The Tamil authors of the period were mostly Shivaites or Vishnuites but sometimes Jains. Among the Shivaite writers was the fourteenth-century theologian Umāpati, who completed the Tamil canon (see Chapter III). He also wrote the *Koyirpurānum*, dealing with the legends of the Shiva shrine in Chidambaram. The late-fourteenth-century writer Svarūpānanda Dēshikar and his pupil Tattuvarāyar prepared two celebrated anthologies of religious and philosophic poetry. Probably the greatest Shivaite litterateur was Arunagirinātha. He was the author of the *Tiruppugal*, a popular fifteenth-century work containing over 1,360 lyrics in various meters; centring in the God Subrahmanya, it presented much of the sacred lore of Hinduism in vivid imagery. Among the Vishnuite authors were Pillai Lōkācārya and Vedānta Deshika, whose work has been noted several times. A Tamil version of the *Bhāgavatam* appeared at the very end of this period.

Of the more secular Tamil poets at least three should be singled out. Poyyāmoli wrote the *Tañjai-vānan-kōvai*, which dealt with the reign of a Pāndya king who died in 1308. Pugalēndi retold in the *Nalavenbā* (which appears to have been written about this time) the tragic story of Nala and Damayanti from the *Mahābhārata*. Probably the best Tamil secular poem of the period was the *Bharatam* of Villiputtūrar (*c.* 1400), which dealt with the theme of the *Mahābhārata* in 4,350 well-turned verses, with a profuse admixture of Sanskrit words.

Another of the Dravidian vernaculars was Kanarese (Kannada or Karnātaka). Kanarese literature was not so old as the Tamil, but it, too, had had a considerable period of development prior to 1300, generally dominated by Jaina productions. From 1300 to 1500, under the Vijayanagar Empire, the dominant literature in Kanarese was the religious writings of the Lingāyats or Vīrashaivites (see Chapter II), although Jaina works continued and Vishnuite works began to appear in that language.

A large part of the Vīrashaivite literature was in the form of simple prose tracts (called *vachanas*) or of *purānas* (mostly in six-line stanzas known as *shatpadī*). The *vachanas* expounded religious ideas, and the *purānas* dealt with religious reformers and devotees. Bhīmakavi's *Bāsava-purāna* (1369), a life of Bāsava, founder of the Lingāyats, became one of the sect's main texts and established the supremacy of the *shatpadī* verse-form among Vīrashaivite writers. Another famous life of Bāsava, the *Mahā-Bāsavarāja-charita*, was written by Singirāja about 1500. Chāmarasa's *Prabhulinga-līle*, a life of one of Bāsava's associates, so pleased Emperor Praudha Deva Rāya of Vijayanagar (1419–46) that he had it translated into Telugu and Tamil.

The Jaina works in Kanarese were for the most part *campūs* (that is, mingled poetry and prose), the verse varying in meter and showing marked literary skill. Other pieces generally were *purānas* dealing with the lives of great Jaina religious leaders or patrons. The Jaina writer Nāgarāja's *Punyāshrava* (*c.* 1331), containing fifty-two tales of puranic heroes, illustrated the duties of a householder. Other Jaina authors were Madhura (*c.* 1385), court poet of Harihara, whose *Dharmanātha-purāna* narrated the life of a Jaina patriarch, and Bhāskara, whose *Jīvandhara-charita* (1424) dealt with a pious prince who was a favourite subject among Jaina writers of this period.

The chief Vishnuite productions in Kanarese came in the late fifteenth century. They included Kumāra-Vyāsa's *Gadugina-Bhārata* (or *Karnāta Bhārata*), an incomplete version of the *Mahābhārata* (c. 1440), and Kumāra Vālmīki's *Torave Rāmāyana* (c. 1500). The longer Vishnuite poems employed the *shatpadī* form.

The Telugu (or Āndhra) vernacular, also a Dravidian tongue, was spoken in the Warangal area of eastern India reaching from Madras northward. Although it certainly had much earlier beginnings, its budding period extended from the late thirteenth century to about 1500 and was closely associated with Vīrashaivism. From the beginning it had a closer connection with Sanskrit than did Tamil or Kanarese, though its link with Kanarese is also very close. During this period the chief belletristic productions in Telugu were *purānas* and epic and lyric poems adapted from Sanskrit originals and Shivaistic devotional treatises of the puranic type. The Telugu version of the *Mahābhārata*, worked on since the eleventh century, was finally completed by Yerrāpragada (1280–1350), who also produced a version of the *Rāmāyana* (no longer extant) and of the *Harivamsha*, the epilogue to the *Mahābhārata*. In the late-thirteenth and early-fourteenth centuries two classic Telugu versions of the *Rāmāyana* were produced—the *Ranganātha Rāmāyana* of Kona Buddharāja and his son, and the *Bhāskara Rāmāyanam* (in *campū* form) of Hulakki Bhāskara and his son and disciples. Pālkuriki Somanātha, probably of this period, was a Lingāyat pamphleteer, who wrote not only in Telugu but also in Sanskrit and Kanarese. He composed a *Bāsava-purāna* and, in honour of Basava, the first Telugu *shataka*. (A *shataka* consists of a hundred lyric verses addressed to a God, saint, hero, or loved one.) In the early fifteenth century, Vemana, a philosophical poet, wrote *shatakas* that, because of their charm and simplicity, were translated into European and other languages.

The towering figure of Telugu literature in the fifteenth century was Shrīnātha (1365–1440), a staunch Shivaite, who shares with the thirteenth-century Tikkana the reputation of being the best poet in the language. He was patronized by various rajas and the ruler of Vijayanagar. His outstanding work was a majestic translation of Shrīharsha's great epic *Naishadha-carita*. His drama *Krīdābhirāmam*, giving a picture of urban society in Warangal, started a new genre in Telugu—a first-person narrative of the narrator's experiences addressed to a listener. His poem the *Haravilāsamu* contained four stories about Shiva. He may also have been the author of a work on poetics and of the earliest known historical heroic ballad in the literature. His brother-in-law, Bammera Potana (1400–75), in his youth wrote the *Bhōginīdandakam*, a love rhapsody on the king's concubine, the earliest work of this sort in Telugu, and he later translated the *Bhāgavatam* with such smooth diction, vivid description, and spiritual intensity that it became the most popular puranic epic in the Telugu language.

Malayalam is the vernacular of the Malabar coast area. It is a Dravidian dialect, closely related to Tamil, and its literature shows marked dependence on Tamil as well as Sanskrit. It was at first a medium of popular ballads and songs, of some longer metrical works, and of a certain type of ritualistic dance-drama. The earliest extant literary work in Malayalam is an anonymous poem of the fourteenth century telling about the transmission of a love message; it is still considered one of the most exquisite poems in the language. To enrich the ritual of the dance-drama, *campūs* and *prabandhas* were written under the influence of Sanskritists. The prose passages of the *campūs* often were satires upon contemporary usages and personalities. Perhaps the most famous Malayalam composer of this genre was Punam Nambudiri of the fifteenth century, whose masterpiece was the *Rāmāyana-campū*. In the next century Malamangalam Nambudiri in his *Naishadha-campū* pictured puranic scenes with an inspired touch, and the epic poet Cheruśśeri Nambudiri dealt with the life of Krishna in the best-known of his works, *Krishna-gāthā*. The Niranam poets of central Travancore, from the fifteenth century onward, sought to develop a Malayalam style free from Tamil and Sanskrit influences. Among this group were Mādhava Panikkār, author of a translation of the *Gītā*, and his grandson, Rāma Panikkār, author of a number of epics including the *Rāmāyanam*, a *Bhārata-gāthā*, and a *Bhāgavatam*.

In northern India the Indo–Aryan vernaculars won out, and of these the Hindi group was one of the oldest and most important. The several Hindi languages include not only Western and Eastern Hindi but also Rājasthānī and Biharī, and each of them, in turn, has its own local dialects. Western Hindi was the most important, Hindi can be traced back to the bards of the Rajputs, but it became a language of literary importance only in the late fourteenth and fifteenth centuries with the lyrics of the early *bhakti* poets of Vishnuism, who sang the praises of Rāma and Krishna. The most significant among the several bards of the fourteenth century was Sarang Dhar (see Chapter VIII). Many of the Hindi lyrics of the early *bhakti* poets have been preserved in the *Adi Granth* of the Sikhs and the *Bījak* of the Kabīrpanthīs, which include works of the eminent religious leaders of the fifteenth century such as Rāmānanda, Kabīr, and Nānak (see Chapter VIII). Most of these writers directed their paeans toward Rāma. Kabīr's numerous poems were unpolished, but his telling satire and epigrams and his fascinating rhythm, though rough, gave great power to his poetry. He did more than any other early writer except Mīrā Bāi (see Chapter III) to create and popularize Hindi literature. Nānak wrote in Punjabi as well as Hindi. Although he was not the equal of Kabīr, his pithy verses of praise and prayer (contained in the *Japjī*) were not without poetical merit.

The finest Hindu lyric poets of the period were Vidyāpati Thākur (beginning of the fifteenth century) and Mīrā Bāi. Vidyāpati wrote numerous short songs or sonnets (*pads*) on the love of Rādhā and Krishna in the Maithili dialect of Bihari and so is claimed by Bengali as well as Hindi scholars. He also wrote in Sanskrit, and although his songs about Rādhā's love for Krishna have been interpreted as allegories of the soul's love for God, fundamentally they continue the Sanskrit tradition of Jayadeva's love-poetry. The excellence of his style and diction gave him considerable popularity throughout eastern India. He was the founder of a school of master-singers, which later spread over Bengal, and his songs unquestionably influenced Chaitanya.

The poetess Mīra Bāi, who came from the Muttra area, sacred to Krishnaites, wrote in the Braj Bhāshā dialect of Western Hindi (the dialect of Muttra). A devotee of Krishna from childhood, she expressed her intense love for him in graceful and melodious verses, which also won a wide popular approval. Her poems stimulated the use of the Braj Bhāshā dialect for the lyric poetry of the Krishna cult. Vitthalnātha, son of the founder of the Vallabhas, was reputed to be the author of the *Mandan*, a short prose work in Braj Bhāshā dealing with the story of Rādhā and Krishna.

The literature in Bengali, another of the old Indo–Aryan vernaculars, perhaps showed more originality than that in Hindi. In the fourteenth century the Māgadhī Prakrit language began to assume its Bengali character, which in its literary form (Sādhu-bhāsā) borrowed Sanskrit words freely. A Hindu reaction to Muslim domination led, furthermore, to a sort of classical revival of Sanskrit influence, without, however, obliterating the popular religious pattern.[13] The local folk culture was made up of several elements. The Tantric Buddhism of Bengal had influenced its local cults (of Manasā, Chandi, Dharma, and other folk deities and heroes), whose mythologies took shape during the early centuries of Islamic control, and these cults with their mythologies were, in turn, gradually absorbed into the Krishna-Rādhā and Shākta religious movements, especially from the sixteenth century on. Bengali literature thus eventually derived its major characteristics from five main sources: Tantric Buddhism, local folk cults, Krishna-Rādhā *bhaktism*, Shākta *bhaktism*, and, of course, Sanskrit literature.

The first important body of Bengali literature to survive appeared in the relatively peaceful fifteenth century. The standard element of Bengali poetry, the *payār*, a heroic or rhyming couplet with four feet in each line, had by that time become fully developed. The religious nature of their subject matter led writers to model their narrative poems on the puranas rather than on the great Sanskrit epics and secular works. In their Bengali versions, the grandeur of the Sanskrit epics 'shrank into thin trickles of rustic piety', for 'the most inferior qualities of Sanskrit . . . seem to have had the greatest appeal for Bengali poets.'[14]

This new literature fell into three divisions, which persisted until the nineteenth century. They were (1) translations, (2) Krishna-Rādhā literature, of which the short lyrical devotional and love songs (*pads*) had a distinct literary beauty, and (3) narrative or epic poems setting forth the stories and myths of the local cults. The narrative or epic poems were called either *vijay* ('victory') *kāvya* ('victory' referring to the cruelty with which the deities treated their opponents) or *mangal* ('benevolence') *kāvya* ('benevolence' referring to the kindness which the deities showed toward their followers). Most Bengali poetry was meant to be sung, and the long poems were composed of pieces for semi-musical and semi-dramatic performance by professional and mendicant minstrels or story-tellers.

The earliest cardinal work in Bengali literature has continued to be regarded as a masterpiece; it was the *Rāmāyana* of Krittivās Ojhā, written at Gaur sometime between 1409 and 1414 in *payārs*. Since the author freely modified the original *Rāmāyana* to suit his own religious purpose and to appeal to the common people, the characters were represented as popular, rustic types with little of the heroic spirit. Its simplicity, charm, and ethical qualities have made it the Bible of the Bengal masses. From both the literary and linguistic points of view, however, the *Shrī-Krisna-kīrttan* of Baru Chandīdās (see Chapter III) was the most interesting work of the early-fifteenth century. It was an epic narrating the conquest (*vijay*) of Rādhā by Krishna. Krishna was pictured as the cunning seducer of Rādhā, who, much the most appealing figure in the story, loved him unselfishly and with her whole body and soul, once her resistance had been overcome. Mālādhar Vasu's *Shrī-Krisna-vijay* was a significant version of the *Bhāgavata-purāna*, written between 1473 and 1480. Rādhā had not been mentioned in the original purana, but the theme of Mālādhar's work was Krishna the lover and beloved of Rādhā.

The first of the surviving epics inspired by the local cults was the *Manasā-mangal* of Vijay Gupta, begun in 1494. It told the story of Manasā (here the daughter of Shiva), who, having left her home because of the cruelty of her stepmother Chandī, tried to gain the worship of Chād Sadāgar, a wealthy merchant, in order to avenge herself by taking worshippers away from Shiva and Chandī. It throws much light on contemporary life in Bengal.

A great literary outburst occurred in Bengal under the relatively enlightened rule of Sultan Hussein Shah (1493–1518). One of his officials, Yasorāj Khān, a Hindu turned Muslim, wrote the *Krishna-mangal*. Sanātana and Rūpa Gosvāmī (see Chapters V and VII) also flourished at the sultan's court before they joined the Chaitanya movement. About this time Kavīndra composed his version of the *Mahābhārata*, and Shrīkaran Nandwi his version of a part of it; Shrīdhar produced the earliest rendering of the Sanskrit Vidyā-Sundar story, a tale of a love intrigue between the Princess Vidyā and a disguised foreign prince, Sundar; and Kaviranjan of Shrīkhanda imitated the amatory Rādhā-Krishna lyrics of Vidyāpati so well as to earn the name Minor Vidyāpati.

The literature in other Indo-European vernaculars of north India developed in much the same way as that in Hindi and in Bengali. Marathi literature was noted for its religious mysticism and pure devotionalism. Most of its important writers were religious poets who sang the praises of Vittoba (Vishnu), the deity of the local Pandharpur shrine. The first important Marathi writer was Jñāndeva, who prepared a commentary on the *Bhāgavad-gītā* about 1290; the foremost figure of the period was Nāmdēv (see Chapters II and III). The development of Gujarati literature was closely related to that of Hindi, although it was perhaps more clearly dominated by the Rādhā-Krishna poets.

Many verses of Mīrā Bāi were well known in Gujarati. Narsingh Mehtā wrote (*post* 1450) some noted Gujarati lyrics about the loves of Rādhā and Krishna. The *Pañchatantra* and other Sanskrit stories were translated into that tongue, and at an early date Islamic influences also appeared in it. Punjabi literature was little developed before 1500. Although the Urdu language matured during this period, no literature of any consequence appeared in it. The most prominent writer in Kashmiri was the fourteenth-century ascetic Lallā, whose lyrical songs paid honour to Shiva. In Assam Shāktism and Tantrism were vigorous, and erotic sentiments were prominent in *pads* and longer songs. The foundations for later literary developments in Assamese were laid, probably in the fourteenth century, by Mādhav Kandali's version of the *Rāmāyana*. Mādhav was also the author of the *Devajit*, a more original poem, in praise of Krishna.

The Literatures of Southeast Asia

The literature of the countries of southeast Asia (except Vietnam) fell under profound Pali Buddhist and Sanskrit influences, but the classical sources in those languages were supplemented by native myths and legends. The works of greatest interest and merit were largely inspired by or derived from the Jātaka stories about the life of the Buddha or from the great Sanskrit epics and puranas. Epic and lyric poetry were the chief literary forms, but some stories and native chronicles were recorded in prose, and the dramatic-ballet, employing verse and pantomime accompanied by music, was also a common medium of creative expression. Authors were generally either monks or courtiers.

In the several kingdoms that now make up Burma, though Buddhist religious and philosophical treatises and poems dealing with the story of the Buddha were often written in Pali, in the latter half of the fifteenth century chronicles, law books, and poetry appeared in the vernacular. In the Ava area a group of monkish scholars wrote in both Pali and Burmese. Ariyavamsa (fl. 1450) composed several poems in Burmese; Uttamagyan (b. 1453) used Burmese for a famous poem on the seasons, the *Tawla* (*A Journey through the Forest*); Silavamsa (Thilawunth, 1453–1520) wrote the mythological chronicle *Yazawingyan* as well as other poems in that language; and both Ratthasara (1468–1529) and Aggathamahdi (b. 1479) wrote Burmese poetical versions of the Jātakas. In Pegu the dominant vernacular was that of the Talaing tribe. The oldest surviving law book of the realm is a translation in Talaing. At Toungoo the royal family was celebrated in courtly verses by one of the king's war boat commanders, Thondaunghmu, and in Arakan the court bard Aduminnyo composed an historical poem (*c.* 1430).

The Tibetan dialects are related to Burmese. For a country of so small a population, Tibet produced a considerable literature, primarily of a religious nature. The two canonical collections, the *Kanjur* and the *Tanjur*, reached their definitive form in the early fourteenth century (the *Kanjur* was printed in 1410). Several of the best of the numerous elaborate histories were essentially accounts of Buddhism in Tibet. Among the biographies of religious leaders was Ge-long's of Geden-dub, the first of the great lamas, written about 1494. And the mythological life of Padma-Sambhava, the celebrated founder of Tantric Buddhism in Tibet, probably belongs in this period too. Tibetan authors also produced folktales, accounts of holy places, and poetry, but no poet came forth to compare with Mila, the most celebrated poet of earlier Tibet.

In Siam, except for the Pali Buddhist canon, Pali literature was less influential than in Burma, whereas as early as the fourteenth century various pieces of literature, including several versions of the Jātakas, appeared in the native Thai languages. Thai literature was also strongly influenced by the Sanskrit epics and puranas that came to Siam by way of the Khmer Empire and Java. These works, along with the Jātakas and native traditions, supplied inspiration for popular mythological or semi-historical prose tales and dance-dramas. Versions of the universally beloved *Ramakien* (*Rāmāyana*) were certainly in existence by the fourteenth century, and so probably were many of the other tales that have since been adapted to dance dramas. The well-known historical romance *Inaco*, of Javanese origin, must have been available before 1500. The early versions of the *Maxims of Phra Ruang*, a classic of Siamese moralistic (*nīti*) literature, most likely made their appearance in the fourteenth century, since Phra Ruang, the Thai national hero, probably was Rāma Kamheng, who lived about 1300. Thai literature was especially noted for its short lyric love songs and its *nirats* (extended narrative love poems), in which a traveller addresses his lady love.

Of the literature of Cambodia before the sack of Angkor (1431) by the Thais little is known. Its strong Sanskrit connections are suggested by the Sanskrit elements in Thai and Laotian literature, doubtless imported by way of Cambodia. After the fall of its capital Cambodia had little political or cultural eminence, but its native chronicles and other forms of literature, strongly influenced by the Pali Buddhist tradition as well as the Sanskrit tradition, continued.

Old Javanese, still preserved in Bali as the language of traditional literature, perhaps reached its zenith before the Majapahit period (1293–1415). It prospered until the fifteenth century, heavily dependent on Hindu and Buddhist ideas. Over half the words it used were Sanskrit, and its great classics were adaptations of Sanskrit and Buddhist texts, though thoroughly naturalized. Among them were the *Kāndā* (*Tradition*), *Rāmākavi* (*Rāmāyana*), *Bhārata-yuddha* and *Arjunavivāha* (both from the *Mahābhārata*), *Nītisārakavi* (based on a Hindu work on ethics and religion), and the *Kamahāyānikan* (a Buddhist work expounding Mahāyāna and Tantric ideas). More distinctly native were the chronicles, the romances, the tales of evil spirits, the dance-dramas, and especially the *wayang* (or shadow plays), employing puppets or masked figures. Probably the most admirable original work of the Majapahit period was the *Nagarakertagama*, a poem composed about 1365 by Prapanca, head of the Buddhist clergy, dealing with the life and times of the contemporary ruler Hayam Wuruk. With the rise of Malacca and Islam and the decline of Majapahit, the production of significant literature in Old Javanese ceased, nor was it effectively replaced by works in modern Javanese or the closely related Malay. Malay was written in the Arabic alphabet after the fourteenth century; the literary language since the fifteenth century has undergone little change.

The Filipinos appear to have had before the Spanish conquest a written literature consisting of epic and lyric poetry. Some of it has been preserved and appears in modern times in the form of oral literature and dance dramas. It incorporates local myths, legends, and heroes, and seems to have been influenced also by the great Hindu epics.

BELLES-LETTRES IN THE FAR EAST

In most of the Far East Chinese was the *langue de culture*. The complicated symbolic nature of the Far Eastern writing systems limited the acquirement of reading proficiency to those who had learned the numerous ideographs. A phonetic Mongol script based on the Uigur alphabet developed shortly after 1200, but only a limited amount of Mongol literature appear in it. By 1434 Korea also had a phonetic alphabet, which was used for popular literature and various other purposes, but it did not succeed in replacing literary Chinese for serious writings. Japan had its own *Kana* syllabary in which (sometimes in combination with Chinese characters) its classics were written, and a truly Japanese literature of this type existed, but the period under consideration in this chapter was not one of the great periods of Japanese literary production.

Printing was in general use in China, Korea, Japan, Vietnam, and central Asia throughout our period, facilitating the dissemination and preservation of literature. Moveable type had been used in China since about 1045. The earliest type was made of porcelain, and later examples were of tin and wood (1313). Wooden type of Uigur words dating *c.* 1300 has been found in central Asia. A type mould from which a more durable metal type could be cast was perfected in Korea or China during the fourteenth century. Moveable type seems, however, not to have been widely adopted in China, block printing being generally preferred. The first large book known to have been printed with moveable type in China was a reprint in 1574 of the great *T'ai-ping yü-lan* encyclopedia. In Korea, on the other hand, moveable type was used a great deal in the fifteenth century. The Yi dynasty established a Department of Books charged with casting type and printing, which, beginning actively in 1403, cast many founts, but after 1544 moveable type ceased to be used until revived in 1770. The first book known to have been printed in moveable type in Japan appeared in 1596, but the use of moveable type ended about 1647 in favour of block printing.[15]

Mongol literature was in its infancy during this period. It consisted of native songs and folklore, probably largely unwritten, some annals, and some translations or adaptations of Chinese and Indian works—the Indian works largely indirectly, from Tibetan translations. The so-called *Tobciyan* was a Mongol account of Genghis Khan and his first four successors; it formed the basis of the early parts of the Chinese *Yüan shih* (see Chapter VIII), but it probably had no wide currency among the Mongols themselves. Some of the translations of Chinese and Indian literature were more popular. The *Pañchatantra* tales were among these, as was also the Buddhist classic the *Bodhicaryāvatara* of Shāntideva, which the translator, the Tibetan monk Čosgi Odsir (early fourteenth century), provided with a commentary. The Mongol version of the Chinese *Classic of Filial Piety* (*Hsiao ching*) was perhaps the finest specimen of this translated literature.[16]

The oldest literary works of Vietnam were not only of Chinese origin but were also written in Chinese, and the earliest native poetry and chronicles were likewise composed in Chinese. In the thirteenth and fourteenth centuries, however, the *chū'-nōm* system of writing developed whereby Vietnamese words were written in modified Chinese characters. Gradually a goodly amount of poetry and tales appeared in this form, along with Vietnamese versions of Chinese dramas, novels, and ethical and philosophical works.

Korean authors also at first wrote in Chinese. A popular work of fiction, the *Adventures of Hong Kil Dong*, by the monk Kasan, probably Korea's most important literary creation of the fourteenth century, was in that language. Both Buddhist and Confucian influences pervaded Korean literature, but after the establishment of the Yi dynasty (1392) Confucian ideas dominated. With the development of the phonetic Korean alphabet, more popular literature, such as folktales, novels, dramas, and adaptations of Chinese classical works, began to appear in pure Korean, while Chinese retained its grip on the more serious literary forms. An upsurge of nationalism and of Confucian idealism under the new dynasty combined with the use of the phonetic script to make the fifteenth century one of the most flourishing in Korean literary history. It culminated in an imposing anthology, the *Tongmun Seon*, prepared by a group of scholars in accordance with a royal order of 1478, which contained selections from about five hundred authors.

Styles of Prose in China

In China the development of the vernacular was somewhat different from elsewhere. The dominance of literary Chinese as the proper language of government documents, learning, and 'true literature' was not seriously challenged, but two new forms of literature, the drama and the novel, emerged, written in *pai-hua*, the colloquial speech. The dramas, having a certain literary elegance, were gradually accepted as literature by the Confucian literati, but the novels, despite their widespread appeal, were not. During our period, however, these 'lower' forms of imaginative letters blossomed and became, despite Confucian purists, the most popular and original.

Some significant work was still produced in the literary language. Prose in that language during our period was of several types—*ku-wen, pien-wen, fu,* and *pa-ku. Ku-wen,* the ancient or loose prose style, was the most used, being employed for most of the *lun* (essays or brief discussions), *hsiao-shuo* (short stories), histories, biographies, and literary criticism. In the Yüan and early Ming periods one of the few well-known essayists was Sung Lien (1310–81), chief author of the *Yüan History.* Short stories in the literary language, once characteristic of the T'ang period, again became popular. They included tales of the marvellous (*ch'uan-ch'i*), fictionized biographies of historical persons, heroic narratives, religious legends, and love stories. The tales of Ch'ü Yu (1341–1427) found in the *Chien-teng lu* and *Chien-teng-hsin-hua* (1378) were widely read. In these and other collections stories of illicit love, verging on the pornographic, predominated. Most of the biographical works were concise, factual, dry, and, while valuable as historical sources, of little literary merit. Among the critics were the early-fourteenth-century scholar Wu Shih-tao, whose *Wu li-pu shih-hua* discussed the principles of poetry, and the late-fifteenth-century statesman Li Tung-yang, whose *Lu-t'ang shih-hua* was critical of poets, past and contemporary.

The other prose styles in the literary language were put to less common use. The complicated *pien-wen* (or parallel-sentence prose) was no longer much needed except in eulogies and formal government documents. The *fu,* originally a rhyming parallel-sentence form of a descriptive or expository nature, had by this time been transformed into the so-called prose *fu.* The *fu* was a genre peculiar to China. It dealt with an assortment of subjects including places, products, animals, scenery, meteorological phenomena, and various emotions such as home-sickness and the sadness of separation. The prose *fu* of our period had a loose structure permitting unpredictable rhymes and parallelisms and allowing considerable freedom but requiring some degree of literary skill to produce anything of distinction. Although many *fu* were written, few, if any, compared with those of earlier periods. The eight-legged essay (*pa-ku*) became the prescribed form for the civil-service examinations, but it promoted a formal and stultified style that did not serve to improve literary standards.

Chinese Poetry

The ability to write poetry was considered one of the accomplishments of the Chinese scholar, and tens of thousands of poems were produced. Most of them were of mediocre quality, and none of the poetry in the traditional style compared favourably with that of the T'ang and Sung periods. It divided into two general groups—the *shih* and the *tz'u*.

The *shih* poems, in turn, were of two general types. The ancient or unregulated type consisted of lines of four, five, and seven words with no fixed number of lines. The modern or regulated type was popularized during the T'ang period. Its standard form was the *lü-shih*, which consisted of lines of five or seven words each in an eight-line stanza that followed a prescribed rhyme-scheme and observed strict rules of verbal parallelism and tonal sequence in certain lines.[17] A diversification known as the *pai-lü* permitted as many as several hundred lines with variations in the rhyme scheme, and another, the *chüeh-chü*, or broken-off line poem, was of four lines, each consisting of five or seven words—just enough to introduce, develop, embellish, and conclude a theme. These conventions determined that most traditional Chinese poems would be short and, to have any merit, would have to reveal verbal dexterity as well as literary inspiration. The imitators of our period could not match the several original types, among other reasons because linguistic changes had altered tones, making the T'ang rhymes, which they had to follow, sound inaccurate. Liu Chi (1311–75) and Kao Ch'i (1336–74) were perhaps the most distinguished traditional poets of the Mongol period, and of the early Ming period Hsieh Chin (1369–1415), one of the editors of the great Yung-lo encyclopaedia (see Chapter XI), Li Tung-yang (1447–1516), and Li Meng-yang (1472–1529).

The *tz'u* poem, having originated during the T'ang period, had reached its highest level during the Sung period. It was at first a vehicle principally for love lyrics that were intended to be sung. Its lines were of unequal length but with prescribed rhymes and tonal sequences, which occurred in many patterns. Despite its adherence to the literary style it admitted elements of colloquial speech. Gradually it expanded in length, became divorced from music, and developed into purely literary verse dealing with other than lyric subjects. Most of the poets of our period wrote *tz'u* also, but none of them measured up to the Sung masters.

The function of the *tz'u* as song was gradually taken over by the *ch'ü*, or colloquial lyric, designed to be sung to a designated tune by public entertainers or sing-song girls. The ancient drum song (*ku-shih*), a rhyming version of the colloquial tale, was similarly meant to be sung or else recited by storytellers. *The Rhythmic Tales of the Twenty Histories* (*Erh-shih-i shih-t'an ts'u*), by the scholar Yang Shen (1488–1559), presented several drum songs of the Ming period. When taken over and polished by literary men, the *ch'ü* and the *ku-shih* became a new, dynamic poetry. The music, songs, and recitations of the *ch'ü* and *ku-shih* entertainers were combined with the prose tale, whether in the literary or the colloquial language, and with various other popular dramatic forms to create the new drama. *Ch'ü* poetry flourished thenceforth in the theatre, while the drum song, being popular narrative poetry, helped to promote the colloquial prose tale and the novel.

Chinese Drama

Chinese drama reached full maturity during the Yüan period. It appealed to the Mongol rulers as well as the general public, and many literary men not employed by the conquerors found an outlet for their talents in writing plays. The plays they wrote were essentially operatic ballets, employing, along with both speaking and singing parts, an elaborate system of conventional gestures with sleeve, hand, arm, foot, leg, waist, or whole body to help explain an emotion or action. The actors wore elaborate costumes but used little or no stage setting. They were accompanied by an orchestra, which played music that exploited popular tunes, for which appropriate *ch'ü* songs were written. Plots were drawn from history or popular tales and were presented in a colloquial or semi-colloquial language. Before 1500 Chinese drama was perhaps further advanced than the drama of the West but seems rudimentary when compared with the best of the Greco-Roman stage or of the later West.

The southern Chinese plays (*nan-hsi* or *hsi-wen*) can be distinguished from the northern ones (*tsa-chü*). The northern play normally consisted of a prologue which was an integral part of it and four acts (with an optional fifth). Only the leading actor sang, and he changed roles from act to act if the leading role changed. The northern drama had its own distinctive tunes, all of which in a given act were in the same key. The southern drama was more colloquial and unconventional. It was generally long and of an irregular number of acts, and the prologue was not an integral part of it. It employed tunes from south China, all songs in the same act were not in the same key, and all characters might sing, often in duets. In the early southern plays tunes from Huei-chou (Anhwei) and I-chiang (Kiangsi) were especially favoured.

Southern dramatists introduced into their productions lengthy historical plots as well as Taoist immortals and supernatural elements. They also tended to emphasize Confucian moral principles. The most noteworthy of the early southern dramas was the *Tale of a Lute* (*P'i-p'a chi*), written by Kao Tse-ch'eng probably late in the fourteenth century. It was a melancholy and highly ethical tale of the responsibilities put upon a young scholar by his Confucian ideals, especially those of filial piety. It had twenty-four acts and was clearly not intended to be presented *in toto* at one sitting. Some southern dramas apparently were already popular in south China before the northern dramas reached their greatest vogue at Peking, but they were at first disregarded by literary men, and not until the latter part of the Yüan period did they compete successfully at the capital with the northern dramas.

Most of the early dramas were moralistic in tone, tending to fall within three general categories—romantic comedies, the 'just official' plays, in which the hero was an honest and sagacious official, and the warrior-hero or historical plays. Stock characters were customary—the elderly man, the just official, the military hero, the country bumpkin, the loving mother, the courtesan, the high-born maiden, the simple country girl. The plots were generally thin, success depending rather on the popularity of the theme and music and the

ability of the actors than on the literary merit of the play. Dreams and supernatural agencies were often called upon to solve impossible situations. Some
of the plays were tragic, but they did not develop the theme of inner conflict
characteristic of Greek and later Western tragedy. Chi Chün-hsiang's early-
fourteenth-century *Orphan of the House of Chao*, however, suggested it: to
save the life of his ward a doctor sacrifices his own son but in the end is
rewarded for having discharged his higher duty.

The titles of over 500 northern dramas of the Yüan period have been
preserved, and about 132 are still extant. The largest number were preserved
in the *Yüan ch'ü hsüan*, compiled during the Ming period. Kuan Han-ch'ing
(c. 1210–1285), Wang Shih-fu, and Ma Chih-yüan probably were the leading
dramatists of the early Yüan period. In Kuan's *Courtesan in Distress* the
heroine is rescued from the villain by her true admirer and another courtesan;
and in his *Gross Injustice to the Maid T'ou*, a girl is executed for a murder she
did not commit, but her father, having become a judge and guided by his
dreams, punishes the guilty. Kuan and Wang were joint authors of *The
Romance of the West Chamber* (*Hsi hsiang chi*), the best-known of the Yüan
dramas. It was a sequence of five four-act plays dealing with the 'wing,
flowers, snow and moonlight' of a frustrated romance, which worked out in
the end, however, to the satisfaction of all concerned. Ma's *Sorrows of Han*
dealt with the suicide of a Han princess sent as a concubine to the chief of the
Huns in order to save China from attack.

In the later Yüan period, when the southern dramas became popular everywhere, the two regional types began to influence each other. In the early Ming
period a mixed type developed in which southern tunes predominated and
formed the transition to the southern *k'un-ch'ü* drama of the sixteenth century
(Chapter XI). *Madame Cassia, or The Tale of a Horse Dealer*, a play in four
acts, was a good example of the mixed play. It dealt with the woes of a horse
dealer whose children were driven away from home by a vicious step-mother.
All are happily re-united in the end, and the villains appropriately punished.

The Short Story and the Novel in China

The short story in the literary language was an old form of belles-lettres in
China, but the colloquial tale (*hsiao-shuo*) became popular only during our
period. The oldest surviving colloquial tales date from the Sung dynasty or
earlier; they survived in story-tellers' prompt books. One of the oldest
collections of Sung stories, the *Ch'ing-p'ing-shan t'ang*, was published only
between 1522 and 1566; another somewhat better collection, the *Ching-pen
t'ung-shu hsiao-shuo*, appears to have come somewhat later. During the Yüan
and early Ming periods numerous stories were produced, some 120 of them
being published between 1620 and 1628 in three separate collections, known
together as the *San-yen* (*Three Collections*). The largest group were moralistic
tales; others dealt with rewards and punishment, fate, happy reunions of
families and lovers, courtesans, talented youths, just officials, immortals, and

swindlers; some were of a detective-story nature, with a clever magistrate solving the mystery involved. The oldest collection of tales of historical fiction, the *Completely Illustrated P'ing-hua* (*Ch'uan-hsiang*), can be dated 1321–24.

Out of drum songs, dramas, and colloquial tales grew the longer colloquial prose stories, or novels. These novels were lengthy, repetitious, and rambling, and their plots were weak, but their characterization was often excellent. They represented a vital and dynamic literature-of-the-people. The oldest were historical and picaresque narratives. One of the most notable before 1500 was *The Romance of the Three Kingdoms* (*San-kuo-chih yen-i*), based on the conflict among the three successor states to the Later Han dynasty; its characters were historical figures, and its episodes elaborations of events mentioned in the dynastic histories. It is attributed to Lo Kuan-chung (1328–98), but the novel of 120 chapters which we have today probably is the product of revision and perhaps supplementation by later hands; the oldest surviving printed version dates from about 1522, but its preface indicates that it must have been in print as early as 1494.

The Water Margin (*Shui hu chuan*, translated by Pearl S. Buck in 1933 as *All Men Are Brothers*) was another notable novel of the period before 1500. It was a Chinese Robin Hood story, written in a more colloquial style than *The Romance of the Three Kingdoms*. It dealt with a large band of men forced by hard times and vicious officials to live as robbers in a marsh in Shantung, generally befriending the poor and weak and wreaking vengeance on the oppressors of the people; ultimately pardoned by the emperor and taken into official service, they were gradually destroyed by the machinations of court officials. Some of the characters and many of the incidents were historical but in reality had been widely separated in time and place.

The history of *The Water Margin* may suggest what happened in the course of time to the original texts of other Chinese novels. Its oldest version in 92 chapters was possibly the joint work of Shih Nai-an and Lo Kuan-chung. In the so-called Kuo edition (*c.* 1550) and several other, almost contemporary editions, eight chapters were inserted describing the robbers' campaigns after they had been taken into the emperor's service. In the 1590's a Fukien bookseller brought out an edition, which, though otherwise abbreviated, gave two new campaigns in addition. Li Chih, a champion of vernacular fiction, revised and enlarged the story of the two recently added campaigns and supplied a commentary but followed the Kuo edition in most other respects. This newer version, published in 1614 in 120 chapters, gave the novel its most complete form. Chin Sheng-t'an, a well-known man of letters of the seventeenth century, considered the work of literary value but did not condone its portrayal of robbers as heroes. In 1644 he brought out an edition, with his own prologue and commentary, that eliminated the last fifty chapters, those which narrated the pardon of the robbers and their employment in the imperial service, and substituted an ending in which one of the leaders in a dream sees the whole band put to death. This disinfected version became the standard and is the one usually presented in Western translations and adaptations.[18]

Belles-Lettres in Japan

Japan's classical literature is that of the Heian era, the pre-feudal period (before the end of the twelfth century) when the imperial court flourished at Heian-kyō (or Kyoto). The language of learning of that period, both secular and religious, was Chinese, while that of popular literature was Japanese, in which women excelled. The works in either medium were produced by a relatively small learned class that lived in comparative luxury and idleness around the imperial court. Almost inevitably the quality of courtly learning and literature declined as the rise of the feudal system transferred economic and political power from the imperial court to more vigorous but less learned military men. Furthermore, during the early phases of the feudal period, Buddhist sects grew in popularity, with a corresponding growth in the emphasis upon religious ideas and the influence of monastic learning. Despite the joint impact of feudalism and Buddhism, the decline of courtly literature and secular learning was not abrupt during the Kamakura Shogunate (1185–1333), for central control remained strong in some regards and the court and nobility at Kyoto still enjoyed a relative prosperity.

Hence the Kamakura period was characterized by a mixed literature that reflected the interests of both the declining courtiers and the rising military and religious groups. Poetry, romantic novels, diaries, travel accounts, and miscellanies or jottings, although of inferior quality, continued to be the products of the classical courtly litterateur while military novels and Buddhist tales, both based on historical episodes, reflected the interests of the new dominant groups. Meanwhile, as Buddhism rose in popular estimation, Chinese learning declined. Those who could write in Chinese became so scarce that as early as the thirteenth century a new mixed Sino-Japanese prose style emerged. It was Japanese in grammar and structure, but its vocabulary was rich in Chinese words and Sino-Buddhist terms. This new style was used for both learned and popular literature. As the old, pure Japanese became obsolete and the feudal regime advanced, women gradually disappeared as literary figures.

With the rise of the Ashikaga shoguns after 1333, decentralizing feudalism gradually triumphed and secular learning, the imperial court, and the court nobility declined to their nadir. In the late fifteenth and the early sixteenth century, meritorious literary works almost ceased to be produced, and literary sterility was avoided only by the emergence of new forms that pointed to the great revival of the seventeenth and eighteenth centuries (see Chapter XI). Among the emerging forms were the *renga* (chain-poems), the *otogi-zōshi* (short, fantastic, fairy tales), and the *nō* (lyrical) drama with its *kyōgen* (farcical interludes). All the new forms except the *renga* owed a good deal to Buddhism and other popular concerns. Much of the literature of the period was sombre, reflecting at once the pessimism of the Buddhists and the uncertainties and heroism of a warring and violent age. Yet most writings of the time mirrored the interest in nature, the courtly, lyrical quality, the lightness and grace, the studied avoidance of roughness and vulgarity, the atmosphere of plumblossoms-and-moonlight, and the slightly effeminate and superficial tone that had been bequeathed by the Heian masters. The interest in nature was reinforced by Zen Buddhism, and the character of the Heian literary heritage as a whole was perpetuated by the triumphant aristocratic, feudal society.

The classical *tanka* (a poem of five lines of 5, 7, 5, 7, and 7 syllables respectively) remained the monopoly of the court poets and those taught by them. The *tanka*'s theme was love or nature, and its tone was one of gentle melancholy. *Tankas* continued to be produced in considerable quantity into the fifteenth century. Five imperial anthologies, containing a total of 8,105 poems, were produced in the thirteenth century; eight of 15,938 in the fourteenth; and one of 2,144, the *New Collection of Ancient and Modern Times Continued* (*Shinzokukokinshu*) in the fifteenth (1433–39). The poetry of the later collections was imitative and uninspired. Its weakness was in all probability accentuated by the development of hereditary lines of court poets, of which the three most prominent (the Nijō, the Kyōgoku, and the Reizei) were descendants of the justly famous Fujiwara Tameie (1198–1275), compiler of two of the imperial anthologies. The Reizei branch was founded by Tamesuke, son of the famous authoress Abutsu, who was the wife or the concubine of Tameie in his old age. It was perhaps more original and vigorous than the others and produced generations of famous poets. It also trained others—for instance, Imagawa Sadoya (Ryōshun, 1324–1420), who was a general of the Ashikagas, and the monk Shōtetsu (1381–1459). The principal compiler of all but three collections of *tankas* after 1144 was a Fujiwara, and the fact that an outsider, Asukai Masayo, was asked to compile the last one probably indicated that the muse was believed to be deserting the Nijō branch of the family. In addition to the imperial anthologies several private collections of *tankas* were compiled; the *Fubokushō* was prepared by Fujiwara Nagakiyo, a pupil of Tamesuke, about 1308–10 and contained over 16,000 poems not included in previous imperial collections.

By the fifteenth century the *tanka* yielded primacy to the *renga* and to poetic forms associated with the *nō* drama. The *renga* was a derivative of the *tanka*. It preserved the syllable arrangement of the *tanka*, but every five-line stanza was the work of two poets. The first composed a seventeen-syllable strophe (5, 7, 5) and the second a fourteen-syllable strophe (7, 7), each taking as his point of departure the immediately preceding strophe.[19] This form gradually developed rigid rules, and a *renga* that happily fulfilled them became the most highly regarded of poetic accomplishments. Its greatest master was the monk Sōgi (1421–1502), who, in 1488, with two disciples composed 100 such linked verses considered the acme of the art.

The *nō* (or lyrical) drama was the pre-eminent literary and artistic product of the Ashikaga period. The great majority of the 235 *nō* dramas contained in a modern collection (*Yōkyoku tsūge*) date from the fifteenth century. Of these the Shinto priest Kwanami Kiyotsuga (1333–84) is credited with 15, and his son Seami Motokiyo (1363–1443) with 93. The *nō* was a dance drama in which a plot of small merit was combined with prose, verse, singing, dancing, and music. Except superficially it had little in common with the Chinese drama and seems not to have been derived from it. On the other hand, it had certain similarities to the Greek drama, including the sparseness of scenery, the use of masks, and a chorus that told the story during the performance.

Nō dramas seem to have originated from a popular form of secular entertainment, a mixture of song and dance known as *sarugaku* (monkey-business). They were probably also influenced by the more religious *dengaku* (field-music) theatricals, associated with harvest and other festivals celebrated at various shrines during the thirteenth and fourteenth centuries. Through the genius of Kwanami and Seami and under the patronage of the Askikaga shoguns at Kyoto, these rustic theatricals were transformed into highly aristocratic and esoteric drama. Each play was performed by a principal dancer, an assistant (generally played by a priest), lesser performers (usually not more than four or five), a chorus, and an orchestra of flutes and drums.

The *nō* play was profoundly influenced by Zen Buddhism both in form and ideas. Its prevailing tone was serious, often tragic. It was rather short. It was symbolic, and its poetry, written in alternating lines of seven and five syllables, was characterized by dramatic and suggestive imagery. The quiet scenes were in prose, but the dramatic episodes were expressed in dances or poems sung to music. *Nō* themes were drawn from Buddhist, Chinese, and Japanese legends and history. The plays generally centred in gods, devils, festivals, warriors, women, or the insane, and echoed sentiments of piety, patriotic and martial fervour, and love of nature. Later, as the *nō* began to be patronized by feudal lords, several schools developed. To break the serious mood and monotony of the *nō*, farces or *kyōgen* (mad-words) were introduced between performances. These *kyōgen* were written in colloquial speech, in contrast to the elegant and flowery court language of the *nō*, and they presented common people such as peasants and priests in skits that often parodied the preceding *nō*.

In practically all Japanese prose literature, verse was liberally interspersed, composed or recited by lovers, officials, warriors, and priests at every turn. Prose stories were usually called *monogatari*, or narratives, whether short or of novel length. The romantic novel had practically ceased to be produced by 1300, and the last historical novel (*rekishi*) of importance was *The Clear Mirror* (*Masu-kagami*), covering the period from the rise of the Kamakura Shogunate to its fall in 1333. The military novel (*gunki* or *senki*) became a favourite form of the early feudal period. It grew out of the historical novel, but it was influenced by the newer and shorter historical and Buddhist tale, and it dealt with military families, especially the Taira and the Minomoto. The most famous, the *Heike monogatari*, which described the decline and fall of the Taira clan, had been written in the early thirteenth century. A number of others followed, the last important one being the *Record of the Great Peace* (*Taiheiki*)—an inappropriate title indeed, since the story was laid in the period (1318–67) of battles and conspiracies that brought the fall of Kamakura, the attempts of the Go-Daigo emperor to regain power, and the rise of the Ashikagas. Pedantic and rhetorical in style, the work bristled with Chinese allusions and Buddhist theological terms and was liberally sprinkled with long poems in alternating lines of five and seven syllables. Its author was probably the Buddhist priest Kojima, who died in 1374.

Of the shorter historical and Buddhist stories, from the fourteenth century on slightly different kinds won special favour. Among these were the *otogi-zōshi*, short tales of fantastic adventure, often much in the nature of fairy tales, and, more or less parallel, the *kōwakamai*, which were recited or chanted (fifteenth and sixteenth centuries). In their archaic grammar and vocabulary they were related to the romantic novels, but in their subject matter they derived, rather, from the historical and military novels and the Buddhist stories.

Some of Japan's best prose went into works of non-fiction. Of the travel diaries, none during our period surpassed the *Izayoi nikki* (*Diary of the Waning Moon*), written in the late thirteenth century by the poetess Abutsu, describing, among other things, her trip from Kyoto to Kamakura. Undoubtedly the finest piece of literature of the period, with the exception perhaps of some *nō* dramas, was the *Grasses of Ennui* (*Tsurezuregusa*), probably written between 1324 and 1331 by the courtier and Buddhist poet Yoshida Kenkō (1283–1350). It was in the *zuihitsu* (jottings) genre, consisting of short sketches, anecdotes, antiquarian notes, and reminiscences interspersed with reflections on life, death, morality, and religion. Somewhat cynical and melancholy in tone and archaic in style, it belonged perhaps, with Abutsu's *Diary*, among the last works of a passing classical age rather than among those pointing to the future.

NOTES TO CHAPTER X

1. The Kings of France—in particular Charles V—and the Dukes of Burgundy—in particular Philip the Good—concerned themselves with the assembly of fine collections of manuscripts, thus effectively encouraging efforts already essentially humanist in character. (Professor Pierre Le Gentil.)

2. In speaking of the contribution of oral literatures, we should not forget the considerable impact of the 'matter of Britain'. It should be added that while epics, romances, and chronicles were at first written in verse form, prose began to flourish as early as the thirteenth century, in particular with the appearance of two masterpieces which played a capital role in the development of the literature of the West: the Lancelot–Grail cycle and the prose Tristan, still appreciated in the fourteenth century. (Pierre Le Gentil.)

3. To Professor Olivier Le Gentil, it would be preferable to say that while Villon's poetry is full of mediaeval themes and reflexes, this traditional aspect of his work in no way detracts from its 'modernity'.

4. In stressing the upsurge of lyricism—above all of the courtly lyric—in the fourteenth and fifteenth centuries, it is necessary to recall that, contrary to what had previously been the case, music and poetry ceased to be indissolubly linked. Not all lyric compositions, even those in set form, were still sung, and when they were, the author of the text was no longer the author of the melody as well.

   In the course of the period after Machaut, the last and most famous representative of traditional musical lyricism, the musician figured side by side with the poet, particularly in Spain and France. The taste for allegory and aberrant parody to which this gave rise is worth mentioning. (Pierre Le Gentil.)

5. In the history of the theatre in the West at the end of the Middle Ages, it is impossible not to make mention of the *Miracles de Notre Dame par personnages* (fourteenth century) and, above all, of the great Mystery plays of Mercadé, Greban and J. Michel—all the more since it is in connection with them that arise such questions as the progress of 'mise en scène', of the theatrical troop, not to mention that of the evolution of sensitivity and of religious feeling. Nor should the 'entremets' of the Burgundian court be neglected, for they provide an excellent illustration of the taste for spectacle then playing a more and more determining role in court life and ceremonials. (Olivier Le Gentil.)

6. Professor P. Le Gentil points out that the origin of the 'danse macabre' is still subject to discussion. It should, however, be recalled that the word *macabre* first made its appearance in France in the form of *Macabré*, and that there is an ancient and famous *Danse macabre* (1424–25) in the Cemetery of the Innocents in Paris. Mention should also be made of the Spanish *Danza general de la Muerta*.

7. Professor P. Le Gentil feels that the case of the novella and the romance receives here somewhat summary treatment. Before the *Cent nouvelles nouvelles*, no longer attributed to Antoine de La Sale, mention should have been made of the latter's *Jehan de Saintré*, rightly recognized as a minor masterpiece. It should also be recalled that the court of Burgundy actively promoted the writing of prose versions of the old *chansons de geste* and Breton romances, an activity leading to the production of splendid manuscripts often magnificently illuminated and later proving useful to printers anxious to cater to their clients' persistent taste for the age of chivalry. Something of the mediaeval message thus survived even at the height of the Renaissance. Viewed in this perspective, it is easier to appreciate the role played by writers such as Malory or Montalvo.

8. Dámaso Alonso, 'The Spanish Contribution to the Modern European Novel', *Journal of World History*, VI (1961), 885.

9. Professor P. Le Gentil emphasizes that it is not easy to understand and to convey to others how, during the second half of the fifteenth century, a new age began to take the place of the mediaeval era which, nevertheless, lived on in so many ways, nor yet how such continuity was successfully reconciled with a virtual revolution. Certain signs, however, did herald a change unmarked by any deep or brutal break: a certain taste for the grandiose, expressed in the ambitious attempts of the *Grands Rhétoriqueurs*, or the authors of the Mysteries; a sharpened sense of philology and history leading to the search for Latinity in Cicero rather than in the works of the Schoolmen, and for religious truth in the New Testament itself rather than in the commentaries with which the centuries had overlaid it; a sense of reality which, without rejecting the achievements of a too-chimerical *courtoisie* and *chevalerie*, sought a closer adaptation to life itself, with its carnal needs and positive ambitions, under cover of historical rather than legendary examples or those endorsed by the great civilizations of the past. A combination of contradictory tendencies appeared which associated in a very complex manner sacred and profane; rejection of certain authorities with respect for others; need for material pleasure with the highest aspirations of the mind; nationalism with the search for a new universalism; conservatism with adventure; docility with iconoclasm; objectivity and observation with the most naïve and tendentious remnants of book-learning.

The authors feel, however, that some of the points made in this comment have been, or will be, made quite explicit elsewhere in the volume.

10. H. A. R. Gibbs, 'Literature' in Sir Thomas Arnold and Alfred Guillaume (eds.), *The Legacy of Islam* (Oxford, 1931), pp. 193–4.

11. See J. Chandra Ghosh, 'Vernacular Literatures' in G. T. Garrett (ed.), *The Legacy of India* (Oxford, 1937), p. 378.

12. See K. A. Nilakanta Sastri, *A History of South India* (London, 1955), p. 365.

13. J. C. Ghosh, *Bengali Literature* (London, 1948), p. 11.

14. *Ibid.*, p. 20.

15. T. F. Carter, *The Invention of Printing in China and Its Spread Westward*, by L. Carrington Goodrich (2nd ed., New York, 1955), pp. 211–37.

16. See William Hung, 'The Transmission of the Book Known as *The Secret History of the Mongols*,' *Harvard Journal of Asiatic Studies*, XIV (1951), 433–92. See also the article by Francis Woodman Cleaves, *ibid.*, XVII (1954), 1–129.

17. See James R. Hightower, *Topics in Chinese Literature* (Cambridge, Mass., 1950), p. 65.

18. Richard G. Irwin, *The Evolution of a Chinese Novel* (Cambridge, Mass., 1953), especially pp. 114–16.

19. See Edwin O. Reischauer, 'The Izayoi Nikki', *Harvard Journal of Asiatic Studies*, X (1947), especially pp. 261, 281–82, 293–303, and 383–87.

LITERARY COMMUNICATION AND BELLES-LETTRES (1500–1775)

LANGUAGE AND LINGUISTICS IN EUROPE

The Rise and Spread of the Vernaculars

THE period under consideration in this chapter is well marked in the history of European letters, though far from exclusively, by a concern with the Bible. It opens with Reformation controversies over whether the Bible should be made easily available to all Christians, clerical and lay alike, and, if so, what versions of the Bible, and it closes with Enlightenment controversies over what significance the Bible might have, if it had any at all. The success of the Protestant Reformation greatly hastened the translating of the Bible into a number of the vernaculars, and authorized or generally accepted translations helped to establish literary standards.[1] Perhaps the most spectacular of the translations was Luther's. It was based on the earlier critical studies of the Vulgate that had begun with Valla and on several scholarly editions of parts of the Bible, including Erasmus' revised text of the Greek Testament (see Chapter X). It had the benefit of Luther's acquaintance with earlier translations, his knowledge of philology in general and of the Scriptures in particular, his linguistic verve and vigorous style, his superb feeling for the nuances of German, and his intensive application to the task of translation. He completed his translation of the New Testament while in hiding at the Wartburg.

The first part of Luther's translation appeared in 1522, after revision by Melanchthon and others. For the Old Testament Luther worked with a team of scholars. The translation of the whole Bible was not ready until 1534. Thanks to the quality of his work and the popularity of his cause, Luther's Bible was widely read and became a landmark in the development of a standard German language. Though German unification was long postponed for other reasons, the concept of a common German culture was nevertheless both a cause and an effect of Luther's contribution. About 430 total or partial printings (probably more than 250,000 copies) of his Bible were issued before 1546, the year of his death, each probably exerting an accumulative impact upon the German style of his compatriots.

Before the end of the sixteenth century printed versions of the Bible were available in Danish, Swedish, English, Dutch, German, Italian, Spanish, French, Czech, Polish, Hungarian, Croat, Church Slavonic, and Russian. At the same time, the Vatican, with the Augustinian monk Angelo Rocca (1548–

1620) at the head of its press and as its editor, issued scholarly editions of the Vulgate and the writings of the church fathers. To be sure, in the countries that remained loyal to the Roman Catholic faith the Latin Bible, the Vulgate, even when slightly revised at the Council of Trent, exerted little influence on —might even have interfered with—the developments of the vernacular language, but in several such countries the inhabitants had first joined the Protestant movement, returning to Catholicism only later (e.g. Bohemia, Hungary, and Poland), or had continued thoroughly divided (e.g. Germany), and so had become familiar, if only in part and temporarily, with a vernacular version of the Bible. Quantity-production of the many translations by means of printing helped to broadcast them, even in Catholic countries, and with them went a heightened familiarity with an approved vernacular style. The nationalization of the churches thus tended to promote a nationalization of language and literature.

Popular poetry had a similar effect. The earliest and perhaps most spectacular instances of the power of the poets in this regard had already taken place in Italy and England (see Chapter X). Before 1500 Dante, Petrarch, Boccaccio, Ariosto, and Tasso had gone far toward making their Tuscan dialect Italy's literary language, and Chaucer had made the best English of his day rather than French the language of England's poetry. In the sixteenth century, but perhaps in a less decisive fashion, Francisco Sá de Miranda and Luis Vaz de Camoëns in Portugal, Joachim du Bellay, Pierre de Ronsard, and their associates in the group known as the Pléiade in France, and Garcilaso de la Vega and Fernando de Herrera in Spain had an analogous influence in determining good usage in their respective languages.

Several of the great literary and scholarly lights, sometimes with deliberate intent, helped to crystallize formal speech in their local tongues. In Chapter X we mentioned Lebrija's valiant efforts to standardize good Spanish usage. Calvin's *Institutes* and Montaigne's *Essays*, though less deliberately, set the standard for French prose. The Accademia della Crusca published in 1612 its *Vocabulario*, a dictionary of Italian based on fourteenth-century Tuscan usage, thus giving to the language of Dante a sanction that practically made it the Italian standard and at the same time furnishing a model of lexicography for other languages. The earliest original writer in Polish, Mikotaj Rey (1505–69), and his contemporary Piotr Skarga (1536–1612), the first rector of the Jesuit University of Wilno, provided the models of good composition in Poland. Elizah Bochur contributed to the fuller development of a standard Yiddish during the sixteenth century. Shakespeare's thirty-seven plays (c. 1590–1611), along with his sonnets and other non-dramatic works, were to become second only to the King James version of the Bible (1611) as a continuing influence on the speech of literate Englishmen, and a somewhat analogous influence is sometimes claimed for the approved translations or adaptations of Shakespeare in several other languages. Ludwig Holberg (1684–1754) found Danish a despised tongue and left it a medium of literature.

From the turn of the seventeenth century on, a number of factors made it possible for literary Russian to steer a middle course between the complicated structure of Church Slavonic and the oversimplification of the current vernacular; among them were script reform (which introduced a simpler alphabet than that of Church Slavonic), the western influences nurtured by Peter the Great, and the grammatical works, prose, and poetry of Lomonosov.

Monarchs striving in an age of ascending absolutism to consolidate their realms easily recognized the value of a common language for their purposes. Consequently, political authority was sometimes exerted in a policy to eliminate or at least subordinate the sometimes too free and intractable local patois. France furnished an excellent example of this policy. In 1539 Francis I decreed that all official publications should appear in French, giving precedence to the *langue d'oil* spoken around Paris. Henry IV, in his endeavours to unite his people after the great dissensions of the religious wars, officially commissioned his councillor François de Malherbe in 1605 to purify the French language. Thirty years later a stalwart exponent of centralization, Cardinal Richelieu, won a royal patent for the Académie Française, 'the Forty Immortals', who from their efforts to appraise literature soon passed also to preparing official dictionaries and grammars of their language. The first comprehensive dictionary of the French language appeared from its hands in 1694, during the reign of Louis XIV; a new edition followed in 1718 and again in 1740. By royal decree the Real Academia Española undertook a Spanish dictionary with the like objective of improving the national speech by distinguishing good from bad usage; eventually it published a *Diccionario de autoridades* in six volumes (1726–39), perhaps the most comprehensive dictionary of its day.

In no other cases was equally systematic attention given to language in the interest of political centralization. Royal activity in Portugal and Sweden pointed to a similar effort but to a more limited extent. In Russia too, Peter I, though not given to dealing with esoteric or aesthetic questions, directed some of his energy to the language problem, insisting on the use of the vernacular rather than Church Slavonic; under his influence and Catherine II's, Russian, already filled with Tatar and Polish words, borrowed technical terms freely from Latin and other western languages, particularly German, Dutch, English, and French. The decentralized Low Countries, on the other hand, during our period failed to develop a uniform Dutch, although the province of Holland set the standard in this regard as well as in others. The preparation of a dictionary of the English language 'by which its purity may be preserved' (as Samuel Johnson's *Plan* put it) was left to the initiative of private booksellers and the genius of Johnson; it appeared in two volumes only in 1755.

Grammatical and lexicographical works helped to create criteria of usage and style, furnishing better tools of communication while perhaps unduly restraining the forces that make learning and language a living, adaptable, and spontaneous part of a people's life. Dialects were no longer on an equal footing with the standard national tongue (which had, however, developed from a particular dialect). They nevertheless persisted, and so did several isolated languages like the Celtic tongues of Ireland, Manx, Scotland, Wales, and Brittany, the Basque of northwestern Spain and southwestern France, and the Sorbic of the Wends of East Germany. Elsewhere schoolmasters could teach more systematically an accepted form of expression in terms of which refinement, elegance, and style might be judged.

If a national language strengthened the cohesiveness among the various peoples within a nation, it also tended to become a barrier against communication with other nations. Yet language provided a link as well as a barrier. In contrast to the twentieth century, some cosmopolitan tongue or other continued to be widely used. The learned and cultivated in all west European lands—since scholarship was handed on in Latin, and cultivation of the mind implied the study of the Classics—could usually communicate with one another; they had not only a common language (despite differences of pronunciation) but also a common literary heritage. During the eighteenth century, when the use of Latin had diminished even in such conservative institutions as universities and when French culture asserted a general dominance in Europe, the French language, for a while at least, played a similar role in the discourse of the educated. In addition, the international-minded among the not always learned aristocracy gave French in the eighteenth century a fashionable appeal. It thus provided at least a temporary means of cosmopolitan communication in a civilization steadily growing more nationalistic. Besides, during this period European languages spread to vast territories outside of Europe. Spanish, Portuguese, English, French, Dutch, Danish and Russian conquerors and emigrants carried their language to new lands, thus spreading their literary heritage.

The languages of the immigrants often became modified by the language of the local populations or by the peculiarities of life in new surroundings. New products, institutions, and ways of doing things were reflected in the development of the migrant tongues. Separated from the mother land and from the steadying or altering influences that were there being exerted in linguistic matters, the European languages abroad developed in different directions. Afrikaans became something different from Dutch, Brazilian different from the Portuguese of Lisbon and Coimbra, Argentine and Mexican Spanish different from Castilian, and American different from the king's English. Wherever the products and practices of the wider world became important for Europe itself, they also brought new words to enrich Europe's vocabularies.

The Study of Language

The humanists of the Renaissance, devoted students of good style as they were, willy-nilly contributed to the development of the vernacular tongues. Their scholarly and aesthetic attitude toward the languages and literature of the Ancients was easily transferable to the modern languages, especially since
x*

all European languages had already been more or less influenced by Latin and Greek. Though their imitation of Ciceronian Latin may often have been slavish and sterile, discouraging originality and variety of expression, it yet developed an increasing sensitivity to good literary taste. The polemics of pro-Ciceronians and anti-Ciceronians stimulated conscious reflection upon good and bad usage in word construction. The study of a Classical language required a refined understanding of grammar and the structure of speech in general. Ardent teachers, such as Comenius (see Chapter XVI), became concerned about the best ways of teaching languages, and this concern stimulated the search for meaningful regularities and linguistic theories.

A number of linguistic works followed which, though probably not comparable to the flood after 1800, contributed greatly to the development of language tools. The humanists of the fifteenth and early sixteenth centuries compiled adages and other elegant, noteworthy sentiments, taken usually from Latin and Greek authors, who were held up as paramount examples of stylistic excellence. Erasmus's *Adagia* was perhaps the most popular compilation of this kind. Gradually, Classical linguistic interests became more systematic with the work of scholars like the Scaligers and the Estiennes. Nonetheless, the Classical languages began in the sixteenth century to give way as subjects of linguistic study before the devoted attention to the vernaculars, and in the case of the French Benedictines of the seventeenth century (most notably represented by Mabillon, Montfaucon, and the lay brother Du Cange) also before medieval Latin and Byzantine Greek, which had been spurned by the humanists as hybrid tongues.

Despite the facts that the study of the grammar, pronunciation, and orthography of several vernaculars had received serious attention since the end of the fifteenth century and that a fair number of authoritative dictionaries were published in the seventeenth and eighteenth centuries, scholarship still was weak on the etymological side. The weakness was due largely to the lack of a comparative Indo-European philology. During our period the scholarly study of comparative linguistics had its beginnings, meagre though they were. Bilingual dictionaries grew in number and precision during and after the Renaissance, and translating became a recognized literary profession. Largely independent of the practical needs of conqueror, administrator, merchant, and missionary, scholars began to investigate the relationships and differences of languages.[2] In 1300 an interest in Greek literature, even though it was one of the sources of Western civilization, was still somewhat rare; by 1500 the study of Greek was respectable and common, but in contrast, students of Hebrew felt called upon to justify their exotic tastes. By 1600 Hebrew had become a common scholarly tool, and Arabic, previously best known among the Christians of Spain, began to be added to the equipment of interested scholars elsewhere in Europe. Gesner in his *Mithridates* (1555) made the first serious attempt to study languages comparatively, but he knew nothing of Sanskrit. Only later did Filippo Sassetti (1540–88), during an extended visit to India, guess from comparable roots and forms that Sanskrit was related to the European languages, a conclusion that was in 1767 with fuller evidence restated by the Jesuit missionary Gaston Laurent Coeurdoux (1691–1779) in a letter to the Académie des Inscriptions. After 1700 Europe's publishers even risked the printing of dictionaries of such languages as Tamil and Algonquin. While Cardinal Ximenez' Polyglot Bible (completed in 1517) had provided texts in only four languages, the polyglot dictionary (*Linguarum Totius Orbis Vocabularis Comparativa*) compiled on the order of Catherine the Great included some 200, the Spanish philologist Lorenzo Hervás y Panduro in his *Catálogo de las lenguas de la naciones conocidas* (1800–1805) was to study 300, and the German philologist Johann Christoph Adelung was to present in his *Mithridates* (1806) samples of 500. Thus, as Europe's separate national languages were replacing the *langues de culture* even for scholars, overseas expansion of Europe's seafaring peoples helped to create an interest in the manifold vehicles of human expression that reached beyond the borders of nations and even of continents.

THE TECHNICAL APPARATUS OF LITERATURE

Bookmaking as a Business

Among the technological factors that fostered the European vernacular languages and literatures, the printing press was the most decisive. Probably, but for the invention of a means of mass publication at the very time that the vernacular tongues were emerging from folk usage to literary usage, they might have remained unacceptable to discriminating readers and writers longer. In terms of quantity and speed of distribution, printing made possible a method of reproducing thought that had never existed before. A writer could now find a wide public in a relatively short time. Thus a thinker or literary artist could within his own lifetime more confidently expect to exert an influence upon his nation or even his entire culture, and a much larger number of men and women could participate in the intellectual and literary life of their age. Since many widely differing ideas could be spread quickly, the printed book became a factor in promoting at the same time both intellectual diversity among the disciples of different writers and intellectual uniformity among the disciples of the same writers.

In an era of rotary presses, binding and cutting machinery, modern paper making, and the ordering of books by telephone and telegraph, the proficiency of the three hundred years between 1500 and 1800 may appear rudimentary indeed. Nevertheless, after the development of printing in Germany and its spread to various regions of the West during the second half of the fifteenth century, the history of printing was a story of amazing technical improvement, entrepreneurial daring, and increase of output. Many printers contributed to these ends. We have already encountered Froben of Basel (see Chapter X); Manutius and Plantin were no less enterprising.

Teobaldo Manuzio, alias Aldus Manutius of Venice (1450–1515), was one of the most productive printers of the sixteenth century. After studying Latin and Greek, and tutoring young aristocrats, Manutius conceived the idea of printing the Greek classics. One of his rich pupils, Alberto Pio, nephew of Pico della Mirandola, proved ready to finance the project, and around 1494 Manutius set up the 'Aldine' publishing house. He chose to do so in Venice, where he could find good libraries, wealthy patrons, wide marketing facilities, and refugee Greeks for editorial tasks. From the handwriting of one of his Cretan assistants, Marcus Musurus, he patterned his Greek type. Paper was obtained from mills in Fabriano (Ancona), famous since the thirteenth century for the excellence of its product. Printing ink was manufactured in Manutius's Venetian establishment, where the binding also was done.

The Aldine press gave to the world some of its first editions of the great classics, sometimes based on the hallowed manuscripts of the Venetian libraries. By 1500 Manutius had published numerous Greek masterpieces, including Hesiod, nine of Aristophanes' plays, and a five-volume Aristotle dedicated to his benefactor Alberto Pio. By the end of his crowded career (1515) he had printed in addition at least some of the works of Thucydides, Herodotus, Xenophon, Plutarch, Sophocles, Euripides, Demosthenes, Pindar, and Plato, to say nothing of a number of Latin works. His editing was a careful scholarly procedure; manuscript versions were collated and texts critically emended. His home was a beehive of scholars engaged in editorial activities. When in 1508 Erasmus's *Adagia* was in the press, the author worked at his final revisions at Manutius' home while Manutius and his proofreader busied themselves with the technical details of editing.

Technologically likewise the 'Aldine' editions were epochmaking. For Latin works Manutius adopted the semi-script type still called *italic*, which was a space-saver. His books were beautifully manufactured in a commendable effort to appease booklovers who resented machine-made products. Their title-pages were adorned with a dolphin-and-anchor emblem, symbolizing speed and stability, and carried the motto *Festina lente*. The volumes were small, a boon to those who actually used books and collected them in libraries. They were remarkably cheap—about two to three dollars a piece in modern currency, much less costly than huge folio tomes or manuscript books. Now, of course, they are collectors' items.

All was not smooth sailing for the new firm. Manutius had labour troubles, problems of distribution, and difficulty with foreign publishers, who 'pirated' his carefully prepared editions. Twice his press had to close because of wars. Meanwhile he had formed a Greek Academy—called *Neacademia*—from his circle of Hellenically inclined humanists. The constitution of the society was drawn up in Greek, Greek was used in its meetings, and most of the members translated or transliterated their names into Greek. Among the honorary foreign members were Erasmus and Thoman Linacre. After Manutius's death in 1515, the Aldine Press carried on under the management of Manutius' relatives and partners until 1597, when his grandson Aldo died. Never a remarkably successful venture from the financial standpoint—Manutius himself died poor and worn out—the Aldine Press was a monument to a practical humanist scholar and his sponsors, who dedicated their energies and fortunes to spreading through the West the literature of ancient Greece and Rome.

In northern Europe the progress of printing was reflected in the career of another great publisher, Christopher Plantin (1514–89) of Antwerp. Plantin started out as a mere bookbinder without much scholarly equipment. He learned to make use of the master engravers of the Netherlands in producing books unsurpassed anywhere for the merit of their illustrations. He printed Latin and Greek classics but is perhaps more famous for various editions of the Bible. One of his Bibles was printed with an exceptionally fine Hebrew type, provided by his partners, the van Bomberghes, descendants of a Dutch Christian, Daniel van Bomberghe, who had specialized in Venice in the printing of works in Hebrew. Another was the famous eight-volume polyglot Bible of Antwerp (c. 1568–71), financed by Philip II, king of Spain and the Netherlands. At the height of Plantin's prosperity his publishing house had somewhere between sixteen and twenty-two presses and between fifty-six and seventy-three pressmen (authorities differ), to say nothing of the staffs and equipment in his branch houses in Paris and Leyden, and Corneille van Bomberghe used a system of cost accounting for its bookkeeping. Today in Antwerp the Musée Plantin, remodelled after his old printing establishment, reveals the remarkable technological progress made by Plantin and other northern printers in the sixteenth century.

During most of that century printers generally used the simple press of the 'incunabula' period. It consisted of an upright frame with a flat, horizontal bed of stone or wood. The type was fitted in the upright frame and the sheets of paper were placed on the horizontal bed. The impression of the type on the paper was obtained by a screw device, which was worked laboriously with a detachable handle in order to apply the proper pressure. When the imprint was made, the pressure of the type-plane on the paper-plane was released by working the same device in reverse. And so on and on, sheet after sheet. With few modifications this sort of press was used till Willem Janszon Blaeu (1571–1638) of Amsterdam produced a better one. The new press, however, merely provided some improvements (which cannot now be exactly determined) in the details of operating the old screw press. Until Charles Stanhope (1753–1816) developed the labour-saving all-iron hand-press, the technical processes of bookmaking retained the cumbersomeness of the inventions of Gutenberg and other fifteenth-century printers.

More appreciable improvements were made in the process of book-illustration. As previously indicated, hand-illustrating of printed books continued during the early decades of printing. In addition, notable examples were provided during the 'incunabula' period of *printed* illustrations. Woodcuts were used, as they had been before the development of movable type—for example, in the *Magdeburg Chronicle*. By the end of the fifteenth century metal engravings had been introduced, though they did not become common until Plantin and other enterprising northern printers adopted them. Etchings came into use still later. From the beginning of printing, colour illustration was employed, done for the most part by hand on black-and-white illustrations that had been printed. Shortly after 1450, however, a remarkable example of multicolour printing appeared in the initial letters and illustrations of a psalter published at Mainz by Fust and Schaffer (1457). More common during this early era were simple initials printed in red and black.

The great printing centre of the fifteenth century was Mainz. During the sixteenth century several other cities achieved fame as printing centres. In addition to Venice with the establishments of Manutius and the Bomberghes, Antwerp with that of Plantin, and Basel with that of Froben, Paris, Leiden, Amsterdam, Leipzig, and Nuremberg (see Chapter XV) also had outstanding printing houses. The proportionally large number of these centres in the Netherlands is a measure of that little country's remarkable progress in the technology of printing as well as in other intellectual activities. Ivan Fedorov was the earliest significant book publisher of Russia. The first work printed in Russian seems to have been an edition (Moscow, 1564) of the Acts of the Apostles by Fedorov and Petr Mstislavets. Among a number of other books published by Federov was the first Russian Bible (Ostrog, 1581).

In its initial half-century the printed book still had to fight an uphill battle against the general humanistic preference for manuscripts. After 1500, however, the printed book almost altogether replaced the work of the scribe and copyist. The volume of printing increased tremendously. A library of machine-produced books was no longer thought of as an odious thing but rather as a mark of culture and learning.

The increase in the quantity of printing after 1500 was tremendous. The Mazarin Bible, one of the earliest printed books, was printed in an edition of 210 copies. Luther's version of the New Testament appeared in an edition of 5,000 copies in 1522 and had to be reprinted in ten weeks. His tract *To the Nobility of the German Nation* sold 4,000 copies in five days—a figure, however, which may be explained in terms of its special situation. In the year 1530 the town of Leipzig, which developed early as one of the book centres of Europe, had forty-six bookdealers. The so-called *Messkataloge* used by the bookdealers and publishers represented at the great fairs in Frankfort listed 256 book titles in 1564, 550 in 1565, 1,211 between 1641 and 1648, and 1,212 between 1649 and 1660; and the bookdealers at Leipzig, which superseded Frankfort by 1700, listed 3,286 titles between 1701 and 1710. Even a sparsely populated area like the nascent United States put out amazing numbers of publications—2,400,000 between 1639 and 1791.

The quality of printing after 1500 varied almost century by century. The sixteenth century was in many ways outstanding in terms of the beauty of the finished product. Manutius in Venice, Froben in Basel, the Estiennes in Paris, and Plantin in Antwerp put out books that were scholarly as well as esthetically pleasing, making good use of the arts of type-making, book-binding, woodcut, and etching. The printers and publishers of the seventeenth century improved the technical quality of the book very little and its artistic quality even less, but editions tended to become larger perhaps, and a few enterprising publishers like the Dutch Elzevir family did much to popularize books further by their economic (and still handsome) editions. During the eighteenth century, printers in England (e.g., William Caslon and John Baskerville), in Italy (e.g. Giambattista Bodoni), and especially in France (where the Imprimerie Royale, established by Richelieu in 1640, and the type designs of Philippe Grandjean set the pace) greatly improved their type and generally succeeded in publishing very attractive and relatively cheap books. As objects of art, the French and the Italian books of the Rococo period were likely to be representative of the contemporary style.

In addition to being a craft, book making was also a business. The gradual trend toward the specialization of labour was in a small way reflected also in printing and publishing between 1450 and 1800. In the beginning the printer had often combined editorial supervision with type-making, printing, illustrating, binding, and selling. Gradually all these functions began to be taken over by specialists with separate establishments and often with competing interests. In general, publishing tended to be a risky business, which seldom resulted in the acquisition of a great fortune. Competition was keen and sometimes unscrupulous. Pirating of texts was fairly common in the absence of copyright laws, the first effective one coming only in 1710 in England. Although the market was considerable, books were by no means cheap,[3] nor could they be produced fast enough for what we would today consider mass consumption. Consequently, publishing tended to concentrate in certain important locations and sometimes depended upon the support of a national government.

The Periodical and Censorship

The speed with which the printed word could reach a large public suggested a new channel for printing. Sometimes printers could exploit a far-reaching crisis, such as a war, a religious struggle, or a political controversy, to sell relatively cheap *gazzettas*, *corantos*, diurnals, newsbooks, or newsletters. The publication of regular newspapers started modestly in the late sixteenth century in Venice with the printing of the *Notizie Scritti* and continued uncertainly in the early seventeenth in Frankfort (*Avisa Relation oder Zeitung*), Antwerp (*Nieuwe Tijdingen*), London (*Weekly Newes*), and other cities. These initial journalistic attempts, despite censorship, bankruptcy, and other hardships, demonstrated that the printing press might be systematically used to satisfy a natural thirst for information on current affairs. The *Frankfurter Postzeitung* started on a long career in 1616, the *Gazette de France* in 1631,

and the *Oxford Gazette* (later the *London Gazette*) in 1665. Enduring maga-
zines came somewhat later. The French Academy of Sciences began publication of the *Journal des Sçavans* in 1665, and the same year the *Philosophical
Transactions* of the English Royal Society followed. The *Mercure Galant*
(subsequently the *Mercure de France*), devoted primarily to literature, first
appeared in 1672. Although still limited in circulation and often hampered by
governmental taxation and censorship, the new media of communication
gained a firm footing. Daily newspapers began to appear only in the eighteenth
century. Most of them were ephemeral or collapsed within a few years, but in
1772 the London *Morning Post* and in 1777 the *Journal de Paris* began a long-
lived existence. In general, the periodical press tended to be a separate part
of the publishing world, providing not only work and profit for a new type of
writer, the journalist, but also a vehicle for men who regarded the printing
press as an educational and propaganda medium.

The slow but constant growth of literacy in conjunction with the wider
spread of the printed word gave literature an increasing persuasive force.
Naturally, conservative institutions such as state or church exhibited deep
concern, on the one hand, for exploiting the printed word in their own
interest and, on the other, for controlling opposing opinions through sur-
veillance of the press. Censorship of literary expression, well known long
before 1500, after that date became more systematic in the hands of a still
powerful church and an ever more powerful state. The Catholic Church as
early as the first decade of the sixteenth century authorized its bishops to keep
a watchful eye over the products of printing. In an effort to reinforce its
foundations after the Protestant revolt, the papacy firmly institutionalized
censorship (see Chapter IV). Though the *Index Librorum Prohibitorum* has
never been so restrictive as has sometimes been claimed, it nonetheless was an
important and largely successful attempt to limit reading.

The European governments also experimented with various modes of
control. Effective use was made by some of them of the 'privilege' or 'license',
a permit which the printer was required to get from the central authority
before publishing a book and which could easily be revoked. In general, this
form of permission was a relatively simple form of prohibition.[4] A publisher,
probably a member of the stationers' guild to begin with and, if so, already
subject to its regulations, was obliged to proceed at his own risk—the risk
being that of subsequent prosecution and loss of license. *Ex post facto* control
of this sort cost the state little in bureaucratic machinery, but it also gave
controversial writings a good chance to 'slip through'. Preventive censorship,
the kind that passed judgment on a manuscript before publication and might
forbid its printing, was preferred by some governments to licensing but,
because of its bureaucratic cumbersomeness, sometimes gave way to a system
of tacit permission. Preventive censorship was abolished in England, for
instance, in favour of punitive censorship (1694). A rather common form of
censorship, partly because it constituted a source of added revenue, was the

taxing of newspapers by means of stamps, which tended to limit circulation by raising the price of papers and pamphlets.

Censorship was the rule in most European countries, but a few allowed unrestricted freedom of publication. Foremost among these few was the United Provinces. Its free press doubtless accounts in part for the intellectual prominence of that small federation during our period. The flood of reading matter emanating from these unrestricted publishing centres in many ways helped to counteract the censorship efforts of other governments. Counting on the great desire of people to say and read what they wished, publishers found many ways of 'bootlegging' literature. One of the favourite ones was to smuggle books into a forbidden area from a free one or merely to falsify the place of publication given on the title page. Occasionally a great public or literary figure openly took up the fight for full freedom of expression, and an eloquent piece of literature like Milton's *Areopagitica* (1644) might result, but most of the time writers battled only with the weapons of wit and satire or with the strategy of evasion by subterfuge and clandestine circulation. That their struggle was neither vain nor personal but was an expression of a general human desire for freedom was perhaps best attested by the universality and force with which freedom of the press was demanded throughout the eighteenth century.

An important outgrowth of the economic possibilities of the printing press and publishing was the growing economic independence of the writer. In former ages writing usually was a luxury which only those could afford who were supported by a wealthy patron or had the economic backing of a powerful institution such as a government, a monastic order, or a university. Some of the writings of the fifteenth-century humanists appear to us in bad taste because they were commissioned works for the glorification of fairly insignificant princes or benefactors, although, of course, many distinguished works also were produced under this sort of patronage. After 1500—the first notable case being Erasmus—the greater market created by the printing press began to make it feasible for a writer to earn a living from the products of his pen. Whether literature improved because writers became less dependent on royal or aristocratic Maecenases and became dependent instead on booksellers will doubtless remain a moot point. Few writers indeed amassed fortunes by relying solely on the income from the sale of their books, and in many cases patrons (among whom the members of the wealthy, book-buying middle class became increasingly consequential) were still assiduously sought. Even so, the man with ideas that did not appeal to the powerful—a radical politician like John Wilkes or an eloquent freethinker like Voltaire—could say what he wished, if he dared, and despite censorship and court penalties could still hope by subterfuge or defiance to find a market and some income.

Libraries and Reference Compendia

The mounting output of books increased the need for storing and in some sense systematizing the written products of the human mind. The number, size, and use of libraries grew tremendously during the period between 1500 and 1775. This growth was both a cause and an effect of the shift in Europe's intellectual life toward secular and temporal influences at the expense of the religious and ecclesiastical. Whereas monasteries or cathedral schools had once provided the great storehouses of manuscripts, the new libraries grew out of the collections of monarchs, rich nobles, universities (which were gradually becoming less and less dominated by clerics and monastic orders), and wealthy members of the middle class. Noteworthy exceptions to this trend were the Vatican Library at Rome and those of the Maurists at Paris and of some Jesuit colleges, where serious scholarly concerns often prevailed. The bigger private collections grew, the more common it became to hand them over eventually to some larger and more public library. The core of many great libraries of our day goes back to such gifts from great collectors. The universities of Europe and, later, the scholarly academics often depended on the contributions of patrons but sometimes were able to accumulate vast bibliographical treasures simply because they could add continually to their collections over a long span of time.

The royal libraries tended to develop into the largest ones. They usually benefited not only from regal munificence but also from the fact that rulers, in their efforts to control publishing, in certain instances created a sort of 'deposit library' to which publishers were required to send one or more copies of the books they published. Especially noteworthy among the new royal foundations of the sixteenth century were Philip II's library at the Escorial Palace near Madrid, the royal Bavarian library at Munich, and the French royal library, which Francis I moved to Fontainebleau, whence later it was returned to Paris, eventually to become part of the Bibliothèque Nationale. Before the end of the sixteenth century other royal collections, destined to be great university or national libraries, had been brought together in Dresden, Vienna, Copenhagen, Cracow, Stockholm, and other capitals. By the early seventeenth century the royal library in Paris had a catalogue of some six thousand volumes.

Other illustrious libraries were instituted during the sixteenth century. Significant book collections had already existed in several universities—e.g. Paris, Salamanca, and Cambridge—and in that century the libraries of some others became the foundations of world-famous collections—e.g. St. Andrews, Glasgow, Aberdeen, Oxford (refounded by Thomas Bodley), Ingolstadt (later removed to Munich), Heidelberg, Basel, Prague, Coimbra, Leyden, Utrecht, and Amsterdam. Municipal libraries became fairly common in urban centres before 1600—e.g. Edinburgh, Angers, Bourges, Carpentras, Clermont-Ferrand, Lyons, Venice, and Modena. The British Museum Library began comparatively late (1700), with the donation of the collection of Robert Bruce Cotton to the nation in 1700. In general, monastic and private collections fell behind in the race, often being absorbed by university or national libraries. Today, in some of Europe's finest libraries the names of some illustrious collection, commemorating a famous private collector such as Chigi, Bessarion, Urbino, Laud, Coislin, Mazarin, and Cotton, give evidence of a voluntary merger by gift or purchase.

The recently settled community of Boston, Massachusetts, created a public library in 1653, but genuinely public libraries, accessible to all comers without fee, did not yet exist in Europe. The Bodleian Library at Oxford, however, had set the precedent for a semi-public library, open to a large if still restricted number of students and other recommended persons, and by the end of the eighteenth century library development had reached a stage that was not far removed from the public libraries of our day; subscription libraries, available to those who paid a regular fee, and book collections of local reading groups (the *sociétés de pensée* of the eighteenth century) filled the needs of a public gradually growing in literacy.

As the sheer bulk of printed materials increased, new tools were developed for the more efficient use of books. Libraries compiled catalogues of their holdings. Scholars and practical bookmen began to publish bibliographies of the available materials on certain subjects. As we have seen, lexicographers made specialized dictionaries of one kind or another. When, in the seventeenth century learned journals began to appear with a certain measure of regularity, they carried sections in which they announced and discussed new publications. Concordances of the Bible and critical editions of basic Classical texts were compiled. This development of special kinds of books for the better use and understanding of other books revealed the mounting significance of books in general.

The accumulating number of encyclopedias also strikingly illustrated the enormous increase in scholarship and literary interest. Compendia of knowledge were known in European antiquity and medieval times and had been still more highly developed in some of the other great cultures, particularly in China (see below). From the thirteenth century on, a good number of compilations of then existing knowledge appeared in Europe. Most of them suffered from the fact that they were the works of a single man. They were usually either ambitious in scope but unreliable or more reliable but limited in scope. One of the more reliable of the one-man compendia was Bayle's *Dictionnaire historique et critique* (1697; English translation, 1710). During the eighteenth century, however, learned men began to work in groups in order to publish encyclopedias that in every sense were worthy predecessors of the great compendia of the modern world. None perhaps ever had greater impact on European intellectual life in its time than the *Encyclopédie* of Diderot and his associates. 'We dare say,' said D'Alembert in the famous *Discours préliminaire* of that work, 'that if the ancients . . . had elaborated such an Encyclopedia and if its manuscript alone had escaped from the fire that destroyed the library of Alexandria, this would have been sufficient to console us for the loss of the rest.'[5]

Libraries outside Europe probably did not arise with equal rapidity, nor did municipal and university libraries for semi-public use develop as fully as in Europe. Nevertheless, in India the great palm-leaf manuscript collections in some monastic and temple schools grew, and the Mogul emperors also collected important manuscript libraries; and in China the libraries of the Manchu emperors exceeded earlier imperial collections. The rate of Chinese book publication rose swiftly; over 15,000 works are estimated to have been published during the K'ang-hsi period alone (1662–1722). Until the middle of the eighteenth century, it has been estimated, China had printed more books than perhaps the rest of the world combined.[6] The enormous *Ssu-k'u ch'uan-shu* (*Complete Library of the Four Branches of Literature*), assembled during the Ch'ien-lung period, was an Imperial Manuscript Library of what was regarded as the best among extant books. It contained 3,461 works in over 36,000 volumes (*ts'e*) of 78,000 chapters (*chüan*), and the printed and anno-tated catalogue (1782) of all the books considered for inclusion contained 10,254 titles in over 171,000 *chüan*. Unfortunately, the editing of this collec-tion was used by the ruler as an opportunity to delete passages or destroy works which criticized the Manchus and other Tatars or otherwise dis-pleased him. Two copies of the yet enormous though purged collection were kept in the Peking area, and others in Jehol, Mukden, Yang-chou, Chin-chiang, and Hang-chou, to make it more accessible to scholars. In China the number of large private library buildings (one of which contained over 100,000 chapters in its founder's day) grew markedly after 1500, more than 500 being famous in the Manchu period. Of these, the T'ien-i-ko of Ningpo, founded in 1550, still survives; it was made of brick and tile without wood, and its staff enforced special rules to prevent fire and other damage. The Yi dynasty of Korea accumulated large libraries at Seoul, and considerable ones arose at Kyoto and Edo in Japan.

POETRY, DRAMA, AND FICTION IN EUROPE

Folk Literature

While brilliant original creative writings immortalized new names between 1500 and 1775, a rich old literature persisted that was nameless and often not dateable. Usually disdained by the educated classes during the first two centuries of our period, it was handed down by oral tradition. Numerous songs, stories, epics, dramas, legends, proverbs, riddles, and fairy tales thus survived many generations, undergoing variations that often further augmen-ted their richness and colour. Some of them were written down by unknown scribes or, on occasion, by writers whose names we sometimes know—e.g. Anders Sprensen Vedel, who in 1591 published a collection of Danish folk-songs, and the Russian Metropolitan Macarius (d. 1563), whose *Chetyi Minei* (*Saints' Calendar*) compiled Holy Scripture, patristic writings, church decrees, lives of saints, and folktales into one huge collection. Sometimes collectors breathed into such folklore their own artistry (see Chapter X), but after 1700 literary-minded persons began to collect it systematically and tried to promote a greater appreciation for the native qualities of its eloquent, if sometimes unrefined, treasures. A great deal of folk literature was then presented to the peoples who had produced it as a part of their respective national heritages. In the late eighteenth and early nineteenth centuries collectors and writers—with a romantic love for tradition, respect for the common people, and belief in the *Volk*—turned to folk-literature as a form of artistic expression fully deserving admiration, study, and even imitation. The vogue of folklore was so pronounced that James Macpherson (1736–96) was able to palm off his own tales as the work of Ossian, legendary bard of the Highlands, until challenged by Dr Johnson and others.

Even though it is quite impossible in most instances to date this folk literature with any accuracy, much of the heritage of song and story either originated or was significantly modified between 1500 and 1775. Identifiable social institutions, moods, and preoccupations, and the impact of particular events are clearly reflected in them. Some German songs were unmistakably associated with the mercenary soldiers (the *Landsknechte*) of the type that flourished roughly from 1450 to 1650. Others reflected the life of the soldier and the horrors of armed conflict in the days of Europe's absolute monarchies. Certain Russian tales centre around the struggle with the 'Golden Horde'; a few disclose the local patriotism of the burghers of Novgorod, Pskov, and other towns subjugated by Moscow or satirize church and state officialdom. Witches, ghosts, and like manifestations of the supernatural were a common theme. Folklore served as a medium by which the unhappy poor released their pent-up feelings against the rich and powerful and by which conquered peoples (e.g. in Mexico, the Balkans, Ireland, and central Europe) managed to preserve some of their 'national' traditions. The unsophisticated stylistic or linguistic characteristics of many of these folk creations, even when poured into a more elegant literary mould by later writers, betrayed their origin as folk literature.

In all likelihood the products of folk literature express to some degree the artistic qualities of the individuals who composed them or gave them their basic formulation, and it would be erroneous to regard them altogether as spontaneous. Nevertheless, this was the literature (rather than the more formal kind soon to be discussed) that thrived among the great masses of people and was most meaningful and accessible to the illiterate. It represented the simple literary tastes of the uncultured and less powerful masses. Its beauty and significance was usually overlooked by the more educated and polished (though they were not entirely free from its pervasive spirit) until the Romantic Movement recognized its intrinsic merit and universal appeal.

New Poetic Forms

The humanists of the Renaissance revived literary forms that had flourished in Antiquity but had been lost or rarely used during the Middle Ages.

Lascaris's publication of *The Greek Anthology* (see Chapter X) was followed by Joseph Scaliger's anthology (1573) of Latin poetry. These anthologies, together with the renditions and translations of Classical poetry by the sixteenth-century French poets Clément Marot and Mellin de Saint-Gelais, gave some of the favourite poetic forms of Antiquity a considerable vogue. For example, the epigram and the ode began to appear frequently in European poetry around 1600.

Other poetic forms usually continued as before, but in some cases, such as the ballade and the sonnet, some refinement took place, so that, for example, the Shakespearean sonnet differed in rhyme pattern from the Italian. Song forms like the Provençal *chanson* and the Italian *canzone* and madrigal (see Chapter XII), frequently written without the intention of musical accompaniment, enjoyed a distinct popularity. Numerous schemes of verse, rhyme, and meter were employed, but the *ottava rima* (eight lines of ten or eleven syllables each) became the accepted stanza of Italian epic poetry after Ariosto and Tasso, Alexandrine verse was almost obligatory for French and other continental epic and tragedy after Ronsard, and Spenser's preference for decasyllabic lines, reinforcing Chaucer's, set the model for English heroic verse. Subsequent epic poets of England—Dryden and Pope, for example—preferred, however, the heroic couplet to the 'Spenserian stanza' (eight decasyllabic iambic lines with a ninth of Alexandrine) of Spenser's *Faërie Queene* (1599–1611). Classical dactylic hexameter was rare before the eighteenth century.

Developments in the Theatre

During this period Classical drama, revived by Renaissance playwrights, merged with Christian spectacle to form the basis of Europe's future dramatic development. The religious play was brought to perhaps its greatest height in the *autos* (*acts*) of the Spanish and the Portuguese dramatists of the late sixteenth and early seventeenth century, of whom Lope de Vega (1562–1635) and Pedro Calderón de la Barca (1600–81) are probably the best known today.[7] The *auto* was usually a one-act spectacle performed outdoors in connection with a church procession and structured around an allegory suitable for the holy day on which it was performed. Such religious dramas were also frequently presented in the Jesuit schools. In general, the religious performances continued longer and flourished more freely in the Catholic and the Lutheran (particularly Scandinavian) areas of Europe than in those dominated by the more iconoclastic Calvinists.

The importance of this kind of religious theatre was greater than the mere number of plays would seem to indicate. It was to a large extent folk drama, enjoyable for all layers of society. It represented a flexible art form (often not even written down), in which improvisation played a good part. It united the common Christian tradition with popular lore. Its patrimony to the professional actors of the *commedia dell'arte* (see Chapter X), which reached its highest elaboration in the sixteenth century, was probably considerable. More important perhaps, the irregular, impromptu dialogue of the religious play and of the *commedia dell'arte* prepared the way for the wider social acceptance of a regular secular theatre. For meanwhile, too, written plays on secular themes (often based on *Schwänke*, *fabliaux*, and historical episodes) had become popular. Of the more than 2,000 dramatic pieces that Lope de Vega is said to have written and the well over 400 of which the text is known, the overwhelming number were on secular themes; and Calderón wrote 120 plays, many of them on secular themes, in addition to numerous *autos*. These two writers (particularly Lope de Vega, whom Calderón often imitated and sometimes, as was a common practice in that day, plagiarized) not only gave form to the Spanish drama but through translations and borrowings also influenced the French and the English stage, both of which frankly exploited their Spanish sources.

Parallel to the rise of the new dramatic literature went a revival of Classical drama—in particular, tragedy. This revival resulted not only in the publication and study of the works of the great Greco-Roman tragedians—Aeschylus, Sophocles, Euripides, and Seneca—but also in a growing awareness of the dramatic theories of Antiquity, particularly Aristotle's. Classical concepts of dramatic form, with the notable exception of the basic role assigned by Ancient writers to the chorus, helped to shape the structure of European drama. Plays were divided into scenes and acts in accordance with Classical conventions. Three acts were used predominantly by Spanish, Portuguese, and Italian writers in imitation of Terence, five by English and French writers in imitation of Seneca. This convention, in turn, influenced the structure and exposition, the climax and denouement of the plot. Meters varied, and the use of rhyme was by no means universal. Toward the close of our period, metric verse was frequently replaced by prose. In general, English and Spanish dramatists developed plays of a freer style than did the French classicists, particularly after a controversy precipitated by Corneille's *Le Cid*. We shall see in greater detail later that the French dramatists attempted to make their plays adhere to fixed rules of dramatic style and form allegedly derived from Aristotle's *Poetics*. Comedy (though more complex because of its association with the looser traditions of farce and burlesque) also was to a certain extent influenced in its formal aspects by the revival of Classical comedy, especially Plautus and Terence (but hardly at all by the greatest comedian of antiquity, Aristophanes).

While religious plays were often performed by amateurs on 'natural' stages (such as the steps of a church), the comedies and tragedies of the modern literary artist called for interpretation by professionals with increasingly elaborate scenery. Repertory theatres with permanent troupes grew up, such as the Globe Theatre, of Shakespearean fame, and the great hall of the Hôtel Bourbon, where Molière's company held forth. More common (and, in a sense, more in keeping with the technical nature of the dramas of a

Racine or a Molière) were the small theatres at royal or princely courts, visited by itinerant companies of professional actors. The Comédie Française founded in 1680, was the first state-supported public theatre. Despite frequent marks of social disapproval the number of theatres, actors, plays, and serious dramatists mounted.

The Ancients versus the Moderns

Great changes in form took place also in prose literature after 1500. While previously prose had, of course, been used extensively in the writing of history, philosophy, and other non-fictional subjects (considered elsewhere in this volume), only rarely was creative writing done in prose. Subsequently a great variety of literary forms employing prose evolved, until literary expression commonly became prose expression. The novelette and the novel emerged as favoured art forms. Collections of short stories, tied together by such simple devices as the single narrator of the *Arabian Nights* or the common audience of Boccaccio's *Decameron*, enjoyed wide popularity. Eighteenth-century novelists frequently used the device of an exchange of letters among their characters to develop their stories. The art of the essay was greatly furthered by such skillful writers as Montaigne and Bayle, Addison and Steele. The increasing number of periodicals, newspapers, and almanacs brought forth a journalistic prose style. Polemic has rarely been more eloquently carried on than in the pamphlets, satires, or letters of Luther, Pascal, Swift, and Voltaire, or memoirs more engagingly narrated than in the auto-biographies of Cellini, the *Raskolnik* leader Avvakum, Rousseau, and Franklin. The epigram was nobly employed by La Rochefoucauld and Franklin, homily by the Polish Jesuit Piotr Skarga, the Russian Archbishop Theofan Prokopovich (1681–1736), and the French bishops Jacques Bénigne Bossuet (1627–1704) and Jean Baptiste Massillon (1663–1742), and oratory by Savonarola and Edmund Burke. And under the influence of Classical examples (especially Cicero's) cultivated Europeans, from the humanists through the Russian tsars to the *philosophes*, lifted letter writing to the level of a highly refined art, of which Madame de Sévigné and Lord Chesterfield were perhaps the leading exponents.

In the Western countries, the generations between the Renaissance and the beginning of the Romantic Movement were exceedingly self-conscious about literary criteria. Standards of criticism were explicit in the minds of literary men, in many ways tied up with and analogous to their philological concerns. All in all this period, and especially the decades of 'the Quarrel of the Ancients and the Moderns'—i.e. the battle of the advocates with the opponents of literary neoclassicism—at the close of the seventeenth and the beginning of the eighteenth century were perhaps the most erudite and form-conscious epoch in the history of Western literature.

The Western literary world of these times was torn by the strife between the defenders of free and spontaneous literary form and the advocates of firm models, rules, and standards. On the one side stood those writers who, with qualifications (since literary men can never wholly escape concern with problems of form), were basically preoccupied with saying what they wished to say without serious formal restrictions and those critics who defended the poet's freedom or the artist's right to deviate from rules and preconceived standards of 'good taste'. On that side were found most of the great Spanish poets and dramatists, Shakespeare, and critics like Bernard de Fontenelle (1657–1757) and Charles Perrault (1628–1703); they generally went their own way without much or only amused attention to the literary quarrels around them. These men and their admirers were sometimes referred to as the 'Moderns'. They did not necessarily look down upon literary traditions (Lessing, for example, while holding up Shakespeare as a better model than Racine, respected the authority of Aristotle), but they did feel that modern literature might have merit of its own even when it did not imitate the writings of Antiquity.

On the other side stood the 'Ancients'. They comprised those writers and critics who believed that literature was a disciplined art with an ascertainable hierarchy of forms, each having its particular qualities from which standards could be deduced for firm judgments. They stood for such qualities as edification, clarity, decorum, and symmetry expressed in preferred forms like epigram, epic, and verse tragedy. Foremost among the Ancients in France were Boileau, Racine, and Fénelon—with some assistance, when 'the Quarrel of the Ancients and the Moderns' moved across the Channel, from Swift, Pope, and (ambivalently, because of his admiration for Shakespeare) Dryden. In the eighteenth century, Johnson impugned the dramatic 'unities' (see below) to defend Shakespeare, but in Russia Alexander Petrovich Sumarakov (1718–77), along with Lomonosov, in tragedies based on themes borrowed from Russian history inaugurated a reign of classicism, looking to Boileau, and later Voltaire, as arbiter.

The 'Ancients' were greatly influenced by the revival of Classical literary theories. It was admiration for Classical epigram, epic, and tragedy that led them to the defence of these forms as the most exalted in the literary hierarchy. Under the influence of Classical literary theories, especially those of Aristotle's *Poetics* and Horace's *Ars Poetica*—and these, more particularly, as represented in Boileau's *L'art poétique* (1674) and Pope's *Essay on Criticism* (1711)—they constructed explicit rules for poetry. In drama they upheld with special rigour the rule of the 'three unities'—of action, time, and place—extrapolated in the sixteenth century by Ludovico Castelvetro and other Italian critics from Aristotle's dramatic theory. The 'unities' were followed in Ben Jonson's *Alchemist* (1610), Jean de Mairet's *Sophonisbe* (1634), and Joseph Addison's *Cato* (1713), to cite but a few examples. Even a fairly formalistic dramatist like Corneille at first fell short of the Neoclassicists' doctrines, but after a pamphlet war precipitated by his partial violation of them in *Le Cid* (1636), he conformed to their standards of unity, purity of genre, decorum, and edification. With Racine's *Berenice* (1670), *Phèdre* (1677), *Athalie* (1691), and other tragedies the dramatic unities became a strict convention of the French stage until the time of the Romantics. The works of perhaps the world's greatest writer of tragedies, William Shakespeare, long remained in the Neoclassicists' sight sadly amorphous and sometimes unedifying constructions, and inferior therefore.[8]

Stringent formalism, combined with an esthetic and moralistic aversion to crudities, resulted in comdemnation of some of the memorable literary achievements of Antiquity and ended in such absurdities as the rewriting and purifying of Homer. On the other hand, the intense preoccupation with the formal questions of literature promoted sensitivity to fundamental artistic values and problems. In addition, it gave a mighty impetus to Classical scholarship and to the stylistic vogue in the arts and letters of Neoclassicism. At the close of our period, with the pre-romantics of France and the *Sturm und Drang* of Germany, and most explicitly in the critical writings of Herder, the Classical criteria of literary taste gave way to a preference for greater individuality of form and more spontaneous norms of style and structure.

Varieties of Literary Moods

Like the good literature of all ages, that of 1500–1775 gave expression to universal interests, values, and problems. Love with all its shadings from the basest passion to the feeling of mysterious union with the cosmos; war with its brutal horrors and brave sacrifices; death and disease with their accompanying fears; beauty whether of the female form or of the setting sun; despair, sorrow, and pain; indignation at injustice and the quest for right; hope, joy, laughter, and fun; adulation, contempt, and satire—all the manifold attitudes, experiences, and desires of man found ample and moving articulation in the poetry, drama, and prose of the epoch. It began with the Renaissance humanism of commanding figures like Erasmus, Rabelais, and Machiavelli and ran through the classical period of several national literatures with such peerless masters as Tasso, Cervantes, Shakespeare, and Racine, to the humanitarianism of the Enlightenment, represented by the mature works of Lomonosov, Rousseau, and Voltaire, and the early works of Goethe. At the same time—and this consideration constitutes our basic concern here—this literature also exhibited in its content, themes, and moods the varying peculiarities of the age. So many contemporary movements and problems were somehow reflected in the *belles lettres* of this era of two hundred and seventy-five years (quite apart from its philosophic, polemic, scholarly, and historical prose) that its imaginative literature forms one of the best media for fathoming its changes of temper.

A most troublesome problem of the era was the passionate religious controversy engendered by the Reformation, the Counter Reformation, and the Wars of Religion. The varying character of the numerous Protestant splintergroups (ranging from individualistic pietism to radical social action) can with simple clarity be sensed in their hymns; except for the ubiquitous translations of the Bible, prayer books and hymns were perhaps the most widely influential literary achievement of the Protestants. The deep devotion of the Puritan found more literary expression in John Milton's *Paradise Lost* (1667) and John Bunyan's *Pilgrim's Progress* (1678–84). John Donne (1572–1631) mixed 'metaphysical' profundity with a deep religious conviction in both poems and sermons. Pascal's posthumously published *Pensées* (1670) combined a Jansenist piety, even mysticism, with touches of irony and epigrammatic wisdom. The religious fervour of Spanish poets and mystics like St Theresa of Avila, Fray Luis de Leon (1527–91), and St John of the Cross amply testify to the emotional intensity of the Catholic Counter Reformation.

The Faust and the Don Juan theme illustrate the persistence of traditional concepts of Hell as the terrible, eternal abode of the wicked and worldly. The bohemian Christopher Marlowe, accused by some of his contemporaries of atheism, was, for all that, troubled by the problems of evil and the renunciation of God; the restless scholar who is the central figure in his *Tragical History of Doctor Faustus* (*c.* 1588), weary of science, bargains away his soul in return for power and pleasure but in the end rues his contract with the Devil. Don Juan's fate, though not the outcome of an explicit bargain, is no kinder. Unmitigated sensualist, seeker after momentary worldly pleasure, enjoying the day and trusting little to the morrow, defying moral and theological principles, Don Juan charmed and seduced for the sheer joy of conquest, but he pays the inescapable penalty in the end. He first appeared in *El burlador de Seville y convidado de piedra* by Fray Gabriel Tellez (pen name, Tirso de Molina, 1584?–1648) and reappeared in Molière's *Le Festin de Pierre* (1660) and other plays before Mozart gave him (1787) operatic immortality.

Nevertheless, the changing mood of early modern man from preoccupation with other-worldliness to skepticism of both heaven and hell and to acceptance of his temporal condition was also easily perceptible in imaginative literature. For one thing, the number of satires on church dignitaries like those in Erasmus's *Praise of Folly* (1509) and in the *Letters of Obscure Men* (1515–17) by Crotus Rubeanus and Ulrich von Hutten increased until the heckling of ecclesiastical obscurantism and *l'infame*, while still risky, ceased to be rare, and passed as a literary heritage to the Enlightenment writers like Voltaire and Diderot. Meanwhile man's conquest of nature through science was eulogized, as in Fontenelle's *Entretiens sur la pluralité des mondes* (1686), and pantheistic nature was glorified, as in James Thomson's *Seasons* (1726–1730). Pagan gods and heroes were more and more substituted in metaphor for saints and angels; Camoëns resorted to this device in *Os Lusiadas* (1572) and Milton, humanist as well as Puritan, in *Comus* (1643) and other poems. The taste for lusty writings like the ubiquitous *facetiae* grew. Marguerite of Angoulême's *Heptameron* and Rabelais' *Gargantua and Pantagruel*, mirroring life in Renaissance France of the sixteenth century, speak candidly of the enjoyment of worldly pleasures, though (as is indicated in other contexts) their authors were greatly concerned with eternal problems and with man's higher nature. The philosophical breadth, not to mention the literary quality, that characterized Rabelais' satire is lacking in some of the libertine writings of the seventeenth and eighteenth century (see Chapter V), but their anti-clerical and pyrrhonist tone is more evident and, if anything, is less jovial and good-natured. Boldness of religious scepticism regarding the Christian tradition culminated with the Enlightenment, and in letters of an imaginative nature (not to rename from Chapter VII the more prosaic titles) it was perhaps most perceptible in Voltaire's *Poème sur le désastre de Lisbonne* (1756), Hume's *Dialogues Concerning Natural Religion*, and Diderot's *Le neveu de Rameau* (the last two published only posthumously).

The Reflection of Current Trends in Literature

The growing consciousness of the inhabitants of the different countries of Europe that they were both heirs and bequeathers of their common culture was enhanced not only by the rise of the vernaculars but by the patriotic trend in poetry, drama, and prose as well. The patriotic spirit manifested itself in the Russian songs and legends celebrating the great victories over Teuton and Tatar, in the Ukrainian *dumy* commemorating the heroic struggles with Tatar, Turk, and Pole, in the plays of Shakespeare about spectacular English kings, in the bitter lamentations of Grimmelshausen's *Simplicissimus* (1669) about a Germany torn by the foreign invasions and internecine strife of the Thirty Years War, in the Alexandrine declamations put by Corneille in the mouths of the patriots of Rome and Spain, and in the dramatizations by Friedrich Gottlieb Klopstock (1724–1803) and Goethe of the lives of German heroic figures.[9]

Polish literature provides a more than typical example of the general literary trend toward national concerns and patriotism. Before 1500 the Polish humanist used the vernacular rarely, perhaps even more rarely than his confreres farther west, but with the Bible translations and the polemics and sermons of the Reformation the foreboding and pride of Polish writers in both camps were often expressed in the vernacular. The Jesuit Father Skarga in his *Parliamentary Sermons* (1547) stirred his hearers and set a standard for Polish prose by his patriotic jeremiads. His lifetime, the turn of the sixteenth century, was also the 'golden age' of Polish poetry. Jan Kochanowski (1530–84) showed convincingly that the vernacular was an excellent vehicle for the Polish muse with his poems *Frazki* (*Trifles*, a collection of proverbs) and *Treny* (*Lamentations*, on the death of his daughter) and with his drama in the Classical vein, *The Dismissal of the Greek Envoys*. His contemporary and successor Simon Szymonowicz (1554–1642) wrote beautiful pastorals, of which *Kolacz* (*The Lake*) may be singled out as perhaps the best and probably the most popular. In the seventeenth century, though Classic (and French) influences still were marked, the intermittent war with the Turks made the patriotic theme more insistent. Woclaw Potocki (1625–96) in *Wojna Chocinska*

(*Chocin Campaign*) and other war epics celebrated the deeds of Sobieski and lesser Polish heroes, reflecting his anxiety about the loss of the ancient Polish virtues. Vespasian Kochowski (1633–1700) also wrote epics of war but is better remembered for his *Polish Psalmody*. The Serbian poet Ivan Gundulić (1588–1638), translator of Tasso and other Latin and Italian poets into Serb, similarly glorified the victory of the Poles over the Turks in his *Osman* (first printed in 1826). If few of the patriotic expressions of this period matched the competitive ardour of nineteenth-century nationalism, they yet reflected the rising national sentiment and at the same time helped to foster it.

Current changes in the political and social order were likewise mirrored in the writings of the day. The general tendency of the patriotic literature was to eulogize princes and dynastic rule, as befitted an era of growing centralization of power. Yet, this tendency was counterbalanced by oft-quoted passages in praise of the republican spirit of Antiquity or in condemnation of the arrogance of rulers in the works of Shakespeare, Corneille, Racine, and Voltaire. Ideals of knighthood, which had strongly coloured the literature of the Middle Ages, were now sometimes treated mockingly as antiquated relics of a no longer viable mode of life; Cervantes' *Don Quixote* (1605 and 1615) gave to literature a new character type—the impractical, simple-minded, visionary but noble knight of the sad countenance, victim of his own illusions, laughable but lovable—*quixotic*, in short. Instead of the knightly ideal writers put forth that of the gentleman, the *honnête homme*, with good manners and good sense, a certain amount of worldly learning and of accomplishment in the arts, a still strongly developed sense of chivalry and honour, and an appreciation of the graciousness of life.

This gentlemanly ideal had been portrayed even before Cervantes made sport of Don Quixote. Alphonse Martinez de Toledo, under the name of the Archpriest of Talavera (as he was), had published as early as 1438 a treatise dealing with worldly love and other questions of common morality and behaviour. Generally known as *El corbacho* (*The Whip*), the book sought to teach more edifying ways, largely through a fictitious misogynist who lashed vice, sin, and bad manners as if they were exclusively feminine weaknesses. Proper behaviour was subsequently held up as an ideal not only in Castiglione's *Il Cortegiano* (1528) and other sixteenth-century writings on education (see Chapter XVI) but also in the seventeenth century in Mme. de Lafayette's novels and Molière's plays, where the crude pretentiousness of the name characters in *Les précieuses ridicules* (1659), *Le bourgeois gentilhomme* (1670), or *Les femmes savantes* (1672) might be set off against the common decency and genuine worth of a lesser character such as Cléante. The gentlemanly hero was thoroughly overdrawn later in Samuel Richardson's *Sir Charles Grandison* (1753) and enveloped in a thick coating of *sensibilité* in the characterization of Wolmar in Rousseau's *Nouvelle Héloïse* (1761)—well-bred, honourable, philanthropic, forgiving, intellectual.

In some ways the counterparts to this urbane ideal were found in the simple heroes of the widespread pastoral literature, who inhabited a blessed never-never-land (Arcadia) where simple shepherds, shepherdesses, and nymphs dwelt in peace and happiness. Their life was rustic but without the harshness of rusticity, for nature was always benevolent and beautiful. The prototypes of this kind of romance are to be found in Greek and Roman literature; but the genre was revived in the *Arcadia* (1504) of Jacopo Sennazaro and was subsequently echoed by Jorge de Montemayor (1521-61), Sir Philip Sidney (1554-86), Spenser, Honoré d'Urfé (1568-1626), Tasso, Cervantes, Milton, and others.

In contrast, the rising bourgeoisie was gaining ground and made its vigour felt. In a way, that vigour was reflected in the 'picaresque' novel, centred in a usually amiable rogue (Spanish, *picaro*), who was sometimes drawn from a historical model. The picaroon was rarely genteel, only occasionally gentle, and nearly always engaged in energetic and merry or exciting frauds and escapades. The first well-known hero of this description was the subject of *La vida de Lazarillo de Tormes y de sus fortunas y adversidades* of unknown authorship but perhaps the work of Diego Hurtado de Mendoza (1503-75). Lazarillo was depicted as a kindly but not very bright beggar boy who serves several masters in turn, not always to his own advantage. His story has been described as the first novel to employ psychological analysis in order to show not only that poverty is not properly a subject of ridicule but also that human character is a mixture of good and bad.[10] It was followed by a number of similar narratives, of which the most famous were Mateo Alemán's *Guzman de Alfarache* (1599), *La Picara Justina* (1605, likewise of disputed authorship), and Quevedo's *Historia y vida del Buscón* (1626). From Spain the vogue spread to the Spanish Netherlands, England, France, and Germany through translation and imitation and eventually found expression at the hands of masters like Daniel Defoe (1661?-1731), Alain René Le Sage (1668-1747), Grimmelshausen, and Henry Fielding (1707-54). Bourgeois vigour appeared to some extent also in the eighteenth-century theatre (for instance, Diderot's realistic plays of 'everyday life' such as *Le Fils Naturel* and Lessing's *burgerliche Trauerspiele* such as *Miss Sara Sampson* and *Emilia Galotti*). Above all, it was revealed by English novelists of the eighteenth century. Perhaps foremost among their novels of middle-class life were Defoe's *Moll Flanders*, Richardson's *Pamela*, and Fielding's *Tom Jones*.[11]

Middle-class vigour at times took the form of a conscientious concern with social problems like poverty and prostitution. Often combined with a delicate sensitivity to humanitarian and esthetic values (*sensibilité*), this concern led to a characteristic kind of sentimentalism that provided the themes and mood for much of the later literary output of our era, paced by Rousseau's *Nouvelle Héloïse*. The numerous Utopias written between 1500 and 1790 (in part, under the impact of contemporary geographical discoveries) were indirect expressions of social criticism, betraying a troubled awareness that man had not yet achieved the nobler things for which he was meant. Their prominent place in the current vogue of the philosophy of optimism led Voltaire to parody them in the El Dorado of his *Candide, ou l'optimisme* (1759).

The increasing contacts of Europeans with other areas of the world not only stimulated some of the utopian conceits but also induced an adulation of much that was foreign. For example, Leibniz and Wolff exhibited a learned curiosity about China, and Montesquieu and Voltaire, at least for literary purposes, showed a perhaps feigned admiration of Islam. In some instances—e.g. Camoëns' *Os Lusiadas* (1572) and Defoe's *Robinson Crusoe* (1719), to choose widely spaced examples from different genres—writers revealed a keen realization that man had achieved greatness in conquering the oceans and surviving strange encounters. Camoëns' epic built an odyssey around the glamorous story of Vasco da Gama; the hero of Defoe's tale was modelled after an otherwise little known sailor. The supposed simplicity of 'the noble savage' and wisdom of the Eastern sages led to an enthusiasm for strange places and characters in seventeenth and eighteenth-century literature that is sometimes called 'exoticism'. The theme of travel was a common literary device—as in Swift's *Gulliver's Travels* (1726), Le Sage's *Adventures de Robert, dit le chevalier de Beauchesne* (1732) and *Gil Blas* (1735), Voltaire's *Zadig* (1747) and *Candide*, Johnson's *Rasselas* (1759), and Sterne's *Sentimental Journey* (1768)—and the heroine of Defoe's *Moll Flanders* (1721) found, while the hero of Abbé Prévost *Mánon Lescaut* (1731) failed to find, refuge from the woes of Europe in the wilds of America.

The conquest of nature through the sciences likewise formed a recurrent theme in eighteenth-century Europe's literature. Schiller later complained that writers in the eighteenth century described the sun as a gaseous fireball rather than as Hyperion's chariot. The triumphs of a Newton or a Franklin moved Voltaire and lesser poets to verses of praise, and men of letters themselves often engaged in scientific research. Yet the attitude toward science was not always respectful. Swift mocked the learned academies in *Gulliver's Travels*. In Le Sage's novel *Gil Blas*, the picaresque hero at one stage of his career was a quack physician. In the two hundred years between Marlowe and Goethe, only slowly did the half-historical, half-legendary Faust, thirster after new experience and power, change from one whom the Devil ultimately claimed to one whom the angels save from Hell because he had served mankind.

BELLES-LETTRES IN THE ISLAMIC LANDS

The rising trend of Islamic prose after Ibn-Khaldun toward commentary and elaboration rather than toward creative scholarship has already been touched upon (see Chapter VII). Poetry continued abundantly, but in Iran at least it, too, was less notable after the fifteenth century. Jamāl-ud-dīn 'Urfī of Shīrāz (d. 1591) composed stately and traditional verse and was the most famous writer of *quaṣīdas* (elegies, odes, panegyrics) of his day. Like many gifted Persian contemporaries, whether philosophers or poets, he went to the

Mogul court of Delhi to live. He was one of those who were more appreciated in India and Turkey than at home, and the same was true in the next century of Sā'ib of Tabrez (d. 1677), whose influence eclipsed that of earlier poets. The classical tradition represented by these men was continued, although less fruitfully, in the eighteenth century. Alongside it other poetic tendencies appeared, notably the Shī'ite devotional poetry of the *marthiyas* (elegies on the misfortunes of Mohammed's family).

Meanwhile, as pointed out in Chapter X, Ottoman Turkish rose to prominence as a literary language. With the advent of the Uzbeks in Turkestan early in the sixteenth century, Chaghatai Turkish, which had been the most important of the three forms of Turkish in the time of Nevā'ī, tended to languish, though it was still used throughout the north. The best work of Fuzūlī of Baghdad (sixteenth century), perhaps the greatest Turkish poet of all time, was done in the Turkish of Azerbaijan (though he also composed in Persian and Arabic). Nevertheless, the western or Ottoman idiom, modelling itself on the master poet Bāqī of the sixteenth century, came on to lead the field. Ottoman Turkish poetry is generally regarded as superior to contemporary Persian poetry. It abounded in *mathnawīs*, commonly of a mystical tenor. Each *ṭarīqa* had its own poetic tradition.

Turkish poetry continued to feel the influence of contemporary Persian and Indo-Persian poets for a long time, though early in the eighteenth century it developed a greater independence of theme. In Turkish (as in Urdu) the trend toward ornateness, prevalent in the Persian zone, was often carried even further than in Iran itself. By the end of the eighteenth century, Turkish poetry seriously declined. Nonetheless, historical and related fields of learning after 1500 stayed on a high level, as the work of 'Ālī Chelebi demonstrated (see Chapter IX). Travel literature and other sorts of descriptive prose also retained a lofty standard.[12]

Persian literature bloomed in India under the patronage of the Mogul emperors and at the courts of independent Islamic sultans. Abu'l-Faḍl, poet, essayist, critic, and historian as well as vizier of Akbar (see Chapter V), was probably the most distinguished Islamic man of letters in the India of his day, but his brother Fayzī stood well toward the top of the list of contemporary poets. Among Fayzī's conspicuous achievements were his translations of Hindu classics, commissioned by Akbar. At least two of the illustrious poets of Akbar's reign were Persian immigrants. In addition to 'Urfī of Shīrāz, there was Muhammad Husain Nazīrī of Nishāpūr, writer of polished *ghazals*. The courts of Jahāngīr and Shāh Jahān likewise were graced by scholars and belletrists. Probably the most famous literary figure of Shāh Jahān's period was his son, Dārā Shikūh, who was executed in 1657 by his brother Aurangzīb in the struggle for succession. He was a Ṣūfī, well versed in Arabic, Persian, and Sanskrit. He assisted in translating the *Upanishads*, the *Bhāgavad-gītā*, and the *Yoga Vāshishtha Rāmāyana* into Persian. He was also the author of the *Majma'-ul-Baḥrayn*, a work harmonizing Hindu and Ṣūfī theosophies, and of the *Safīnat-ul-Awliyā*, a collection of biographies of the saints of Islam as well as of a separate biography of the saint Mian Mīr. In contrast, Aurangzīb's religious bigotry led him to discourage art, music, history, and literature, and from his time on, as Islamic control disintegrated, Persian literature in India tended to decline.

A number of ladies of the Mogul court were learned in Persian and Arabic literature and were talented writers. Bābur's daughter, Gulbadan Begam, was the author of a history of Humāyūn's reign. Humāyūn's niece, Salīma Sultāna, composed several poems. The extraordinary woman who was the wife of Jahāngīr, Nūr-Jahān, was also esteemed as a woman of letters. Aurangzīb's daughter Zayb-un-Nisā was a gifted poetess and calligrapher.

Early Urdu literature was largely secular. Although Urdu was extensively used at the court of Akbar, it first developed as a literary language in the Deccan at the end of the sixteenth century under the patronage of the sultans of Bijapur and Golkunda. Urdu poetry generally followed Persian verse forms —*ghazals, rubā'īyats*, etc.—and the ornate Persian style. It developed not only traditional Persian themes but also themes taken from the Hindu background. By the eighteenth century Urdu had come to be used likewise in the north and produced masters who were esteemed by certain groups of Hindus as well as by Muslims. The most celebrated poet of the Deccan area was Walī of Aurangabad (b. 1668). His poetry stimulated various eighteenth-century writers—such as Zuhūr-ud-din Hātim (1699–1792) and Khān Ārzū (1689–1756)—who are considered the fathers of Urdu literature in north India and the Punjab. Urdu was ultimately to become the literary language of Pakistan. The disintegration of the Mogul Empire and the decadence of the imperial court fostered the more corrupt aspects of the Persian tradition. The body of the Urdu poetry of the time is said 'to combine a high order of verbal ingenuity and prosodic dexterity with a range of subjects almost exclusively restricted to homosexuality, the cult of the courtesan, and rakish and sadistic cynicism.'[13]

In the other languages spoken by considerable numbers of Muslims the literary achievements of this period were generally of local interest only. Literature in Gujarati remained oriented to the local sects and in good part was translated from Arabic and Persian. Other than the various chronicles mentioned in Chapter IX, modern Javanese and Malay produced little of wide significance. The spread of Islam in Malaysia did not result in conditions conducive to the encouragement of native literature: Islam's literary masterpieces were in Arabic or Persian, and its sacred *Koran* was not to be translated; furthermore, after 1511 it had to compete with Western conquests. The oldest surviving manuscript in Malay seems to date from about 1600. Islamic literature in Javanese and Malay consisted of various adaptations from Arabic, Persian, or Urdu—religious romances, moral exhortations, mystical treatises, and legal works. A more distinctly native tradition endured in proverbs, folktales, and *wayang* (marionette shadow) plays. The Islamic areas of the southern Philippines, which were not conquered by the Spanish, produced, besides some chronicles and law codes, several epic poems celebrating the glories of particular tribes, such as the *Sulayman* of the Moros.

OTHER BELLES-LETTRES IN AND AROUND INDIA (1500–1775)

In eastern Asia during this period printing with movable type had an uneven history, which has already been sketched (Chapter X). In south Asia, printing underwent no significant development except in Vietnam. Even after it was introduced by Westerners, it did not take good hold in India and southeast Asia outside the areas they controlled.

Sanskrit Literature

After a display of renewed vigour in the sixteenth and seventeenth centuries Sanskrit declined rapidly again in the eighteenth as a medium of wide communication. Works continued, however, to appear in Sanskrit. Poets of genuine merit, of course, were rare, here as everywhere. Although epic, lyric, and dramatic poems were produced, at best they were imperfect imitations of older pieces and without beauty of locution or other poetic qualities. Sanskrit verse conveyed the growing interest in *bhakti* devotion, the poems related to the Krishna-Rādhā sects becoming increasingly erotic. While writers in Sanskrit showed greater strength in non-fiction, here too they generally were content to rework the older literature, and the best among them tended to become pedantic and to engage in hair-splitting philosophical discussions.[14]

Among the Sanskrit writers were Appaya Dīkshita (see Chapter VII) and his nephew Nīlakantha Dīkshita. Appaya Dīkshita, a south Indian philosopher and man of letters, was probably the outstanding Indian polymath of his day. He was the author of many devotional poems, two works of literary criticism (the *Citramīmāmsā* and *Lakshanāvalī*), a discussion of figures of speech (the *Kuvalayānanda*), and an analysis of the poetic use of words. He was concerned with the meaning rather than the sound of poetry. Nīlakantha Dīkshita was probably the most accomplished Sanskrit poet of the seventeenth century. His epic *Shiva-līlārnava* sang the praises of Shiva, while his collection of didactic verse, the *Kalividambana*, exposed human weaknesses and pled for a higher code of conduct. In the area of the longer romance, the Sanskrit *campū* (prose and poetry intermingled) became popular in the seventeenth century, and one of the outstanding *campūs* was Nīlakantha Dīkshita's *Nīlakanthavijaya*. It dealt with the ancient story of the churning of the milky sea by the gods, the resulting creation of poison, and Shiva's salvation of the world by consuming the poison.

Jagannātha, of the Mogul court of Shāh Jahān, was the finest critic and literary mind of the period. His *Bhāminivilāsa* was at once an erotic poem, an elegy, and a collection of gnomic sayings. He was most famous for his *Riasagangādhara*, an original treatise on poetics, which re-examined earlier works in the light of his own standards. Differing thoroughly with Appaya Dīkshita, he defined poetry as primarily sound (though it also conveyed meaning), a sort of contemplation that produced transcendental pleasure.

The literary attainments of other authors of the period who wrote in Sanskrit were perhaps less distinguished. Rūpa Gosvāmī (see Chapter VII) was the author of the *Padyāvalī*, which contained many passages of lyric poetry honouring Krishna, and of two religious dramas, the *Vidagdha Mādhava* and the *Lalita Mādhava*. The ingenuity of Sanskrit poets was illustrated in Rāmachandra's sixteenth-century *Rāsikarañjana* (*Delight of Connoisseurs*), which appeared to be, if read in one spirit, a eulogy of asceticism and, if in another, an erotic poem. About 1650 Meghavijaya produced the *Pañchākhyānoddhāra*, modelled upon the *Pañchatantra*; it contained a number of fables that gave evidence of the intercultural connections of India with the West. *Srīvāhāsudhākara*, a *campū* by Nārāyana, described in idyllic fashion the love of Svāhā, the wife of Agni, the god of fire, for the moon.

Tamil, Kanarese, Telegu, and Malayalam Literature

Literature in the Dravidian vernaculars (Tamil, Kanarese, Telegu, and Malayalam) rarely sought inspiration outside Hindu sources. In the Tamil literature of the sixteenth and seventeenth centuries *purānas* dealing with legends relating to famous shrines were particularly popular. In 1,225 easy flowing verses, the *Ariccandira* (1524) of Nallūr Virakavirāyar set forth the trials that the mythological king Harishcandra had to endure because of his devotion to truth. Probably the leading work of this mythological genre was the early seventeenth-century *Tiruvilaiyādal* of Parañjōti, describing the sixty-four sacred sports of Shiva at Madura. Kumāragurupara and Turaiman-galam Shivaprakāshar, both of the seventeenth century, were perhaps the best writers in Tamil of the period. The former was the author of many poems honouring Shiva and other deities, of other kinds of devotional and ethical poetry, and of a work on Tamil prosody. The latter, a Vīrashaivite of liberal persuasion, composed poems on the deities of various shrines, a work of ethics, and a refutation of Christianity and translated into Tamil verse various Kanarese and Sanskrit writings on philosophy and Vīrashaivism. The beautiful devotional though anti-Brahman poetry of the Sittars (see Chapter III) preserved in the *Shiva-Vākyāni* probably belongs to this period, but it may have been earlier. In the eighteenth century the most famous scholar of Tamil Shivaism, Shivañānar, compiled, with his pupil Kānchi Appar, the *Kānchi-purānam*, which retold the legends of the sacred city of Conjeeveram. Among the more secular writers in Tamil were the Pāndyan king Ativīrarāma (*c.* 1564) and his cousin Varatungarāma Pāndya. The king translated several works from Sanskrit, prepared a small book on morals, and wrote an epic, the *Naidadam*; his cousin produced poems on Shivaite shrines and theology and translated the *Hokhoha*, a Sanskrit work on eroticism; and together they translated the Shivaite *Linga* and *Kūrma purānas*.

After 1500 Vishnuite authors, stimulated by the Chaitanya movement, dominated Kanarese literature, although Vīrashaivite writers remained active and some Jaina works also appeared. The rise of Vishnuite preponderance corresponded with the glorious period of the Vijayanagar Empire under Krishnadeva Rāya (1509–29), who, himself a poet, patronized all learning and literature, especially that in Sanskrit, Kanarese, and Telegu. The blossoming of Vishnuite letters under his patronage betokened a temporary increase in the influence of Brahmanic ideas and Sanskrit literature. Kanarese Vishnuite literature was largely made up of reproductions, in one form or other, of Sanskrit works. In the sixteenth century the Vishnuites produced, besides, a large number of popular songs extolling Vishnu, the most famous of the song writers being Purandaradāsa (d. 1564) and Kanakadadāsa. Kanakadadāsa also wrote the *Mohana-tarangini* (*River of Delight*), consisting of puranic stories about Krishna, and other moral and devotional poems in *shatpadī* verse. Among the Lingāyat contemporaries were Mallanārya of Gubbi, author of the *Vīrashivāmrita* (1530), a popular poetic explanation of the faith; Virūpāk-shapandita, author of the *Channabāsava-purāna*, a most venerated work of the Lingāyats, which dealt with the life of Bāsava's nephew; and Sarvajñamūrti (c. 1600), author of the *Sarvajña-padagalu*, a book of verses frequently on the lips of the common man.

In the late seventeenth and the eighteenth century, after the Vijayanagar Empire was disrupted by the Muslims, Kanarese literature was patronized especially by the rajas of Mysore. Having become independent about 1610 and having given up the Lingāyat faith, they now favoured Vishnuism. Many new versions of Sanskrit writings sacred to the Vishnuites and numerous collections of stories followed, generally in prose but sometimes in verse. King Chikkadēvarāja Odeyar (1672–1704), who persecuted the Jains, was himself an author, and so were several of his ministers and of the ladies at his court. The most eminent Kanarese Vishnuite poet, however, did not have royal patronage. He was Lakshmīsha, author of the *Jaimini Bhārata* (before 1700), the finest and most popular *shatpadī* poem in Kanarese. A very free adaptation of the Sanskrit original, it dealt with an incident from the *Mahā-bhārata* associated with the horse sacrifice, but its real purpose was to extol Krishna. Among the contemporaneous Lingāyat writers was Shadaksharadēva, who wrote poetry in both Kanarese and Sanskrit. Besides composing *campūs* on Bāsava (1671) and on the sports of Shiva, he elaborated an old story in his principal *campū*, the *Rājashekhara-vilāsa* (1657), which became one of the most highly esteemed poems in Kanarese. After him belles-lettres in Karanese were undistinguished. A new type of popular literature, the *yakshagāna*, emerged, however; it consisted of rude dramas or operatic pieces suited to rustic audiences and possessing neither dramatic skill nor literary merit.

The golden age of Telugu letters fell in the sixteenth century and likewise came under the patronage of Emperor Krishnadeva of Vijayanagar. Vishnuite influence became prominent in it. The principal poetic form was the *pra-*

bandha (grand epic), which like the Sanskrit *mahākāvya* contains descriptions of many things—cities, rivers, mountains, forests, lakes, seasons, sun, moon, travel, politics, battles, birth, marriage, pinings, morals, sex affairs, gambling, and kings. Telugu literature no longer counted so much as previously on translation, and the great *prabandhas* were independent creations, based on some puranic event. Krishnadeva's own epic, the *Āmuktamālyada* (see Chapter IX), is now ranked among the so-called 'five great *prabandhas*' in Telugu for its insight into human nature, its political philosophy, and the light it sheds on the social history and institutions of his reign. It dealt with the life and thought of a Vishnuite saint and the love of his foster daughter for the God Ranganātha.

The 'Eight Elephants' (or pre-eminent poets) of Telugu literature adorned this period. The foremost of them was Allasāni Peddana, the 'grandfather of Telugu poetry', whose simple and dignified *Manucarita* was another of 'the five great *prabandhas*'. It was a puranic story built around the refusal of a Brahman to accept the love of the divine courtesan Varūthinī. Another 'elephant' was Nandi Timmana, author of the *Pārijatāpaharana*, which elaborated in beautiful verse an episode in the life of Krishna, introducing the motif of jealousy in the characterization of Satya, one of Krishna's mistresses. Only three of the remaining 'elephants' were of truly imposing stature. They probably did their work between 1540 and 1590. One of the trio, Pingali Sūranna, was the author of two epics, both of which are sometimes included among 'the great five'. They are the *Kalāpūrnodayam* (*Birth of Kalāpurna*), essentially a novel in verse, which occasionally is regarded as the finest poem in Telugu (and has been compared with Shakespeare's *Comedy of Errors*), and the *Prabhāvatī Pradyumna*, which deals with the marriage of Prabhāvatī and Pradyumna, son of Krishna. Bhattumūrti (or Rāmarajabhushana) was another of the three. His leading poem was the *Vasucaritra* (*c.* 1570), telling a simple story of the love of Prince Vasu and Princess Girika, daughter of a river and a mountain. Tenāli Rāmakrishna (or Rāmalinga), the third of the trio, was the author of the *Pānduranga Māhātmya*, which narrated the rescue of the soul of a dissipated Brahman from the servants of Yama, king of the dead, by those of Vishnu.

With the collapse of Vijayanagar Telugu literature began to deteriorate. The feudatory courts of Nellore, Tanjore, Madura, and other strongholds were the centres of Telugu literature during these centuries of decline. In the seventeenth century Raghunātha Nāyaka, raja of Tanjore, wrote the *Valmīki-caritram*, the first important prose work in Telugu. The great Telugu literary figure of the century was Chāmakūra Venkatakavi, of Raghunātha's court, whose *Vijayavilāsam* was often rated among 'the five great *prabandhas*'. It dealt with the adventures and loves of the semi-divine hero Arjuna. In the eighteenth century Telugu literature reached its nadir, 'the Age of Despair', unrelieved by the number of popular *shatakas*, prose works, and colloquial dramas of the *yakshagāna* variety that it produced but somewhat brightened by Tyāgarāju of Tanjore, perhaps the greatest of Hindu musicians (see Chapter XII).

After Cheruśśeri (see Chapter X) little Malayalam literature was put forth other than local songs and ballads. Tuñcat Rāmānujan Eluttaccan (c. 1700), author of a number of works dealing with Indian mythology, religion, and monistic philosophy, gave shape to the modern speech. He produced Malayalam versions of the *Rāmāyana*, the *Mahābhārata*, and the *Bhāgavata*. Of the popular dance-dramas the *Rāman-āttam* of Kottārakkara Tampurān (perhaps sixteenth century), a work meant to be completed in eight performances, is the oldest extant example. In the seventeenth century the *Shiva-purāna* and the *Brahmānda* were translated into Malayalam.

Hindi Literature

The heyday of Hindi literature was the century (1556–1658) between the beginning of the reign of Akbar and the rise of Aurangzīb. Its glory was a response, in part, to the upsurge of the Vishnuite *bhakti* movements centred on Rāma and Krishna and, in part, to the era of patronage and good will inaugurated by Akbar and continued, though more restrictedly, by his two immediate successors. It took on an artistic and sophisticated character and soared to heights rarely, if ever, attained again. During this period the *Bījak* (c. 1570) and the *Ādi Granth* (1604) were produced and the greatest figures of Hindi literature flourished. Religious devotion was its dominant motivation and supplied its main themes. Lyric poetry retained its prominence, but epics and other poetic forms also thrived.

Many first-rank Hindi writers set an elevated literary tone at Akbar's court, but three towering figures of his reign were not under his direct patronage. Of these the senior was the Krishnaite Sūr Dās (d. c. 1563), 'the blind bard of Agra'. The others were Tulsī Dās and Kēsab Dās. Sūr Dās generally is listed among the eight great Vallabha poets, and he is considered by some to be the greatest Hindi poet (although this honour is generally reserved for Tulsī Dās).[15] He reproduced a large number of episodes and passages from the *Bhāgavata-purāna*; his lyrics relating to Krishna and Rādhā were collected in the *Sūrsagar* and the *Sūrāvalī*. He is said to have written as many as 75,000 verses, noted for the polish, ornament, and variety of their style and for their picturesque images and similes.

Kēsab Dās (1555–1617), of Orchhā in Bundelkhand, was the first significant Hindi writer on poetics. His most admired work, the *Kavi Priyā*, undertook to describe the qualities required of a good poem. Among his other writings were the learned *Rasik Priyā*, dealing with poetical composition, and the *Rām Alankrtmañjarī*, dealing with prosody. Since he illustrated his points with original poems, each of these books constituted also a collection of his own poetry.

Tulsī Dās (d. 1623), of Benares (see Chapter V), is the most celebrated and, as already indicated, is generally considered the best, of the Rāmat writers. His well-known *Rāmāyana* (more moralistic than the original), begun in 1575, is one of the noblest epics ever penned, ranking with *Paradise Lost* among the masterpieces of religious poetry. Written in old Eastern Hindi, which thereafter became the literary language for Rāmats, the poem became household knowledge, revered throughout north India. Tulsī Dās was the author of many other highly moralistic poems, all venerating Rāma. The *Rām Gītāvali* was composed in verses adapted for singing, and the *Vinay Patrikā* was a group of hymns. His *Sāt Sāi*, a discussion of poetics, was illustrated with devotional verses, also on Rāma.

A fourth famous literary figure of the period was Bihārī-Lāl Chaube (*c.* 1603–63), the most celebrated of many Hindi authorities on the art of poetry. He lived in Muttra and wrote in the Braj Bhāshā dialect. His major opus was a *Sāt Sāi* (1662), a collection of about seven hundred original couplets intended to provide illustrations of various kinds of poems, styles, heroic characters, rhetorical figures, and related subjects. A majority of these verses were in the form of amorous utterances by Rādhā and Krishna, since the author was a Krishnaite. This type of work was quite common, but Bihārī-Lāl's revealed particular skill and excellence of expression.

Of the bardic poems in Hindi, the *Padumāvatī* of Malik Muhammad Jāyasī (see Chapter IX) was easily the most impressive. Its theme, the seige of Chitor by Emperor Alā-ud-dīn (1303), permitted a striking admixture of Hindu and Islamic lore. It was written in a local Hindi dialect of Rajputana in Persian characters with some admixture of Persian words and idioms. Its originality and poetic beauty make it one of the Hindi masterpieces.

Aurangzīb's anti-literary and anti-Hindu policies helped to inaugurate a steady decline of Hindi literature. Civil strife, political and economic disintegration, and the degeneration of the *bhakti* movements prolonged this literary decadence beyond our period. It was characterized by ornateness of style, overattention to form, lack of emotional depth, and increase of eroticism. It was productive of a mounting number of undistinguished translations of the *Rāmāyana*, the *Mahābhārata*, the *Bhāgavad-gītā*, the *Bhāgavata-purāna*, and other Sanskrit classics.

The lesser Hindi authors of the period fall into five groups—court poets and writers, Rāmats, followers of Kabīr, Krishnaites, and bardic chroniclers. Among the first were Rājā Bīrbal, Akbar's poet-laureate, noted for his witty and humorous verses; Ganga Prasād, renowned for his comic style and descriptions of battles; Balbhadra Sanādya Mishra, brother of Kēsab Dās, remembered especially for a *Nakhshikh* (a popular type of poem which described every part of the body of a hero or heroine from toenails to top-knot); and Dev Kavi (*c.* 1673–1745), of whose works thirty are extant, disclosing good form and diction, an ornamental style, striking descriptions of heroines, and patent eroticism. After Tulsī Dās the Rāmat writers were not distinguished; probably the best known was Nābhā Dās, author of the *Bhaktimālā* an account of the lives of Vishnuite devotees. Nor did the followers of Kabīr, although prolific as writers, excel as creative literary lights. The Krishnaite authors were perhaps more memorable; they produced a good deal of poetry of estimable quality, marked by erotic phrasing and sensuous imagery, describing the soul's devotion to the divine as a reflection of Rādhā's surrender to her beloved.[16] Gokulnāth (fl. 1568), author of the *Chaurāsī Vārtā*, a prose work that retold the legends of the Vallabhas, and Hari Dās (fl. 1600) were among the most able of this Krishnaite group. Lāl Kavi (see Chapter IX) was perhaps the best of the numerous eighteenth-century bardic chroniclers.

Literature in Bengali and Other Indo-European Vernaculars

From about 1500 on, the Chaitanya movement and the local Shakta cults dominated Bengali literature, and their joint impact produced the golden age of traditional Bengali literature. After 1650 Shākta influences waxed, as Chaitanyaism waned. The Portuguese had the Christian gospel translated into Bengali and made serious efforts during the seventeenth century to spread it, but the Westerners' Bible seems not to have contributed to the development of Bengali prose before the nineteenth century. The period from 1500 to 1800 is often known as the Nadiyā period, since that city became the centre not only of the Chaitanya movement in particular but of the economic and cultural life of Bengal in general.

Chaitanya poetry was of three kinds: (1) *pads* (short, lyrical, pastoral songs about the love of Krishna and Rādhā), (2) biographies of Chaitanya and other leaders, and (3) expositions of doctrine and practice. Of the last only those disquisitions on *rasa-tattva*, or the cult of love and devotion, were of a belletristic nature. They were based upon the Sanskrit treatises of Rūpa Gosvāmī, and of the disquisitions in Bengali the sixteenth-century *Prem-bhakti-chandrika* by Narottam, who was also an outstanding *pad* writer, was representative. The theological theory they presented, of course, promoted the Krishna-Rādhā love poetry of the *pads*. The standard biographies of Chaitanya by Vrindāvan Dās and Krisnadās Kavirāja have already been mentioned (Chapter V), but numerous poets combined legend and fact in order to present biographies of Chaitanya and other leaders in verse. Pre-eminent among these poetical versions was the eighteenth-century *Bhakti-ratnākar* of Narahari Chakravarttī, which, in addition to its biographical accounts, presented discussions of theology, rhetoric, literature, and related subjects. Narahari also wrote on versification, made a collection of others' *pads*, and was himself an able *pad* writer.

The finest literary products of the Chaitanya movement and perhaps of the whole of Bengali literature were *pads*. More than 3,000 of them by over 150 writers prior to the nineteenth century testify to their popularity. They were greatly influenced by the earlier lyrics of Vidyāpati. Written in a language called Vrajabuli, which was a mixture of Bengali and Maithili, they told of the love of Krishna and Rādhā in lyrics of passionate intensity and undisguised sensuousness, intended to symbolize the love of man for God. They presented the story in its several stages—the dawn of love, the message, the tryst, union, separation, and reunion in spirit; and to heighten their intensity, they introduced an unconventional touch by making Krishna a cowherd and Rādhā a married princess. *Ecstasy* and *emotional madness* were favourite words. The most skilful sixteenth century writer of *pads*, Govindadās Kavirāja, was unrivalled for verbal harmony and alliteration. Among the numerous seventeenth-century writers, both Hindu and Muslim, the Muslim Ālāol stands out, but the general quality of seventeenth-century *pads* was below that of the sixteenth. In the eighteenth century, a further decline in originality took place as numerous anthologies were compiled and the *pad* became more stereotyped.

During these centuries several long narrative poems were produced in Bengali. Among about twenty Bengali versions of the *Rāmāyana*, that by Adbhut Āchārya (seventeenth century) was the most commonly accepted. Of some thirty of the *Mahābhārata*, that of Kāsirām Dās (seventeenth century) was the masterpiece. Of the *mangals* dealing with Krishna, probably the foremost was the *Govinda-mangal* of Kavichandra Chakravarttī (eighteenth century), who was also the author of an excellent version of the *Mahābhārata* and perhaps of a version of the *Rāmāyana*.

A good deal of Bengali literature was inspired by the various local cults, especially those of Shakti (see Chapter V). The outstanding Manasā poem was produced by Ksamānanda (*c.* 1650); it avoided the prolixity and coarseness of much of the other Manasā literature. The praise of Chandī in her genuine character as a local goddess became a common literary theme during the seventeenth century, with accent upon the episodes in which she conferred her favours on a humble male follower, Kālketu, and a female devotee, Khullanā, daughter of a rich merchant. The *Chandī-mangal* of Mukundarām Chakravarttī, written during the late sixteenth century, was peopled with realistic characters. It pictured the harsh life of the Bengal villages and the piratical activity of the Portuguese and appealed to the goddess to better the people's lot. The many Chandī poems of the seventeenth and eighteenth centuries in Bengali did not measure up to it, perhaps because of the competition of the Sanskrit *Mārkandeya-purāna*, which depicted a Brahmanized Chandī, or (as she was more generally known in her Brahmanized form) Durgā, wife of Shiva.

In the seventeenth century the number of poems about Shiva also began to mount, although Durgā often 'stole the show'. The Shiva of Bengal folklore was a rustic plowman or vagabond who ran after low women, but in these poems he was elevated to be the head of a respectable middle-class household, who occasionally got into difficulties as the old husband of a young wife. Dharma, originally the Buddha but now completely distorted by tantric ideas and local lore, was often identified with Shiva. Dharma-cult literature also made its appearance in the seventeenth century, relating the exploits of the

Y*

hero Lāusen, aided by Dharma. The best of the *mangals* dealing with Dharma was completed by Ghanaram Chakravarttī in 1711, and the *Shiva-samkīrttan* of Rāmesvar Bhattāchārya (eighteenth century) was unsurpassed among the Shivāyan poems.

In the eighteenth century Bengali literature underwent a general deterioration, but with certain redeeming features. Some purely secular poems of merit appeared, of which the elegant love lyrics of Nidhu Bābu decidedly belonged in the drawing-room rather than the village street. Moreover, two of Bengal's ablest poets adorned the century. Ramprasād Sen (*c.* 1718–75), the outstanding song writer of his day, composed and dedicated to the terrible goddess Kālī some simple devotional lyrics that have remained beloved to the present day. In contrast to him, Bhārat-chandra Rāy (1722–60) was a basically secular, courtly writer, whose dexterity has remained unequalled in Bengali poetry. Each of these poets wrote a *Kālikā-mangal*, of which Bāhrat-chandra Rāy's was the more celebrated. It was in reality a trilogy, completed in 1752, of which the Vidya-Sundar love-story (see Chapter X) has particular charm. He contrived to introduce the Goddess Kālī into it, but his absorbing theme was a secular story of illicit love, expounded in sensuous, witty, and elegant phraseology. Although drawn from Sanskrit literature and clearly influenced by Mukundarām Chakravarttī, the poem also showed Islamic influence.

The authors in the other Indo-European vernaculars of India were nearly always religiously inspired. *Bhakti* poetry was a distinct factor in stimulating the Maratha nationalistic movement under Sivājī and his successors (see Chapter V). Ekanātha (d. 1608), Rāmdās (seventeenth century), and especially Tukārām (also seventeenth century) were the foremost Marathi poets of this period. Rāmdās wrote not only a *Rāmāyana* but also two hundred and five verses to the mind. While Gujarati poetry could boast the Krishna poets Nākar and Premānand, Gujarati literature became almost barren in the later seventeenth and eighteenth centuries, except for the lyrics of the Shivaite writer Shivānand (fl. 1750). The ablest examples of Punjabi letters were the poems of Nānak (early sixteenth century) and of other Sikh writers in the *Granth* (see Chapter V).

Literature in Assam, Nepal, Burma, and Siam

Assam, which gallantly maintained an uncertain independence of the Mogul Empire, enjoyed its age of literary glory during the sixteenth and early seventeenth centuries. Assamese literature burst into flower under the Krishna *bhakti* movement led by Shankar Deb and his successor Madhab Deb (d. 1596). Shankar Deb's *Kīrtan-ghosa* was a series of renderings from many puranic sources; he began the use of dramas drawn from the puranas as a means of popular religious instruction. Madhab Deb made translations of Sanskrit ethical and philosophical works and composed devotional songs (*bargīts*) and dramas. Later, Bhattadeva (*c.* 1558–1638) laid the foundation of Assamese prose in the translations of the *Bhāgavata-purāna* and the *Bhāga-*

vad-gītā. After 1650 the Krishna movement declined, and literature, which passed under the patronage of the Shan Ahom kings, grew more secular. Prose then became a commoner literary vehicle, as court poets glorified their kings in prose-and-verse chronicles known as *buranji* (eight of which were written between 1648 and 1742). Biographies of religious leaders (in either prose or verse) shared popularity with romances in *kāvya* style and with Shākta poems in praise of Durgā, Chandī, and Kālī.

Most of the works in the Nepali vernacular were either inspired by or were adaptations of Buddhist and Hindu religious literature, especially *tantras* and puranas. Some independent chronicles or genealogies (*vamshāvalis*) were produced in the seventeenth and eighteenth centuries. Perhaps the most meritorious native literary product was the sixteenth-century *Svayambhū-purāna,* a legendary account of the origins of Nepal under the guidance of the bodhisattva Mañjushrī.

In Burma after 1500 Pali literature remained abundant, but vernacular compositions steadily increased. Translations or adaptations of Pāli philosophical works and of Jātaka tales made up one part of the vernacular output; legal treatises and chronicles made up another; still another comprised *niti* literature (traditional tales illustrative of conduct or dealing with national heroes); and there were poems and dance-dramas, drawn not only from the Jātakas, Indian epics, or puranas but also from native tradition. Several of the Toungoo kings (1531–1752) were patrons of letters and maintained royal chroniclers. Literature bloomed especially under King Bayin Naung (1551–81), when Siamese captives apparently introduced the variety of songs and dances known as *Yodaya* (*Ayuthia*). Zeyyayandameik, a courtier of King Anaukpetlun (1605–28), was the author of a poem entitled *Natshinnaung,* after a Burmese adventurer associated with the Portuguese buccaneer De Brito. In the eighteenth century, under Alaungpaya (see Chapter IX) and his immediate successors, a number of famous poets prospered. Seindakyawthu (1736–71) was especially noted, for his *Kawiletkanathatpon,* a poem in a philosophical vein, and his *Awwadatupyo,* which set forth guiding principles in the pursuit of wisdom.

Most Siamese rulers maintained poets and chroniclers, and kings and other royal personages sometimes were prominent authors. Among the more important of the prose tales, which were popularized through the epic dance-dramas, were new versions of the *Ramakien* and the *Inaco* (see Chapter X). The earliest extant complete version of the *Ramakien* is that of King P'ya Taksin (1767–82); the oldest extant version of the *Inaco* dates only from the nineteenth century. Other tales told of wondrous things—of the origin of mankind from the egg of a sacred goose; of a king who became an ascetic upon contemplating a withered tree; of a princess who was beloved by an elephant; of a princess who was carried off by a crocodile and rescued by her lover; of the love of a dragon princess disguised as a mortal; of a princess betrothed before birth to a giant in return for a piece of fruit her mother wanted;

of a princess guarded by an enchanted spear which fatally stabbed her prince when he climbed to her bower; of the wars of King Mahasot; and of Anuruddha, demi-god grandson of Krishna. Many stories dealt with the life of Buddha, the *Pathomma Somphothiyan* becoming standard by the eighteenth century. Thai literature perhaps found its best expression in its poetry, unrivalled for elegance of diction and musical sound, especially in its *nirats* and shorter love songs. Its *khon* dance-dramas used masked dancers and were usually based on incidents from the *Ramakien*; its *lakon* dance-dramas did not use masks and might be drawn from any source.

BELLES-LETTRES AROUND AND IN CHINA

Literature in Tibet, Mongolia, Manchuria, Vietnam, and Korea

In Tibet the flood of religious literature and folklore went on, particularly in the form of histories of the lamas. Probably the weightiest Tibetan literary achievement of this period, however, was not in Tibetan but in the translation of the *Kanjur* into Mongol (1604–34). From this source there sprang a number of widely accepted religious works in Mongol. Among the Mongolian people the legends of Gesser Khan and Siddhi-kūr (from the Sanskrit) and the Mongol heroic epic *Jangariad* also were favourites. In the seventeenth century Prince Sanang Setzen produced a *History of the Eastern Mongols*, and Saya Pandita devised (1648) an improved alphabet, the Kalmuck, which spread among the western Mongols. In 1748 Čosgi Odsir's rendition of the *Bodhicar-yāvatāra* (see Chapter X) was re-edited.

In 1599 the Manchus also had adopted the Mongol script. Some documents, chronicles, and other materials appeared in Manchu, and Dahai began the translation of some Chinese works. Little, however, was done in the way of an independent Manchu literature.

Vietnamese writers continued to use both Chinese and *chũ-nōm* after 1500, but the best expressions of the Vietnamese literary genius were in the native script. Novels and dramas were especially popular. Written shortly after our period ended, the *Kim-vân-kiêu* of Nguyên-du was the best known and best liked Vietnamese *truyên* (narrative in verse); it was inspired by a Chinese novel. The *Cung oan ngam-khuc*, which was purely Vietnamese in origin, was also a favourite. Some missionaries contrived a romanized script, the *quôc-ngũ*, in the seventeenth century; in modified form it gradually supplanted *chũ-nōm* as the written medium and ultimately became the official national script.

In Korea a good literary standard was maintained during the sixteenth and seventeenth centuries, but with the eighteenth a decline in quality if not in quantity set in. Translations and popular renderings of Chinese works kept up, but native ideas also found expression in novelettes, short stories, and works on ceremonies. Conflicts of loyalty were a major theme and provided the plot in two popular novels, the *Chunhyang Jun* (*Spring Fragrance*), in which the heroine remained loyal to her lover, and the *Simchung Jun*, in which the heroine remained loyal to her father. After Hideyoshi's invasions began (1592), war too became a common theme. The mid-seventeenth century was dominated by the writings of Song Sol (fl. c. 1650). In 1774 an elaborate set of works dealt with the ceremonies of marriage, death, ancestor worship, hospitality, and war.

Chinese Literature in the Traditional Style

In China after 1500 the largest number of writers remained faithful to the traditional literary style and idiom. Their products were perhaps superior to those of the earlier period. Despite the frowns of literati drama, the novel, and other popular forms of literature were more and more generally accepted.

In addition to a supplement of the canon (1607), a number of Taoist works were published during this period. Tung Han-shun, early in the sixteenth century, put out a collection of extracts from Taoist authors, ancient and modern (Ch'ün-hsien yao-yü), and in 1566 Yao Ju-hsün issued a popular treatise on Taoism in its modern form (Chih yu tzu). In 1640 Hsüeh Ta-hsün published the Shen-hsien t'ung-chien, an extensive, illustrated work, giving biographical sketches, largely legendary, of about 800 Taoist immortals, saints, and sages (some of whom were Buddhists). This Taoist Acta Sanctorum and its imitations helped to popularize Taoist lore and exerted considerable influence upon Chinese literature and art.

Most of the literary men of the period wrote essays along traditional lines in the involved, elliptical ku-wên form. Those of the literary critic Yao Nai (1732–1815) were among the most celebrated. The complicated parallel-sentence prose (see Chapter X) revived somewhat, but it did not seriously threaten the dominance of ku-wên. Most of the essays, whether in one form or the other, were more distinguished for elegance of style than for originality of thought. Yüan Mei (1716–98) was a noted practitioner of parallel-sentence prose. His collected works, first published in 1775, contained poetry, fu, essays, letters, literary criticism, short stories, and miscellaneous pieces, all fairly representative of contemporaneous literary efforts.

In the late Ming and Ch'ing periods notable anthologies of earlier tales, especially those of the T'ang, were compiled. Original short stories in the literary language also attained a new eminence in the Strange Stories (Liao-chai chih-i) of P'u Sung-ling (1640–1715). Though his preface was written in 1679, his 431 stories circulated in manuscript until printed in 1766. Their subjects were similar to those of the T'ang tales, but he achieved a new realism in his handling of the supernatural, which he depicted in a distinguished yet simple style. Whereas P'u's stories recited only weird adventures, those of Yüan Mei dealt also with everyday events.

During the centuries here under consideration literary critics were numerous. Yüan Mei and Yao Nai (as already mentioned) were prominent among those who adhered to conventional standards. Other outstanding critics were also of that persuasion. Wu Ching-hsü (early Ch'ing) produced the Li-tai *shih-hua*, a monumental critical review of poets, ancient and modern, and Wang Shih-han completed about 1768 a compendium of critical scholarship relating to the *Wen-hsüan*, an early general collection of prose and poetry. On the other hand, Li Chih,[17] a late-Ming freethinker (see Chapter V), and the eccentric Chin Sheng-t'an (*c*. 1610–61) were less conventional. Both praised more recent literary forms like novels and dramas and were critical of past standards, though they readily conceded enduring glory to some ancient writings and authors. Chin was particularly active. He published an annotated edition of the T'ang poet Tu Fu, of the novel *The Water Margin*, and of the drama *The Romance of the West Chamber* (see Chapter X), an anthology of T'ang poetry, a general anthology, various critical essays, and an original novel. In a fashion, the disagreement of these critics of China parallels the Quarrel of the Ancients and the Moderns in the West.

The poetry written in the literary language developed few new forms, and these centuries were famous rather for monumental collections of earlier verse. An enormous amount of new poetry of a fairly high technical quality was produced, to be sure, but most of it was imitative and uninspired and exploited traditional themes. No *fu* of special distinction was produced, but numerous *shih* writers attained eminence. One was Wang Shih-chen (1526–90), who was also counted among the leading literary critics. Of various *tz'u* writers only the Manchu Na-lan Hsing-te (1655–85) showed exceptional merit; his love poems, which developed new patterns, compared favourably with those of the *tz'u* masters of the Sung. Under the patronage of the Ch'ien-lung emperor (1736–95) several poets achieved a lasting fame but made no new contributions to poetic form.

Drum Song and Drama in China

In vernacular literature, the Chinese exhibited greater talent. Perhaps the best of the various drum songs was the epic *Love in Reincarnations* (*Tsai-sheng yüan*) of the poetess Ch'en Tuan-sheng of the late eighteenth century. It was probably inspired by her unhappiness over the exile of her husband. *Ch'ü* poetry reached new heights in the southern *k'un-ch'ü* dramas. The *k'un-ch'ü* tunes originated in K'un-shan, in the Soochow area of Kiangsu, a province whose economic and cultural prominence attracted many visitors. Soochow sing-song girls came to be widely employed throughout the country and helped spread the popularity of the *k'un-ch'ü* songs and dramas. The musician Wei Liang-fu, of the early sixteenth century, adapted native tunes to operatic scores and enlarged and improved the orchestras (see Chapter XII).

Under Wei's inspiration some dramatists produced polished, elegant texts for the plays, which rose in popularity throughout the sixteenth century. During the Wan-li reign (1573–1620) the *k'un-ch'ü* established its ascendency as the preferred dramatic form of the people, claiming 77 playwrights and over 150 new dramas. Many of these dramas were exceedingly long, running to fifty or sixty acts, and were often intended only to be read, although parts might be performed. They were sometimes more profound and possessed better characterization than earlier drama. The earliest *k'un-ch'ü* dramatist of lasting reputation was Li K'ai-hsien (1501–68). A portion of his *History of a Sword* has survived under the name *Lin Ch'ung Flees by Night*. It deals with a character from the *Shui hu chuan* (*Water Margin*), who, having been unjustly sentenced for murder, escapes. Another dramatist, Liang Ch'en-yü, contributed to the stage success of the *k'un-ch'ü* plays with several romantic plays, among which the *Wash-Girl of the Huan-sha Stream* found special favour. Some playwrights stressed the musical side of the dramas, as did, for example, Shen Ching. Three of his seventeen plays have survived, but his collection of the songs of the time was perhaps an even greater contribution since it served others as a guide. His followers emphasized music and acoustic values. A play by Wang T'ing-no, *The Tale of the Roaring Lioness* (*Shih hou chi*), was a light comedy about shrewish wives, written about the same time as Shakespeare's *The Taming of the Shrew*.

Unquestionably the greatest dramatist of the Wan-li period was T'ang Hsien-tsu (1550–1617), who strove for thoughtful dialogue and interesting plot. *The Romance of the Purple Flute* and *The Peony Pavilion* (*Mu-tan t'ing*) were perhaps his most famous plays. *The Peony Pavilion* was a melodrama of 55 acts, which presented the romance of a prefect's daughter and a young scholar by means of devices involving dreams, supernatural agencies, and resurrection. Some of its scenes had little connection with the main story, and each act had separate titles and could be produced independently. Especially in demand were the scenes entitled 'The Dream Betrothal', 'The Dream Comes True', and 'Spring Perfume Turns the Schoolroom Topsy-Turvy'.

With the fall of the Ming dynasty and the rise of the Ch'ing, scholars undertook to formalize the *k'un-ch'ü*. They encountered the opposition of the leading literary figure of the period, the poet, dramatist, essayist, and fictionist Li Yü (1611–80?). Li was the author of at least sixteen plays, *Feng-cheng wu* (*Tangle of the Kite*) being perhaps the best of them; he also revised several earlier plays; and his *Hsien-ch'ing ou-chi* (1671) was the first Chinese book on dramatic theory. In addition he wrote a number of short stories, and two novels are attributed to him—one of which, *The Flesh Cushion* (*Jou p'u-t'uan*), was later banned because of its eroticism. Li objected to the scholarly formalization of the *k'un-ch'ü*, insisting that the ideal was to express 'profound ideas in plain language, without the least smell of bookishness.'[18] Nevertheless, the language of the plays now became more literary, the style more florid, and the ideas and themes more acceptable to the literati.

The growing academicism of the *k'un-ch'ü* tended to divorce it from its popular roots, threatening it with extinction by competition from more widely accepted forms of drama. It was saved by imperial patronage, which began about 1670 with the K'ang-hsi emperor and continued throughout the eighteenth century under the Ch'ien-lung emperor. Imperial patronage attracted talented poets and writers and encouraged the production of a number of significant plays. The foremost ones were *The Palace of Everlasting Life* (*Chang-sheng t'ien*) of Hung Sheng (*c.* 1650–1705) of the north and *The Peach Blossom Fan* (*T'ao-hua shan*) of K'ung Shang-jen (1648–1708 ?) of the south. *The Palace of Everlasting Life* was based on the actual tragedy of the T'ang emperor Ming-huang and his beautiful concubine Yang Kuei-fei, which culminated in rebellion and the death of Yang. In the play, however, although separated in the twenty-fifth act, the lovers are reunited in the fiftieth. *The Peach Blossom Fan* was more authentic. It dealt with the tragic love of Hou Fang-yüeh, a famous author of the late Ming period, for Li Hsiang-chüng, a celebrated sing-song girl and poetess, and the author contrived no happy ending. Both plays were exceedingly long but were considered literary masterpieces because of their structure, literary quality, and skilful characterization. The principal dramatist of the Ch'ien-lung reign was Chiang Shih-chüan (1725–84), who wrote nine well-known plays, mostly built around historical events of a tragic nature, one being a dramatization of Po Chü-i's famous lyrical poem *The Walking Guitar* (*P'i-p'a hsing*). Despite lavish imperial patronage, the *k'un ch'ü* (or 'elegant drama', as it was now called) began to yield to several colloquial forms, which eventually grew into the capital or mandarin drama of the nineteenth century.

Short Story and Novel in China

The popularity of colloquial short stories likewise increased during the late-Ming and Ch'ing periods. Numerous anthologies were issued, of which the *San-yen* collections, published between 1620 and 1628 by Feng Meng-lung (*c.* 1574–1645), were among the more eminent. Feng, a scholar and minor official of Soochow, was also industrious as an editor, compiler, author, and publisher of novels, anecdotes, and plays as well as of stories in the literary language. His contemporary Ling Meng-ch'u brought out two further collections of stories (1627 and 1632)—some being imitations of *San-yen* stories, others new productions. In the interval between 1633 and 1644 forty stories from these earlier collections appeared in the justly renowned *Strange Tales Ancient and Modern* (*Chin-ku ch'i-kuan*), selections from which have become widely known in the West. The detective story also became increasingly popular, and many of them reached short-novel length.

Contemporaneously with a similar development in the West, the Chinese novel reached its full growth during late-Ming and Ch'ing times. Historical and picaresque novels lost none of their general esteem, but the novel of ordinary life also emerged and ultimately became the most noteworthy type. Hundreds of all kinds appeared. Perhaps the best of the numerous historical novels were the *Sui-T'ang yen-i*, dealing with the rise and fall of the Sui and T'ang dynasties, and the *Lieh-kuo chih*, dealing with the period of the Warring States. Five novels are often thought to excel the others of the period: *The Record of a Journey to the West* (*Hsi yu chi*) belonged to the picaresque group; *A Warning to the Generations Regarding the Destiny of Marriage* (*Hsing-chih yin-yüan chuan*) was of a mixed type; and *The Golden Lotus* (*Chin P'ing Mei*), *The Dream of the Red Chamber* (*Hung-lou meng*) and *The Unofficial History of Officialdom* (*Ju-lin wai-shih*) were realistic novels of everyday affairs.

Several novels were concerned with religion and the supernatural. Of these *The Record of a Journey to the West*, one of the five most esteemed novels just mentioned (written by Wu Ch'eng-en about 1550), had an exceptional vogue. Based on the journey of a Buddhist monk, Hsüan Tsang, to India during the seventh century, it presented allegorically the exploits of supernatural agents, with a strong undercurrent of satire on society and bureaucracy. In solving the superhuman problems confronting him, Hsüan Tsang was aided by an invincible stone monkey, the novel's real hero (hence the title *Monkey* for Arthur Waley's translation). The monkey ultimately brought the journey to a successful end in the Western Paradise. Another work with a supernatural motif was the *List of Canonized Saints* (*Feng-shen jen-i*) of Hsü Chung-lin (*c.* 1560), a novel despite its unenticing title. It was filled with Taoist mythology and dealt with the founding of the Chou dynasty. Still another was the *Hsi-yang chi* of Lou Meng-ting (*c.* 1597), which centred on the great voyage of Cheng Ho into the Indian Ocean during the early fifteenth century. In a fashion reminiscent of Dante's *Divina Commedia*, it described a journey through hell, which was discovered to be far to the west of Mecca; both accounts of hell may have drawn on common sources.[19]

A Warning to the Generations Regarding the Destiny of Marriage, another of the five generally preferred novels, was a lengthy work, probably of the early Ch'ing period, often attributed nowadays to the short-story writer P'u Sung-ling. Combining the supernatural with the natural, it consisted of two virtually separate stories: the hero and his concubine, who drove the wife to suicide in the first part, suffered under the abuse of the wife in their second, reincarnated state. The novel turned a glaring light upon lower-middle-class family life.

The Golden Lotus was the first significant novel to be largely divorced from the historical past, legend, the supernatural, and mythology. It was written in the sixteenth century under another title, for its original title (*Chin P'ing Mei*) consists of the names of three of its chief female characters and is untranslatable. An English rendition carried the title *Hsi Men and His Seven Wives*. The novel described the life of a wealthy businessman bent on sensual pleasure and the catastrophes that overtook him and his companions. The author was the first Chinese writer to portray female characters convincingly. Who he was is uncertain. A sequel to the story appeared in the seventeenth century, and various similar erotic novels followed.

The Unofficial History of Officialdom, another of the novels described above as realistic, was by Wu Ching-tzu (1701–54). It might be called 'The Book of Snobs', since it was a satirical attack on the examination system, the literati, and the corruption, inefficiency, and hypocrisy of officialdom by an independent-minded if profligate member of the class he attacked. It lacked plot and was essentially a series of tenuously connected episodes involving different characters. It inspired a series of realistic, satirical, and sometimes salacious works about particular social groups.

Probably the most distinguished of all Chinese novels was the lengthy *Dream of the Red Chamber*, begun by Ts'ao Chan (d. 1763) and completed by Kao O (*c.* 1795). It dealt with the declining fortunes of a once wealthy and powerful official family. The first part apparently was autobiographical, but the semi-happy ending supplied by Kao in the last forty chapters perhaps was not intended by Ts'ao. Despite digressions and sub-plots, it had a better plot than most Chinese novels. While it presented a picture of the life of almost every social group in China in a more realistic fashion than earlier novels, it was in particular an indictment of the great households dominated by women. The story centres upon the search of a sentimental, effeminate, and pampered youth of a scholarly family for affection; because his family prefers another as his wife, his favoured girl combines with her frustrated love a jealousy and self-pity that ultimately destroy her. The author's insight into the psychology of love makes the work unique in Chinese literature.

IMAGINATIVE LITERATURE IN JAPAN[20]

The New and the Traditional in Japanese Literature

Japan's letters of the Tokugawa period mirrored the interests, ideals, and conflicts of the country's two most articulate classes—the samurai and the *chōnin* (the rising middle-class townsmen). The literature reflecting samurai culture was traditionalist, often moralist, and generally without vigour or inspiration. Its chief forms were *nō* drama and poetry and various kinds of prose in the customary Sino-Japanese style. The literature reflecting the *chōnin* culture was new, vigorous, vulgar, erotic, witty, dynamic, often satirical, and critical of traditional ways and values. It was normally written in colloquial language and presented in new forms. This new literature aroused the ire and contempt of the government and hence incurred censorship, regulation, and suppression, but it grew in popularity not only among townsmen but also among samurai and even at the imperial court. It reached full flower during the Genroku period at the end of the seventeenth century. Its major centres were the principal cities of Osaka, Kyoto, and Edo.

The more time-honoured types of literature persisted under the patronage not only of the great courts of the shogun and the emperor but also of the lesser courts of powerful feudal lords (*daimyōs*). Poets at the imperial court and samurai writers continued to turn out *tankas*, while Shinto nationalists deliberately tried to revive and promote traditional Japanese poetic forms. Samurai writers kept on producing uninspired *rengas* (chain-poems) also, while Ieyasu, the founder of the Tokugawa shogunate, and his early successors as earnest patrons fostered the esoteric *nō*. The Confucian moralist Arai Hakuseki persuaded the shogun in 1711 to abandon the *nō* at court banquets in favour of certain kinds of ancient music, but as a traditional art it still won the favour of several *daimyōs* and conservative samurai.

Prose literature was of the most varied types, both new and traditional. Some excellent Japanese prose works of the seventeenth century were the *otogi sōshi*, or children's fables. While this is a type of folk literature familiar in all cultures, such stories as *The Rat's Wedding, The Hare's Revenge,* and *The Battle of the Ape and the Crab* have a uniquely Japanese quality. The few traditionalist *monogatari* of the early seventeenth century, such as the *Mokuzu* and the *Usuyuki*, were unimpressive, melodramatic tales of love, passion, intrigue, and revenge. The *Taikōki* (1625), a somewhat legendary biography of Hideyoshi, was of little literary merit. Undoubtedly, the best traditional prose of the period was that of the moral philosophers of the Chinese school. They introduced many new Chinese words, thus greatly enriching the Japanese language, and some of them contributed to the development of a prose that was to meet the needs of modern Japan. Kaibara Ekken's treatises on morals (see Chapter VII) and his books on travel were intentionally written in a simple, semi-colloquial style to appeal to the many.

As traditionalists of a reactionary bent, the Shinto nationalists sought to cultivate the most ancient Japanese forms and ways. In the field of literature Mabuchi and Motoori took a leading part in a deliberate effort to throw off Chinese influence and promote the study of early Japanese. They, too, made a contribution to the modern prose style—in their case, by trying to exclude Chinese words from their vocabularies in favour of the *wabun* (or pure Japanese) style. Furthermore, Motoori laid the foundations of Japanese grammar. One of his many writings, the *Tama Kushige* (*Precious Casket*), giving his views on how a feudal domain should be governed, was written in a simple, straightforward prose suitable to the popular needs of the eighteenth century. Although not a Shinto nationalist, Tokugawa Mitsukuni published in 1678 the *Fusōjiuyoshiu*, an anthology of traditional masterpieces in the pure Japanese style. Shinto nationalists had little in common either psychologically or socially with the rising culture of the middle class, but they were revolutionary in their own way, and they were distinctly modern in their nationalism.

Meanwhile a new urban literature was reaching maturity. It was the literature of the *ukiyo*, the 'floating world' of the theatres, restaurants, brothels, and other merry haunts of the growing towns. Its subjects were actors, dancers, courtesans, wrestlers, singers, and similar inhabitants of a universe of fleeting joys, whose usual patrons were the prosperous bourgeois, the dissolute samurai, and the 'naughty apprentice'.[21] Some of the authors in the new style were samurai, some were *chōnin*, but most were denizens of, or otherwise well acquainted with, the life of 'the nightless city', the amusement area of the towns. Three writers of this school stand out above the rest: the poet Matsuo Bashō (1644–94), the dramatist Chikamatsu Monzayemon (1653–1725), both of whom were samurai, and the novelist and short-story writer Ihara Saikaku (1642–93), who was of lower-class origin.

Poetry and Fiction in Japan

In the sixteenth and seventeenth centuries, in keeping with the new literary freedom, poetic forms became less rigid. The *haikai*, or 'free' chain-poem, tended to replace the older *renga*. Avoiding the formal rules of the *renga*, it loosely employed colloquial or Chinese words and popular, even vulgar, ideas. Its opening verse, which consisted of three lines of 5, 7, and 5 syllables respectively, also developed into an independent genre known as the *haiku*, which, since a *haikai* could not be very successful unless all those participating were of eminent ability, ultimately became the most widely used poetic form. Both forms were imagist poetry, requiring extraordinary skill (even though the *haiku* required less) if they were to come off well. The *haiku* in particular was to influence later Western writers. Saikaku was illustrious in his time as a writer not only of stories but also of *haikus*. A kind of narrative poem known as the *utazaimon*, an often bawdy ballad about contemporary events, was also generally approved during this period, and some of this kind, such as *Osen, the Cooper's Wife* (*Taruya Osen*), dealt with incidents found in some of Saikaku's stories.[22] Another current poetic form was the *kiōka* (mad poetry), a comic, merry, vulgar, and witty variety of the *tanka*. The *senryū*, a type of satirical poem made familiar by Karai Senryū (1718–90), likewise had wide appeal.

Bashō was the pre-eminent poet of the period. A samurai turned Buddhist monk, he travelled a great deal and often joined with local poets in writing *haikai*. His poetry became known throughout the land not only for its cleverness and originality but also for its refinement and purity, in contrast to much of the new poetry. He insisted that the important principles of prosody were change and permanence[23]—change, because style should always be new, fresh, and original; permanence, because the poet should attempt in his own way to solve the eternal problems. Bashō's travel diary, *The Narrow Road of Oku*, contained a number of his poems and sometimes described the circumstances surrounding their composition. His many disciples and imitators dominated the eighteenth century. Though Bashō himself had preferred nature as a subject, his imitators drew their material from 'the floating world'.

Though also a poet and dramatist, Saikaku is best remembered for his colloquial fiction. His novelettes, tales, and sketches marked a departure in Japanese prose, a new type of erotic fiction. While his accounts of contemporary manners and customs were reminiscent of the *monogatari* of the classical period, the social class he described was different; he was concerned in the main with the life, habits, and manners of the nightless city of Osaka.

Harlots, rakes, pederasts, tricky merchants, and even plain middle-class characters who dared to transgress custom or feudal law were prominent in his stories. Women reappeared as notable figures, although they were generally courtesans or daring townswomen rather than highborn ladies. Although some of his plots showed a pronounced inventiveness, he was especially noted for his polished, witty, and realistic pictures of contemporary life. His stories brought out the injustices and inanities of many contemporary practices and pleaded for greater liberty, equality, and humanity.

Saikaku began his career as a writer of fiction with *The Love Rogue* (*Kōshoku ichidai otako*) in 1682, and from that time until his death he turned out a steady stream of best sellers. He has sometimes been compared with Boccaccio; in one of his tales, *The Rise and Fall of Gallantry* (1688), as in one of the *Decameron* stories, an amorous young woman employs an unsuspecting monk to entice a young gallant to her boudoir. His *Five Women Who Loved Love* (1686) dealt with middle-class and lower-class women who risk all for love; four of them lose their lives, not so much because they must pay for their immorality as because they overstep class lines or violate established custom. Saikaku's portrayal of ordinary townswomen as heroines gave rise later, in the middle of the eighteenth century, to a genre employing this device, known as the *yomihon*. His *Tales from the Provinces* (1685) reflected the regionalism of Japan. The *Treasury of Japan* (1688) told how to make and lose a fortune. *A Mirror of the Beauties* (1684) was his only story of suicide for love, of which he disapproved.

Despite the eroticism of Saikaku's works their basic purpose was not pornographic. In fact, his *Tale of Virtuous Conduct* and *Twenty-Four Examples of Unfilial Behaviour* engaged in a moralizing sort of edification. But the same cannot be said of some of his contemporaries. The works of his Edo contemporary Tōrindō Chōmaro and of the Kyoto-Osaka bookseller Jishō (d. 1745) and the latter's collaborator Kiseki (d. 1736) depicted 'the floating world' of Kyoto and Osaka. Though embellished with a good deal of humour, they were largely pornographic. Publishers of this type of literature, known as *sharébon* (or witty books), appeared in the main cities and, despite efforts of the authorities to censor them in 1723 and later, carried on until rather thoroughly suppressed in 1791.

Of course, fiction of a more sedate variety was also produced. The seventeenth-century stories about a hero named Yuriwaka, who, after winning great victories abroad, was abandoned by his evil companions on an isolated island, may possibly reflect Japanese acquaintance with the Ulysses story. A type of historical novel that developed in the eighteenth century dealt with wars and vendettas, some of which revolved around relatively recent personages. One such novel centring on Hideyoshi was a best seller, and the *Ōoka seidan*, recounting the cases of a celebrated judge of the early eighteenth century, was even more so. The *Wasōbē* (1774) was a sort of *Gulliver's Travels* filled with fantastic and impossible adventures.

The Japanese Theatre

Drama was the field of highest literary achievement of the early Tokugawa period. Popular dramatic performances were of two types—the *jōruri* and the *kabuki*. Both types appeared at the beginning of the seventeenth century and reached full maturity by the beginning of the eighteenth. They seem to have grown out of the *nō* with its humorous interludes (*kyōgen*), temple dances and performances, and the chanted or recited metrical romances of the *kōwakamai* variety. The plays that came to be known as *jōruri* (after a legendary princess in one of the favourite pieces) used puppets to enact a story told by a chanter to musical accompaniment. The music was provided by the *samisen* (a three-stringed guitar), after it was introduced (beginning of the eighteenth century) from the Ryukyu Islands. The *jōruri* theatre evolved in Osaka, Kyoto, and Edo. With improvements in the manufacture and manipulation of the puppets, it reached its fullest development at Osaka in the early eighteenth century under Chikamatsu Monzayemon, who also dominated the *kabuki* theatre.

The *kabuki* theatre is believed to have begun in the Kyoto-Osaka area in 1603 with the performances of Okuni, a shrine dancer, who had deserted her temple in Idzumo. It seems certain that the earliest *kabuki* were mostly lascivious, humorous dances and farces put on by prostitutes and their hangers-on to attract customers; in the early stagings women generally played male parts and men often played female parts. From the first, the *Bakufu* (the shogunate) disapproved of these exhibitions and tried, without success, to keep the samurai away from them.[24] It banned women's *kabuki* in 1628, but the ban did not become effective until the 1640's, when the government began to imprison offending theatre managers. Before that date, *kabuki* troupes of boys and young men had appeared, but they, too, soon displeased the authorities, for they seemed to promote homosexuality, especially among the samurai. First female impersonation alone and then (1652) youths' *kabuki* altogether were banned, but afterward male *kabuki* was permitted on condition that female impersonators shaved their forelocks and dressed their hair like men instead of like women.

Both the *jōruri* and the *kabuki* plays rapidly developed into organic dramas of from three to five acts. From Chikamatsu's time on most of them either were historical or dealt with social life and manners. They were full of shocking action, excitement, and melodrama. Edo was noted for actors who specialized in heroics, or 'rough business', and Osaka for actors who depicted the romantic emotions, or 'moist business'.

Most *kabuki* dramas of the seventeenth century were the joint product of the troupe and not the outcome of a single author's effort, but during the eighteenth century several individual authors stood out. None was more imposing than Chikamatsu, even though almost all of his more than fifty plays were written not for *kabuki* but for the puppet (*jōruri*) theatre of Osaka. He defined art as the slender margin between the real and the unreal and considered the puppet theatre best adapted to portray that marginal realm.

Nevertheless, most of his plays were also adapted to the *kabuki*. Like Shakespeare, Chikamatsu wrote both comedies and tragedies, combined poetry with prose, and mixed elegant diction with extreme colloquialism. His characters, however, were not comparable to the English dramatist's.

Most of Chikamatsu's plays were built around some social conflict that resulted in an emotional crisis, and most of them had a highly moralistic tone. The most successful of them was *The Battles of Koxinga (Kokusenya kassen)*, written in 1715. Its hero was the memorable Chinese pirate and Ming loyalist, Cheng Ch'eng-kung (1624–62), whose mother was Japanese. Two hundred and forty thousand spectators are estimated to have seen it in seventeen months at Osaka. Chikamatsu's *Sagami Lay Monk and the Thousand Dogs* (1714), while ostensibly portraying the last of the Hōjō regents (1303–33), was a political satire on the shogun Tsunayoshi (1681–1709), who, under the influence of Buddhist teachings, had forbidden injury to dogs. Chikamatsu's historical plays were peopled with military and abounded in intrigue, combat, torture, murder, and suicide. His plays of domestic life were about merchants, clerks, prostitutes, and middle-class women who became involved in heroics of the bedchamber, embezzlements, elopements, and suicide for love. He borrowed the themes of several of them from Saikaku's *Five Women*. Perhaps the most familiar one, *The Love-Suicide of Amijima*, told the tragedy of lovers frustrated by the social and class restrictions of their time. While Chikamatsu's plays were not without erotic elements, many other *jōruri* and *kabuki* dramas were more openly lascivious.

Takeda Izumo (d. 1756) was perhaps the most esteemed *kabuki* dramatist of the Edo theatre in the eighteenth century. His best-known play (written with two collaborators and published in 1748) was the *Chūshingura (Magazine of Faithful Retainers)*. It was based upon an actual vendetta that ended in the suicide of forty-seven *rōnin* ('masterless samurai') involved in a conflict between loyalty to their lord and obedience to the laws of the Bakufu. The story had previously been dealt with by Chikamatsu and was a favourite theme of dramatists and others.

After Takeda's time, Chikamatsu Hanji (*c.* 1725–83) came to dominate the Japanese stage. His plays emphasized ethical problems, contained little poetry, and made a greater use of dialogue. From his time on, the *jōruri* theatre steadily declined, but the *kabuki* theatre continued to thrive.

NOTES TO CHAPTER XI

1. It must be emphasized, however, that translations of the Bible had very little influence in Italy, France, and Spain. In these countries, the expressive and literary qualities of the national language, the nobility of which was held comparable to that of classical languages, were recognized. An excellent example of this attitude is given by Du Bellay's *Défense et illustration de la langue française* (1549). Literature in the vernacular developed contemporaneously with the existence at court, among the aristocracy and in certain strata of the bourgeoisie, of a reading public for such works. (Raymond Picard.)

2. See G. Bonfante, 'Ideas on the Kinship of European Languages from 1200 to 1800', *Journal of World History*, I (1954), 679–99.

3. For example, a new tragedy by Racine, a small in-16° booklet of 70 pages, cost between 30 sols and 3 livres, or approximately the equivalent of three to six dollars. Volumes of larger format or containing a greater number of pages often cost as much as the equivalent of about 50 dollars. (Raymond Picard.)

4. Professor Raymond Picard notes that the system of 'Privilege', a perfectly normal procedure, implied no particular risk for the publishers and did not necessarily lead to prohibitions. Furthermore if on the one hand it did make preventive censorship possible, since the manuscript to be printed was submitted to the royal censor, on the other hand it guaranteed to the author or his publisher ownership of the work for a certain fixed length of time, within the boundaries of the kingdom. Political and police control was thus accompanied by a form of economic and intellectual protection.

5. *Encyclopédie* (new ed., F. Picavet, Paris, 1894), I, 143.

6. Ping-ti Ho, *The Ladder of Success in Imperial China, Aspects of Social Mobility*, 1368–1911 (New York, 1962), p. 214.

7. Professor Le Gentil notes that Gil Vicenti (c. 1465–1537) should be mentioned in connection with the theatre in the Iberian peninsula. Vicenti has sometimes been called 'the Portuguese Shakespeare'.

8. Professor Raymond Picard points out that the value and use of the unities was not really at issue in this Quarrel. Perrault, champion of the Moderns, never advocated a spontaneous literature freed from all regulations, asserting only that the tragedies of Corneille, for example, were superior, or at any rate equal, to those of Sophocles or Euripides. The elaboration of the system of the unities (1580–1630) dates from well before the beginning of the Quarrel.

   Having considered this opinion, the authors made the following comment: 'The text perhaps overemphasizes the problem of rules and form in "the Quarrel of the Ancients and the Moderns", but the text, when speaking of 'the Quarrel', subsumes it under 'the Western literary world of these times', meaning the years 1500–1775 and not 'the Quarrel' alone. The writers mentioned above lived from the sixteenth to the eighteenth century inclusive and, as the text shows, frequently were interested in forms and rules as well as the relative merits of Classic and modern authors. See Perrault's Parallèles des Anciens et des Modernes *(4th Dialogue, part iii), where he argues that "all the arts have been raised in our time to a higher degree of perfection than where they were among the Ancients because time has revealed several secrets in all the arts which, joined to those which the Ancients left us, have rendered them more accomplished, art being nothing other, according to Aristotle himself, than an accumulation of rules (préceptes) for doing well the work which is its objective." Perrault obviously means that the Moderns not only had more but also better rules than the Ancients.'*

9. For Professor Raymond Picard the patriotism discernible in the work of Grimmelshausen bears no relation to that of Corneille's heroes. There is no element of French national feeling in the declamations of Horace or Sertorius. Their attitude, like the rhetoric in which it is expressed, derives from the classical texts themselves.

   The authors do not agree with Professor Picard's reading of Corneille. They write: 'Corneille does make Sertorius say: Rome n'est plus dans Rome, elle est toute où je suis. *We find it difficult to believe that, writing his best plays under the patronage of Richelieu and during the French participation in the Thirty Years' War, Corneille did not mean his lofty declamations to rouse his hearers' patriotic sentiments as Frenchmen (or that he would have succeeded if he had intended not to do so).'*

10. Dámaso Alonso, 'The Spanish Contribution', *loc. cit.*, pp. 888–89.

11. The development of the romanesque novel is one of the great events of the literary history of the eighteenth century. The French tradition of the psychological novel, which derives its scheme from tragedy, produced works remarkable for their unity and truth from *La vie de Marianne* by Marivaux (1731–42) to *Les Liaisons Dangereuses* by Laclos (1782). In his novels written in the form of dialogue, *Le Neveu de Rameau* and *Jacques le Fataliste* (c. 1755–70) Diderot embarked on a bold experiment foreshadowing the modern novel. (Raymond Picard.)

12. Among Turkish poets should also be mentioned Nef'î (d. 1634), one of the great classics, famous for his satirical verve. Mention should also be made of the *Divan* of Nedim (d. 1730), which gives expression to the refined taste of the 'Tulip' period: the stirring songs of Nedim are sung to this day. (Raymond Picard.)

13. J. C. Ghosh, 'Vernacular Literature', in Garratt (ed.), *op. cit.*, p. 380.

14. See C. Lahiri, 'Sanskrit *Kāvya* Literature' in *The Cultural Heritage of India* (Calcutta, 1937), III, 650.

15. See F. E. Keay, *A History of Hindi Literature* (London, 1933), p. 67.

16. See *ibid.*, p. 72.

17. See K. C. Hsiao, 'Li Chih: an Iconoclast of the Sixteenth Century', *T'ien-hsai Monthly*, VI (1938), 317–41.

18. Yao Hsin-nung, 'The Rise and Fall of the K'un Ch'ü', *ibid.*, II (1936), 77.

19. See J. J. L. Duyvendak, 'A Chinese "Divina Commedia"', *T'oung-pao*, XLI (1952), 255–317.

20. This discussion has employed quite freely several papers prepared for the International Commission for a History of the Scientific and Cultural Development of Mankind: Ishida Ichiro, 'The Urban Culture in the Japanese Feudal Age', Richard Lane, 'Saikaku and Boccaccio: the Novella in Japan and Italy', and Donald H. Shively, 'Theater and Government in Tokugawa Japan'.

21. G. B. Sansom, *Japan, a Short Cultural History* (New York, 1943), p. 474.

22. See Richard Lane, 'Saikaku's "Five Women"' in W. T. de Bary's translation of Ihara Saikaku's *Five Women Who Loved Love* (Tokyo, 1956), pp. 236, 244, and 251.

23. See Donald Keene, *Japanese Literature* (London, 1953), p. 38.

24. See Donald H. Shively, 'Bakufu Versus Kabuki', *Harvard Journal of Asiatic Studies*, XVIII (1955), 326–56.

CHAPTER XII

THE VISUAL ARTS AND MUSIC
(1300–1775)

THE FINE ARTS IN EUROPE

ACHIEVEMENT in the visual arts has rarely, if ever, attained a higher level than that of this period in the Western world, which includes the late Gothic, the Renaissance, the Baroque, the Rococo, and the early Neoclassical eras. Many important centres produced works of extraordinary merit, but the major changes in style originated in Italy and, with the late seventeenth century, in France. Innovations leading to Europe's Renaissance and later styles came first in painting early in the Middle Ages (before 1300), and for that reason painting will be given first place in the account below of European developments in the visual arts. It will be followed by a section on sculpture, the art most closely related to painting in Europe of that day, and then by sections on architecture and the decorative arts. A section concerning the changing theories of art and the role of the artist, which were derived in great part from the innovations of practising artists, will conclude our discussion of the visual arts in Europe before we take up music in Europe and the arts in Islam, the Hindu and Buddhist areas, in China, Japan, and neighbouring countries, and in Africa and the Americas.

Painting in the Later Middle Ages

The ancient Hellenistic understanding of plastic form and spatial illusion survived in Byzantine art, but it had become attenuated in the course of time, particularly during the iconoclastic period of the eighth and ninth centuries (see Volume III). After the eleventh century the Byzantine tradition of icon-painting persisted in the churches of Russia—so much so that the word *icon*, when it denotes a representation of a religious subject on panels, has largely lost its original Greek identity and has become closely associated with Russian art. By the end of the fourteenth century the iconostasis, a screen or wall covered with icons and separating the sanctuary from the main part of the church, had become characteristic of the Russian church. The Russian icon-painter for the most part developed a colourful, crowded, two-dimensional, linear style, but artists like Theophanes the Greek (late fourteenth, early fifteenth century) and Andrei Rublev (c. 1370–c. 1430), probably his disciple, both of whom also painted frescoes on church walls in Novgorod, Vladimir, and Moscow, succeeded in eliminating hieratic non-essentials and in at least suggesting three-dimensional forms. Russian icon-painting sought chiefly, however, to depict a mystical world beyond sense experience and was only incidently concerned with the realities of space and movement. Until late in the seventeenth century when Western standards began to affect Russian art conspicuously, the Russian artist knew little about the ancient Hellenistic tradition. (Pl. 1, a, b.)

Meanwhile, during the centuries here under consideration Western European painting developed a distinctive system of monocular perspective that approximated the homogeneity of the visual world. It was based upon the study of optics and was probably stimulated by literary accounts of spatial illusion in the paintings of Antiquity.

In the early Middle Ages, in contrast to the essentially linear and two-dimensional art of northern Europe, Italian artists had retained the more plastic forms of the Byzantine tradition. There they found reminiscences of Hellenistic modelling, foreshortening, and spatial depth that had been all but lost in the north of Europe. This inclination to seek remnants of the Hellenistic tradition in Byzantine art (and later in the Ancient sources themselves) may have had its origin in a growing desire for concreteness or actuality in representing the events of sacred history. Certainly the somewhat austere symbols and conventional arrangements of the thirteenth century were inadequate to express the Franciscan's desire for a vivid, readily understandable re-enactment of Biblical events. A current belief, based on William of Ockham's philosophy (see Chapter VI)—that reality could best be defined by the particular and individual qualities of things—may have been another stimulus toward more exact detail. Northern European artists, to be sure, often revealed a parallel interest in careful delineation of details, but their more concrete moments were overshadowed by decorative passages of diapered patterns, gold grounds, and ornamental calligraphy. The artists of Tuscany, on the other hand, dedicated themselves to the attainment not only of the actuality of isolated objects but also of spatial unity and homogeneity.

Early in the fourteenth century, Giotto gave clear expression to these aims in the Arena Chapel of Padua and in the Bardi and Peruzzi chapels in Santa Croce of Florence. He gave his forms a convincing life in the round by the use of modelling and by increasing the variety of angles from which to view them. To allow adequate space for his columnar figures, he deepened the platform and rocky ledge used by Byzantine artists and elaborated the small-scale structures that indicated the locale of the sacred event portrayed. His acute depiction of gestures and facial expressions made emotional relationships clear, and aided by the established physical types and by the symbols gradually built up in the Christian world, he encouraged the spectator to participate in the emotions he portrayed. (Pl. 2a.)

Giotto's art pointed the direction that painters of the Renaissance ultimately were to follow, but the artists of the fourteenth century for a time demurred. They tended to develop the genre aspects of Giotto's art rather than his interest in the illusion of solidly modelled figures and clearly defined intervals.

Nevertheless, Duccio da Buoninsegna of Siena, his contemporary, shared some of his spatial and psychological interests, and in the middle of the fourteenth century the Sienese artists Ambrosio and Pietro Lorenzetti painted interiors of remarkable spaciousness (notably Pietro's 'Birth of the Virgin') as well as panoramic views of the city and its countryside (i.e. the 'Allegories of Good and Bad Government'). Furthermore, the dim interiors and extensive landscapes of the anonymous painter known as the Master of the Heures du Maréchal de Boucicaut in the late fourteenth century and the miniatures of the Limbourg brothers in the early fifteenth reveal that the development of pictorial space was occurring also in the French miniature tradition.

In most of the rest of Europe this interest in pictorial space was supplanted by an emphasis on decorative rhythms. The calligraphic art of Simone Martini, developed from the curvilinear grace of Duccio and the French miniaturists, spread over the Continent during the latter half of the fourteenth century, and it continued in many centres until the middle of the fifteenth century. (Pl. 2b.) This vogue was the last flowering of Gothic art, called 'the International Style'. It was characterized by courtly elegance of figures, preciousness of detail, and rhythmic vitality in the cursive line. From the relative homogeneity of this style, distinctive schools of painting emerged in Flanders, Germany, Poland, Bohemia, Hungary, Venice, and elsewhere.[1]

Florentine and Flemish Painting in the Fifteenth Century

Meanwhile, in the early fifteenth century Florentine painting had become distinguished by a new system of spatial construction, now called 'artificial perspective', demonstrated by Filippo Brunelleschi in 1419 and systematized by Leon Battista Alberti in 1435. It made possible the illusion of a continuous space of measurable depth in which all objects were scaled according to their distance from a point symbolizing the spectator's eye and shaped according to their position above, below, or on the level with that point and to the right or left of it. It was a highly intellectual system and not readily understandable to contemporaries. It demanded a new training of the eye to retain the perceptual image, to enable the spectator to interpret the spatial significance of the varying shapes, and to grasp the spatial relations of things in a complex painted scene. It created a new association of viewer to painting—one that aided the immediacy and vividness of the viewer's participation in the event depicted.

Gothic painters had arranged pictorial symbols according to conventions that had little to do with their way of seeing, but now painters faced the varied problems of designing in depth. Their concern for a convincing illusion of space also led to a preference for a rectangular format composed of the vertical and horizontal co-ordinates on which perspective is constructed. Such a self-contained visual world, gathered around its own centre, was more naturally enclosed within the architectural framework of a wall or large 'easel' painting than on manuscripts or chests or within the decorative frames and small panels of retables.

The paintings of Brunelleschi's young contemporary Masaccio in Florence, in contrast to the decorative poetry of the International Style, were severe essays in modelling and spatial construction. Masaccio rejected bright colours, stamping, gilding, undulating lines, and precious details in order to model clearly shaped figures that occupy space and possess weight. He painted the human body not simply as a sum of parts but as a volumetric unit, firmly held together by broad passages of light and shade and, in so doing, strongly intensified Giotto's use of light and re-affirmed his predecessor's emphasis on the block-like totality of figures existing in the round. The fresco the 'Trinity', painted by Masaccio in Santa Maria Novella in 1425, was a major step in the realization of the spatial unity of artificial perspective. (Pl. 3a.)

Painters who followed Masaccio employed this 'scientific' system for creating the illusion of pictorial space without diminishing the individuality of their art. Witness Fra Angelico's delicately but firmly modelled volumes, clear colours, and exquisite detail, Paolo Uccello's foreshortened silhouettes and decorative colour areas, Piero della Francesca's breadth and dignity, and Andrea Mantegna's minutely defined surfaces and sculpturesque shapes. (Pl. 4a, b.) For less creative artists of the period Brunelleschi's artificial perspective provided a secure basis within which their decorative talents might thrive. French illuminators of the fifteenth century, like Jean Fouquet, sometimes expressed sympathy with the new spatial order by reserving for each miniature a whole page free from lettering. (Pl. 5a). These departures from the purely ornamental role of illumination signal the surrender of the Gothic tradition to the new Tuscan ideals.

In the second half of the fifteenth century, the knowledge of the structure and appearance of natural forms was markedly refined. Followers of Masaccio tended to avoid his strong contrasts of light and dark, which disturbed the clarity of colour areas, but they sought to achieve the appearance of roundness that he gave to his figures. An ingenious pictorial solution was suggested by the 'modelling line' introduced around the middle of the century by Donatello in sculptural reliefs. Andrea del Castagno, Antonio Pollaiuolo, and Andrea Verrocchio developed this contour line to give the impression of three dimensions, while Domenico Veneziano, Paolo Uccello, and Sandro Botticelli explored its decorative possibilities. Unlike strong light, line as a dominant modelling agent did not disturb the colour area and was readily adjusted to the ambiguity of its actual life on the surface and its illusory life in depth. Furthermore, the Renaissance predilection for the human body, particularly the nude, as the major subject of painting gained from a growing knowledge of it. Pollaiuolo, Verrocchio, and Leonardo da Vinci studied not only the anatomical structure and mechanism of the body but also the way in which its parts were reshaped by movement and bodily tension. Their figures in motion provided another affirmation of the depth and continuity of pictorial space.

Movement was also intimately related to the Renaissance interest in depicting the 'mind of man'; Leonardo's well-defined descriptions of the histrionic attitudes associated with basic emotional states lived on in the academies of Europe into the eighteenth century. Other observations made during the fifteenth century contributed to a still more convincing representation of space. Some of them centred on 'aerial perspective', or the effect of atmospheric haze on the clarity of outline and the vividness of colour in distant objects. The intimate link between discoveries in optics and innovations in pictorial form became a central feature of Western art and the basis for an unparalleled rapidity of change in the formal aspects of painting.

During this period, the Italian artist also attained but temporarily put aside a space construction that the Baroque artist was enthusiastically to develop later. Andrea Mantegna, in his mid-fifteenth century frescoes of the life of Saint James in Padua's Eremitani Chapel, used eccentric angles and a perspective point that fell beneath the lower edge of the scene. (Pl. 3b.) In his frescoed ceiling in the Ducal Palace in Mantua, he delineated a circular opening with a sharply foreshortened parapet over which leaning figures looked down, with a blue sky above them. Correggio in the early sixteenth century was to realize fully the illusional possibilities of this use of perspective in his frescoes on the domes of the Cathedral and of San Giovanni Evangelista in Parma, but it was avoided by most Renaissance artists in central Italy, who were inclined to respect the surface on which they worked as the beginning plane of a world like that of the spectator but not as one continuous with it.

Shortly before Brunelleschi and Masaccio demonstrated artificial perspective to fellow Tuscans, Hubert and Jan van Eyck in Flanders developed a pictorial form characterized by great spatial depth and most exacting natural detail. This art form was derived from the French illuminations, particularly those of the Limbourg brothers, in which, as already mentioned, some of the illusional possibilities of the Tuscan tradition had been developed. The Van Eycks' Ghent altar-piece, finished in 1432, shows an encyclopedic interest and a marvellous attention to infinitesimal details—in floor tiles, individual leaves on distant trees, and precious stones on the crown of the Father. (Pl. 5b.)

One marvels not only at the Van Eycks' infinite observations and patience but also at their skill in ordering this multiplicity. They were enabled to achieve this effect by means of a new oil technique. 'Tempera' was the technique then used in most areas of Europe including Italy; it was earth or mineral pigment moistened with water and mixed with an oily, fatty, or resinous substance to make an emulsion. The Tuscans commonly made use of egg yolk to bind the ingredients. The resulting surface had a somewhat chalky and opaque appearance, which was counteracted usually by a coat of warm-coloured varnish. Some artists of northern Europe, omitting the egg yolk, had been experimenting with boiled or sun-thickened oils. The Van Eycks adopted this oil technique. It produced sticky substances that facilitated the minute touches, heightened the suggestions of texture, and made transparent films of colour ('glazes'), which gave unity to a multitude of small parts. In contrast to the rationally and quantitatively constructed space of Tuscan art, that of the Van Eycks was a qualitative one, depending on the delicate nuances of colour, fused and flowing within the broad tones of the glazes.

This subtle artistry had little immediate following. It was overshadowed by the more vigorous and dramatic style of the painter known as the Master of Flemalle (probably Robert Campin) and of Rogier van der Weyden, which appears to stem from a monumental art like that of the sculptor Claus Sluter (see below) rather than from the illuminated manuscript tradition. The accentuated individualities and intense expressions of sorrow and pain of the Master of Flemalle's figures were continued in the work of Rogier van der Weyden, but Rogier's art is distinguished by a strong, rhythmic line that organized his panels in large-scale, diagrammatic patterns. In his large 'Deposition' in the Prado (1438), the long curving contour lines of the limp body of Jesus and the lines that describe the garments and sorrowful contortions of the Magdalene reveal his full mastery of the style. Various aspects of his art continued in the Low Countries (in Hans Memling, for example), in other areas where the Gothic style had left a special preference for line (such as Germany, Spain, and France), and even in north Italian artists like Cosimo Tura. Jerome Bosch's imaginative fantasies and, in the mid-sixteenth century, Pieter Bruegel the Elder's landscape and genre scenes were based on northern traditions, but the art of others, such as Quentin Matsys and Jan Mabuse (Gossart), reveals that the pictorial concepts of central Italy were by their time being accepted in the Low Countries.[2]

German Painting, Woodcut, and Engraving

The German School, which in a short life produced works of great emotional intensity and realism of detail, was based in the fifteenth century on contemporary Flemish art and was later influenced by fifteenth-century Italian art. In spite of its affinity with the earlier Flemish and Tuscan schools, German painting boasted several varied art forms. Conrad Witz's Geneva altar-piece exhibits amazing clarity in the depth of its space and in its full volumes. (Pl. 6a.) Martin Schongauer's style is represented by his delicately executed 'Virgin of the Rose Arbor'. Mathias Grünewald ranges in his Isenheim altarpiece from a realistic portrayal of a writhing, brutally beaten Jesus on the cross to a visionary image of the resurrected Christ suffused with white light within an aureole of rainbow colours. Albrecht Altdorfer placed Biblical events in verdant and moody landscapes. Albrecht Dürer's draftsmanship imparted powerful volumes and emotional intensity to his figures. (Pl. 6b.) Hans Holbein the younger executed exactly observed and precisely delineated portraits; he obtained an international reputation, carrying out commissions throughout Europe and leaving a strong impression on the art of sixteenth century England. With the painting of Holbein and Lucas Cranach (Pl. 7a.), this imposing display of German talent ended, never to regain a comparable place in European painting. (Pl. 7b.)

Schongauer, Dürer, Holbein, and other leading German (as well as Italian) painters did some of their most significant work in woodcuts and after 1460 engraving on copperplate. The origin of these techniques is conjectural, but by the early fifteenth century woodcuts were already used for printing sacred images and playing cards and, by the middle of the century, for illustrating popular legends such as the 'Dance of Death'—for which Holbein later did a famous set—and printed books. Print-making spread rapidly, and many capable though frequently anonymous artisans were at work, particularly in Germany, where the special feeling for line and texture was readily expressed by this new pictorial process.3 Variations (such as dry point and, by the sixteenth century, etching) on the earlier intaglio process of engraving revealed considerable technical inventiveness and produced an increasing variety of effects. These media were widely used to copy paintings, and by way of prints many motives, figures types, and compositions were rapidly diffused. With Schongauer, engraving and, with Dürer, woodcut attained the stature of independent art forms. In several of Dürer's woodcut series— e.g. the 'Passion of Christ' and the 'Life of Mary'—and in his individual engravings—e.g. 'The Knight, Death and the Devil' and 'Saint Jerome in His Study'—both media reached a technical and esthetic level never attained again. While admired all over Europe, Dürer's prints were especially praised in Florence during the early sixteenth century, particularly by artists like Andrea del Sarto and Jacopo da Pontormo, who were prominent in the formation of the so-called Mannerist style (see below). Thus German woodcut and engraving, along with German portraiture, had greater international repercussions than other spheres of German art. Perhaps the most important result of the invention of print-making was the acceleration of the interchange of artistic ideas among the leading centres of Europe.

The Venetian Form and Technique

Venetian painters meanwhile had been spurred by their contact with Tuscan art to create a pictorial form that was to be studied through the centuries by artists from all parts of Europe. The sejourn of Jacopo Bellini and his sons in Padua in the mid-fifteenth century, bringing them in contact with the sculpturesque art of Mantegna, led to their fusion of the sumptuous colour of Venice with the clear spatial order of Tuscan painting adopted by the Paduan school. To the Venetians, colour was not simply, as it was in Florentine art, an addition to the basic structure of the drawing; it was the principle element in the shaping of parts and in the achievement of pictorial unity. The new kind of painting was most impressively demonstrated by Giorgione, a creative follower of the Bellini, in his 'Tempest' and 'Fête Champêtre'. (Pl. 8.) Idyllic landscapes (as settings for arcadian adventures) and reclining nudes became popular subjects in Venice and eventually in all of Europe; Titian, while developing still further the bucolic and sensuous aspects of Giorgione's art, emphasized dramatic action rather than poetic reverie. The vigorous, spiralling movement of his Virgin of the 'Assumption' in the Frari Church in Venice (1516) brought a new vitality of movement into the art of Venice. (Pl. 9a.) Giorgione's half-length portraits of moody and self-conscious youths, which recall the intimate aspects of Flemish portraits, were transformed in the hands of Titian into the dignified three-quarter or full-length portraits that became the 'official portrait' type of Europe for the next one hundred and fifty years. Titian's equestrian portrait of Charles V (Pl. 9b.) was also to serve as a model for Baroque painters such as Rubens, Van Dyck, and Velasquez (see below Pl. 17, 18, 20a). Although the Bellini and Giorgione had learned to paint with the more successful oil techniques of Flanders and Germany, Titian was among the first to use oils not simply as a variation on tempera but with a feeling for the substance of the pigment. His rich variety of heavy impasto strokes, the web-like intermingling of the trails of his brush, and the transparency of his glazes, in which subtle details could be laid one upon another, developed oil painting beyond anything attained by the Flemish. The Venetians, using raw oil rather than the sticky sun-thickened or boiled oil of the Flemish, achieved a broader, more fluid kind of brushwork, which became a vehicle as characteristic as handwriting for the expression of the artist's personality.

Painting in the Sixteenth Century

Rome in the early sixteenth century became the art metropolis of central Italy, attracting artists from various local schools. The resulting style, dominated by Tuscan traditions, has been called 'High Renaissance' to indicate its maturity and fullness of realization. In a sense it resolved the many conflicting ideals that earlier generations of the Renaissance had created, attaining an admirable balance of surface and deep-space design, integrating the modelling roles of light and line, and subduing the decorative colour areas in favour of more sculptural aims. Completely in command of the devices that create the illusion of space and volume and lend anatomical vitality to the figures, Leonardo da Vinci, Michelangelo, and Raphael enriched scientific spatial construction with a new rhythmic articulation of space. No longer treating figures and objects as isolated guardians or markers of space, they began to harmonize movements, silhouettes, and volumes so that individual figures fused into groups of three or five or more. These groups, in turn, were so disposed that they formed a flow of masses guiding the viewer's eye along a rhythmic path through the depth of the painting. At the same time the subordination of decoration or descriptive details to the large, simple shapes of the figural and architectural parts brought a new monumentality to the art of Italy. (Pl. 10a, b.) As a result the total configuration of huge paintings composed of many figures (like Raphael's in the Stanza della Signatura) can be seen with an immediacy unequalled in the earlier Renaissance. Leonardo, Michelangelo (particularly in the Sistine Ceiling), and Raphael created, besides, ideal physical types, a 'new race of men', handsome beyond any creation of Nature. While in some ways the fruition of the fifteenth-century artists' study of optics and the natural world, the painting of the High Renaissance became a new art, more decorative and beautiful than the visual world. (Pl. 11.)

Contemporary artists were apparently overwhelmed by these perfect physical types and adroit pictorial arrangements. They tended to avoid the imperfections of nature and to depend directly on painting and engraving after the masters they admired. Yet none of the followers of Michelangelo could successfully imitate his particular rhetoric, lacking the tragic intensity that sustained his figures. The imitative followers of Raphael and Michelangelo are called 'Mannerists'. Although their complex artifice and 'attitudinizing' are often disturbing, they nevertheless made original contributions by new adjustments of surface and space design less dependent on artificial perspective and more dependent on the new ideal of rhythmic or ornamental relationship. The Florentine Mannerists Pontormo, Bronzino, and Il Rosso, together with Parmigianino of the Parma school, frequently attained an elegance in their figures, a refined sensuousness in their surfaces, and a subtle, minor-key colour harmony unequalled in the High Renaissance. Theirs was an art whose form and often obscure allegorical subject-matter appealed to subtle intellects and tastes. It was this style and not that of the High Renaissance which was successfully transplanted to Fontainebleau in France, and the subtleties, elegance, and refined sensuousness of the Tuscan Mannerists have since remained fairly characteristic of French art.

Venice, under the guidance of Titian and the superb decorator Paolo Veronese, remained relatively independent of Mannerism. The style of Tintoretto, in the second half of the sixteenth century, while different in some aspects from that of his Venetian contemporaries, was equally far from that of the Mannerists. He did not merely follow the elongated and contorted figures of Michelangelo but within the broad tones of the Venetian tradition, achieved an intense dynamism of flickering light, which gave his figures and deep space a striking vitality.[4] (Pl. 12a.)

El Greco (d. 1614) was a kindred spirit. After a period of study in Venice and Rome, he found a stimulating atmosphere in the intensely devout Toledo of Spain. There he acquired a unique style, characterized by an ecstatic energy that absorbed and reshaped his figures, and by a new palette of fierce, sulphurous colours that are both icy and vivid at the same time. (Pl. 13.) His austere and vibrant art has much in common with the flame-like figures of the earlier Toledan sculptor Alonso Berruguete but contrasts with the equally vibrant but voluptuous art of Correggio, Federigo Barocci, and later Baroque artists.

Painting in the Seventeeth Century

The style of art known as Baroque is conventionally said to have begun in Italy in the late sixteenth century. It developed further through two strikingly different departures by opponents of the Mannerist style. The first, initiated in Bologna by Lodovico Carracci and his nephews, Agostino and Annibale Carracci, was carried by Annibale to Rome in 1595; the second was largely a Roman development initiated by Caravaggio.[5]

The Carracci, though diverse in style, had much in common. They all admired the drawing of Raphael and his ideal but still natural figures, the warmth of Venetian colour, and the art of Antiquity. Lodovico's more painterly manner, based on colour and light effects, inspired the Baroque style of Guido Reni and Guercino, while Annibale's vigorous, sculptural, and Classicist tendencies influenced Domenichino, Francesco Albani, and the French painter Nicholas Poussin. (Pl. 14a.) Pictorial form still rested, as it had in the Renaissance, on the arrangement of modelled volumes in the illusory depths of the painting, but Baroque space was more dependent on nuances of light, colour, and atmospheric effects than on linear perspective, and in addition provided the spectator with more eccentric and diagonal points of view. The Tuscan insistence on drawing as the basis of painting was not completely abandoned, but momentary, accidental light became during the Baroque period the vital element in the definition of shapes.

These formal changes from Renaissance painting contributed to the success of a pictorial marvel of the seventeenth century in Italy—the illusory frescoes that opened the vaults of a room onto a spectacle attended by heavenly hosts floating freely in an infinite expanse of blue sky. Pietro da Cortona's fresco of the 1630's in the Palazzo Barberini, glorifying the magnificence, virtue, and wisdom of Pope Urban VIII, is filled with hundreds of robust and vigorous figures. Massed and entangled, all are possessed by a common state of excitement; each silhouette and surface is restless and vibrant. This suggestion of energy does not depend on a convincing portrayal of anatomical movement but rather on a fluid and all-pervading dynamism which unites many complex parts into one vision of ecstatic intensity. As mentioned previously, Correggio had pioneered in this kind of illusion a century earlier, and Cortona's fresco is a panoramic extension of Correggio's frescoes in Parma. In the late seventeenth century, Andrea Pozzo's frescoed vault in the Church of San Ignazio in Rome continued the rise of the wall by means of painted architecture creating the illusion of a space twice as high as it actually is. Beyond, one sees Saint Ignatius in glory, while allegorical figures representing the four parts of the earth pay homage. Exalted themes and grandiose ensembles like these represent the climax of the Baroque style in Catholic countries and have few analogies in Protestant areas.

In Rome Poussin was imbued with Annibale Carracci's fondness for Classic and High Renaissance models, firm contours, and Venetian colour. The mature Poussin with the dignified rhetoric of his ideal types, the sculptural clarity of his figures, and the calculated and rhythmic arrangement of his groups more completely realized the art of Raphael than did any other painter in the seventeenth century. Poussin's was an unusually restrained, even stoic, and noble utterance, perfectly sustained. For him Biblical events required a deliberate classicism characterized by geometric shaping and arrangements of parts, while subjects like 'The Reign of Flora' called for softer and more sensuous treatment of flesh and more delight in colour. (Pl. 14b.)

Although he did not form a 'school' of followers, Poussin's calm, reasoned, tectonic art with its noble and moral content appealed to Charles LeBrun, leader of the new Royal Academy of Painting and Sculpture in Paris. Chapter XVI will describe the rise and influence of Europe's academies of art. None of them made a more serious effort to mould national standards than the French academy. It gave a firm direction to the training of artists and to the formation of a French school of painting. Poussin's art, as interpreted by the Academicians, became the basis for the 'Grande Manière' of the French tradition.[6]

Landscape painting of several different kinds also flourished in Rome in the early seventeenth century. Annibale Carracci brought the idyllic, arcadian landscape of northern Italy. Paul Brill was representative of the rich Flemish tradition, which boasts the extensive, detailed and delightfully varied terrains of such a master as Joachim Patinir. Adam Elsheimer depicted nocturnal landscapes with the exuberant vegetation typical of the German school. Drawing on Italian traditions, Poussin constructed magnificent landscapes.[7] His compatriot in Rome, Claude Lorrain, developed subtle tonalities on far-reaching views of the Roman countryside broken by an occasional ruin or of a harbour bordered by grandiose palaces; Lorrain's landscapes conveyed a special mood by captivating light effects, particularly the warm glow and low angle of twilight.

While the art of the Carracci initiated one significant direction in European art, Caravaggio was the originator of another. (Pl. 12b.) Most late sixteenth-century opponents of Caravaggio's painting objected to his 'artless' naturalism and his ordinary rather than ideal physical types. The most influential aspect of his work, however, was not this realism but his use of chiaroscuro. The unusually harsh contrast of his light and dark causes the contours of his objects to be almost lost in broad passages of impenetrable darkness. His denial of the Tuscan-Roman belief in clear drawing as the basic element of painting was more in accord with Lombard and Venetian art. The strong contrast of light and dark found in Giorgionesque night scenes, particularly those of Correggio, and the monochromatic tonalities and the sometimes violent light and dark of the later Titian and Tintoretto provided possible models for Caravaggio's use of 'artificial' light.

Even before Caravaggio, several artists, particularly when endowing the

Nativity with a mystic light, had shown great skill in the use of chiaroscuro. In Spain Navarrete had worked in the tenebrist manner of the Venetians at the Escorial near Madrid, and his follower Francisco Ribalta had carried that manner to Valencia. There José Ribera received his early training; then, after acquiring the realism and the more intense chiaroscuro of Caravaggio, he formed a style of painting in Naples that was followed through the seventeenth century.

Most of Europe came to know Caravaggio's style through his followers Saraceni and Orazio Gentileschi and various Dutch artists in Rome rather than from his own paintings. These painters emphasized 'cellar' lighting effects, tavern or street scenes, and ignoble physical types, overlooking Caravaggio's profound understanding of mental states and human relations. Many also failed to duplicate his clear structure of space and the volumes within it. A provincial French follower, Georges de la Tour, however, succeeded in developing a highly personal style in which a warm light appears to glide out of utter darkness onto the smooth surfaces of extremely simplified shapes of silent and humbly devout people. Valentin de Boulogne, who spent most of his life in Rome, followed Caravaggio's art less creatively. Simon Vouet, after an initial attraction to tenebrism, found himself—as did most Frenchmen—more in accord with the Carracci current than with the harsh realism of Caravaggio.

The Dutch Baroque style meanwhile also departed markedly from the exalted manner of Italy. Dutch artists were now deeply rooted in fifteenth century Flemish realism and in the genre art initiated in the sixteenth century by Pieter Brueghel. Hence they readily accepted the ordinary faces and everyday events of the 'Caravaggisti'. Jan Steen executed rowdy scenes like Brueghel's; Pieter de Hooch presented the unspectacular life of that class of Dutch homes in which women tended their own children and quietly performed household chores; Gerard Terborg as well as Honthorst depicted a more genteel, elegantly dressed set politely conversing or playing musical instruments.[8] Paintings of such unimportant, easily recognizable subjects provide a more complete pictorial record of Dutch life than those left by any other cultural area. (Pl. 15a, b.) The relative calm of the figures and the adjustment of the main wall planes to parallel the surface of the painting contrast with the dramatic events, dynamic figures, and diagonal movement of space in the Italian Grand Manner. In further contrast with contemporary Italian painting, the patiently recorded patterns of floor tiles and of multi-coloured carpets, and the minute details of the maps hanging on the walls were all kept firmly in place within the varied lighting of the interior by the perfection of each colour within its tonal area. Less tenebrist and anecdotic than most Dutch painters, Jan Vermeer carefully adjusted delicately varied colours to subtle areas of tone without dimming the beauty and clarity of the individual colour.

In the sixteenth and particularly the seventeenth century two subjects, formerly subordinate to the primarily narrative purpose of painting, gained a new independence. They were the non-figural landscape and the still-life. Both were given a more prominent place in Dutch painting than in that of any other cultural area of Europe. Pieter Claesz' and Willem Kalf's pictures of abandoned dinner tables laden with the torn and nibbled left-overs of a meal, although accidental in appearance, are most skilfully contrived; the luscious, tempting colours and textures of food scattered among shining silver, pewter, and glass reveal the epicurean side of Dutch upper-class life. Views of the sea, cities, and open country, independent of any narrative, were aspects of the Dutchman's biography which he apparently enjoyed contemplating in pictorial reproduction. The landscapes of Jacob van Ruysdael and his pupil Myndaert Hobbema not only recorded the topographical peculiarities of Holland but also expressed the dynamic character of nature; billowing clouds, patches of shadow across a field, and vigorous vegetation revealed an interest in growth and change that was characteristic of Baroque painting.

Rembrandt, the giant among the Dutch painters of this golden age, did some of his most memorable work as portraits. Portraits had become an important art form among the Flemish and the Italians of the fifteenth century. The Flemish patiently depicted every detail of face and costume, and the Italians tended to glorify the beauty, dignity and even grandeur of Man. In contrast, Rembrandt subordinated much of the setting and the costume in a warm umber spaciousness, defining selected details with crisp touches of impasto. Usually presenting Man as humble and contemplative or seriously and frankly concerned with life, he seems to glimpse into the inmost mind of the portrayed. (Pl. 16a.) The laughing eyes and animated spirits of Frans Hals' extroverts or the carefully composed mien of Valezquez's regal personages do not so cogently invite exploration of the psyche.

While Rembrandt also did some mythological paintings and landscapes, his favoured subject (if his etchings, drawings, and paintings are all considered) was the Biblical event. (Pl. 16b.) After a period in which he followed the rhetorical gestures of the Italian tradition, he tended to concentrate increasingly on the inner reactions of the participants. His art represents the ultimate potential of Caravaggio's chiaroscuro as a means of creating space and placing figures within it, but Rembrandt's light and dark are less harshly separated than Caravaggio's, and his light is more intimately fused with warm, earthy colour tonalities (sometimes accented with brilliant colour, in keeping with his admiration for Venetian painting).

Rembrandt's relatively sombre paintings in Protestant Holland contrasted dramatically with the predominately light-filled and vivid colour of the Catholic painter Peter Paul Rubens in nearby Flanders. Although Rubens' special sensibility to varied textures and light-reflecting qualities has deep roots in Flemish art, his opulent colour was derived from Venetian painting, and his grand rhythmic movements, his groupings of figures, and their rhetorical gestures draw upon the Tuscan-Roman tradition and, perhaps, the

ecstatic dynamism of Correggio and Barocci. Rich and vivid in hues, his
'Rape of the Daughters of Leucippus' in Munich reveals his unique characteristics; the soft and heavy white bodies of the women contrast with the
hardened, sun-tanned skin of the men, the turbulence of their twisting bodies
magnified by a vitality that permeates all the canvas. (Pl. 17.) The same
pictorial qualities with which he portrayed indulgences of the flesh contributed fervour to his depiction of a triumph of faith or an apotheosis of a saint.
In him and Pietro da Cortona in Rome the Grand Manner of the seventeenth
century reached its zenith.

Technical ability also reached its zenith about the same time. In the handling of oil paint, Rubens stands out along with Rembrandt and Velasquez, the
heirs of Titian, as a most accomplished technician. The variety of ways in
which pigment can be smeared, trailed, touched, or glazed over the surface—
and endure—has remained unexcelled, and the manipulation of pigment as a
vehicle of individuality was brought to its highest pitch, remaining a model
for painters to this day. Rembrandt also raised etching to a technical and
aesthetic level never equalled for variety of texture and tone.

The national school of Spain in the seventeenth century provided not only
her golden age in painting but also the clearest and most austere pictorial
statement of the Counter-Reformation in Europe. The mature Velasquez,
to be sure, was a court painter, particularly noted for the magnificence
and mastery of his portraits in the Venetian tradition and for the colour
and aerial perspective of his historical paintings (e.g. the 'Surrender of
Breda').[9] (Pl. 18.) Other Spanish painters, however, received most of their
commissions from the church. Francisco Zurbarán created a non-sensuous
world of quiet surfaces and clear shapes that effectively conveyed the chaste
life or the intense visions of the white-habited monks whose life he portrayed.
Valdes Leal's disturbing reminders of the death of the body and the eternal
life of the spirit emphasized the ephemeral nature of matter by the insistent
actuality of the physical substance he depicted. Murillo, while creating
an unrivalled representation of the Immaculate Conception and tender
images of the Holy Family, developed an atmospheric spaciousness that
gently merged the physical world and the celestial vision, effectively portraying
the intimate relation between the material and the spiritual in Spanish
Catholicism.

Painting in the Eighteenth Century

In the early seventeenth century, Europe had become a cosmos of richly
varied national styles. By the eighteenth century, however, the Flemish,
Dutch, and Spanish schools had lost their creative vigour, leaving Venice
rivalled for leadership only by England and, more particularly, France.
Throughout the seventeenth century the artists of Europe continued to make
the pilgrimage to Venice to learn the colour secrets of Titian and Veronese.
In the eighteenth century, the superb Venetian colourist and decorator

Giovanni Battista Tiepolo won international fame and was called upon to carry out huge frescoed ceilings in the illusional tradition of Italy not only in his own country but in Würzburg and Madrid. (Pl 19a.) Antonio Canaletto's and Francesco Guardi's views of the piazzas and canals of Venice, memorable for the shimmering blues and greens of water and sky and the warm rose and tan of buildings, were painted in response to a steady demand from tourists, particularly English, who flocked to Venice. (Pl. 19b.)

England during the eighteenth century was not only a good market for landscapes but, for the first time, could boast a native group of painters who ranked among the major figures of European art. In the seventeenth century some brilliant pupils or followers of Rubens—Anthony Van Dyck, Peter Lely, and Godfrey Kneller—had gone to England from the Continent. Van Dyck was the most influential of them. His manner was facile but less vigorous and sensuous than Rubens', and his figures were more dignified and elegant. (Pl. 20a.) These immigrant artists provided England with a basic type for its portrait school. Joshua Reynolds and Thomas Gainsborough followed that type (Pl. 20b), and George Romney helped to carry the tradition into the nineteenth century. Gainsborough also painted hastily executed and sparkling landscapes that recall Rubens (as well as Watteau) in their vibrancy and Hobbema and the Dutch school in the dynamic and irregular character of the nature they portray and in their lack of historical or narrative reference. (Pl. 21a.) Reynolds appears to have adapted the landscapes of Claude Lorrain to the role of background for his fashionable portraits. (Pl. 21b.) In the eighteenth century, watercolour became a prominent medium for landscapes and views of towns in the skilful and sensitive hands of Paul Sandby and John Robert Cozens. One of the most insistently 'English' painters of the period, William Hogarth, painted and engraved shrewd commentaries on contemporary morals and customs (see Chapter IX and Pl. 23a).

In France the exalted and domineering voice of the Royal Academy had not gone unchallenged. The latter half of the seventeenth century was characterized by arguments between the 'Rubensists', who emphasized colour, and the Classicists of the Academy, identified as 'Poussinists', who emphasized drawing. By the early eighteenth century the argument had lost its significance, because the important place claimed for colour by the Rubensists was accepted, and a leader of that group, Antoine Watteau, was a member of the Academy.

Watteau, although essentially a colourist like Rubens, is notably different. His paintings tend to be quite small in contrast to Rubens' monumentality, and unlike Rubens' full, rich colour, Watteau's tends to be subtle, delicate, and iridescent. (Pl. 22.) Watteau's 'well-groomed wilderness,' peopled for the day by dreamy, fragile youths and maidens of the leisure classes, glitters with the bright sheen of silk against the soft, misty hues of the woodlands. His loose brush reveals great facility in the Rubens tradition, but the present deteriorated state of his works testifies to a less exacting craftsmanship. The vagueness of the events in Watteau's 'fêtes galantes' and their aspect of reverie as well as their blond tonality recall the pastorals of Giorgione's followers in Venice, but the French scenes have more of a touch of languor or nostalgia shading their participants' pleasure.

By its variety, delicacy, elegance, feminine grace, and emphasis on genteel and sensuous pleasures, Watteau's art gave direction to the 'Rococo' style in early eighteenth-century painting. Lesser artists, such as Jean Baptiste Pater and Nicholas Lancret, repeated Watteau's subjects, and Jean Honoré Fragonard and Madame de Pompadour's favourite, François Boucher, continued his love themes. The works of Fragonard revealed more tenderness and genuine voluptuousness than the calculated, erotic works of Boucher. While Boucher and Fragonard followed Watteau's colour and sensuousness, they looked also to Italian artists of the decorative tradition, such as Tiepolo, for models for their mural designs in the intimate salons and boudoirs of the Rococo hôtel. Nicholas Largillière's portraits were ornamental and flattering versions of the Van Dyck portrait, while Maurice Quentin de la Tour and Jean-Etienne Liotard executed more intimate portraits in pastel, a delicate medium permitting the most gentle transitions and subtle nuances of colour, and thus particularly pleasing to the Rococo taste.

In striking contrast with this group, Chardin painted middle-class life and (more memorably) still-lifes. His paintings contain no obviously contrived or complicated arrangements but a careful ordering of simple shapes, rich, low-key colours, and homespun textures. In this way he pointed toward a kind of 'pure painting' that remains an ideal in French art to the present day. Greuze's paintings also mirrored the village life of his day, reflecting more than Chardin the contemporary vogue of *sensibilité* (see Chapter IX and Pl. 23b).

About the mid-eighteenth century, a new burst of admiration for the Greco-Roman world was set off by some extraordinary archaeological excavations, particularly at Herculaneum and Pompeii. The archaeologist Comte de Caylus, Anton Raphael Mengs, painter and director of the Vatican Academy of Art, and the art historian Winckelmann urged the study of Ancient art not only for its form and appeal to the senses but also for its appeal to virtue and the elevated emotions (see Chapter IX). It was not, however, the bourgeois morality of a Greuze that the lovers of Antiquity had in mind. The noble ideals envisioned by these Neoclassicists were to be exemplified rather in the last quarter of the century by the tales of civic virtue, courage, and patriotism painted by Jacques Louis David.

Although the Europeans faced many of the same problems in the depiction of space encountered centuries before by Chinese artists, the solutions the West found suggest no awareness of the Far Eastern tradition. When Europeans finally came in contact with the Chinese pictorial form, they were so completely conditioned by the homogeneous space of their perspective system that the Eastern space devices appeared to them simply naïve. On the other hand, the most insistent efforts of religious orders such as the Jesuits to teach

z*

Western painting in China and Japan won a number of apt pupils but brought no general disturbance to the continuity of the Eastern tradition. The Chinese were not inclined to base their paintings on natural science or to subordinate pictorial arrangement to discoveries in optics (see below).

Sculpture in France, the Germanies, and Northern Europe (c. *1300–1500*)

European sculpture underwent style changes similar to those of painting but with some important differences. Unlike northern miniature painters, who reacted early in the fourteenth century to the illusional spatial depth of Sienese and Florentine painting, northern sculptors remained relatively unaffected by Italian sculptural developments until late in the fifteenth century. In certain areas, indeed, the Gothic tradition of polychrome wood sculpture, in opposition to the unadorned bronze and marble statuary of central Italy, persisted until the late eighteenth century.

In the medieval tradition, sculpture was associated predominantly with cult images, altar retables, church façades and portals, and tombs. During the thirteenth and early fourteenth centuries the main portals of cathedrals were profusely decorated with sculptured figures and scenes sacred to the church. Carved on archivolts and tympanums from the stone with which the cathedral was built, sculpture was scaled and aligned like an architectural feature. Many of the great portals had been completed by the fourteenth century, but important sculptural programmes were still under way on the cathedrals of Strasbourg, Lyon, and Rouen in France, Exeter in England, and Augsburg, Nuremberg, Gmünd, and Ulm in Germany. Sculptors of this period tended to free portal figures from their somewhat columnar compactness by permitting the arms to move out and the drapery to fall more freely from the body. In the fourteenth century an 'S' curve, rising through these figures and released by the tilt of the heads, lent a gracefulness that relieved the earlier rigidity. The tendency toward grace and ease was accentuated when the artist, now rarely called upon for monumental stone sculpture, instead did small devotional images in ivory, silver, alabaster, marble, or polychrome wood.

Leadership in setting style passed during the fourteenth century from the Île-de-France to several new centres. While the style of the French centre continued (and even reasserted itself in the Loire valley during the so-called 'Détente' of the late fifteenth and early sixteenth centuries), Prague, the Low Countries, Burgundy, and Germany became hubs of more realistic styles that contrasted with the idealized types, simple shapes, and gentle dignity of the Île-de-France. The Parler family, radiating from Prague, formed a style characterized by weighty volumes and realistic surface details like those of the bust portraits in the triforium of the Prague Cathedral. (Pl. 24a, b, c.) Patrons all over Europe ordered many works from Dutch and Flemish centres, but wholesale destruction of sculpture in the Low Countries during the religious strife of the sixteenth century makes difficult an estimate of the amount of work done there. During the last third of the fourteenth century, the Flemish André Beauneveu, particularly renowned for the realism of his effigies, carried out some important sepulchral commissions around Paris, notably those for King Charles V and King Philippe VI in Saint-Denis.

The major figure of the Burgundian school, Claus Sluter, is believed to have come from Holland during the last decade of the fourteenth century to complete the work initiated by Jean Marville for the Carthusian monastery at Champmol near Dijon. His effigies of the duke and duchess of Burgundy (placed with their attendant saints on brackets on either side of paired façade portals) adore the Virgin and Child located between the two portals; larger than life-size, fully round, and animated by vigorously swirling draperies, these figures are more independent of their architectural setting than any in the Île-de-France Gothic tradition. Sluter's ponderous and energetic prophets, carved around a base for a huge calvary in the same monastery's cloisters, suggest that this calvary was probably the most impressive sculptural monument in the Europe of 1400. The magnificent drapery arrangements with the deep, shadowed recesses of their folds, the realism of detail, and the fierce alertness of the prophets' faces impart a physical forcefulness and a dramatic intensity equalled only by Donatello in the following century. (Pl. 25.)

The sculptural production of Germany during the fifteenth and sixteenth centuries is better preserved than that of the Low Countries. In sculptural form northwest Germany was close to the Low Countries, while southern and eastern Germany created more original styles. Most German sculptors worked predominantly in wood. One of the best preserved works of the Franconian Veit Stoss is the huge retable of polychrome wood begun around 1477 in Cracow. The definition of his figures, in contrast to those by Sluter or the sculptors of the Île-de-France tradition, depends on applied colour and on the light and shade and suggestion of line created by abrupt changes of surface and by deep undercutting in the draperies. These 'pictorial' characteristics of his sculpture, particularly his angular drapery patterns, and the dramatic intensity of his figures call to mind the paintings of Rogier van der Weyden. German technical mastery of wood is exemplified by Stoss's 'Annunciation', carved within a rosary and suspended over the choir of Saint Lawrence in Nuremberg (Pl. 26a); its small, delicate parts and its many perforations lend an immaterial, visionary aspect to the scene. Tilman Riemenschneider, though also a Franconian, reflected the lyric and melancholy spirit of Swabian sculptors rather than the vigorous and dramatic character of Stoss. Although most of Riemenschneider's work is in wood, his nude statues of Adam and Eve are stone. (Pl. 26b, c.) Their simple shapes and somewhat stiff appearance disclose that his knowledge of anatomy was more limited than that of contemporary Italians (see below). Bernt Notke's decorative Saint George killing a fierce and fanciful dragon, made for the Church of Saint Nicola in Stockholm in 1489, displays a rearing horse that recalls Leonardo's designs for the Trivulzio monument, but it suggests none of the Italian's understanding of the anatomy of a body in motion. (Pl. 28a.) Peter Vischer excelled in bronze casting. His technical proficiency in that medium stemmed from a long German tradition in metal work, but some of his isolated motifs show a growing awareness of the classical vocabulary of Italy. Such were the putti and the leaf forms among the slim shapes and lively silhouettes of his early sixteenth century shrine of Saint Sebald in Nuremberg.

Sculpture in Italy (c. 1250–1600)

In medieval Italy the lingering of the Romanesque style and the relatively slow acceptance of Gothic forms reflected the continued vitality of the Classical tradition there. Striking references to ancient sculpture were also to be found in French works, notably the 'Visitation' on the façade of the Cathedral of Reims, but they were isolated instances. In Italy such references were less exotic. In the middle of the thirteenth century, when the Gothic style was spreading to all of Europe, Emperor Frederick II in southern Italy commissioned artists to copy ancient sculpture in an effort to enhance his imperial status by reminders of the Roman Empire. Nicola Pisano's reliefs on the pulpit of the Baptistry of Pisa (completed in 1259) indicated a careful study of Classical models. (Pl. 27a.) Giotto's paintings of well-rounded figures disposed in a clearly defined interval were an added stimulus in the direction indicated by Nicola Pisano. Although Giovanni Pisano, his son, turned to northern Gothic models, Andrea Pisano followed the more Classical tradition of Giotto and Nicola in his bronze reliefs for the early fourteenth-century door of the Florence Baptistry and in his stone reliefs for the Cathedral tower.[10]

During the early fifteenth century, much sculptural work went on in Florence. More-than-life-size statues of saints and apostles were commissioned for the Cathedral and the Oratory of San Michele, and reliefs in marble and bronze for the Baptistry, the Cathedral, and the Oratory. Florentine sculptors were stimulated by the desire, which they shared with contemporary painters, to regain the perfection of Ancient art. Donatello and Ghiberti, the leading sculptors of the period, collected and studied Ancient bronzes and marbles (probably small or fragmentary pieces) and also Ancient gems and coins. Furthermore, the keen observation of nature that was transforming painting was also changing sculpture. The bronze panels depicting 'The Sacrifice of Isaac' submitted by Brunelleschi and by Ghiberti in the competition in 1401 for the Baptistry doors reveal attempts to create the pictorial illusion of adequate and convincing space.

About 1417, Donatello carved the marble relief of 'Saint George and the Dragon' for the base of his Statue of Saint George for the Orsanmichele Church. (Pl. 28b.) It ranged from half-round figures in the foreground to very low relief in the background to create another version of the pictorial relief. Delicate variations of light give to the subtly bevelled surfaces of the background an almost atmospheric softness and distance that contrast with the effect created by the broader expanses of light on the strong relief of the figures in the foreground. In making these suggestions of depth, Donatello was 'painting with light' on marble, a technique which the sixteenth-century art historian Giorgio Vasari said he had learned from Ancient gems.

In the square reliefs for his 'Gates of Paradise' (as Michelangelo is supposed to have called the Baptistry doors) Ghiberti incorporated some of Donatello's subtle devices. He was able to create a homogeneous space that continues from the almost free-standing figures in the foreground into the low relief and illusional depths of the panel. (Pl. 27b.) The twisting life of Ghiberti's figures can be seen from a variety of angles, and their more natural scale in relation to their architectural setting contribute pictorial effects that compare favourably with contemporary painting. The association of sculptural relief with the spatial illusion of painting continued as a dominant attitude until recent times. The detail and surface refinements of Ghiberti's reliefs surpassed the work of the most accomplished heirs of Germany's long tradition of bronze casting. As early as 1414 he had successfully cast an eight-foot bronze statue in one piece—a technical feat seldom accomplished in Europe since Antiquity, though contemporary bronze-casting traditions to compare with those of Florence and Germany were to be found, we shall soon see, in China, Japan, India, and Benin.

Donatello's over-life-size figures in marble for the tower of the Cathedral and the exterior of the Orsanmichele Church were formed with a non-ornamental, 'scientific' purpose comparable to those later painted by Masaccio. The clear volumes that compose his statue of Saint George are confined by undisturbed surfaces, simplified for the sculptural effect of lights. (Pl. 29a.) Its forceful modelling and its compactness suggest density and weight and lend to the figure an appearance of physical energy, enhanced by its broad stance, which braces it against the pull of gravity. This clear interdependence of bodily parts within an organic unit distinguishes Donatello's sculpture and that of the later Renaissance. Another characteristic of Donatello's sculpture is the careful control of the contours of the silhouette to form rhythmic continuities that make a precisely frontal view the most harmonious and satisfying. This frontality reflects the influence of *disegno* ('drawing'), which was considered by Florentines to be fundamental to both painting and sculpture. Donatello's severe monolithic statues contrast with the fluidity and subtlety of surfaces, the looping folds, and the gracefully meandering edges of the draperies—vestiges of the International Style—in Ghiberti's figures of Saint John the Baptist and Saint Stephen on the Orsanmichele Church. (Pl. 29b.)

On the other hand, Donatello shares with Ghiberti a sensitivity to the adjustment of a figure in height and volume to its niche. Both sought to place their statuary in such a way that it was neither overwhelmed by a huge cavity nor cramped by inadequate space. Their suggestion of the complementary nature of solid and void, within the homogeneity of figure and space, tended to a close balance comparable to that sought in contemporary painting. Sculptors also shared the contemporary painters' concern for the optical effect of foreshortening, on occasion noticeably enlarging the upper part of a figure placed on high in order to counteract the illusory diminution of size.

One of the most stimulating problems of the fifteenth century was that of free-standing sculpture, unrelated to the architectural background and visible from all sides. The columnar female figures rising freely from the parapet of the fountain begun about 1414 by Jacopo della Quercia for the main square of Siena and the bronze 'David' (1430-40) made by Donatello in the court of the Medici Palace in Florence are the first free-standing nude statues known to have been erected since Antiquity. (Pl. 31b.) Although in-the-round figures, they were clearly designed to be most informative and most esthetically satisfying from the front view. Even the famous equestrian monument of Gattamelatta in Padua was intended to be seen from the two profile views. (Pl. 30b.) When, however, the triangular base for Donatello's bronze 'Judith and Holofernes' was completed (c. 1455) for the Medici Gardens, it indicated a plurifacial concept of sculpture; the limbs of the dead Holofernes hanging beyond the base form a departure from the earlier compactness of marble sculpture around its own core and prepared for a more lively interchange between the free-standing figure and space. Bodily parts were flung even more vigorously beyond the sculptural core in Pollaiuolo's triangular based statuette of 'Hercules Strangling Anteus'.

The boldest step in the plurifacial concept of sculpture came with Verrocchio. His bronze putto posed on tiptoe and affectionately clutching a dolphin was completed (c. 1470) for the gardens of the Villa Careggi. The later installation of this statue in the court of the Palazzo Vecchio in Florence probably re-emphasized its original plurifacial aims since it was made to resolve, constantly presenting a new angle, by the pressure of water that passes through the figure and out through the mouth of the dolphin. The placement of Verrochio's equestrian statue of Colleoni (Pl. 30a) in 1489 in the square of Saint Giovanni e Paolo in Venice reflected a similar consciousness of multiple views, in this case obtained from the five or six entries into the square. Nevertheless, both of these statues have readily recognizable primary views more satisfying than the several secondary ones.

The vigour of the free-standing figures by Pollaiuolo and Verrocchio was made still more convincing by the sculptors' increased knowledge of anatomy. Though only about thirty years separated Verrocchio's bronze 'David' (1460) from Donatello's, Verrocchio's showed more advanced anatomical knowledge. (Pl. 31a.) Growing knowledge freed the artist of the late fifteenth century from the limited repertory of poses used during the Middle Ages and enabled him to present the human body persuasively in any action or arrangement he chose. Leonardo's 'Rider on a Rearing Horse,' delineated in his plans (1511-12) for the Trivulzio monument, presented not only a new intensity of action but in addition a rotary kind of movement; his curvilinear silhouette forced the eye to return to the core of the statue.[12] This revival of compactness of sculptural form and of balanced stability of parts without sacrifice of the ease or vigour of the figure in space was to become characteristic of the High Renaissance.

During the quattrocento several other notable accomplishments were recorded. Desiderio de Settignano and the Rossellini brothers translated the subtle surfaces and light effects of Ghiberti's bronzes into marble and attained a refinement in the treatment of marble surfaces that was to be equalled only by Bernini and, eventually, by the French sculptors of the eighteenth century. This refinement together with the careful study of human anatomy at various ages enabled this group to fashion sculpture (portrait busts of women, a youthful Saint John, a child Jesus) with amazing delicacy of structure and apparent softness of surface. (Pl. 32a.) Donatello, Verrocchio, and Benedetto da Maiano did male busts of a more vigorous and harshly detailed character but with the aim in each case to suggest a living presence. The Rossellini brothers and Desiderio also formed a favoured sepulchral type composed of an elaborately carved sarcophagus and an effigy of the deceased, both enclosed within a symbolic triumphal arch. In the second quarter of the fifteenth century Luca della Robbia initiated glazed terra cotta sculpture. (Pl. 32b.) While Luca restricted the use of blue, lavender, or green glazes for details on the predominantly white surfaces of his sculpture, more elaborate colour schemes are characteristic of his followers. The school founded by Luca represents the major continuity of polychrome statuary in central Italy.

While sculptors in Lombardy and Emilia produced impressive works, Florentine sculptors attracted to the papal court preserved the main tradition in Rome. The fullness of volumes, the heroic types, and the easy grace of the early sixteenth century are exemplified by Michelangelo's 'Pieta' in Saint Peter's in Rome and his gigantic 'David' in Florence and by Andrea Sansovino's 'Virtues' in the niches of the triumphal-arch tombs in Santa Maria del Popolo in Rome. (Pl. 31c.) These figures reveal the confidence with which sculptors of the High Renaissance employed the technical skills, the anatomical knowledge, and the standards of beauty developed during the fifteenth century. Andrea's favoured pupil, Jacopo Sansovino, continuing the master's sculptural types, emphasized the graceful and even elegant aspects of the human figure in such works as the 'Apollo' and the 'Mercury' of the Loggetta in Venice. Michelangelo, on the other hand, created a new sense of spiritual tension, which he enhanced by arranging the limbs so as to seem to compress rather than release the energy pent up in his figures. His 'Saint Matthew', his so-called 'Slaves' (initiated for the ambitious tomb planned for Julius II), and his figures sculptured for the Medici tombs are accommodated to rhythmic configurations essentially different from the natural positions designed by fifteenth-century sculptors.[13] His figural inventions were much admired and accepted as models by painters and sculptors during the cinquecento.

How to relate a statue to surrounding space and how to design it so as to allow an advantageous view from many angles persisted as sculptural problems. Michelangelo's youthful, inebriated 'Bacchus' lifting his wine cup into space, Jacopo Sansovino's 'Bacchus' with even more extended limbs, and Benvenuto Cellini's 'Perseus' holding forth the head of Medusa are examples both of the often abrupt extension from the central core and of the invitation to secondary views. Tribolo, Pierino da Vinci, and Bartolomeo Ammannati, in sculpture planned for garden and fountain settings, made notable contributions to the development of statues in contorted Michelangelesque positions placed precariously on the edge of a fountain pedestal or a basin. Cellini, in arguing the superiority of sculpture over painting and the greater difficulties faced by the sculptor, claimed that the sculptor was not concerned simply with one but with 'forty angles of view,' all of which must be painstakingly designed and adjusted to one another. Despite the advocacy of a plurifacial ideal, Cellini and other cinquecentists generally remained under the spell of a primary, frontal view.

Cellini's aim was realized most fully by Giovanni da Bologna. A Fleming by birth, he came from a sculptural tradition less under the compulsion of a primary view. Out of the Verrocchio-Leonardo-Michelangelo tradition, he developed a *figura serpentinata* that spiralled about a stable central axis, encouraging the continual movement of the spectator around it by presenting no view that was in itself completely satisfying. His bronze 'Mercury' (1564), balanced on tiptoe on one leg with arms and the other leg flung into space, his small marble 'Venus' in the Grotto of the Boboli Gardens, covering her nakedness with her arms, while turning to look at the satyrs peeping over the edge of the basin, and particularly the three struggling figures of his 'Rape of the Sabines' demonstrate a rhythmic spiraling of forms within a column of space. (Pl. 33a.) This organization of figures maintained the autonomy and composure of the free-standing figure, releasing the sculptured limbs in an easy interplay with space, and provided a maximum number of pleasing views with easy passage from one to another.

Spread of Italian Sculptural Ideals

Italian sculptural ideals of the Renaissance penetrated into other parts of Europe to varying degrees. Reacting only little to Italian developments, England for the most part continued her own rich decorative vocabulary, evolved during the late Middle Ages. Among the earliest and most accomplished sculptors outside Italy to follow the Renaissance manner were certain Spaniards. Bartolomé Ordóñez, Diego Siloé, and Damián Forment revealed a clear grasp of Renaissance forms, and so sometimes did the anonymous sculptors of arabesque ornaments in the highly ornamental Spanish architectural style known as the 'Plateresque'. Nevertheless, polychrome wood sculpture and a less Classical aim became dominant among Spanish sculptors (see below).

Germany's political and religious disturbances, reinforcing her strong Gothic tradition, seem to have limited her participation in the elaboration of Classical ideals, but Germans readily followed Italian interest in bronze statuettes and plaques, with an excellence of workmanship in metal work drawn from their medieval technical tradition. By the end of the sixteenth and the beginning of the seventeenth century, Giovanni da Bologna's spiralling figures were adopted in Germany and the Low Countries. Notable among his followers were Hubert Gerhard, who cast bronze figures for fountains in Augsburg and Munich, Andriaen de Vries, who worked in The Hague and Augsburg, and Jacques du Broeucq, who took Bologna's type of sculpture to the Low Countries after a period of study in Italy. The decorative vocabulary of arabesques and other Classical motifs diffused more readily on the Continent than most other aspects of Italian Renaissance sculpture. In Protestant lands, however, nothing significant was contributed to the development of Italian sculptural forms.

Italy's principles of sculpture were transferred more successfully to France than elsewhere. Various Italian sculptors—Leonardo da Vinci, Francesco Laurana, Rustici, Cellini, several members of the Fontainebleau School, and other lesser lights—worked in France during the late fifteenth and the early sixteenth century[14] So little of their work has been preserved or identified that it is difficult to reconstruct the nature of the stimuli they provided. Major French sculptors of this period, such as Michel Colombe and Jean Goujon, are known to us only by way of a few mature pieces, which clearly reveal their awareness of Italian Renaissance and Ancient art, but the formation of their artistic personalities also remains conjectural. Colombe, probably trained in the calm and idealized forms of the 'Détente', readily responded to the motifs and sculptural attitudes of the Italians. His free-standing marble tomb for Duke Francis II of Brittany in the Cathedral of Nantes followed French sepulchral types, but he employed medallions and apostles in niches, framed by half-round arches, elaborately carved pilasters, and Classical mouldings that reflect the clear geometric shapes and minute goldsmith detail of the Tuscan-Lombard tradition. His four 'Virtues', arranged as guardians at the corners of the sepulchre, were carved in the round, attaining a stability of balanced weight, an anatomical 'correctness' of bodily parts, and a fall of draperies that reveal the fusion of Italian ideals with those of the 'Détente'. Goujon worked in co-operation with the outstanding architect Pierre Lescot (see below). Goujon's often low reliefs of decorative and elegant nymphs and allegorical figures, made in the 1540's to ornament the façade of the Louvre, the court of the Hôtel Carnavalet, and his Fountain of the Innocents, employ the elongated figure types and the contrived and subtly sensuous poses of the Italian Mannerists. (Pl. 33b.)

On the other hand, Pierre Bontemps' contemporary work suggests no admiration for such decorative figural inventions. He did much of his work in conjunction with another major architect of the period, Philibert de l'Orme (see below). The tomb of Francis I in Saint Denis, surmounted by precisely finished and boldly shaped bronze effigies of the royal family, is a foremost example of their sober and accomplished workmanship.

After the 1560's the prominence of Catherine de Medici, widow of King Henry II, and her Italian superintendent of art, Primaticcio, encouraged French inclinations to follow Renaissance models. Germain Pilon received commissions from Primaticcio and probably carried out plans designed by him. Pilon was famous for effigies and allegorical figures for sepulchres, and for carefully observed and meticulously executed bronze busts, such as that of Jean de Morvillier, in the Museum of Orleans. Although most of his sculpture is generally quite static, several religious works of the 1580's, particularly his terra-cotta 'Virgin of Sorrows' in the Louvre and his 'Saint Francis in Ecstacy', attain a surprising emotional intensity not only in the expression and gestures of the personages but in undulating surfaces and linear complications. Sculptors in France were rarely called upon to do figures completely free of architectural or sepulchral settings, but, in the late sixteenth century and after, statues of the kings, frequently equestrian, were erected in the centre of the Place Royale of several cities. Although some of these statues were destroyed during the French Revolution as 'monuments of feudalism and idolatry', surviving examples and engravings make it evident that these free-standing equestrian statues depended on Italian models. Pierre Francheville and others continued Giovanni da Bologna's sculptural types into the seventeenth century. Particularly notable is the bronze figure of 'Fame' (modelled on Giovanni's 'Mercury') originally mounted over the tomb of the Duc d'Épernon. French sculptors of the sixteenth century are less important for innovations than for the absorption of Italian and then Ancient ideals into the French tradition, thus giving a Classical direction to the country which was to become the leading art centre of Europe during the late seventeenth and eighteenth centuries.

Polychrome Wood Sculpture

In Spain and Germany while some native sculptors were accomplished in Renaissance forms and Italians were invited to court centres, the Italian Renaissance influence was opposed by those who continued the Gothic tradition of polychrome wood sculpture. Statues of cold marble and bronze may have served the esthetic needs of those who judged by standards of correctness and beauty, but they did not convey the warmth and the impression of actual presence demanded by devout Germans and Spaniards. In the polychrome statuary of the sixteenth and seventeenth centuries, the great variation of physical types, emotional expression, formal arrangement, and treatment of colour testify not simply to a lingering of the medieval tradition but to its prolonged vitality.

Customarily, in this tradition, one artist carved the figure; another completed the costumes, often enriched by designs scratched through upper layers of colour to reveal threads of the gold leaf beneath; and a third did the flesh. The full volumes, the realism in details, and the clarity of local colour in the 'Entombment' of Juan de Juni in Valladolid, completed in the mid-sixteenth century, remind one of the similar groups favoured in France and northern Italy a century earlier. The many figures of Berruguete's huge retable, now in the Museum of Valladolid, have something of the sublime and tragic intensity of Michelangelo's but augmented to a frantic state and absorbed by a flame-like energy. Early-seventeenth-century polychrome sculptors, particularly Gregorio Fernandez in Valladolid and Martínez Montañez in Sevilla (Pl. 34a), employed more limited and subdued colour over figures of greater calm and monumentality. Fernandez' 'Pieta' displays some of the realism for which Spanish and Latin American sculptors of this period are famous: Jesus' deep wounds and open mouth with carefully carved teeth and tongue accentuate his last painful breath. (Pl. 34b.) Although the polychrome sculpture of Germany in the late sixteenth and the early seventeenth century did not match earlier German accomplishments, the works of Ignaz Günther and the Asam brothers in the eighteenth century betokened a renewal of vitality.

Bernini and the Baroque Style

During the seventeenth century, the Classical tradition of Italian sculpture was transformed into the Baroque style largely by the emotional exuberance of Giovanni Lorenzo Bernini, a Neapolitan sculptor who worked chiefly in Rome. Although much of his sculpture was carried out in marble, his technical mastery permitted him to shape and finish his figures as if they were made of wax. In his early busts, such as those of Cardinal Scipione Borghese and of Costanza Bonarelli, he surpassed the effect of living presence in the Renaissance portrait through his startling ability to translate into stone not only the physical structure, softness, and texture of skin and hair but also the state of mind of an alert individual caught in an unguarded moment. His 'Santa Teresa in Ecstasy' is an unexcelled example of the Baroque effort to penetrate the psychology of the persons represented; it portrays the saint's emotion at the moment of spiritual union with Christ, recalling the ecstasies painted by Correggio and Baroccio or the excited sculptures of Berruguete and Stoss. (Pl. 35a.) Like the Gothic sculpture of Germany, Bernini's pieces are often described as 'pictorial': his subtle and fluid surfaces dissolve the hardness, weight, and even bulk of the marble; his gradations of light and shade are the result of studied concern; and his works in architectural settings, like the Santa Teresa and the equestrian statue of Constantine in the narthex of St Peter's, were usually conceived from a primary view. Yet his soft and discontinuous contours do not confine his sculpture so firmly within a primary view as the more precise and coherent contours of Renaissance sculptors confined theirs, and as a result the figures and objects of Bernini's fountains, tombs, and free-standing groups present multiple views and intermingle freely with surrounding space.[15]

Another major seventeenth-century figure in Rome was Alessandro Algardi. He showed greater faithfulness than Bernini to the Classical tradition in his clear opposition of sculptural volume to spatial voids and in the greater restraint of his emotional display. The relatively static forms of Algardi's tomb for Leo XI and the fluid energy of Bernini's tomb for Urban VIII, both in Saint Peter's in Rome, reveal the fundamental difference in their art.

Bernini's art was greatly admired by contemporaries, but few of his followers matched his emotional gusto or his sensibility to the textural and colouring possibilities of light and shade in sculpture. Jacques Sarazin adopted certain aspects of Bernini's style, but most French sculptors working in Rome and the influential François Duquesnoy, a Fleming, were closer in spirit to Algardi. Most Berninesque among the sculptors in France was Pierre Puget; his marble statue of Milo of Crotona attacked by a lion, carved originally for the gardens of Versailles in the 1670's, reveals a comparable technical facility, particularly in the suggestion of the softness of the flesh rent by the lion's claws. In the Low Countries and in Germany during the seventeenth and eighteenth centuries, sculptors more readily adopted, even intensified, the turbulence of Bernini's draperies and the excitement of his figures and frequently equalled his marvellous technique. Among the most lavish sculptural works in these northern areas, and particularly the Low Countries, were church confessionals and pulpits. The confessional in the Church of Ninove by Theodore Verhaegen, the pulpit in Saint Andrew's in Antwerp by Jan van Greel and Jan van Hool, and that in Saint-Gudule in Brussels by Henri François Verbruggen are among the most impressive Dutch and Flemish examples. Andreas Schluter's equestrian statue of the Great Elector in Berlin, Balthasar Permoser's sculptural decoration on the pavilions of the Zwinger in Dresden, and Egid Quirin Assam's excited figures of the 'Assumption of the Virgin' in the Convent Church of Rohr, exemplify the continuity of the Bernini style in eighteenth-century Germany. (Pl. 35b.)

The Classical and the Rococo

Except for Puget, French sculptors, under the watchful eye of the Royal Academy of Painting and Sculpture, rarely approached the emotional and pictorial tendencies of Bernini. In the early seventeenth century, academicians shifted from Italian Renaissance to Ancient models and thus gained a degree of independence from Italian sculptural developments. When Bernini, as leader of the new Italian Baroque style, presented his exuberant bust and equestrian statue of King Louis XIV in Paris in 1665, French sculptors found that they lacked the dignity and restraint appropriate to the person of the king. The Classical ideals of the French Academy were revealed by the sculpture commissioned for the palace and gardens of Versailles and by the many copies of ancient marbles made by French students in Rome and installed in Versailles in the 1680's. The sculpture of Versailles, dedicated to the glorification of the Sun-King, formed a rich, planned concentration of sculptural work equalled only by the Gothic cathedral.

François Girardon was the leading sculptor during the period in which LeBrun directed the art of Versailles. The heroic, idealized figures of Girardon's 'Rape of Proserpine', although in violent poses, are transfixed by the calm and hard surfaces that enclose the figural volumes, with no suggestion of fleshly softness or vitality comparable to Bernini's surfaces. Even Girardon's somewhat pictorial group of 'Apollo and the Nymphs', an allegorical reference to Louis XIV, aimed at the statuesque clarity of bodily parts rather than the sense of breathing life sought by Baroque sculptors in Italy.

The later, more spirited, and less monumental work of Charles Antoine Coysevox, probably stimulated by Puget and other Baroque artists, introduced the Rococo style in sculpture. This style spread rapidly to other court circles in Europe, but the voices of Classicism were never stilled, and throughout the eighteenth century in much of Europe conflict raged between these contrasting points of view. The Rococo style fostered by Coysevox was carried on with an unusual constancy into the nineteenth century by a sequence of sculptors, who were frequently related not only by sculptural traditions but by family ties. Guillaume and Nicolas Coustou, nephews of Coysevox, trained Jean-Baptiste Lemoyne, whose son, Jean-Louis Lemoyne, became the teacher of such important Rococo sculptors as Jean-Baptiste Pigalle and Etienne-Maurice Falconet.

This style was well suited to the portrayal of intimate, playful, or tender moments of life but was less effective in subjects of a heroic nature. Coysevox's sprightly figure of the Duchess of Burgundy as 'Diana', made originally (1710) for the Château of Marly, and Falconet's small and charming 'Bather' (1757) are examples of the special talent of the Rococo sculptor for the portrayal of the softness, delicacy, and grace of the feminine figure. (Pl. 36a.) Pigalle's children in playful activities and his 'Mercury Attaching His Sandals' are examples of the small scale and the light and often trivial subjects of Rococo works. The statuettes by Clodion (Claude Michel) of nymphs and satyrs reveal the joyful and sensuous inclinations of this style. The departure from the monumentality and grandeur of French Classicism is further emphasized by the ceramic figurines, popular items of ornament during the eighteenth century in Europe, for which many Rococo sculptors designed pieces. Perhaps the sculptural acme of the Rococo group was reached with their highly individualized, life-size busts, which projected emotional warmth, intellectual alertness, and love of life in a manner that transformed the momentary character of Bernini's portraits into a peculiarly Rococo, and French, vivaciousness. Coysevox's 'Self-portrait' and his bust of Robert de Cotte are examples of this type. It culminated during the late eighteenth century in the lively and penetrating portraits of Jean-Antoine Houdon. (Pl. 36b.)

During the seventeenth and eighteenth centuries sculpture usually attempted to attain effects associated with painting. Girardon's marble relief 'Nymphs Bathing' recalls the Donatellesque tradition of utilizing subtle surface variations and delicate linear passages to represent an atmospheric spaciousness behind the half-round of the forward figures. This type of relief sculpture developed fragile pieces of virtuosity and pictorial effect such as the 'Horses of the Sun', carved by Le Lorrain over the entrance to the stables of the Hôtel de Rohan. The Rococo style also entered more monumental statuary. Such works as the 'Horse Tamers of Marly', carried out by Guillaume Coustou in 1740 and now on the Place de la Concorde in Paris, reveals the sensibility to fragile projections and the lively variations of surface and silhouette characteristic of Rococo.

The soft contours and the vitality of small Rococo sculpture enhanced the suggestion of life-in-the-round, but monumental works showed a marked tendency toward a preferred, most informative viewing point. Although European sculpture had been freed from subservience to architecture, large-scale, free-standing statues and monuments continued to be affected by the overall sense of order which spatial complexes such as courts, gardens, and public squares imposed. With the acceptance of axial principles of architectural planning in most parts of Europe in the seventeenth century, the sculptor was somewhat released from demands for an infinite number of views imposed during the Renaissance by centripetal placement. Rococo sculptors usually planned a major and several secondary views, on the assumption that the spectator would follow the axial paths planned by the architect.

Monumental and profusely sculptured tombs afforded a major opportunity to French sculptors. During the late seventeenth century the traditional praying attitude of the sepulchral effigy was transformed into one in which the deceased offers himself to the Deity. Early examples are the figure of Colbert on his tomb in Saint-Eustache and that of Mazarin, both by Coysevox. Among the most elaborate allegorical tombs of the period were those made by Pigalle for the Comte d'Harcourt in Notre Dame in Paris and for the Comte de Saxe in Strasbourg, both of which employ the shrouded skeleton, a medieval symbol of death, and figures that plead or weep for the dead.

Eighteenth-century sculptors all over Europe by the excellence of their workmanship and the suggestion of a living presence in their sculpture revealed their indebtedness not only to the strict standards and philosophical principles of the French Academy but also to the keen observations and formal inventions of the artists of the earlier Tuscan-Roman tradition. The lively, pictorial quality of Rococo sculpture was increasingly opposed during the third quarter of the eighteenth century by Neoclassic standards of statuesque calm and by idealized figure types modelled on ancient Greek works. The Neoclassic style was to be most fully realized in sculpture during the last years of the eighteenth century by the Italian Canova and the Dane Thorwaldsen.

Architecture in Pre-Petrine Scandinavia and Russia

In regions where timber was easily available, a style of architecture had arisen in the Middle Ages that combined function with both the limitations and the flexibility of wood as a building material. Few examples of the stave church of the Scandinavian countries and the timber church of northern Russia survive in their original form because of the combustibility and the perishability of wood. Yet some of them have been preserved in some state of repair or restoration.

The wooden church of Russia revealed certain features that may be Byzantine, Tatar, or Gothic, but it remained essentially Russian. The octagonal central space and the pyramidal exterior, traceable to the eleventh-century Cathedral of Sancta Sophia in Kiev, was probably derived from the need to adapt the Greek-cross plan to the most ample practical arrangement to which a log structure could aspire. The tall roof, resembling a tent and frequently called a tent roof, built of planks laid on vertical rafters, is known by the Tatar name of 'shater'. The high vertical reach (obtained by a shater resting on an octagonal drum and topped by a spired, bulbous cupola) may suggest that Gothic influence came into northern Russia from German and Polish contacts with the merchant city of Novgorod even before the arrival of Italian craftsmen at the court of Ivan III in the fifteenth century. But the octagonal drum, the shater, and the cupola, characteristics of the Russian church, probably were themselves the answer of the Russian carpenter-builder to the problem of adapting his materials to his objectives, as were also the *bochki* ('barrels'), or omega-shaped broken arches, with which he decorated the exterior of his churches. One of the best examples of the carpenter-builder's craft, though sometimes considered too extravagant, was the Church of the Transfiguration at Kizhi, built in 1714, with twenty-three cupolas and numerous bochki. (Pl. 37b.)

Russian masonry churches followed the same general structure. They were essentially octagonal, pyramidal, tent churches on the cross plan even when stone permitted, if desired, a greater variety of ornamentation, subsidiary chapels, and more massive dimensions. The Cathedral of St Basil the Blessed, built by Ivan IV in 1555–60 and noted today because it dominates the square outside the walls enclosing the congeries of buildings known as the Moscow Kremlin, is perhaps the outstanding example of the Russian masonry church. Its nine towers are each topped with a polychrome cupola. Built (notwithstanding a persistent legend to the contrary) by the Russian architects Postnik and Barma, it remains, despite or perhaps because of its exuberance, one of the most celebrated landmarks of pre-Petrine architecture. (Pl. 37a.)

Gothic Architecture

The Gothic style, characteristic of most of Western and Central Europe's architecture in 1300, had likewise been developed primarily in the design of churches and cathedrals. Neither belief nor ceremony had been static, and builders had been called upon to shape interior spaces to meet the changing demands of the cult. A search for a greater structural and stylistic unity of architectural elements also favoured change. The Classical rules for the arrangement of architectural elements had been in part lost and, more significant, in part invalidated by an architectural inclination unknown to Greek and Roman architects—the Christian aspiration to create a vast interior reaching toward unprecedented heights. The Île-de-France cathedral was accepted as a model by most of the Continent, but by 1300 adjustments to varying local traditions resulted in several distinct styles.

A Gothic church was a stone skeleton composed of rib-vaults supported by piers and sustained against the outward thrust of the vaults by buttresses. In the second half of the thirteenth century, piers became slimmer and taller, articulated by shafts that continued directly into the ribs of the vaults; arches became more sharply pointed; and all parts seem to have been shaped by a wish to attain an ever higher interior. The huge cathedrals (Reims, Amiens, Cologne, Beauvais, and Troyes) on which work continued during the fourteenth century present dramatic evidence of local devotion and civic pride in their tremendous interior height. (Pl. 38a, b.) In 1284, however, when the vaults of the Cathedral of Beauvais crashed from the unprecedented height of 157 feet, cathedral-builders apparently recognized that they had reached the limit of their structural technique.

The vast, tall interior unity of the Christian cathedral, essentially founded on the technological and esthetic development of the rib-vault, had no parallel outside Europe. It differed strikingly, for example, from the low, horizontal compartments of the hypostyle Islamic mosque. With every step inside his mosque the Muslim experiences change along severely channelled aisles in a space shattered in all directions by a forest of columns, inducing him to draw within himself to pray. The Christian, upon entering his cathedral, becomes part of a continuous space that expands into the light-filled upper reaches of a central nave, inducing him to feel united with the rest of the congregation and the main altar.

Although few cathedrals were initiated in the fourteenth and fifteenth centuries and activity centred around parish or monastery churches and secular buildings, the ideal of expansive space continued to dominate their interiors. In Germany architects formed a great unity of space and light by raising the side aisles and eliminating the independent reaches of the transept. In this new type of church, the 'hall' church, the unbroken rise of the slim shafts of the piers into the vaults gave a new emphasis to the overhead as the final gathering place of the structure's linear energy. Unity in width as well as height was gained by interweaving ribs and intermediary mouldings to form an ornamental web that spanned the full length and breadth of the interior. Outstanding examples (1200–1500) of the German 'hall' church are Saint Elizabeth's in Marburg, the choir of Saint Lawrence's in Nuremberg, Saint Stephen's in Vienna, and Saint Lawrence's in Landshut. (Pl. 39a, b.)

An altogether different sense of spatial unity was characteristic of southern France and Catalonia. The Cathedral of Albi, completed in 1380, provided an interior space dominated by a vast single nave, evenly lighted by tall lancet windows, well suited to the bright sun of the south, and covered by vaults of exceptional spans. The fortress-like exterior is characterized by a taut alternation of half-round buttresses with shallow rectangular chapels surrounding the nave. Its impressiveness is accented by a tower that forms the single western entry. (Pl. 40a.) Another striking example of this type, the Cathedral of Gerona in Catalonia, is covered by a vault with an amazing span of 73 feet—an engineering miracle of the early fifteenth century that drew upon the combined knowledge of architects from all over Europe. (Pl. 41a, b.)

The Hispanization of the Île-de-France cathedral can be followed from its faithful reproduction in the Cathedral of Léon through its variations in the cathedrals of Burgos and Toledo to the uniquely Spanish form of the Cathedral of Seville. The Cathedral of Seville was begun in 1401 with the famous resolution—expressive of the grandiloquent aspiration which continued to motivate Gothic Europe—to build 'such a church that those who see it will take us for mad' to have begun it.[16] It completely covers the 250 feet by 400 feet rectangle originally occupied by the main Muslim mosque and thus has a rectangular plan, five aisles wide and nine bays long. (Pl. 40b.) This aspect of the ground plan, the block-like clarity of the exterior parts, and the acceptance of the old minaret as the cathedral's bell-tower were frank admissions of the Islamic heritage, which, moreover, lived on in the art of Christian Spain. Like Germany and England, Spain preserved an amazingly creative vitality within the forms of the Gothic style. In Spain it lasted until well into the sixteenth century.

Maintaining a marked degree of architectural independence until the seventeenth century England initiated a late phase of Gothic architecture, which subsequently took root also on the Continent. English architects began to move toward a frankly decorative treatment of vaults and window traceries in the early fourteenth century. The names given to English architecture during this period—'decorated' or 'curvilinear'—are clues to its ornamental and lively nature. Small-scale motifs were spread over the surfaces of spandrels and tympanums of cusped, mixtilinear, and, occasionally, ogee arches, but the main areas of innovation were the vaults, where the various ribs rising from the piers were elaborated by intermediary and interlocking ribs in such a way that complicated 'star-like' patterns were created. The spectacular stellar vaults of the cathedrals of Gloucester, Canterbury, Wells, Ely, and Exeter have spatial implications; they seem to be ornamental webs that merge all the individual bays into a continuous decorative unit. Architects in nearby

Normandy appear to have taken over the ogee arch and the curvilinear rhythms to form the French 'flamboyant' style, which was readily diffused over most of the Continent.[17] The exuberant, if no longer transcendental, energy of this style rises through the fragile pentagonal porch of Saint-Maclou in Rouen (1434) and the north portal of the Cathedral of Strasbourg (1495).

Meanwhile, England had abandoned the 'curvilinear' style and, in the late fourteenth century, had initiated a new one called 'perpendicular' or 'rectilinear'. Exceptional fifteenth-century examples of this kind of ornament are the lantern over the crossing of the Cathedral of Ely, the chapels of Eton College and King's College in Cambridge, and, not completed until the next century, the Saint George Chapel of Windsor Castle. (Pl. 42a, b.) The terms 'fan', 'palm', or 'conoidal', used to describe their vaults, suggest spreading, curving surfaces that rise directly from the walls or piers to form the vaults.

Surfaces had been of secondary importance in the Gothic style of the thirteenth century, but in the fifteenth century they became the main realm of decorative invention, a major factor in the unity of interior space, and the conqueror of the linear skeleton that had previously characterized Gothic architecture. This sensibility to the concreteness of the decorative surface was the common denominator of the architectural styles of many parts of fifteenth-century Europe. The 'Isabeline' in Spain, the 'Manueline' in Portugal, and the 'Florid Gothic' in Venice have an opulence of decoration and an excellence of craftsmanship comparable to contemporary works in England, France, and Germany.

In keeping with the general trend toward secularization, this style was most successful in the secular architecture of the late Gothic period. It was adopted for city halls like that of Compiègne in France and of Lübeck and Stralsund in Germany, for châteaux like that of Josselin in Brittany, for bourgeois mansions like Jacques Coeur's in Bourges, and for English manor houses. (Pl. 43a.) Perhaps the outstanding example was the Palais de Justice in Rouen, begun in 1493. Its windows and portals assume ornamental shapes; its walls terminate in a fragile arcade along the roofline; the piers sectioning its façade gradually diminish into delicately carved finials; and the lace-like frames of the dormer windows join with these features to carry its wall decoratively into the steep rise of a tall roof. Among the most exceptional of the many Gothic merchant palaces of Europe was Marino Contarini's Ca' d'Oro on the Grand Canal in Venice. (Pl. 43b.) Its several stages of galleries are supported by elaborately carved and ornamentally shaped arcades, and the preciousness of its white marble and pale rose-coloured walls is lavishly enriched with gold and the flicker of light reflected from the canal.

The Beginnings of Italian Renaissance Architecture

While Tuscan painters had long been stirred by a new ideal, Tuscan architects continued to build in the Italian Gothic style until the fifteenth century.

By 1420, however, Brunelleschi established an essentially different architectural 'vocabulary' and 'syntax' based on his understanding of ancient Roman architecture. In a spirit that paralleled that of his contemporaries in Florence who waxed enthusiastic about the ancient forms in literature or the visual arts, he and his followers believed that Greco-Roman architectural forms were superior to the 'unmeasured and mixtilinear' forms of the Gothic, which they attributed to Germanic 'barbarians'. In pursuit of their aim, they gave unprecedented deference to the rules of architecture laid down in a treatise by Vitruvius in the first century BC and eagerly studied the architectural and decorative vocabulary of Roman ruins. Where the lessons learned from the actual monuments did not coincide with the advice given by Vitruvius the motifs or solutions found in Roman ruins won out, along with those derived from Early Christian, Byzantine, or Romanesque buildings believed to reflect ancient forms. In this way, the architects of Tuscany conjured up an image of Roman architecture that was amazingly complete. Brunelleschi's churches (San Lorenzo and Santo Spirito) in Florence gave a new architectural ideal to Italy and eventually to the whole of Europe and America. (Pl. 46a.) The models for his supports and ceilings were not provided by the local Gothic churches; rather the columns and half-round arches, the flat ceilings, and the boxlike nave and transepts were fashioned on the Romanesque Church of SS. Apostoli, which, his contemporaries believed, was built by Charlemagne.

The architectural vocabulary which Brunelleschi used was based on the ornate 'Corinthian order', composed of a pedestal, round shaft, capital, abacus, and entablature (made up of a lower moulding or architrave, a frieze, and a top cornice). Each of the ancient orders, however, whether Corinthian, Doric, or Ionic, came to be defined by rules for the shape, the scale, and the sequence of its parts, and practice allowed only a limited variation in specifications. The parts of Brunelleschi's order were held together as a continuous system by the contrast of the grey stone of which they were made with the white plaster of the walls; and the careful ratios of parts within the order were reflected in the simple 1:2 and 3:5 ratios that determined the length, width, and height of nave, crossing dome, arms, and chapels. Visual awareness of these ratios adds to the harmony and coherence of structure and interior space.

In Brunelleschi's Latin-cross plan the dome at the intersection, especially the large dome he designed for the Cathedral of Florence, provided a central core to which all parts referred. (Fig. 1; Pl. 46b.) This ordered stability, based upon a building's central vertical axis, is more readily seen in his early Pazzi chapel and most impressively developed in his last work, the unfinished Church of Santa Maria degli Angeli in Florence. Derived from the domed rotunda-with-ambulatory of late Antiquity, this architectural type is characterized by massive piers and chapels arranged around a rotunda dominated by a dome.[18]

FIG. 1. Ground-plan of Santa Maria delle Fiori, Florence (after Fletcher).

Alberti, the leading theorist of the fifteenth century, defined the essence of Brunelleschi's architectural form as the proportional harmony of all parts to the whole.[19] He also fostered the idea that the noble orders served to decorate the wall, dramatizing its inherent strength and proportions. Furthermore, he held that new forms could be created by merging several ancient models or

FIG. 2. Plan of Palmanova

by combining an ancient form with a Christian one. This merging was particularly evident in the variety of basilican church façades that he devised from the triumphal arch and the pedimented temple façade of the Romans. Alberti, like most of the architects of the fifteenth century, looked upon the basilican church with its high central aisle and its lower side aisles as an unfortunate historical accident, which should be corrected even at that late date. His effort at correction in the barrel-vaulted church of Sant' Andrea in

Mantua was particularly ingenious but was not generally followed until, shortly after the middle of the sixteenth century, it was taken as a model for the Gesu, the mother church of the Jesuit Order. On the other hand, his church of San Sebastiano in Mantua, planned in 1460 and apparently based on the domed, Greek-cross churches of the Byzantine tradition, did gain a wide following.[20]

During the late fifteenth century and the early sixteenth, several architects contributed to the formation of compactly ordered central churches. The designs of Antonio Averlino, called il Filarete, and the exploratory sketches of Leonardo da Vinci were especially significant. Contemporaries extolled Santa Maria delle Carceri in Prato, Santa Maria della Consolazione in Todi, and San Biagio in Montepulciano, outstanding examples of this central type, as the most perfect expression of cosmic order and thus appropriate symbolically, if not ceremonially, for Christian worship. So convinced were they of the superiority of the central plan that even Saint Peter's in Rome, the most revered basilican church in the Christian world of that day, fell victim to their criticism, and a domed Greek-cross church, the largest in the Western world, arose in its place (with the religious and political repercussions examined in Chapter IV). The new Saint Peter's was planned and initiated by Donato Bramante but was continued according to a revision by Michelangelo and was completed only in the early seventeenth century merely to be redesigned again (see below). The central church, in its clear reciprocal relation of exterior to interior and its careful balance of spaces around the central cavity of the dome, was the ultimate statement of an architectural order stabilized around its own centre.

Centrally ordered architecture was set up as the ideal in secular enterprises as well. Its formal aim led to the square, block-design palace with façades of three graduated stages and an arcaded central court, of which the Palazzo Riccardi-Medici, planned during the second quarter of the fifteenth century, and the Palazzo Strozzi are magnificent illustrations. (Pl. 47a.) Central symmetry, being considered practical for defence purposes, was also accepted for the overall plan of a city. Filarete and Francesco di Giorgio in the late fifteenth century fostered this type of city plan, and its long life is evidenced by Scamozzi's design for Palmanova in 1593 (Fig. 2), Christopher Wren's for the centre of London in 1666, and L'Enfant's for Washington in 1791. The rectangular grid-plan, however, proved a more practical, if less ornamental, basis for the organization or expansion of a city. In south and Central America Spanish architects planned the most impressive examples of this type. (Pl. 83.)

Further Developments (from the Sixteenth to the Eighteenth Century)

Some aspects of the Florentine style were accepted in Milan and Urbino, and in these secondary centres Bramante, the leading architect of the early sixteenth century, acquired his training and carried out his first works.

Although he developed a more severe and monumental architectural style in Rome after 1500, his early works in Lombardy reflected the local admiration for rich terra cotta and plaster decoration. The most profusely ornamented of these is the façade of the Certosa of Pavia, which was more admired by visitors from the rest of Europe than the more restrained architecture of Tuscany; its relatively clear framework in horizontals and verticals is charged with a multitude of small figures, geometric inlays, and vegetal courses in a variety of colourful marbles and in varying degrees of relief. Lombardy and, to a lesser degree, Naples, probably because of their geographic positions, became the centres in which most of Europe encountered the new architectural style. The French and the Spanish who came to Italy in the late fifteenth and early sixteenth century as conquerors were impressed by the architectural wonders they saw and, within the next few decades, deferred to Italian Renaissance forms.

Until the middle of the sixteenth century, the advance of the Renaissance in France was fostered mainly by its kings, Charles VIII and Francis I. They imported works of art, designs, engravings, and even artists to make the royal palaces and chateaux appropriately sumptuous. In his enthusiasm Francis I initiated many works, but he was dependent on architects and masons for whom Italian Renaissance forms meant an abrupt disturbance of the accustomed way. The large, block-design palace with a square central court designed by Pierre Lescot for the Louvre in the middle of the sixteenth century merged the French tradition of pavilion-and-corridor architecture with the central plan of Italy. In this work and that of the more traditional Hôtel Carnavalet, Lescot (working, as we have seen, with the sculptor Goujon) created elegantly proportioned and richly sculptured façades that reveal a tendency toward 'correctness' in the proportions of the orders, a tendency which France (in contrast with Italy) was to intensify during the seventeenth century. (Pl. 47b.) Sebastiano Serlio's designs and his 'model books' on architecture, though more inventive and less 'correct' than the growing awareness of France would tolerate, were nevertheless important steps in the formation of her Renaissance ideals. De l'Orme in the third quarter of the sixteenth century ran more parallel to contemporary works in Italy in the fullness of his forms, the use of rustication, and the aim of monumentality, but he used Italian models along with traditional French types in a completely sovereign way.

During the first half of the sixteenth century, Spain was even more prolific than France as a follower of the Lombard Renaissance. The Spanish 'Plateresque' style is characterized by profuse and small-scale decorative motifs carved as textural patterns within the confines of pilasters, pedestals, friezes, window frames, and parapets along the roofline. The 'Puerta del Pardon' of the Cathedral in Granada (Pl. 44a) and the City Hall in Seville are its foremost representatives. It was not limited to secular structures and ornamental portals because, unlike France, Spain had to provide impressive cathedrals—

not only for the major cities of Andalusia, recently re-won from Islam, but also for the new cities of the New World. (Pl. 44b; 45a, b.)

Juan de Herrera, following the trend of which Serlio was an outstanding exponent, formed an architectural style of unprecedented gravity that contrasted sharply with the Plateresque. As architect to the king, Herrera was able to impose his style on Spain and the New World (see below). His gigantic square palace of the Escorial with its twelve courts, church, monastery, palace, and royal residence was considered by contemporaries to surpass anything built in ancient times. The majesty and sobriety which characterize his architecture were still more magnificently revealed in his design for the Cathedral of Valladolid, which, enhancing the traditional rectangular ground plan of the Cathedral of Seville with four corner towers, he made into a centrally ordered rectangle of most impressive dimensions and grandeur.

Next to France and Spain, the most significant architectural development outside central Italy occurred in the Venetian Republic. Venice also had encountered the Tuscan forms clothed in the ornate and polychrome vestments of Lombardy, but, in the last years of the fifteenth century, a Venetian, Mauro Coducci, brought a clearer understanding of the Albertian concept of architecture. Coducci's Palazzo-Corner Spinelli and Palazzo Vendramin-Calergi provided a Colosseum-like façade, divided into several stages by entablatures, supported by piers and arcades and constructed not of the light and bright materials of the Ca'd'Oro but of grey stone. (Pl. 48a.) Jacopo Sansovino in Venice and Michele Sanmichele in Verona designed successively more monumental versions of the stylar façades introduced by Alberti in the Rucellai Palace in Florence and by Bramante in the 'House of Raphael' in Rome. In so doing, however, Venetians put aside a palatial type ideally suited to the watery setting of their city.

In the third quarter of the sixteenth century Andrea Palladio emerged from this sober Classical atmosphere. He demonstrated again the fruitfulness of the centripetal principle of arrangement in his Villa Rotonda near Vincenza. (Pl. 49a.) Perhaps the most influential feature of this villa, particularly upon English country houses during the seventeenth and eighteenth centuries, was the temple-like façade with which he faced its four sides. In the church façades of San Giorgio and Il Redentore in Venice, Palladio furthermore made the most important innovation in the temple-type façade since it was initiated by Alberti. (Pl. 49b.) The Ancient temple façade, fundamentally a colonnade surmounted by a triangular pediment, had caused embarrassment to those who attempted to use it to front the tall centre and lower sides of the Christian basilica, but Palladio solved the formal difficulty by interpenetrating two pedimented temple façades, a broad one on the lower level of the side chapels under a tall one with two-stage columns rising to the height of the centre nave. This solution was used in many variations for the next two hundred years.

Palladio's architecture was put aside by most of Catholic Europe in favour of the sixteenth-century idiom of central Italy, but it won a limited favour in England when it was introduced by Inigo Jones in the Banqueting House at Whitehall, London, in 1619, and it gained more general recognition when fostered by Richard Boyle in the early eighteenth century. England, her colonies, and Protestant countries generally continued the Palladian tradition of Renaissance architecture in opposition to the exuberant Baroque of Catholic Europe and America.

Meanwhile, in central Italy a movement paralleling Mannerism in painting had taken place in architecture. Most Renaissance designers had accepted the separate existence of the plane of the wall and its openings behind the self-sufficient grid of horizontals and verticals that comprise the architectural orders, but in the second quarter of the sixteenth century architects sought a greater decorative coherence of wall and order. To this end, the self-sufficiency of the architectural order was violated. Parts were made to overlap, interlink, or participate in patterns of rhythmic intervals, textures, colours, or shapes, so that the elements of the order and of the wall were brought into a decorative relationship to each other. Giulio Romano's house and his Palazzo del Te in Mantua, Baldassare Peruzzi's Palazzo Massimi in Rome (Pl. 48b), Serlio's published designs, and Vignola's Palazzo Farnese in Caprarola reflected this new attitude toward the treatment of the wall.

Michelangelo, recognized as an early leader of the revolt against Vitruvian rules, had initiated the new approach in his designs (1519) for the façade of Brunelleschi's Church of San Lorenzo and had further developed it in the Laurentian Library and the Medici Chapel of Florence. The style requires a sculptural organization of shapes so as to make them seem to react to one another, with no individual part autonomous and all equal before the modelling force of light. Starting with a completely traditional form, such as his original design for the wall niches alongside the Medici tombs, Michelangelo gradually caused the interaction of adjacent shapes, and the compressing and interlinking of parts, until he transformed the whole into something quite unique in its inherent order. The arrangement of parts was no longer dependent on Alberti's sense for an anthropomorphic balance of weights and supports but rather on a sense of decorative unity; and the size of architectural elements was no longer scaled in relation to man. They became gigantic, scaled to pilasters or columns that rose through several stages, like those on the Palace of the Conservatori on the Capitoline Hill (1536) or on the apse of St Peter's in Rome (1546). The new attitude tended to make the solution of each architectural problem unique and, thus, to a degree not known before, transformed architecture into a medium for personal expression. Few contemporary architects outside central Italy grasped the significance of this attitude, and even in Italy few were able to act as arbiters of architectural form with the self-confidence of Michelangelo.

★   ★   ★

Another important change in the architecture of central Italy (and eventually much of the rest of Europe) was the displacement of the Renaissance preference for a centripetal order by a new axial continuity along an ideal line of vision or movement. This inclination had been expressed as early as the fifteenth century in the relation of Tuscan villas to surrounding gardens. Bramante provided an important preparation for the new inclination in his early-sixteenth-century design for the great complex of levels in the Vatican's Belvedere Court, which he ordered along a longitudinal axis of view, if not of movement. A dramatic instance of the transformation of the centrally ordered palace occurred in the modifications planned in 1546 by Michelangelo for the traditional block-type Palazzo Farnese in Rome. Here he planned a longitudinal continuity that, starting in a carefully ordered piazza in front of the palace, passed through an open loggia at the rear of the court into the gardens and finally, by means of a projected bridge across the Tiber, to the Villa Farnesina on the other side. Michelangelo also designed the Piazza of the Campidoglio in Rome along axial schemes of movement[22] (Pl. 50a), Ammannati transformed the Pitti Palace in Florence, and Vignola provided a more complex axial order for the Villa Giulia outside Rome. (Pl. 50b.) This axial scheme was favoured in the seventeenth century. The ideal building no longer turned introspectively toward its own centre but opened expansively to become part of a larger plan.

The growing interest in movement and in long continuities gave unprecedented importance to staircases as dramatic elements of an architectural complex. Among the first products of this development was the monumental stair planned by Bramante to connect the several levels of the Belvedere Court. More imposing examples followed in the seventeenth and eighteenth centuries. The axial stairway (enhanced by watercourses and fountains) that serves to relate the elevated Villa d'Este to its lower gardens, and the ornamental Spanish Steps constructed on the steep slope before the Church of the Trinity in Rome were among the most spectacular. Interior staircases also became important as decorative ensembles in most of Europe. The main staircases of the Escorial in Spain, the Scala Regia leading from the vestibule of Saint Peter's to the Vatican apartments of the pope, the Staircase of the Ambassadors at Versailles (destroyed in the eighteenth century), and the grand staircase of the Archbishop's Palace in Würzburg served as models until modern times.

Grand-scale planning was most impressively developed in France. Early efforts were the palace and town built by Jacques Lemercier for Vicomte Richelieu (1631) and the château Vaux-le-Vicomte (1657), begun by Louis Levau and completed with gardens by Le Nôtre. (Pl. 51a.) These architects and others had a hand in designing the Palace of Versailles, begun in 1627 as a château, enlarged in the 1660's as the royal residence of Louis XIV, and elaborated until well into the eighteenth century. (Pl. 51b.) It was built not only to house the ten thousand people who made up Louis' court and the embassies sent by the other governments of Europe but also to impress the world with visual attributes of his political power and patronage in the form of decorative marvels and to serve as the focus and pinnacle of European aristocratic society. Portions of the interior such as Jules Hardouin Mansard's Hall of Mirrors, rich in glass, multicoloured marbles, gilding, fabrics, painting, and sculpture, flaunted a magnificence unrivalled in Europe. The interior decoration depended less on the finish of individual parts than on the grandeur of the ensemble. Derived from Annibale Carracci's interiors in the Palazzo Farnese in Rome, it also recalled the Gallery of Francis I at Fontainebleau, carried out by Florentine artists a century earlier. The most impressive evidence of the Sun King's power was the very scale on which the palace and its dependencies were planned. With its approaching roads, huge cour d'honneur, wide-spreading wings, terraces, pools, fountains, geometric gardens (by Lenôtre), radial avenues, play villages, and parks, all arranged on an axial plan, the palace dominates the landscape as far as the eye can see.

Versailles became a model of grand-scale architecture for all of Europe. German princelings built impressive palaces of the Versailles type such as the Palace of Pommersfelden in Franconia and the episcopal residence at Würzburg. The palaces of La Granja and Aranjuez in Spain, Peter the Great's Peterhof, Frederick the Great's Sans Souci, and Maria Theresa's Schönbrunn clearly follow the same model. Even relatively conservative English architects designed large Palladian complexes, such as Blenheim Palace in Oxfordshire and Castle Howard in Yorkshire, both by John Vanbrugh. For all their grandeur, however, these European projects do not surpass the extensive architectural complexes of northern India or Peking (see below).

The Baroque Style in Architecture

In central Italy in the sixteenth century the central church was transformed by the same axial order that re-shaped the plans of palaces and city squares. The church that gathered around a circular dome was superseded by the oval church, which produced the effect of a dynamic interior space guiding the entrant along the longitudinal axis from the entry to the altar and expanding into an oval dome that lent unity to the enclosing surfaces. Two of the most important examples of this type were Vignola's churches of San Giacomo degli Incurabili and Santa Anna dei Palafrenieri in Rome. Among the most impressive variations of the oval plan in the seventeenth century are Borromini's San Carlo alle Quattro Fontane and Bernini's Sant' Andrea al Quirinale in Rome and, in the early eighteenth century, Fischer von Erlach's Karlskirche in Vienna. The domed Greek-cross church of the Renaissance lived on into the seventeenth century in other longitudinal variations. Examples are Levau's church of the Collège des Quatre Nations (now the

Palais de l'Institut), Mansart's huge Saint Louis des Invalides (Pl. 52a) in Paris, Wren's Saint Paul's in London (Pl. 52b), and Fischer von Erlach's University Church in Salzburg.

The most influential type of church of the post-Tridentine world, however, was the one designed in 1568 by Vignola for the new order of the Jesuits in Rome. Commissioned, in the new reform spirit, to build an inexpensive church with a single vaulted nave and side chapels but to follow the rules of good architecture, Vignola apparently took as his model the Church of Sant' Andrea in Mantua, designed in 1471 by Alberti. The resulting edifice, the compact Latin-cross Gesù with barrel-vaulted nave and arms and a tall crossing dome, became the church most often imitated in the next two hundred and fifty years. (Fig. 3; Pl. 53a, b.) Even Michelangelo's central church of Saint Peter's in Rome was redesigned in 1606 by Carlo Maderno to become a gigantic three-aisled version of the Gesù. Architects in France and in Spain and her colonies enthusiastically followed the Gesù plan until the middle of the eighteenth century. The Gesù façade designed by Giacomo della Porta was equally influential. Following a façade type invented by Alberti for Santa Maria Novella in Florence in the use of the scroll to bind the lower sides to the higher centre, he attained a greater compactness of form around the centre axis, anticipating the Baroque architects' more dramatic culmination along the centreline. In façades such as that of the Saint Gervais in Paris, France produced some of the most impressive variations on the Gesù. The Jesuit order, in its faithfulness to the plan and the façade of the Gesù, played an important role in the spread of Baroque architecture.

Although Italian architects of the late sixteenth century departed notably from Renaissance models in the basic order of their ground plan and in their organization of façades, they tended, under the leadership of Carlo Maderno, to return to the more 'Classic' and more robust architectural elements of the High Renaissance, abandoning the ambiguously interlinked and interacting shapes of the Mannerists of the mid-sixteenth century. To be sure, Bernini and Pietro da Cortona lent excitement to their structures by utilizing multi-coloured marbles and strongly shadowed intervals between parts, and their curving walls and ornamental ground plans brought a ponderous vitality to their architecture, but the separate parts were relatively static and dense volumes that participated in a system of burdens and supports not unlike that of the Renaissance.[23]

In France, where the Royal Academy of Architecture (founded 1670) more strictly maintained the rules of the orders, proximity to the Renaissance was even greater. In addition, French architects tended in their arrangements of the orders to avoid the more lively groupings and curvatures and the inter-ruptive shadows employed by the Italians. The more rational and staid character of French architectural ideals is evident in the rejection of the curving façades planned by Bernini for the Louvre in 1665. England, Holland, and much of northern Europe, inclined toward a free Palladianism, main-

FIG. 3. Ground-plan of the Church of Il Gesù, Rome (after Fletcher).

tained an attitude closer to the refined and reserved Classicism of France than the more vigorous Baroque of Italy.

When, in the early half of the eighteenth century, Peter the Great and his successors undertook to build on marshy land the Western metropolis which today is known as Leningrad (formerly St Petersburg) and the neighbouring town of Pushkin (formerly Tsarskoye Selo), they deliberately imported Western architects and adopted Baroque and Rococo architectural models. Foremost among the Western architects were Jean-Baptiste-Alexandre Le Blond (1679–1719) and his young Italian assistant Bartolommeo Francesco Rastrelli (1700–71), who arrived in Russia in 1715. With the aid of Russian labour and Russian architects such as Mikhail Grigorieivch Zemtsov (1688–1743) they made St Petersburg a capital of stone churches, palaces, and government buildings contrasting vividly with the many wooden structures of Moscow, destined to burn down during the French invasion of 1812. The Baroque trend in both Russian cities was checked when, in 1757, Tsarina Elizabeth decreed the establishment of the Academy of Fine Arts, which became independent of the University of Moscow only in 1763. Its regulations were modelled upon those of the French Academy, and like its model it prodded young artistic talents to follow the Neoclassic trend of the late eighteenth century.

The Rococo Style in Architecture

Borromini's sensibility to the fluid unity of all parts proved to be the initial step in the formation of the graceful Rococo of the eighteenth century. Exponents of Classicism like Claude Perrault in France, the theatrical Vanbrugh and the flexible Wren in England, and even the most vigorous of the Italians, Pietro da Cortona, were not inclined to follow Borromini's unusual attitude toward the shaping of architectural parts. Borromini's method of designing of the 1630's is evident in the ground plan of San Carlo alle Quattro Fontane in Rome. (Pl. 54a.) Commissioned to make a church, refectory, dormitory, library, cloister, and garden on a small plot, he compressed the parts, causing one to accommodate itself to another until the church had completely departed from a simple oval and had been shaped into a lobed oval with membrane-like walls. Architectural parts became flexible and malleable before the action of space, taking on some of its fluid vitality. In this respect, Borromini recalls not only the architecture of the Mannerists of the middle of the sixteenth century but also that of Gothic designers. The important façade of San Carlo, animated by alternating concave and convex surfaces, presents the first monumental example since late Antiquity of the undulated wall, a basic feature of the Rococo style. Borromini's Church of Sant' Ivo della Sapienza in Rome achieves a still more intricate interpenetration of geometric shapes; a stellar ground plan gives rise to alternative convex and concave walls, which continue directly into a uniquely shaped dome. (Pl. 54b.) The style of Borromini, not directly but as modified and elaborated by his followers Guarino Guarini and Filippe Juvara, passed to France, Portugal, Germany, Austria, and Bohemia as well as to Spain and Latin America, where it reinforced the Churrigueresque style—i.e. the style named after the exuberantly adorned architecture of Jose Churriguera (1650–1725).

In France the new Italian style was refined by a sense for the delicate, subtle, and harmonious. The architecture that resulted was truly one of 'youthfulness and spirit', as Louis XIV described the art that pleased him. The Rococo continued the vivaciousness and voluptuousness of the Baroque but called for more subtle variations of colour, shape, texture, and rhythm, and a lighter and more playful mood. The best examples of Rococo are found in the residences of the wealthy bourgeoisie and nobility of the city-centred court in the seventeenth and eighteenth centuries. Absenting themselves from their grand châteaux in the country, the nobles tended to build *hôtels*, more intimate and less palatial dwellings, in Paris and Versailles. (Pl. 56a.)

Since the fifteenth century, in houses such as that of Jacques Coeur in Bourges, the hôtel had maintained a fairly standard form. Although frequently building on irregularly shaped lots, seventeenth century architects attempted to arrange the hôtel along a longitudinal axis. A typical plan, such as that for the Hôtel de Bretonvilliers in Paris, provided a cour d'honneur screened from the street by a one-storey wall, flanked by offices and stables in wings to the right and left, and terminating with a corps de logis, with other private rooms facing the gardens to the rear. Among the more famous seventeenth-century examples are François Mansart's Hôtel de la Vrilliere (now the Bank of France) and Levau's Hôtel Lambert in Paris. The Petit Trianon, the week-end house in the gardens of Versailles designed for Madame de Pompadour in 1762 by Jacques Ange Gabriel, was most influential. (Pl. 56b.) This elegant structure, and particularly its west façade, served as an architectural model for several generations.

Many of the interiors of these buildings were decorated in the Rococo style. The intimate atmosphere of the eighteenth-century salon encouraged the Rococo artist to create his liveliest and most exquisite works. Although the delicate motifs in some French interiors tend to follow the rectilinear panelling of the room, the oval Hall of Princes in the Hôtel de Soubise in Paris, decorated by Germain Boffrand in the 1730's, is characterized by a more fluid passage of the wall into the vault. *Chinoiserie*, borrowings from Chinese and other Eastern works of art, played a prominent role in the mid-century wall paintings of the Hôtel de Rohan in Paris and appeared frequently in the wall paper, ornamental motifs, and furnishings of the houses of the well-to-do. (Pl. 57a.) Beyond this decorative vogue in the West and the influence of the Chinese garden in Western landscape architecture, Europe's intensified contact with the Far East produced no fundamental effect upon the architecture of either cultural area.

In Austria and southern Germany the new style won enthusiastic approval. The interiors of the palaces of Nymphenburg, Würzburg, and Potsdam

Feet
50
40
30
20
10
0

FIG. 4. Ground-plan of the Church of Vierzehnheiligen
(after Fletcher).

(Sans Souci) were enriched with equally delicate but more exuberant decoration. (Pl. 57b.) All their surfaces and architectural courses undulate gracefully, avoiding the strength of straight lines and geometric shapes, and depending on a fluid and lively continuity to unify the many small parts into a decorative ensemble. German and Austrian architects extended the Rococo style to religious architecture, creating the most impassioned and visually exciting churches on the Continent. The luminous interiors of the Vierzehn- heiligen in Franconia by Johann Balthasar Neumann (Fig. 4; Pl. 55a), the Benedictine abbey of Ottobeuren by Johann Michael Fischer, and the pilgrimage church of the Wies (Pl. 55b) in Bavaria are characterized by a fluidity of space within a diaphanous white structure, gilded and frescoed to evoke an emotional exhilaration which contrasts strikingly with the intellectual curiosity summoned by the spatial complications of Guarini in Italy. Decor- ators of elaborate altars and restless surfaces, such as the Asam brothers and the stucco-workers of Wessobrunn, played unusually important roles in Rococo architecture. A major feature of these south German churches was the frescoed ceiling toward which all parts of the interior rose in excited cur- vilinear movements. Fully populated with a multitude of active figures, seen from below against a delicate blue sky in the Italian and particularly the Tiepolo manner, the vaults served as avenues for the final release of emotional fervour. (Pl. 19a.) The only other works in Christendom to compare with these exuberant Germanic creations were made in Spain and Portugal and their colonies in America.

England remained relatively aloof from the decorative excitement of Rococo style on the Continent. The bold architectural types of Wren and Vanbrugh continued in its churches, city squares, and country houses. The most original English architectural contribution of the period was the English landscape garden, which, in its irregularities and picturesqueness, makes a pleasing contrast to the formality of 'Georgian' architecture (the English adaptation of the Palladian style) and directly opposes the geometric patterns of French or Italian gardens. Probably the landscapes of Claude Lorrain were leading incentives toward this new ideal, and probably also it reflects English admiration for the Chinese garden not only by ornamental pagodas and bridges but also by the nascent Romantic sense of irregularity and freedom with which the elements of nature were arranged. These Romantic inclina- tions expressed themselves also in a mid-century interest in Gothic forms.

Yet the main direction of English architecture was along more Classic lines. Richard Boyle actively marked out this direction by sponsoring the English publications of Vitruvius, Alberti, and Palladio and also of model-books of the works of Inigo Jones and John Webb, the seventeenth-century architects who had first introduced England to the Palladian style. The Society of Dilettanti, founded in 1732, and chiefly interested in Classical archaeology, sent James Stuart and Nicholas Revett to Greece in 1750 to make measured drawings, which were eventually published in 1762 under the title *Antiquities of Athens*.

AA*

Illustrated publications on the ruins of Palmyra, Baalbek, and Herculaneum also appeared about this time, and the first systematic excavation of Pompeii was undertaken in 1763. In this atmosphere Robert Adam and his contemporaries in the third quarter of the eighteenth century led the way to a more direct dependence on Greco-Roman architectural models.

A similar Classical tendency meanwhile had been initiated in Paris. In 1732 the Palladian design of the Italian-born Jean Nicholas Servandoni won a competition among the plans submitted for the façade of the Church of Saint-Sulpice. By the 1760's the even more Classic forms of Gabriel's Petit Trianon at Versailles and Jacques Germain Soufflot's Church of Saint Geneviève (today the Panthéon) signalled the rise of Neoclassicism and the decline of Rococo on the Continent.

THE DECORATIVE ARTS IN EUROPE

The gradual separation of the decorative (the so-called 'minor') arts from the fine (the so-called 'major') arts of painting, sculpture, and architecture was a phenomenon peculiar to Europe during this period. Artists of medieval Europe, the Far East, Islam, and apparently also pre-Columbian America did not make any such distinction. Although many artists of this period in Europe worked in the decorative as well as the fine arts, and some objects occupy a position between the two, the distinction, nevertheless, has some justification. Artisans who made furniture, textiles, pottery, metalware, and glassware or who carved, painted, or inlaid designs on art objects did not have the same claim to scientific knowledge or intellectual accomplishment that enabled Renaissance painters, sculptors, and architects to demand successfully the status of liberal arts for their media. The making of utilitarian objects, the shape of which was largely determined by custom and by the purpose for which they were used, and the distribution of decorative motifs over the surface of such objects were believed to be less complicated and difficult formal problems than those faced in the major arts. Painting, sculpture, and architecture were also considered to be more capable of embodying the profound and elevated truths of science, philosophy, and Christianity, which the Western artists sought to represent in art. Some decorative motifs —emblems, for example—had specific meanings or associations, but from around 1500 many motifs were more generally used as ornament than as meaningful symbols. Decorative motifs from Antiquity, Islam, and the Far East were incorporated into the European repertory with little regard to their meaning. For all these reasons, when the minor arts were not actually small versions of the major arts, their content was considerably less coherent or less profound.[24]

Ornament and Decoration

The decorative tradition of Christian Europe during this period was not so homogeneous or so stable and independent as that of Islam or of China. Among the most widely used of decorative motifs were the architectural elements employed in contemporary buildings. Cusped and mixtilinear arches, interlaced or simply applied to a surface as blind arcades, were favoured during the Middle Ages. The Gothic triforium was enriched by ornamental arcades. Arcuated forms were effectively accommodated to the wheel-like tracery of the rose window. Late Gothic designers gave much attention to the invention of decorative treatments for architectural surfaces and thus created an increasingly rich repertory of decorative motifs. Reliquaries and shrines of wood or metal took on the structure of miniature Gothic edifices. Architectural motifs were used for the ornament of tombs, chests, and ecclesiastical furniture such as choir stalls, altar canopies, and frames for retables.

During the Renaissance architectural motifs continued to be the leading decorative elements, but the unique vocabulary of the Gothic style was replaced by the orders of Antiquity. For a period during the late fifteenth and early sixteenth centuries, the motifs of the Flamboyant and the Renaissance styles were decoratively merged in most areas of Europe outside central Italy. The autonomy, clarity, and static character of Renaissance motifs and designs contrasted with the lively and fluid shapes and rhythmic continuities of the Flamboyant elements, but some magnificent hybrid forms were created. The ancient architectural vocabulary, although not so flexible or readily combined in a rhythmic or ornamental way as the Gothic elements, gradually took over the traditional decorative functions of architectural elements. The severely tectonic arrangement of architectural orders used by decorators in the Renaissance was replaced by the less restrained, more dynamic combinations of architectural elements employed by Baroque designers. During the early eighteenth century freely varied shapes and asymmetrical rhythms departed from the tectonic ideals of the Renaissance. By the third quarter of the eighteenth century Neoclassic architects led the return to the ancient orders, then clarified by a growing archaeological knowledge.

Personal emblems and coats of arms were prominent decorative elements inherited from the Middle Ages. They were used on banners, shields, clothes, tapestries, armour, silver plate, illuminated manuscripts, bookbindings, furniture, fireplaces, portals, and façades. As the social significance of the coat of arms waned, it was transformed into the completely decorative 'cartouche', an elaborately scrolled oblong frame with a decorative or even blank centre. Mottoes, sometimes revised to commemorate important events, together with personal initials, ornamentally shaped and intertwined, became favourite motifs in the late fourteenth and the fifteenth century.[25]

Plant motifs comprise another special category of European ornament. The intensified study of plant life (see Chapter XIII) led to a naturalism that contrasted strikingly with the stylized forms of Islam. Flowers and leaves were favoured during the fourteenth and fifteenth centuries in the delicately and elaborately designed borders painted around manuscript miniatures and woven into the borders of tapestries. In some tapestries, known as 'verdures', the entire background behind the large figures is a flat floral and foliate pattern. Plant motifs were also embroidered in cloth, worked on leather, engraved in metal objects, and carved on ecclesiastical furniture and on architectural elements such as brackets, capitals, and frames of windows and doors. The Flamboyant Style readily accommodated the naturalism of these motifs to its fanciful and curvilinear inclinations. Plants, as well as the older repertory of animals, were readily exchanged for designs modelled upon the ancient Roman 'grotteschi' (so called because the first examples were found in grottoes under the Palatine in Rome), which are composed of fanciful hybrid creatures formed of vegetable, animal, and human parts and joined in continuous arabesques. 'Grotteschi' were widely used during the sixteenth and seventeenth centuries on pilasters, friezes, panelled sections of walls and ceilings, borders of bookplates, and parts of armour. Natural plant motifs, however, were never abandoned.

Perhaps the most unique tendency of European decoration was the ever-increasing use of painting and sculpture to ornament surfaces. Gems, metal cups, furniture, and the walls of rooms often provided surfaces for sculptural reliefs. Pottery was frequently ornamented with scenes comparable to contemporary painting in the illusion they created of depth. When ornament is literally sculpture or painting, it often evidences little sensitivity to the continuity of the surfaces, and hence the basic shape, of the object decorated. As a result, a new ornamental entity, composed of actual and illusional shapes, is created.

Tapestries, stained glass windows, and intarsia (inlay in wood), which are essentially two dimensional in character, became subdivisions of painting. Tapestry technique permits the insertion of many short pieces of yarn and, thus, a great variety of subtle changes of colour. During the fourteenth and fifteenth centuries the hunt, courtly love, the Crusades, and Ancient or sacred history provided subjects for Flemish tapestries. Later Raphael's 'Acts of the Apostles', designed for the Sistine Chapel and made in Brussels, revealed the degree to which tapestries aspired to look like paintings. The sixteenth-century painters Bernard van Orley, Lucas van Leyden, and Jan Mabuse frequently provided cartoons for Flemish tapestries. The Gobelin factory at Paris and the factories at Beauvais and Aubusson, all of which became prominent during the last third of the seventeenth century, increased the variety of colours and tones in the threads to attain the subtle suggestions of modelling and the atmospheric effects characteristic of contemporary painting. Toward the same end, the small pieces of stained glass which created the mosaic-like splendour of medieval windows were replaced by larger pieces of painted glass creating the illusion of modelled figures and deep space. Intarsia often replaced painting as a decorative treatment for furniture.[26] In the early fifteenth century, contrasting woods formed various two-dimensional geometric designs, probably indicative of the Islamic origins of the craft. As the century advanced, historical events or landscapes and still-life subjects were represented. Very small pieces of wood together with new methods of staining half-tones with oils and acids created many subtle variations of golden tans, browns, and greens and enabled intarsia workers to approximate the effects of painting.[27]

* * *

The decorative objects of the period 1300–1775 in Europe are conveniently grouped under the materials from which they were made—yarn, clay, glass, metal, gems, and wood. Moreover, this arrangement helps to emphasize two developments that the decorative arts conspicuously illustrate—the alliance of art and technology, and intercultural borrowing.

Textiles and tapestries

The yarn from which the most elaborately woven and decorative textiles were made was silk. Before the thirteenth century Europe had imported practically all its silks from the Middle and the Far East to serve as church vestments, burial robes, and court costumes. Although Hispano-Islamic centres continued to produce magnificent fabrics, the supply of silks was rendered unsteady in the thirteenth century because of the Mongol invasion of the Near East and the decline of silk factories in Sicily. Muslim silk weavers were thereupon invited or even forced to bring their skill to Christian Europe. Lucca, Florence, and Venice in Italy, Lyons in France, and Bruges in Flanders early became important centres of the European silk industry. Luxurious brocades were made also in Russia, Bulgaria, and Greece as well as Turkey and Persia. Western Europe, however, having reached a technical skill comparable to that of Islam and the Far East, began to supply most of its own needs.

Italian weavers had long been famous for fine woollen cloth, but silk soon won favour also. It was not readily destroyed by pests, took dyes beautifully, and folded luxuriously. In the fourteenth century Italian silk designers borrowed generously from the Islamic lands and the Far East, but their inclination toward naturalism greatly enlarged their decorative repertory and resulted in novel compositions. They adopted the animal and bird motifs that Islamic artists had inherited from the Sassanian-Byzantine tradition but often abandoned the heraldic aspect of confronted positions and frequently removed the animals and birds from the confines of the interlaced roundels so characteristic of Islam to dispose them more freely in diagonal rows. The tendril and other plant motifs were more naturally varied and, once released, along with the animals and birds, from the stylized forms of Islam, gained vitality. Fourteenth-century Italian textiles were often more directly copied from Chinese gold-brocaded satins of the thirteenth century. Lotus tendrils, flaming rays, phoenixes, pheasants, cranes, and other Chinese motifs were used in Italian silks, particularly those made in Lucca, although sometimes transformed to resemble the flora and fauna of Europe. A pseudo-Kufic script, inspired by Persian or Hispano-Islamic textiles, became fashionable in the mid-fourteenth century, and in the fifteenth the pine cone, or so-called pomegranate, pattern. Italian textile designers avoided the pictorial inclinations that transformed several other decorative arts. They showed a tendency to eliminate small tendrils and delicate irregularities in order to attain greater scale and boldness of contour. With this interest in bolder designs, velvet came to the fore, particularly the polychrome velvet made in Florence and later in Genoa.

The most decorative use of the fine woollen cloth produced by European weavers was in tapestries. Scaled to the huge interiors of castles, palaces, and churches, tapestries were monumental mural-like fabrics that served not only to decorate but to keep out cold. (Pl. 58a.) Arras, Tournai, and Paris were most important for tapestry production until the fifteenth century, when Brussels and Bruges became the major producers. French factories, particularly the one created by the Gobelin family near Paris, were foremost during the late seventeenth and the eighteenth century as royal enterprises, but most of their early weavers were Flemish. (Pl. 58b.) At Savonnerie about 1590, the French opened a rug factory, where the knotted technique and the floral designs of Persia were imitated, but Europe never learned to produce rugs comparable to those of the Near and Far East and continued to import its finer rugs.

Lace, the most fragile fabric made of yarn, consists of delicate threads of flax, cotton, and silk intertwined. Good lace requires great skill and patience. Lacemaking may have evolved from the *reticella* work of the Ionian Islands during the late fifteenth century, but it became a peculiarly west European art, centred at first in Venice, Milan, and Genoa but shifting to France and Belgium during the late seventeenth century. It was used as trim on women's clothing, men's shirts, bedspreads, altar cloths, and church vestments. Rose point, flat point, and grounded point were among the lace techniques that the rest of Europe learned from Venice. The 'point d'Alençon', built upon the firm base of a fine net and enriched with 'cordonnet' ridges buttonholed over horsehair, was a French invention that heralded the leadership of France in lacemaking. Argentan, Le Puy, Chantilly, and Valenciennes became famous for fine lace. So did Barcelona in Spain, and Brussels and Malines in the Low Countries.

Plain cloth was frequently decorated by means of embroidery. Gradually Europe had become conscious of the richly embroidered textiles of Persia, Morocco, Turkey, India, China, and Japan. In Europe, England became particularly famous from the fourteenth century on for its embroidery, known then as *opus anglicanum* and widely used for church vestments, court finery, and (in later centuries) upholstery. This art was one of the few not restricted by the requirements of skill to professionals; gentle ladies occupied themselves with the embroidery of domestic articles and clothing.

The stamped, printed, and resist-dyed cottons and silks of India stimulated one of the major textile industries of Europe. Marco Polo in the thirteenth century and Portuguese adventurers in the fifteenth noted that stained and printed cottons were highly prized fabrics in India, and in the sixteenth century England and the Low Countries began to import Indian palampores in great quantities. Although Europeans admired this type of textile and used it for clothes, curtains, and furniture covers, they were not satisfied with the Indian designs, and English craftsmen were sent to teach Indian printmakers the designs preferred by Europeans. The demand for these prints became so great that England, Holland, and France decided to produce them. Among French textiles 'toile de Jouy' became particularly famous. The changes in weaving methods during the late seventeenth and the eighteenth century (connected with 'the Industrial Revolution', which we shall consider in Chapter XV) reduced costs, regularized patterns and assured more uniform colours but diminished the quality of Europe's prints and chintzes.

Ceramics

Potter's clay provided another good medium for decorative expression. Several Spanish regions had borrowed from the Moors the low-fire process of baking the glaze with moderate heat, and it moved from Spain to other Christian areas. Majorca in the twelfth century, Malaga in the fourteenth, and Manises near Valencia in the fifteenth became famous for a gold and ruby lustreware decorated with plant life, Kufic script, animals, concentric circles, and European coats of arms, in brown, violet, and cobalt blue, frequently modelled in low relief to give emphasis to the main part of the design. Italy at first imported this ware from Spain, but by the late fourteenth century Faenza (whence the word *faience*) began to make it, and in the fifteenth century Urbino, Gubbio, and other Italian towns followed suit. The Spanish-Italian ware was called *majolica*. Italian potters were attracted to the low-fire treatment not so much by the lustre it gave as by the greater range of colours it permitted than the high-fire treatment that European potters commonly used. They adorned their plates and bowls, predominantly blue and yellow and often very large, with pictorial effects that contrasted with the two-dimensional motifs of Islamic potters. (Pl. 59a.)

Increased contact with the Far East provided an impetus that elevated ceramics to one of the leading decorative arts—and industries (see Chapter XV)—of eighteenth-century Europe. European potters attempted to make a ware comparable to Chinese and Japanese porcelain. The handsome wares of Delft, Rouen and Sèvres approached the thin translucence and delicate qualities of Far Eastern porcelain. The ware developed at Meissen near Dresden shortly after 1709 was accepted as the equal of Chinese porcelain. Ansbach, Vienna, Capodimonte near Naples, and Buen Retiro near Madrid were other centres established during the eighteenth century. The porcelain factories of Germany and France produced colourful and delicately fashioned figurines depicting playful activities. (Pl. 60.) Although some English ware such as Lowestoft was hard-paste porcelain, the pottery made at Chelsea, Staffordshire, and most other English centres was soft-paste porcelain. Wedgwood ware, characterized by white cameo-like figures in relief on blue, rose, green, and tan grounds, is still numbered among England's most distinctive products.

Glass

Glassware was one of the decorative arts in which Europe excelled even during the Middle Ages. Stained and leaded glass windows reveal the feeling of medieval Europe for the splendour of light-filled and colourful materials. Those of Saint-Nazaire in Carcassone exemplify the tiered arrangement of figures and events, the larger pieces of glass, and the greater array of colours and tonal variations characteristic of fourteenth-century windows in contrast to earlier ones. These tendencies were furthered during the fifteenth and sixteenth centuries by the more widespread acceptance of paintings as models for stained-glass windows.[28] Unevenly coloured glass provided the suggestion of shading in figures and draperies, and transparent enamels applied with a brush enabled the artist to come closer to pictorial effects. The strong two-dimensional design of the leads and the armatures was eliminated whenever possible to create an illusory depth, constructed by means of the devices used to give perspective in painting. In the first decade of the sixteenth century Guglielmo de Marcillat created some of the earliest examples of frankly pictorial stained-glass windows for churches in Arezzo and Cortena. Pictorial aims continued to dominate through the seventeenth and eighteenth centuries.

The craftsmen of medieval Venice, heirs to the Byzantine tradition of glassmaking, improved their processes under a cloak of secrecy and remained unsurpassed if not unrivalled as producers of fine glass until the eighteenth century. Glass goblets, cups, vases, dishes, table decorations, and beads (the mainstay of the Venetian industry) were made in great variety. Among the most famous of Venetian glassware are 'crackled', 'marble', and 'millefiori' glass, and glass with goldleaf either on the surface or worked in. 'Lace' glass, characterized by opaque white lines that create delicate patterns, and glass of the *reticella* ('net') type, with bubbles of air enclosed at the intersections of a network of white lines, were other marvels of technical skill. The *avanturine* type, an amber-coloured glass speckled with myriads of burnished-copper flecks, was the result of a process invented in the early seventeenth century and effectively guarded for two hundred years. The Low Countries, the British Isles, Germany, Bohemia, and France originally made glass on Venetian models and then gradually developed decorative types of their own (see Chapter XV). Gold ruby glass, invented in the late seventeenth century in Potsdam, and cut glass, which appeared also in the seventeenth century (see Chapter XV), were among the innovations that caused the decline of the Venetian market. (Pl. 59b.)

Metal works

Metal provided still another medium of decoration. Near Eastern and Hispanic centres of Islam had gained fame in Europe during the medieval period for steel swords ornamented with inlays of brass and silver. Armour became impractical for military use after the invention of gunpowder but was maintained for ceremonial purposes, and swords, too, became increasingly ceremonial. Ceremonial swords not only were made of precious metals but also were often beautifully adorned and studded with jewels. Ceremonial weapons and armour presented an unusually good opportunity to decorative artists and became more and more elaborate. Designs were frequently etched or inlayed with contrasting metals into the armour plate, and sculptural reliefs of figures or *grotteschi* often embellished breast-plates and helmets.

The metal objects required for the Christian service were numerous. Insistence on rare and costly materials and on elaborate workmanship for ceremonial objects led to some of Europe's most unique and decorative forms. Reliquaries, monstrances, processional crosses, candlesticks, croziers, chalices, patens, and alms dishes were made of gold and silver. These metals, rich in colour and light-reflecting properties, were decoratively pierced, chased, or worked in filigree or repoussé, and often enriched with enamel, carved ivory, and precious stones.

Brass, bronze, and copper objects were frequently enriched with enamels. Medieval Europe continued an enamel technique known as *champlevé*, which had been practised by the ancient Romans: enamel, in the form of powder or paste, was laid into cells which had been engraved into or scooped from the metal surface, and then was fired to attain a glass-like quality. The enamels in the European *champlevé* technique were usually opaque, in contrast to the translucent enamels used by Byzantine craftsmen over a gold base to produce an opalescent effect. During the fifteenth century the technique of painting with enamel on a copper base became prevalent in Europe. Like so many other kinds of decorative artists in Europe, enamel artists attempted to duplicate the effects of contemporary painting.

In the sixteenth century, secular, and particularly domestic, items became an increasingly important part of the goldsmith's work in Europe. Goblets, standing salts, basins, and plates were made of gold or silver. By the sixteenth century, huge collections of silver plate had been amassed by the dukes of Burgundy and the kings of England, France, and Spain. Guilds, colleges, town halls, and wealthy families owned silver plate especially designed for them. The desire to display silver service made the sideboard, and later the buffet, increasingly important. During the fifteenth and sixteenth centuries France, Italy, and particularly Augsburg and Nuremberg in Germany became prominent centres of the goldsmith's and silversmith's craft. Silver service complemented tableware of fine porcelain. French silversmiths at Bordeaux, Strasbourg, Lille, and Paris made table service treasured all over Europe. The introduction of coffee and tea to Europe resulted in the late seventeenth and the eighteenth century in decoratively shaped and richly ornamented silver coffee pots and teapots, as well as cream pitchers and sugar bowls. The silver of Holland and of England and her American colonies, while somewhat more sturdy and less ornamental in shape and surface than contemporary French and German work, nevertheless furnished notable examples of the silversmith's art.

Designs were enamelled, engraved, chased or carried out in repoussé on the gold or silver surface. Some works, like the large salt cellar made by Cellini for Francis I, were fashioned as miniature works of sculpture. Reliquaries and standing cups were occasionally carved of rock crystal, amber, agate, or coconut shells and set in gilded silver or in gold. Renaissance artists also made commemorative medals in bronze, silver, and gold. Although major painters and sculptors such as Pisanello and Cellini occasionally prepared designs for medals, some, particularly in Germany, France, and Italy, devoted themselves primarily to the making of medals.

Jewellery

Jewellery engaged not only the goldsmith or silversmith, but also the lapidary. In Europe, pendants, often worn on the forehead, rings, brooches and necklaces were favoured. Table-cut emeralds and rubies, gems with carved reliefs in the manner of the Ancients, enamel insets, and pearls were given fanciful settings of foliate and *grotteschi* forms in gold and silver. The jewellery of France during the late sixteenth and the seventeenth century was greatly admired, and the designs of Jacques Androust Ducerceau, Etienne Delaune, and Pierre Woeriot of Lorraine were copied in all parts of Europe. Paste, textured and coloured to look like gems, was introduced in the seventeenth century along with other shams of mass-produced jewellery. The aigrette, a cluster of precious stones set in enamelled gold and mounted on movable stalks, and sprays of leaves and flowers with knotted and flowing ribbons were among the most delicate and precious works of eighteenth-century craftsmanship. The magnificent jewellery of the Far East and the Islamic countries (see below) appears to have begun to impress European artisans in the late seventeenth century.

Woodwork

Wood as a medium of decorative art was used in Europe most elaborately in the making of furniture. The Christian church required many wooden objects—retables, altars, canopies, pulpits, and huge choir stalls. These furnishings demanded not only appropriate symbolic references but also richness in materials and workmanship. Domestic furniture during the

Middle Ages was, on the other hand, made of plain, sturdy oak wood, though frequently ingeniously built to serve several purposes. It was restricted to trestle tables, benches, beds, and chests, which were rigid and box-like with only occasional carved panels or arcade motifs. With the Renaissance more attention was given to the decoration of domestic furniture, and more varied types of furnishings were developed. Bureaux with drawers, tables, chairs, *cassoni* (or marriage chests), wall cupboards (or credences), and (later) sideboards were elaborately ornamented. The painting of panels, intarsia (particularly on *cassoni* and cupboards), and the carving of table and chair legs were favoured methods of decoration. During the sixteenth century the boxlike shapes and the relatively flat surfaces of Gothic furniture were replaced by more bulbous and vigorous shapes, which nevertheless retained a compact structural aspect. Robustly shaped caryatids, allegorical figures, medallions, *grotteschi*, garlands, emblems, coats of arms, and (later) *cartouche* frames were frequently carved in the wood or plastered on it in relief. Architectural elements such as columns, entablatures, pediments, mouldings, and brackets often enhanced the tectonic appearance of Renaissance and Baroque furniture in Italy.

During the sixteenth and seventeenth centuries, French furniture gradually gained prominence in Europe. French *armoires* (or cabinets), desks, tables, chairs with leather or cane seats, and reclining couches became elaborate. As the seventeenth century advanced, novelty and magnificence became more and more conspicuously the aims of decoration. Marquetry (as intarsia was called in the north) was carried out not only by inlays in wood, preferably rare woods, but also by incrustations of mother-of-pearl, metal, and ivory. Chairs and couches were upholstered in the late seventeenth century and onward with multicoloured fabrics such as tapestries, needlepoint, embroideries, velvets, and brocades. Colbert established the royal manufactory of furniture in 1667 and brought artisans from all parts of Europe to teach French workmen. New designs and decorative treatments of furniture were readily available to artisans by means of engravings in model books. The engravings of De l'Orme and Ducerceau in the sixteenth century and Jean Lepautré in the seventeenth were among the most influential. Although the richly ornamented pieces of the wood carvers of Augsburg and Nuremberg were widely admired and although England maintained an independent style favouring traditional motifs such as the linen-fold design and turned or spindle supports with 'melon-bulb' protuberances, French furniture designers eventually provided the models for all of Europe.

Those English and French designers who worked within the dominant Rococo style of the eighteenth century not only created more varied, comfortable, and luxurious furnishings but they also elevated their craft to a highly personal art. Furniture was relieved of its earlier tectonic heaviness and bulkiness. The rhythmic curvatures of slim supports and the undulation of surfaces produced a lighter appearance and more ornamental shapes. Surfaces reached an ultimate refinement with inlays of rare woods, porcelains, ivory, tortoise shell, and brass and with veneers of mahogany, rosewood, satinwood, and walnut. Lacquered surfaces, imitating the technique developed in Japan and known in France as *vernis Martin*, had reached a high point of elegance early in the seventeenth century. Soft colours and gilding further enhanced the look of delicacy in this Rococo furniture. Decorative handles, corner mountings, and gilded-bronze supports were added to chests and tables. The contrasts of these various materials and textures resulted in an exceptionally rich and sensuous effect unequalled by earlier European furniture.

The variety and value of the materials, the excellence of the craftsmanship, and the ornamental purpose of Rococo interiors encouraged talented artists to occupy themselves with the making of furniture. Jean Baptiste Pillement and Philippe de Lassalle were foremost among the designers who gained fame for their upholstery fabrics during the latter half of the eighteenth century. By means of the shaping, scaling, finishing, and arranging of parts, eighteenth-century designers frequently impressed a readily identified personal style on their furniture. André-Charles Boulle employed a type of tortoise-shell-and-brass inlay which came to be known as 'buhl' or 'buhlwork'. Thomas Chippendale, drawing upon French predecessors, published an illustrated furniture book, *The Gentleman and Cabinet Maker's Director*, in 1754 and thereby initiated a series of influential English furniture styles. George Heppelwhite and Thomas Sheraton during the late eighteenth century brought England to a foremost place in furniture fashions.

THEORIES OF ART AND THE ROLE OF THE ARTIST

The universe of art in which the European artist of 1775 was educated not only was infinitely more complex than that of his counterpart in 1300 but also offered a much greater freedom for his orientation within it.[29] The status of the European practitioner of the arts changed between 1300 and 1775 from that of a relatively nameless 'artisan' to that of an 'artist'. In the early fifteenth century he became a friend of humanists, philosophers, mathematicians, and poets, and as a result, he freed himself from the control of the guild. Except for an occasional autodidact the artist received his professional training in ateliers and, by the seventeenth century, in academies (see Chapter XVI).

A significant stimulant to change in the prestige of the artist during this period was his role in establishing and clarifying the theory that art is an imitation of nature. Renaissance writers occasionally noted the importance of fancy or imagination and, while generally upholding the intellectual nature and didactic purposes of art, recognized also that sensuous pleasure was to be derived from it. They never succeeded in synthesizing the various ideas derived from the Ancients or inherited from the Middle Ages, but among those ideas the principle of imitation was most influential.

While previously art theory had been written predominantly by philosophers and theologians, that of the Renaissance was primarily the creation of practicing artists who began to theorize about the nature of their practice. Concerned with the imitation of natural forms, they studied optics, developing a linear system of monocular perspective and devices for aerial perspective that in painting and in relief sculpture approximated the visual experience of figures and objects in space. Optics and perspective became a central subject of theoretical notebooks on art, notably those by Alberti, Ghiberti, Piero della Francesca, Leonardo, Jean Pélerin, and Dürer. The foremost object of study, however, not only by painters and sculptors but also by architects, was the human body. An understanding of its anatomical structure, its laws of movement, and the proportional norms on which its beauty depends became an essential part of artistic training in the Western tradition. Leonardo and Dürer stated the proportions of beauty in arithmetical fractions (as the Ancients had) in contrast to the geometric schemes prevalent in the Middle Ages. Leonardo, in the notes and drawings for his encyclopedic treatise on art, epitomized the fifteenth-century concept of art as a demonstration of the artist's knowledge of optics and of nature and its underlying laws. Ghiberti, Alberti, and Leonardo, insisting that the artist deal exclusively with what he saw, abjured metaphysical explanations of the origin of art. An interest in the physical facts of man and nature remained characteristic of Western art and caused Europeans to concentrate their attention upon the corporeal aspects of man's existence rather than the spiritual or religious.

At the same time that early Renaissance artists attempted to approximate the physical appearance of objective natural forms, they saw in the physical world a revelation of the beauty, harmony, and order of the Deity, and they imitated the 'best' parts of nature in creating their own forms. This 'best' came to mean a criterion of perfection. It led Raphael and Michelangelo to shape human figures of a beauty far superior to that of the average human being, and they disposed limbs and grouped figures so as to present rhythmic intervals between the solids and the voids that gave natural forms and events a decorative or artful arrangement. Raphael achieved a subtle balance between approximation and superiority to Nature, but Michelangelo moved farther toward the decorative and away from verisimilitude in the colour, shape, and arrangement of the human figure. Contemporaries accepted the art of Raphael and Michelangelo as revelations of beauty greater than those of natural forms and referred to the revealers of this beauty as 'the divine ones'.

The followers of 'the divine ones' were the Mannerists. They probed the subjective realm of fantasy, depending on what was called the *idea interna* more than on visual experience for the forms of their art. For the Mannerists art was no longer a vehicle for the demonstration of objective knowledge of the world and man but the revelation of a highly subjective sense of perfection or truth. This mystic attitude, probably nourished by Neoplatonic ideas of the visual arts and poetry, accepted the sensible form of art as a means by which the soul could be awakened to intellectual beauty and led to Ultimate Beauty, which is God. Various aspects of the Mannerist idea of art and the artist were codified by Vincenzo Danti in 1567, Giovanni Paolo Lomazzo and Giovanni Battista Armenini in the 1580's, and Frederico Zuccari in 1607. Although the significance of the artists' creativity in this connection appears to have been only vaguely appreciated, they were considered revealers of truth, often independent of the clergy, who were the guardians of Christian Truth. The Council of Trent recognized this invasion of ecclesiastical functions by stating, in effect, that what pertained to theology belonged to the theologians and what pertained to poetic invention to the artists (see below). That dictum, however, did not end the association of artists with the revelation of truths of a mystic or spiritual nature. On the contrary, the association persisted and gathered strength.

The Attitude of the Churches toward Art

While the church remained the dominant patron during the Renaissance (even for profane subjects in painting and sculpture for the palaces and villas of the clergy), its previously overwhelming control of commissions began to diminish.[30] Gradually the earlier restrictions of the artist to works that were useful in the Christian ritual or in perpetuating the faith began to loosen. Yet probably at least 75 per cent of the works commissioned in the Renaissance were still of a religious nature, and that percentage continued into the seventeenth century in Catholic countries.

To Protestant minds, on the other hand, art became something a church could do without—mere ornamentation, which detracted from spiritual growth rather than aided it. Protestants stripped the old churches they had taken over and tended in the new ones they built to avoid images, objects of beauty, and distracting ornament. The visual arts in Germany, vigorous and inventive until the sixteenth century, declined by the middle of that century. Cranach may have intended to convey a Lutheran point of view (as opposed to the Anabaptists) in his scenes of Christ surrounded by little children ('Suffer the little children to come unto me'), but most of his paintings until his death in 1553 were of secular subjects. England's foremost position in architecture and decoration appears to have been relinquished upon departure from the Roman church. The only Protestant country that achieved an art of international importance before the eighteenth century was Holland during the seventeenth century, her golden age. Most Dutch artists devoted themselves, however, exclusively to secular subjects—interiors, tavern scenes, still-lifes, landscapes, and portraits. Rembrandt's depiction of Biblical scenes is unusual for Holland; apparently most of them were not commissioned but were motivated by a personal inclination to probe the significance of sacred legends by means of pictorial realizations of them.

Catholic art of the late sixteenth and seventeenth centuries reflected the split in the Christian community. The twenty-fifth *sessio* of the Council of Trent (December 4, 1563) affirmed that art was the handmaiden of the church and instructed members of the clergy at all levels to take responsibility for the 'correctness' of the images on display in their areas. Innovation was curtailed so far as to require all ecclesiastics to submit any 'unusual' images to the bishop for approval. Gilio da Fabriano in 1564, Carlo Borromeo in 1572, and Gabriel Paleotti in 1582 wrote treatises that defined 'correctness' in greater detail than had the Council of Trent, but they followed the council's affirmation that painters and sculptors were poets and not priests by praising those who subordinated their art to Truth rather than allowed Truth to be distorted for the purposes of art. These writers explained that the matter deserved great attention because images are more impressive than words, and they reminded the artist of his responsibility.[31] Nudity was specifically restricted by the Council of Trent as not conducive to pious thought on the part of the beholder.

The official attitude of the church toward art had prompt effects. Daniele da Volterra, an artist otherwise well worthy of respect, became notorious as *il braghettone* ('the pants maker') by painting clothes on the figures of Michelangelo's 'Last Judgment' by the order of Pope Paul IV. Ammannati in a letter to the Accademia di San Lucca in 1582 expressed his regret for having sculptured nudes, and he disavowed the view that the beauty of the human body was a channel for the realization of the beauty of the Deity. Veronese, when asked by the Inquisition in 1573 to explain the 'extra' figures and distracting events that he had placed prominently in his 'Feast in the House of Simon', now in the Accademia in Venice, was less penitent but apologetic still.

The church's policy on art had visible if more subtle and less frank effects upon subject matter and style. Post-Tridentine Catholic artists favoured themes that sustained beliefs disputed by Protestants—for example, the God-given role of the pope as head of Christendom, the belief in saints as intercessors, the efficacy of prayer and penitence in the attainment of salvation, and the validity of visions as revelations of Christian truth. Events of sacred history were no longer simply narrated by clearly identifying persons and establishing the emotional relations among them, as had been done from Giotto's time through the early sixteenth century. Rather, they were interpreted with a Counter-Reformation emphasis. For some subjects, such as the Immaculate Conception of Mary, a new image was developed to connote the context without direct references to the event itself. Catholic artists tended to depict scenes from sacred history, and in the Grand Manner of the Renaissance, rather than ordinary types and realistic actions, which Protestant artists preferred. If seventeenth-century Spanish and Neapolitan artists employed realism, it was in order to emphasize the low and transient nature of the physical world in contrast to that of the spiritual.

Architecture also reflected the new spirit of the Counter-Reformation. The cosmic order represented in the central church was put aside by Borromeo, and architects were advised to abandon that pagan form. Because preaching had again become important, particularly among the Jesuits, they laid down requirements in 1568 for their mother-church, the Gesù at Rome, as a single nave and vaulted structure, which was readily accepted elsewhere as a compact setting suitable for a sermon. (Pl. 54b; Fig. 3.) The increasing importance of the sermon led also to the elaboration of the pulpit in the seventeenth and eighteenth centuries until in some churches it became the most ornate part.

The Rise of Art Criticism

By the late seventeenth century the judgment of art was subject to the influence of writers and critics, most of whom were not artists. While Italians and some Spaniards continued to exalt fancy or imagination, the most influential works of criticism were published in Cartesian France. There theorists attempted to systematize the more concrete ideas put forth earlier in Italy in order to attain a more objective basis for the judgment of art. The Renaissance categories of primary emotional states[32] (codified by Leonardo and emphasized by artists from Donatello to Poussin) were further clarified by Descartes' *Traité des Passions* and then finally conventionalized by Le Brun and the Académie Royale.[33] Art subjects also were graded—according to the talents they required and the nobility of expression inherent in them. The Renaissance idea persisted that the artist's most worthy subject was man in the act of expressing his most noble emotions, and in consequence the most respected themes were those derived from the dramatic episodes of history, both sacred and profane. Portraiture, animals, landscapes, and still-lifes ranked afterward in respectability in that order. André Félibien (1619–95) and Roger de Piles (1635–1709), outstanding historians and critics of art, fostered a simple, flexible, and, they believed, objective method for judging relative perfection in art by separating and scoring a work's various aspects, such as drawing, colour, composition, expression, and invention, and then totalling the score. This quantitative approach to the quality of art aimed at universal validity by recognizing that weakness in one regard might be compensated by excellence in another. The separate aspects were not considered mutually exclusive, the greatest artists, such as Raphael, being ranked very high in all categories. Some critics were inclined to consider excellence in drawing more important than excellence in colour. The argument between the 'Rubensists', who held that colour was the life of painting and the 'Poussinists', who maintained that drawing was its essential element, became an important part of the literary 'Quarrel of the Ancients and the Moderns' (see Chapter XI), which in art became a quarrel between advocates of the Classical and of the Baroque. It was settled in the last decade of the seventeenth century, when colour and drawing were given equal status.

During the seventeenth century, theorists began to recognize a variety of art categories (in addition to classes of subjects), each with its own aims and conditions of judgment. Frederico Zuccari in 1607 distinguished three kinds of art—natural, artificial, and fantastic. Poussin described several 'modes' of arrangement, each appropriate to a different emotion evoked by a particular kind of event, and (according to Félibien) tried to understand the reasons for various kinds of beauty. The faculty of 'Taste' was first referred to by the Spaniard Baltasar Gracian in 1642, and it was accepted into the domain of esthetics by La Bruyère in 1688. It was, however, too indeterminate for most French theorists, intent as they were on establishing an intellectual basis for judgment.

The expansion of art categories was probably stimulated by the increased range of art forms known to the seventeenth and eighteenth centuries; in any event, the several categories provided a more specific framework for judgments of taste than did the vague but apparently single and absolute norm of 'perfection' by which works had been gauged in the Renaissance. Thinking within these categories, critics became more concerned with relative 'quality' than with 'perfection'.

In the eighteenth century, when writers were especially prone to put order into nature's variety by grouping things into categories, the idea developed of 'species of art', as Hume called them. Giovanni Gravina (1718) inferred that the laws of judgment were as numerous as the things to be judged. Jonathan Richardson (1719) suggested that a work of art was most appropriately judged within the setting of the local school or historical period to which it belonged. Edmund Burke (1756) distinguished two categories of art, the sublime and the beautiful. Raphael Mengs (1762) defined three additional ones—the expressive, the graceful, and the natural. Each of the five was accepted as a kind in which varying degrees of perfection could be reached, but the most noble was generally believed to be that classified as beautiful.

The Debate over the Criteria of Feeling and of Reason

Much attention was given during the eighteenth century to the nature of art and, particularly, of the experience to be derived from viewing works of art. Some of the most interesting and novel observations were made in respect to the non-rational associations with art—the imagination and the feelings. These observations threatened the major premise on which art theory had been based since the beginning of the Renaissance. Although Italian Mannerists had expressed admiration for the elusive quality of *grazia* and Charles Alphone Dufresney (1611–65) and De Piles had given great stress to the factor of 'genius', art was generally regarded as primarily an intellectual activity that could be learned and understood by reason.

Among the eighteenth-century critics of pure rationalism, especially the British, this manner of thinking lost ground. Joseph Addison claimed that imagination combined with reason to produce the wonders of art. Francis Hutcheson suggested that beauty was understood by an 'inner sense' and could not be perceived by reason. David Hume contended that the role of reason was to distinguish truth from falsehood and such a distinction was not basic to the discernment of beauty. Nevertheless, a large group of other

English theorists, although they likewise tended to associate art with non-rational faculties, also assumed that the more disorderly forces might be guided during the creative act by reason. They believed that the attraction of beauty was somehow related to man's God-given sense of pleasure by his preference for order, uniformity, and regularity. They held also that good taste could be taught and that reason paved the way for pleasure in art. In this way, after some foraging into the unexplored areas of the imagination, the English empiricists before the end of the century returned to a rational basis for the understanding of art.

Meanwhile on the Continent the same argument was going on. In Italy Vico, as early as 1725 and without qualifications, had claimed that imagination, not reason, was the essential faculty of the artist. In France Jean Baptiste Dubos (1719) and Charles Batteux (1746) were leading figures in a school of thought that tended to regard engaging the emotions as the chief aim of art, but Batteux still expected to find a clear and distinct idea at the base of the arts and wanted 'to clear away the mists and establish the precepts'.[34] In Germany, Alexander Gottlieb Baumgarten (who in 1735 was the first to use the word *aesthetic* for the science of art) likewise observed that the material of art was not precisely intellectual, and Johann Georg Sulzer (1774) described the aesthetic idea as not sufficiently distinct to be cognitive. These men suggested that the basis for art was not learning, science, or rules but feeling and imagination. These ideas, however, were not synthesized sufficiently to withstand the clear expositions of the rationalists. Diderot, leader among the rationalists, rejected Hutcheson's 'inner sense' and assured his readers that ideas of order, unity, symmetry, and proportion, on which beauty was based, were as 'positive, distinct and real'[35] as the length, breadth, and thickness of things.

Neoclassicism reflected in art the rationalism of the eighteenth century. It was a most effective and widespread theory reaffirming the rules, the ideal types, and the intellectual basis of art. During the third quarter of the century, Caylus, Winckelmann, C. L. Hagerdorn, Mengs, and Lessing eulogized Greek works of art as the most perfect creations of Man. Reynolds also pointed to Greek models, though along with Italian masters as well. His suggestions that the artist observe, digest, compare, and systematize his visual experience reflected the rational approach of Italian and French theorists also. Even Hogarth, who ridiculed rule-ridden academicians, expressed admiration for Greek art and established a law of his own to the effect that beauty is based on a 'precise serpentine line' (probably echoing the claim of the sixteenth-century historian-painter Giovanni Paolo Lomazzo that Michelangelo considered it 'the line of beauty'). These Neoclassicists admired the majesty and repose of the ideal but 'natural' figure, in contrast to the 'affections' of the Rococo, and pointed out that perfection in contour was the chief characteristic of Greek art. Neoclassicists were basically different from Renaissance theorists, although both found inspiration in Antiquity. For one thing, the artists of the eighteenth century looked to Classical Greek art and those of the fifteenth century to Hellenistic Roman art as the acme of Ancient achievement; for another, the more exact archaeological knowledge of the Neoclassicists gave them a better idea of Antiquity than that which Renaissance artists had formed from scattered comments by Ancient writers and from the few fragments of Ancient art known to them.

The pre-eminent speculative genius of the late eighteenth century, Immanuel Kant, attempted to establish intellectual principles of judgment in opposition to the concept of 'taste', but a new attitude fostered by the 'Sturm und Drang' school promised to dislodge the belief that art is an intellectual activity subject to rational judgments. This group, in art as in letters (see Chapter XI), demanded originality rather than correctness and elegance, and intensity of feeling rather than adherence to rules. It accepted the senses as the source of art and lauded creative activity as the most exalted occupation of man. Even Diderot and particularly Rousseau fostered some of these ideas, and thus gave expression to the movement that later was to be known as 'Romantic'.

The Rise of Art History

In contrast to the artist of the early eighteenth century, the artist of 1300 had been relatively unaware of historical change in art forms. Artists began to be conscious, however, of being part of a historical process during the fourteenth century, when Dante, Boccaccio, Petrarch, and Villani described three major phases of art history—that of the great Ancients, the 'barbaric' art of the 'Dark Ages', and the revival evident in their own time. Ghiberti and Alberti continued these historical divisions and expressed confidence that they were about to regain the 'good arts' of Antiquity. Ghiberti interpreted the history of Ancient art and that of his own period as a series of pictorial and sculptural inventions or innovations which gradually would bring art to perfection, or an approximation of nature. Vasari in the mid-sixteenth century thought that his contemporaries, particularly Michelangelo and Raphael, had surpassed not only the Ancients but nature itself, bringing the continuous progress since Giotto and Nicola Pisano to its climax.[36]

Whereas Renaissance artists had been stimulated by the idea of contributing to this progress toward perfection, after the late sixteenth century changes were thought of more as differences of manner brought about by leading artists than as evidence of progress. Few critics in the seventeenth or eighteenth centuries believed that any of their contemporaries had surpassed Raphael; on the contrary they frequently looked back to his art as the most nearly perfect. Although Félibien, De Piles, Richardson, C. H. von Heineken, Hagedorn, and other critics affirmed a greater interest in the style and method of the best artists than in anecdotes about them, the history of art remained an account of the men whose distinctive manners had changed its course. Thus, during most of this period, artists associated change and innovation with the genius of individuals.

Historians of the eighteenth century introduced some new attitudes which gradually altered the artist's view of his place in history. The influence of local cultural differences on art had been recognized earlier, but Johann Friedrich Christ (1726) and A. J. Dezaillier d'Argensville (1754) emphasized the importance of an artist's national art tradition to his style, and Caylus dramatized the persistence of national characteristics by describing chronological changes within the art of a country simply as gradations of tone within one colour continuity. The artist of the 1750's began to think of his national origin as something affecting him, perhaps even inescapable. About the same time Caylus and Winckelmann, presenting a new concept of the history of art, emphasized another historical force acting on the artist. They conceived of art forms as having lives and destinies of their own, and therefore of artists as actors in, rather than creators of, their development. The artist's accomplishment was thus held to be determined at least in part by the people among whom, and the time at which, he was born.

The Development of Art as a Profession

Another important change which occurred between 1300 and 1750 was the new evaluation of a work of art as a collector's item. Independent of its ritual or decorative function, an art object came to be looked upon primarily as evidence of the artistry of the man who had made it. Early collectors, such as Federigo of Urbino, Cosimo de' Medici, Isabella and Alfonso d'Este, Francis I, Charles V, and Federigo Gonzaga, at times expressed the desire to have 'a work by the hand of' a specified artist. Some of these works were selected to give pleasure or edification or to provide models for local artists, but whatever the reason, they suggested that the designated work was believed to have an intrinsic aesthetic value. Collections gathered on this basis were different from church treasuries—the only 'collections' of the Middle Ages. They also tended to become more specialized than the collections of gems, odd stones, coins, relics, and occasional works of art housed in the fifteenth-century 'Wunderkammer', or 'room of marvels'. During the Renaissance the palace court, the villa garden, or the 'studiolo' became display areas for private collections of paintings, drawings, engravings, and sculpture. Princely collectors vied with the clergy for the artist's services. Artists themselves collected—at first, generally pieces to serve as models in their workshops but by the late sixteenth century works reflecting more interest in connoisseurship than in practical use. Art academies formed collections of winners in their competitions or of examples submitted for election to membership. These collections, as well as many private ones, were available to the artist for study, and toward the mid-eighteenth century some of the larger ones, having been taken over by the national governments, were opened also to the public. By the end of the century the artist had begun to look to the collector and the museum as patrons. When the new British Museum failed to buy contemporary English works, Hogarth led an attack on those British who purchased the art of the Continent or of the past exclusively.

Not only had the artist become accustomed to thinking of his art as eventually belonging to a collection and displayed as a self-sufficient work in a gallery but he had begun to depend on exhibitions also as a means of reaching the public and patrons. Since 1663 the Académie des Beaux Arts in Paris had displayed the works of its members. Although they were available for purchase, only about a dozen are recorded to have been sold during the last third of the seventeenth century. By that time, however, the artist was beginning to think of his creation less in relation to a particular use or decorative purpose and more as an independent memorial to his genius, permanently housed in an art collection. Before the seventeenth century artists had rarely undertaken work that was not ordered for some specific purpose. The patronage of collectors and museums, as well as the artist's own concept of his product as primarily an embodiment of his artistry, induced painters, with growing frequency, to initiate pieces that were not commissioned. During the seventeenth century, painters, particularly those of Holland, began to place their landscapes and still-lifes in the hands of dealers, who sought purchasers for them. (Pl. 22.) Sculptors and architects, however, because of the costly nature of their materials and technical processes, were less likely to undertake works that were not commissioned.

Freedom from the taste of a specific patron and from the requirements imposed by a specified assignment allowed an artist like Rembrandt to regard an uncommissioned painting as an avenue of unrestricted intercourse with his genius and conscience. But frequently lesser men found themselves at the mercy of untrained bourgeois tastes. As the artist became increasingly dependent on the patronage of a broader segment of the public, he attempted to improve the general level of taste. Academicians and Neoclassicists alike became concerned with the instruction of manufacturers and craftsmen in the minor arts. Artists and theorists extended their roles as creators and educators of taste from their original concern with the princely patron and other artists to the European public as a whole.

By the end of our period, as a result of both the changes noted above and the influence of the schools and academies to be noted in Chapter XVI, the European artist had ceased to be a humble artisan. He had gained a dignified professional status; he had become a man of recognized intellect and creative genius; he was accepted as a director of the public taste. An artist now tended to think of his works as self-sufficient objects, as expressions of his personality, and as enduring evidence of his genius. Technical facility was, to be sure, an aspect of his art in which he still took pride, but he regarded it as only a means of releasing his particular sensibilities and sense of form, which were for him the most important constituents of his art. Art, which had once been essentially a collective effort by a community of artisans in the service of the church had now become largely an expression of individual creativeness.

THE DANCE AND MUSIC IN EUROPE

In Europe before 1300 dancing was usually under explicit religious controls. The Roman Catholic clergy discouraged processional dancing inside the church edifice and discountenanced Maypole dances elsewhere as an unbecoming pagan practice. Still, in Spain, the region *par excellence* of the western European dance, they were unable to eliminate religious processional dancing. To the present day, Easter processions in Seville, with elaborately adorned images of the Virgin, retain much of their primitive emotionalism. In more subdued form, controlled, rhythmical movement survives in the processional, recessional, and canon of the Roman Catholic mass and in other ritualistic acts, such as the swinging of the censers.

Before 1300 dancing was rarely encountered as a conscious and avowed form of amusement except among the peasantry. Nevertheless, rustic folk dances, sometimes violent and even ribald, were being adapted, refined, and embellished for the entertainment of all classes in town and country. A famous instance was the 'morris dances' of England. Though linked to the Robin Hood legend, they were probably originally called 'Moorish dances' and imported from Spain. Whatever their origin, they were modified to fit English preferences and were early associated with the medieval May Day celebration and Maypole dance, with its varied foreign embellishments.

Pantomime and procession were important features of primitive and rustic dances. When knights and noble ladies took to dancing, the peasants' freedom of movement was denied them by their courtly tradition and dress, which lent themselves rather to stateliness. The two forms nevertheless developed side by side, and as court dances evolved in the fourteenth and fifteenth centuries, they readily borrowed from the more vigorous and less seemly rustic dances. Gradually the 'dancing master' acquired professional standing, thus widening the distance between the dances he supervised and those of the folk, without destroying the possibility of mutual borrowing.

The custom soon arose of alternating slow dances with fast ones. Such couplings of dances remained fashionable under different names to the end of the sixteenth century. Most of the fourteenth century dances were carried over into the fifteenth century, when little was added to the dance-repertory except the *gaillarde* and the *basse danse*. The latter derived its name from the 'low' (walking) steps of the dancers, which contrasted with the 'high' (jumping) steps of the *danses hautes*, such as the *gaillarde* and the *tourdion*. Later, some of these dances were replaced by various *branles* (English, *brawles*), which became so popular that they figured prominently in all kinds of social entertainment.

After 1500, Spanish and Italian dances, modified by the sophistication demanded of royal entertainment, were performed at various courts. Aided by the patronage of the Bourbon kings, French modifications and nomenclature eventually triumphed. Today the names of the courtly dances of this period are commonly French, although the dances themselves are sometimes not French in origin—for example, *sarabande, pavane*, and *gaillarde*. So great was the social prestige of Louis XIV's court that France was able to take the local dances of other peoples, refine them, and then export them as French cultural influences to all the rest of western Europe. Dances of peasant origin, some of them ages old, developed into polite, mincing steps suitable to aristocratic tastes—e.g. the formalized *minuet*, the *gavotte*, the *bourrée*, and the *passepied*. Series of such stylized dances figured in the new *ballets de cour*.

The ballet began in Italy and France. At occasional festivities in the late fifteenth and early sixteenth centuries costumed dancers would perform for royal guests amid sumptuous scenery and to musical accompaniment.[37] In the second half of the seventeenth century the French ballet attained a high degree of excellence and passed from the court to the theatrical stage. Professional dancers were now trained by ballet-masters, and the best contemporary talent wrote much of the music to which they performed. Jean-Baptiste Lully (1633–87), the foremost composer of the period, though born in Italy, had a spectacular career at the court of Louis XIV, rising from a simple violinist in the royal orchestra and *baladin* ('dancer') to the rank of plenipotentiary director of the Paris opera. He not only provided fine music for the *ballets de cour* but also introduced formal ballets into his operas. Moreover, in co-operation with Molière he created the *comédie-ballet*, a combination of theatre and dance, exemplified in *Le Bourgeois Gentilhomme*. By that time the *ballet de cour* was so popular that princes, princesses, and courtiers often took part in them. Louis XIV himself sometimes consented to strut in ballets written to commemorate his greatness. One of these was Lully's 'Ballet de la Nuit' (1653), in which the king took the part of the *roi soleil*, a role that gave him a lasting sobriquet.

In Lully's time ballet-music became an art-form, and theatrical dancing an art in its own right. Subsequently, the ballet was so much in demand that it remained an indispensable part of operatic work well into the eighteenth century. That a ballet presented in several acts could successfully fill an entire evening was proven by Lully's illustrious successor, Jean Philippe Rameau (1683–1764). In the eighteenth century several dancers of both sexes became famous performers, and several treatises on the art of the dance appeared, Jean Georges Noverre's *Lettres sur la danse et les ballets* (1760), being perhaps the most notable of them.

While the *ballet de cour* flourished in France, England developed its own version of courtly and aristocratic entertainment in the masque. Introduced into England from Italy and France, the masque inherited certain characteristics, such as mythological plots and lavish settings, but it also developed its own distinctive features; stereotyped formal dances performed by aristocratic maskers often were interspersed with dialogues and songs performed by professional actors. That the English masque became a sophisticated art-form is due in great part to the co-operation of such eminent literary men as Ben Jonson, Thomas Campion, and Milton, who supplied the texts, and to artists like Inigo Jones, who designed the masks and stage-settings. The decline of the masque began with intrusion of comic and grotesque scenes and dances, called antimasques.

By the end of our period, the dance had become a profession for the vur-tuoso as well as a pastime for the amateur, and it was no longer necessarily an expression of religious devotion or of rustic merriment. From Europe it passed to the European colonies in the Western Hemisphere, where it both enriched and was enriched by the tribal dances of the American Indian and possibly also of the African slave.

The Ars Nova of the Fourteenth Century

The history of the dance is in large part also the history of music. Although spontaneous, unrecorded folksongs and dances never lost their appeal, before 1300 the cultivated music of the Western world consisted almost entirely of church hymnology. In its earliest phases Catholic Church music was repre-sented by the pure, unaccompanied (monophonic) Gregorian chant. The gradual addition of melodic lines to the unalterable Gregorian chant (i.e. to the so-called cantus firmus) marked a signal advancement, and from the twelfth century on, contrapuntal or polyphonic (many-voiced) vocal compositions became increasingly customary. By 1300 primitive counterpoint, which set note against note (point counter point) had progressed to the organum and discantus of the Notre Dame School, and musical composition had become fairly complex.

The church looked with disfavour upon the 'deterioration' of the Gregorian chant. In 1324 a papal bull laid down severe restrictions upon innovations. Nevertheless, ecclesiastical displeasure could neither check the growth of the polyphonic style nor prevent the increasing infiltration of secular elements into religious music. The trend was well illustrated by the development of the motet, the representative musical form of the 'Gothic' period. It was originally a three-part contrapuntal composition sung to sacred Latin texts, with the leading Gregorian melody, the cantus firmus, in the tenor; the added voices were called duplum and triplum. When a text was assigned also to the second voice (usually a paraphrase of the fundamental thought expressed in the tenor) it was called motetus (i.e. 'worded part'), and this term eventually was attached to the entire composition. From the fourteenth century on, the motet was adopted also outside the church. Sometimes contrasting melodies and texts were combined in the same motet, and sometimes, too, the liturgical tenor melody was replaced by worldly tunes. The French folk melody 'L'homme armé' became famous because between the fifteenth and the seventeenth century more than thirty motets based on it were written by outstanding French, Flemish, and Italian masters.

The amalgamation of sacred and secular elements led to the emergence of the *ars nova*, so named by the fourteenth-century musician-poet Philippe de Vitry to distinguish it from the *ars antiqua*, the style of the previous century. The composers of the *ars nova* tried to break away from the *ars antiqua*, which in their opinion was characterized by stiffness. They strove for greater rhythmic-melodic freedom and, above all, for a greater liberty of expression. With them, a new spirit came into music—a spirit that paralleled the lyric quality and the rebellion against rigidity that was expressed in the poems of Dante and Petrarch and in the frescoes of Giotto and Fra Angelico. Nevertheless, the contrapuntal technique dominant in church music continued to influence the construction also of worldly music. Under this influence emerged the secular motet and the catch (or canon), a more or less elaborate part-song in which the voices fell in one after the other, imitating and trying to 'catch' each other. The earliest example of this kind of song is the famous canon (or round) 'Sumer is icumen in', attributed to the English monk John of Fornsete (thirteenth century).

Machaut (see Chapter X) and Francesco Landino (*c.* 1325–97) were the ranking masters of the *ars nova*. Being poets as well as musicians, both put inventiveness and charm into their works. Machaut, born in Champagne, excelled in *ballades*, *rondeaux*, and *virelais*, subtle, sophisticated songs and dances that had sprung up in France. Landino was a master of the Italian *ballata* and the early madrigal, in which a few stanzas sung by a sole voice alternated with instrumental sections. Educated amateurs all over Europe enthusiastically performed the new French and Italian art-forms, and probably for that reason music found an established place in the cultured secular society of the epoch.

In church music the organ was the principal instrument. While of imposing size and tone-power in many a cathedral, it also came in smaller form, such as the 'positive', a stationary chamber-organ, and the picturesque organetto, a small portable instrument carried by a shoulder-strap, the right hand manipulating the keys and the left the bellows. Many other instruments were in use, however; Machaut himself mentions thirty-six kinds. When the wandering musicians of Paris founded a Confrérie et Corporation des Ménestrels (Minstrel's Guild) in 1321, an applicant for membership was expected to play no less than nine different instruments. The strings of the time included various fiddles, which were bowed; harps, zithers, psalteries, and lutes, which were plucked; and the dulcimer, which was beaten. Woodwinds took forms such as the bombarde, the cromorne (from *Krummhorn*, i.e. 'curved horn'), and the shawm or other ancestor of the oboe family. Other wind instruments were the slide-trumpet (not unlike the modern trombone) and the bagpipe. Several types of drums were also used. During the fifteenth and sixteenth centuries some of these instruments became obsolete, others refined. Many of them appear in contemporary paintings and sculptures and survive in the collections and museums of our own day.

The 'Netherlands School' and Modern Notation

In the fifteenth century the seat of musical activity shifted to England and the Low Countries. During the first decades the leading role fell to England's foremost composer John Dunstable (d. 1453), renowned also as a mathematician and an astrologer. Although steeped in the traditional polyphonic style, he transcended it in the free, melodic imagination with which he adorned the *cantus firmus* and in the distinctive euphony of his masses and motets. Thereby he greatly influenced the musical language of his disciples, among whom were Guillaume Dufay and Gilles Binchois, who were to become known as the founders of the Burgundian School of music.

On the Continent musical leadership had already begun to pass from Italy and France to the Low Countries. In Italy, though popular music still flourished, the higher musical art-forms lagged in the competition for talent, with the result that music fell far behind the visual arts, while in France the trials of the Hundred Years' War had temporarily brought exhaustion. About the same time, the Low Countries entered a period of economic and cultural prosperity, and many outstanding French musicians migrated to Flemish Burgundy. Together with talented natives of those parts like Dufay and Binchois they founded the Burgundian School of music, the initial phase of the great grouping usually but inaccurately called the Netherlands School, which comprised three generations of late medieval and early Renaissance composers.

The leader of the Burgundian School was Dufay. Born around 1400 in the county of Hainaut in the borderland between France and the Low Countries, he started out as a choirboy at the Cathedral of Cambrai and died in 1470 as one of its canons. The enterprising Duke Charles (the Bold) of Burgundy made Flanders a centre of musical attainment, and the cathedral school of Cambrai became a seat of musical education. Dufay also spent some years in Rome, where he was exposed to the 'anti-Gothic' spirit of the Italian Renaissance. On the one hand, this spirit modified Dufay's 'Gothic' musical construction; on the other, his solid contrapuntal style decidedly affected Italian music.

Dufay's influence in Italy was reinforced by the great masters of the second generation of the Netherlands School (1460–1500), best represented by the Flemish Johannes Ockeghem (1430–95), Dufay's outstanding disciple, and the Dutch Jacob Obrecht (1430–1505). Ockeghem dominated the second half of the fifteenth century as the creator of exalted religious works in the so-called neo-Gothic style and also as the teacher of practically all the famous composers of the next generation. His name and that of Obrecht are linked to a momentous change in musical thinking that took place in the course of the fifteenth century.

In its early stages polyphonic composition had been primarily the inter-weaving of strands of melodic voices—without much concern, however, whether the harmonies (chords) resulting from the coincidence of different melodic lines clashed or blended. The old contrapuntal practice was, figura-tively speaking, 'horizontal' (each part having its own melodic design), the 'vertical' (or chordal) aspect being more or less unplanned. The incidence of clashing sounds was somewhat diminished by the limited *tessitura* (i.e. the prevailing, average pitch) of the participating voices. Combinations of melody and harmony, already successfully attempted in the secular music of the fourteenth-century *ars nova*, had developed more fully in the worldly French *chanson* of the fifteenth, but in learned church music Ockeghem and Obrecht were the first masters to base intricate polyphony and expanded *tessitura* on a groundwork of firm harmonic structure—a principle that still is valid in contrapuntal composition.

A third generation of 'Netherlanders' arose at the end of the fifteenth century. Some of them, now the heirs to a highly developed contrapuntal tech-nique, put a finishing touch on it by writing mammoth canons, sometimes for more than thirty separate voices, or by devising part-songs that could be per-formed forward and backward (the so-called crab-canons). Others underwent a southern harmonic influence, which gained momentum with the growing migration of Flemish musicians to Italy. Both developments were summed up in Josquin Des Prés (1450–1521), who fully attained the art of combining expressive voice-parts with ordered, meaningful harmonies. Born in France, he became Ockeghem's pupil in Paris, lived in Italy for thirty years, and got to be as celebrated for his music—both sacred and secular—as Leonardo and Raphael for their paintings.

Josquin was the first great master in a true musical Renaissance. His mature works reflect the ideals of balance, clarity, and symmetry of form dear to Renaissance artists. He not only could command the styles and techniques of the time, he also is credited with introducing the method of composition by which a musical work is unified through 'imitation'—i.e. the reiteration of the same motif as it passes from voice to voice. This device, which still is used in polyphonic music, is known as continual imitation (*durchimitierender Stil*). Josquin's masses, motets, and chansons remained the model for two genera-tions of composers all over Europe. His influence was made all the more pervasive by the contemporary development of the printing press and its adaptation to music.

Unlike the products of the visual arts, musical composition comes to life only through actual performance, and performance requires a system of notation. The music of the Middle Ages had been couched in manifold, involved notations, but with the accumulating innovations in music, com-posers had slowly and laboriously been elaborating a modern scheme of representing musical sounds and idiom. By 1500 musical notation had moved decisively from the medieval toward the modern script, and thenceforth the steady accumulation of printed scores hastened the dissemination and cultivation of music. In the course of the next few centuries the medieval script gradually fell into disuse, and for a long time modern musicians were unable to read and hence to perform the music of the Middle Ages. Only a few decades ago musicologists began to decipher it and to reconstruct its performing practices. Thanks to their efforts, combined with those of dedicated artists and recording companies, the gap has now been largely filled.

Music of the High Renaissance

In the sixteenth century leadership in music was on the wane in the north, and it passed to Italy. The music of the Italian Renaissance developed along two main lines: it attained an unsurpassed level in vocal polyphony, and it began a new polyphonic instrumental style. Vocal part-music reached a summit in the secular chanson and madrigal, and an unexcelled perfection in the masses of Pierluigi Palestrina (1525-94).

Palestrina, chapel master of St Peter's in Rome and honorary *maestro compositore* to the pope, was no innovator; he was, rather, the crowning figure of a long historic evolution. His popular fame rests on a now disproved legend. The pure, dignified style of his masses is supposed to have convinced a group of musical judges (appointed by Pope Pius IV in keeping with a resolution of the Council of Trent) that polyphonic music had a rightful place in the church and thus to have averted the reinstatement of the monophonic Gregorian chant. Though not by any such direct route the saviour of Catholic music, Palestrina was the greatest composer of sacred music within the Catholic Church. The serene spirituality of his masses, motets, and other religious compositions sets him apart even from the few contemporary masters who approximated the perfection of his blending of counterpoint with harmony.

Though they are overshadowed in historical importance by the majesty of his church music, Palestrina also wrote numerous secular pieces. The principal secular songs of the day were the chanson and the madrigal. The chanson, of French origin, was a finely wrought part-song for several voices with the leading melody in the treble. It was written to short poetic texts, and whether the poems were lyrical, contemplative, humorous, or frankly frivolous, they usually dealt with love in all its aspects. Some composers—Palestrina's contemporary Clément Jannequin conspicuous among them—delighted also in chansons of a descriptive character—e.g., 'La Guerre', 'Le Chant des Oyseaux', and 'Le Caquet des Femmes'.

The Italian counterpart of the chanson was the sixteenth-century madrigal (not to be confused with its fourteenth-century predecessor). Like the French chanson, it was a kind of vocal chamber music, written for four, five, or six unaccompanied voices. The madrigalists of the High Renaissance tried to translate the varying moods and ideas of the underlying poem into an equally varying flow of musical invention, adapting meter and rhythm, mode and harmony to the nuances of the text. Thereby they often succeeded in adding variety, flexibility, and finesse to the polyphonic style. Among the musically most advanced madrigals, in addition to those by Palestrina, there must be counted some composed by Giovanni Giacomo Gastoldi (c. 1550–c. 1610), Luca Marenzio (c. 1560–90), and Don Carlos Gesualdo, prince of Venosa (c. 1560–1613). Full of dramatic suspense and bold chromatic inflections, the works of Gesualdo were modernist in their own time and still sound modernist. The musical versatility of both men and women of Italy's patrician circles enabled them to perform this elegant sort of vocal polyphony sitting around a table with their part-books in front of them.

From Italy the madrigal spread to Germany and to England. In England it flourished for four decades of the Elizabethan and Jacobean era in a vital, 'naturalized' form. The foremost composers of those decades were Thomas Tallis, Orlando Gibbons, William Byrd, Thomas Morley, and John Dowland. Their madrigals, songs, and anthems still delight music lovers everywhere.

Palestrina's great Continental contemporaries were the Flemings Roland de Lassus (c. 1525–94) and Philippe de Monte (1525–1603), the Spaniards Cristobal Morales (c. 1500–53) and Tomás Luis de Victoria (c. 1540–c. 1613), who was known as 'the Spanish Palestrina', and the Venetians Andrea and Giovanni Gabrieli (1510–86 and 1557–1612 respectively). Lassus stands out as the most versatile composer of the century. Unlike Palestrina, who hardly ever left Rome, he lived and worked in many countries and spent the last decades of his life in Munich, at the ducal court of Bavaria. He produced some 2000 works and excelled in many different styles, including masses, Latin motets and psalms, French chansons, Italian madrigals, and German part-songs. A truly cosmopolitan figure, he embodied the spirit of the late Renaissance. On the other hand, the Spanish priest Victoria wrote sacred music of a kind that imparts the passionate spirit of the dawning Baroque era. Likewise, the works of the two Gabrielis bear the marks of the early Baroque in their predilection for double and multiple choirs with colourful orchestral accompaniments that suggest the splendour of contemporary painting. Their providing for the participation of instruments in their church music, however, was not a complete innovation. Though previous centuries had been dominated by purely vocal church music, instruments had often been used to support or supplant vocal parts, and as early as 1526 Erasmus had complained that churches reverberated with the sound of flutes, pipes, trumpets, and trombones.

Music in the Baroque Era

At the close of the sixteenth century the musical stiaution was exceedingly complex. On the one hand, the vocal polyphonic style, which had taken about four hundred years to mature, was at its peak, and, on the other hand, new trends held forth the promise of fresh achievements in the future. At that juncture music entered the stage of development known as the Baroque, which was to close some one hundred and fifty years later with the death of

Johann Sebastian Bach (1685–1750) and George Frederick Handel (1685–1759). Their most important German forerunners were Johann Hermann Schein (1586–1630), Samuel Scheidt (1587–1654), and Henrich Schütz (1585–1672). With the works of these three masters, particularly with the oratorios and passions of Schütz (who was in a sense a runner-up to Bach as much as his forerunner), Protestant Germany rose to the rank of a full-fledged partner in the musical development of the Western nations.

Until then, German music had been remarkably slow in asserting its individual quality. To be sure, the country's native folksong had flourished at all times, and the Meistersingers had produced a widespread, petty bourgeois musical practice (see Chapter X), but the cross-currents of northern ('Netherlands') and southern (Italian) cultural influences had to be absorbed before German music could reach its height. From the sixteenth century to the end of our period (and beyond), it remained ascendant.

The earliest known examples of polyphonic music based on German folksongs appear in the so-called *Lochamer Liederbuch* (c. 1450). Germany's subsequent contribution to the evolution of music coincided with the rise of Protestantism. Luther was a talented and trained musician, and in the seventeenth century the Pietist musician Paul Gerhardt wrote some of Germany's finest hymns (see Chapter IV). Reared in the musical traditions of the Roman Catholic Church, Luther became familiar with the great polyphonic works—secular as well as religious—of the masters of his time, Josquin being his favourite. He is credited (though not uncontestedly) with the authorship of the so-called battle-hymn of the Reformation ('A Mighty Fortress is Our God') and other religious songs. At any rate, as the founder and organizer of a new liturgy he based the musical part of the service on the chorale—i.e. on simple metrical hymn-tunes with devotional German texts. They were sung in unison by the congregation—first without, and later with, organ accompaniment. The chorale, in turn, gave rise to the chorale-prelude, the chorale-fantasy, and the chorale-variation, art-forms that permitted organist-composers to display their instrumental and contrapuntal skill.

The chorale also found its way in Protestant Germany into larger forms of music, the most important being the cantata, the oratorio, and the passion. These were religious but non-liturgical compositions, characterized by the blending of traditional polyphonic technique with new, dramatic elements. The first German master to achieve this blending was Schütz. He introduced into his oratorios and passions not only the new Italian monody and recitative (soon to be described) but also the alternation of accompanied solo voices and massive choral sections which he had learned to compose in Venice under Gabrieli. The monumentality and the eloquence of Schütz's choral compositions guarantee him a place among the first great figures of the Baroque era.

The century and a half of Baroque music corresponds roughly to the Baroque period in the visual arts and to the so-called scientific revolution. The name *Baroque* when applied to music tends to associate it with some of the characteristics of Baroque art—the mixture of worldliness and piety, the quest for complexity within unity, the monumentality of Baroque architecture. It may suggest association also with some aspects of the scientific spirit of the day—a quest for precision, a restraint of self-expression, a growing knowledge of acoustics (see Chapter XIV), an improvement of techniques and instruments, and a respect for regularity of form.

Early in the Baroque period instrumental music, hitherto secondary, emerged into the foreground. In the sixteenth century, to be sure, *toccatas* ('touch-pieces') and *ricercari* (complex musical designs) had been expressly written for the organ, and dances and all sorts of transcriptions for the lute, the all-purpose instrument of the day. Nevertheless, most compositions still bore the instruction *da cantare o suonare* (to be sung or played), without specifying a particular instrument. Only in the seventeenth century did composers begin to show interest in writing music to be performed on a specific instrument. They invented more and more musical designs and patterns to suit the nature of the chosen medium, bringing out in each instrument its characteristic potentials. In Italy and the northern countries the organ, in Spain the lute, in England the virginal each acquired its own repertory. The organists of the time—even Girolamo Frescobaldi (1583–1643), the greatest among them—perhaps because of the traditional prestige of the organ as the church instrument par excellence, clung more or less loyally to forms inherited from the preceding century. In contrast, the Elizabethan composers created a music that effectively exhibited the merits of a newer and simpler keyboard instrument, the harpsichord. In their so-called 'grounds' (variations written to a recurrent bass-figure) and particularly in the free-and-easy variations on popular songs (some of which were prescribed by Shakespeare for use as incidental music in his plays) Morley, Gibbons, Giles Farnaby, and others plumbed all the resources that the keyboard offered—swift scale and chord passages, trills, and the like.

The harpsichord served also as the favourite medium for another important art-form of the Baroque, the dance-suite. From the great wealth of seventeenth-century dance-forms emerged the German *allemande*, the French *courante*, the Spanish *sarabanda*, and the English *jig* as standard movements. Around 1700 the harpsichord suite was enriched by the inclusion of optional numbers, such as the gavotte, the bourrée, and the minuet, all of which figured also in the ballets and operas of Lully, Purcell, and Rameau. The eighteenth-century dance-suite was to reach its ultimate perfection in Bach's clavier-suites and partitas, as well as in his suites for orchestra.

The fuller development of literature for bowed instruments began in the seventeenth century, coinciding with the great period of violin craftsmanship at Cremona in Italy. The making of the best violins began about 1630 and lasted well into the eighteenth century. Its most famous and still unsurpassed masters were Nicolo Amati (d. 1684) and his pupil Antonio Stradivarius (1644–1737). The German composers of the time stressed the virtuoso rather than the expressive side of violin playing, whereas the Italians used the 'singing' quality of the violin tone to full advantage. In the violin sonata and the sonata da camera (both with an accompanying harpsichord) and in the Baroque solo-concerto and the concerto grosso for string orchestra the Italian masters Archangelo Corelli (1653–1713) and Antonio Vivaldi (1680–1743) created novel art-forms for the violin-family. Guiseppe Tartini (1692–1770), a brilliant violinist as well as a composer, developed a virtuoso style for its dominating member, the violin.

On the whole, the evolution of instrumental music in the seventeenth century was but a diversified continuation of earlier developments. The only relatively unprecedented event was the rise of the *dramma per musica*. The new Italian music-drama owed its existence to the scientists, literati, and musicians who gathered around 1600 in the drawing rooms (the *camerata*) of the Florentine music lover Count Bardi. Tired of polyphony, which, in fact, obscures the text of vocal music, they believed that the future of music lay in the rebirth of the Greek music drama and the adoption of a monodic, declamatory style for its singers. Monody—i.e. the accompanied solo (*monos*) song—was no novelty in itself; it had long been practiced by folk singers and amateurs. Polyphony, however, still enjoyed undisputed hegemony, and the introduction of the monodic style into dramatic art-music marked a turning point in the development of music because it challenged that hegemony. So as to accentuate diction, the composers of the camerata employed the *recitative*, a kind of musical recitation accompanied by sparse chords. The resulting declamatory style inevitably involved a certain dryness and monotony. Hence Claudio Monteverdi (1567–1643), the ranking figure and the only man of genius in the group, interspersed lyrical *ariosos* in his *recitativos*, thereby enriching the scope of the new style. The effort to represent in this fashion the personality of the characters of a musical drama was given the name *stile rappresentative*. With the rise of the monodic style a new kind of notation came into use—the *basso continuo* or figured bass, which is a method of indicating an accompanying part by the bass notes, together with figures indicating the chords and intervals to be played above the bass. This practice lapsed with the passing of the Baroque era; in the eighteenth century the modern system of notation became common and was generally used for all types of music.

The somewhat experimental music drama of the early Baroque was soon superseded by the Italian opera, which had begun its triumphal march in the 1630's. The first permanent opera house was opened in Venice in 1637. When Rome, Naples, Paris, Vienna, and other cities followed suit, opera became an international concern. Dramatic action was no longer placed in the foreground; from the words to be set to music, the emphasis shifted to the music itself, and above all to the arias. In its typical form, perfected by Alessandro Scarlatti (1659?–1725), the leader of the Neapolitan school, the so-called *da-capo aria* became the main vehicle for lyrical expression, while the *coloratura aria* gave the singers an opportunity to show their virtuosity. How highly the art of *bel canto* was thought of (and paid for) in the seventeenth and eighteenth centuries is perhaps correctly measured by the fame and wealth of the *castrati*, for whom roles were specially composed that would reveal their brilliant soprano and contralto voices.

France was somewhat late in producing an operatic style that could match the dramatic art of Corneille and Racine or of its highly developed courtly ballet. In Lully (whose ballets we have already considered) French opera had its first worthy representative. A first-rate theatrical composer, he adapted his music to the classicist style of the libretti he chose, occasionally with Molière's advice. Some of Lully's operas and ballets remained on the French repertoire for almost a century.

In Germany opera was a product of the late Baroque. From humble beginnings in the popular *Singspiel* there evolved the *opera seria*, Italian in style but with German libretti. It attained a certain eminence under a few composers affiliated with the Hamburg Opera, founded in 1678. Their leader, Reinhold Keiser (1674–1739), was much admired; even Handel borrowed from him for some of his own forty operatic works, written between 1711 and 1741. After a span of fifty-odd years, however, most of the German opera houses either closed down or were taken over by Italians and Italian or Italian-style opera, as was true all over the Continent. Not until the advent of Christoph Willibald Gluck (1714–87) was Germany to produce its next great opera-composer.

If the German-born Handel is not counted as English, England produced only one distinguished opera-composer—Henry Purcell (1659–95)—perhaps, at least in part, for the reason that it possessed its home-grown version of the musical drama in the masque. Purcell's 'Dido and Aeneas' is a masterpiece ranking with his many pieces for harpsichord and chamber music, his incidental music (incidental, that is, to spoken dramas), and the anthems and hymns he wrote as organist at Westminster Abbey and the Chapel Royal.

With the works of the generation after Purcell the music of the Baroque reached its height. François Couperin (1668–1733) and Rameau in France, Vivaldi and Domenico Scarlatti (1685–1757) in Italy, Bach in Germany, and Handel in Germany and England were the leading masters of the period. Couperin and Rameau excelled in music for the harpsichord. Rameau also wrote operas and ballets. Some of them were written to traditional Classic, mythological, or allegorical plots; others featured the current interest in the exotic (e.g. 'Les Indes Galantes'). Though Rameau's musical innovations brought on several bitter controversies with Rousseau and other influential contemporaries, he was perhaps more significant as a musical theorist. In an epochal work, the *Traité de l'harmonie* (1722), he laid down the principles of harmonic functions in musical phraseology. This treatise had a far-reaching influence upon generations of composers and still is not obsolete.

While Italy continued to make important contributions to instrumental

BB*

music, opera, and oratorio, in the first half of the eighteenth century musical leadership fell to Germany. That period is often called 'the Age of Bach and Handel', and with good reason. The works of those giants transformed the various national styles of the period into a higher unity, a perfect fusion of Italian, French—and, in Handel's case, English—elements with a fundamentally German background. Moreover, although both spoke the complex musical idiom of their day, the personal characteristics of their art outweighed the typical Baroque features they had in common.

Handel was at his best in large, dramatic forms. After having written a great number of successful operas during his 'Italian' period, he settled down in London and turned definitely to the composition of oratorios, of which he wrote more than thirty. Most of them depicted heroic episodes derived from the Old Testament (e.g. 'Saul', 'Israel in Egypt', 'Esther', 'Judas Maccabeus'), with pathos, grandeur, and dramatic eloquence. They took England by storm and won vast audiences abroad. The secret of the strong emotional impact that Handel's oratorios have always exerted lies partly in their melodic appeal but mainly in their mighty choruses. Yet it was not the forceful spirit of his Biblical 'chorus dramas' that made Handel world-famous. It was 'The Messiah', the only oratorio from his hand in which lyric and contemplative elements predominate. With 'The Messiah', Handel became a national figure in his adopted country. The work itself came to be considered all over Europe as the archetype not only of the Handelian oratorio but of 'the oratorio' in general. Handel made generous contributions to almost all branches of instrumental music also, and the organ concerto with orchestra was his specific addition to that genre. Since, however, in one or another kind of instrumental music Bach or some other contemporary master may occasionally have overshadowed him, his glory rests on the oratorio, in which he was unsurpassed.

Handel was a man of the world; his was the grand Baroque manner, reflected equally in his life and in his work. Bach's spiritual attitude was entirely different. His cantatas and passions were a musical embodiment of Protestant piety, and his numerous instrumental compositions mark the acme of musical architecture, logic, and inspired craftsmanship. An organist, choirmaster, and church-composer in central Germany, he led the simple, well-regulated life of a hard-working middle-class citizen. In the toil of creative fulfilment Bach knew no bounds. While some of Handel's large-scale works show traces of improvisation here and there, Bach's compositions, whether conceived on a large or a small scale, bear the imprint of his genius to the last detail. This quality holds true for his didactic works—such as the *Inventions*, the forty-eight preludes and fugues assembled in the *Well-tempered Clavier* (that is, for the clavier tuned in the equal temperament universally used today) and *The Art of the Fugue*, which is an exegesis of polyphonic composition—and it holds just as true for the many musical works in which he gave free rein to his imagination. In his organ-fantasias and organ-toccatas,

'Chromatic Fantasy and Fugue' for clavier, 'Chaconne' for solo-violin, and certain mystic-symbolic cantatas—to give but a few examples—Bach is widely believed to have surpassed all his contemporaries, including Handel.

Bach and Handel appeared at a time when the polyphonic and the monodic style had reached a high degree of integration. Bach, essentially a contrapuntist, leaned more to the former style; Handel, essentially a dramatist, to the latter. Bach's and Handel's monumental works sum up a long musical evolution. Yet, whereas some of Handel's works (e.g. 'The Messiah') never ceased to be performed (particularly in England, where he spent most of his life), Bach's music was wellnigh forgotten after his death and had to wait for revival until twenty-year-old Felix Mendelssohn performed the 'Passion after St Matthew' in 1829—exactly a hundred years after it was written.

From Bach to 'the Viennese Classics'

In the generation after Bach the feeling prevailed that the grandiose, complicated contrapuntal style had outlived its day. The reaction against the musical tradition asserted itself, on the one hand, in the so-called 'style galant' —an echo in music of the Rococo in architecture—and, on the other, in a new emotionalism (*Empfindsamkeit, sensibilité*), which stressed the milder, more intimate feelings or 'affects'. The slogan of the innovators of the latter persuasion was 'back to nature', and in music at least, this urge can be correctly associated with Rousseau. Once again new esthetic needs led to the quest for new art-forms. It found vent in a movement that paved the way for the compositional technique of those paragons who were to become known as the 'Viennese Classics', Franz Joseph Haydn, Wolfgang Amadeus Mozart, and Ludwig van Beethoven. Three of Bach's sons were pioneers in this movement.

These pioneers inaugurated the sonata-form. The merit of the new form lies in its 'dialectic' nature—i.e. in the opposition of contrasting themes within a single movement, a signal change from the 'monothematic' construction that prevailed in the instrumental music of the Baroque period. Although experimental and frail in its incipient stages, the new form proved to be viable. As finally brought to perfection under Haydn, it was integrated with two or three independent movements in what is generally known as the 'classical sonata at large'. In its broader acceptance, the term *sonata* now covers any large-scale work written on this basic plan, whether for a single instrument (e.g. the piano), a larger group of players (e.g. a string quartet), or an orchestra (in which case it is called a symphony.)

A favourite medium of the post-Baroque composers was the pianoforte. This new keyboard-instrument, first designed by Bartolommeo Cristofori in 1709, superseded the competing harpsichord in a period which valued the expression of tenderness and delicacy. On the harpsichord only the most skilful player could produce anything but abrupt contrasts of 'forte' and 'piano'; on the new instruments, which even then possessed the complicated lever-action of our modern piano, the tone could be modulated by the mere pressure of the fingers. Thus allowing many shadings of intensity, the pianoforte lent itself admirably to the requirements of the new style.

The pioneering endeavours of Bach's sons and their followers were paralleled by the innovations in orchestral music and performance cultivated by the so-called Mannheim School, connected with one of the German ducal courts. Here a group of conductors and composers were brought together, largely from Austria (e.g. Ignaz Holzbauer) and Bohemia (e.g. Franz Xaver Richter and Johann W. A. Stamitz). They laid the foundation for the modern orchestra (the celebrated orchestra of the Mannheim court had a goodly number of wind and string instruments, aided occasionally by drummers) as well as for the symphonic style of the Viennese Classics. They enriched the tonal palette of orchestral performance by introducing unexpected dynamic accents, sudden pauses, extended crescendos, and other hitherto little used or unused devices, which were eagerly taken over by Haydn, Mozart, and particularly Beethoven.

In the operatic field the striving for 'true, natural feelings' found its champion in Gluck. His 'reform-operas' (as he called them) reveal not only an outstanding composer but also a man of profound esthetic principles. Like Monteverdi a century and a half earlier, he stressed the organic unity in opera of text, acting, and music—a principle that was to find its greatest champion in Richard Wagner a hundred years later. Consequently, Gluck banned coloratura arias from his operas, which were all written around plots taken from Classical literature, and allowed ballets only if they did not retard the action. An ideological and literary battle ensued between the Gluckists, his adherents, and the Piccinnists, adherents of Niccola Piccinni, the leading composer in the traditional Italian operatic style. Queen Marie Antoinette, for political rather than aesthetic reasons (Gluck too was Austrian), supported Gluck, and Rousseau, consistent with his avowed opposition to artifice, likewise sided with him. Posterity also seems to have vindicated Gluck. Piccinni's music fell into oblivion while some of Gluck's works still form part of the operatic repertoire.

In the eighteenth century, the three classical masters, Haydn, Mozart, and Beethoven, made of Vienna the musical capital of Europe. Haydn, chronologically the first of the three (1732–1809), had by 1775 composed a number of his finest symphonies and sonatas, helping to perfect those musical types. He also wrote oratorios, masses, and songs, and an astonishing number of string quartets and other kinds of chamber music. Many of his best compositions, however, were to come after 1775. Mozart was only nineteen years old in that year. Having begun to compose when he was five, he had already written a number of operas and symphonies and a good deal of church music as well as sonatas and concertos for his favourite instrument, the piano. All of these early compositions show his extraordinary, if yet not fully matured, gift for melody and harmony and his amazing ability to see a projected composition at once and whole as a mental picture.

The culmination of Haydn's career, the full development of Mozart's genius, and the whole of Beethoven's contribution belongs to the period of Volume V. As if to put a finishing touch upon our period, in 1776 Charles Burney and John Hawkins each began to publish a lengthy history of music, without which much of the knowledge of early music would have been lost. Both of these works are now considered classics in their field.

Music as a Profession

Since the fourteenth century the musician had changed his status considerably. The eighteenth-century musician of reputation might still be a choirmaster, like Bach, or connected in some other way with religious services, but he was not necessarily a functionary of a church, particularly in Protestant countries. More commonly now he was also or entirely in the service of a prince or a bourgeois patron. He might even be a private entrepreneur like Handel, who made and lost fortunes in producing operas and oratorios in England, or like Haydn and Mozart, who composed on commission for special occasions. Purcell, Lully, Bach, Handel, Haydn, and others were happy enough to have royal patrons. Since copyright did not exist and borrowing others' work was common, a royal patron was an especially good asset, for such patrons not only could reward handsomely but also might grant privileges amounting to copyright by placing restrictions upon competitors. With *concerts spirituels* (initiated in Paris in 1725) and operas as well as public concerts becoming regular events in a number of European countries, the works of contemporary composers reached ever widening audiences on more and more social levels. Music in Europe was now not only an art but a secular, even a competitive, profession as well.

THE ARTS OF ISLAM

Architecture

Among the visual arts in the civilization of Islam, architecture remained supreme. Islam perhaps owed much more than the West to the Chinese in the decorative arts, but it was largely exempt from Chinese influence in architecture. After the Mongol invasions the lands of the Persian-using zone (largely under Turkish rule) excelled in architecture, but it continued to be very fruitfully cultivated likewise in the Arabic countries (some of them also Turkish-ruled), especially before 1500. The greatest monuments still were religious buildings—mosques, khānaqāhs (Ṣūfī meeting-places), madrasas (schools for 'ulama'), and great mausoleums often with mosques attached. Care was taken also with secular buildings, such as fortresses, caravanserais, and especially palaces, as well as with the homes of the wealthy.

In the Arabic lands the fourteenth and fifteenth centuries were the great age for the building of madrasas. In Egypt and Syria a madrasa was associated with the mausoleum-mosque of its founder; it was commonly cruciform, allowing classes to meet, according to the hour or the need, in each of the arms of the cross. This complex pattern was broken up toward the end of our period as social needs changed; in later centuries separate portions—such as a school centred on a fountain—were built as individual foundations. The most noticeable monuments that survive from Mamlūk Egypt are its many mosques with their delicately silhouetted minarets and luxuriant use of geometric interlacings. Farther west the tradition of the solidly square minaret was maintained, and the numerous *madrasas* were built more simply. In contrast to the Gothic cathedral, the mosque was hypostyle, many columns breaking it up visually into horizontal compartments (see above). Palace architecture persisted in the rich strength represented by the Alhambra, the fourteenth century palace-citadel of the kings of Granada. (Pl. 61a.)

In Iran and Turkestan the Mongols took readily to buildings in the old Islamic manner, with even increased magnificence. The tombs of rulers were built with an especially massive majesty, usually culminating in a high dome, such as was cultivated also in India. Early in the fourteenth century the tomb of Uljaitu (d. 1316) at Sultaniya helped set this pattern; the blue and gold mausoleum of Timur in Samarkand, erected a century later, is its most impressive example. (Pl. 61b.) Mosques in Iran also emphasized the great high dome, displaying the brightly coloured tiles distinctive of Iran, but they retained the open court as the main body of the prayer space. After 1500, in the Ṣafavid Empire, Iranian architecture was represented at its best in the magnificence of the imperial city of Isfahan, with its garden boulevards and open, landscaped palaces set off by the impressive use of columns. The floral type of decoration was enriched by numerous kinds of ornamental forms, some based on motifs borrowed from Europe and China. A high level of elegance was maintained till the end of the seventeenth century, when political catastrophes put an end to the great age of building. To Julfa, a suburb of Isfahan, Shah Abbas in 1603 transferred a number of Armenian Christian families, whose cathedral, decorated inside with murals depicting scenes of Christian martyrdom painted by Italian journeymen artists, was made externally to look like a mosque.

In the Turkish countries in the fourteenth and especially the fifteenth century there was introduced, perhaps after the Byzantine pattern, a form of mosque in which the main prayer room was placed under the dome instead of in an open court. In the Blue Mosque of Tabriz of the later fifteenth century, the main prayer room was so placed. In the design of some sixteenth century mosques Muslim architects partly adopted the Hagia Sophia in Istanbul as a model, using half-domes to buttress the great central dome. Sinān, the famous Albanian architect of the Sulaymāniyya and other Istanbul mosques, created imposing variations of this central form, originating a fully new and integrated type. With Ottoman domination after 1500, the domed mosque of this general type spread widely in the Arab countries,[38] where otherwise, however, architecture was largely static or even declined. In the eighteenth century in the Turkish provinces of the Ottoman Empire, an Italianate style, modelled on Western Renaissance architecture, came into favour for palaces and homes.

Miniature painting

The best Muslim painting was of miniatures. After 1300 Muslim miniature painting was confined chiefly to the zone, from the Balkans through India, where the Iranian tradition predominated. A sound foundation had been laid for it before Mongol times by both Arab and Persian miniaturists, who stressed colour and pattern, but Chinese influences became strong in the Mongol era, and with them developed the brilliant schools of Islamic painting admired today. This kind of art reached its peak in book illustration, which sometimes affected mural painting. Eventually separate sheets were collected, as individual artists (from the fifteenth century on) received recognition as such. Painting was closely connected with the development of Persian calligraphy, in the *nasta'līq* style (see below), into a cascade of harmoniously flowing lines. In such centres of royal patronage as Samarkand and Herat the Chinese impulse was gradually absorbed, until a new form of aesthetic imagination was produced. At the end of the fifteenth century the miniaturist Bihzād of Herat (1450–*post* 1520) exemplified the establishment of an independent art, relatively more realistic within what was still a largely stylized decorative form. He was the master of the long-lived and varied Tabriz school. Early in the seventeenth century the school of Isfahan, latter-day capital of the Ṣafavids, found its outstanding master in Riza 'Abbāsī, who excelled in portraits and in genre scenes, in which he showed a subtle sense of humour. (Pl. 62a.) He was not altogether uninfluenced by Western painting.

In the eighteenth century the art of miniature painting declined in Iran and imitations of Western as well as of Indian art failed to revive it. The miniatures of the Ottoman Empire, where painting was vigorously frowned on by religious puritans (as was even more the case by then in Arab countries), were abundant but are not thought to have achieved such high distinction as those of Iran and Turkestan. In India (see below) a distinct and vigorous school developed at the Mogul court and influenced non-Muslim art as well.

Decorative arts

In the decorative arts, Islamic craftsmen lent much to and borrowed little from their European colleagues. They borrowed more from the craftsmanship of cultures farther east, but in some crafts—pottery, for example—lent to them also. In the visual arts of all kinds, after the Mongol invasions Iran and the other countries where Muslims used the Persian language were in the forefront, the Arabic countries gradually, especially under Turkish rule, learning to follow their patterns. Iran continued to set the tone for carpets of all sorts, which, like pottery and other types of decorative pieces for regular use, achieved in the Ṣafavid period an unsurpassed refinement of craftsmanship and elegance of design. In all these objects the Chinese influence had become, since the Mongol invasions, unmistakably strong in motifs and even in manner.

The luxurious rugs of the Near East (and of the Far East, too) were made predominantly of wool-and-silk yarn. The technique of rugmaking, which originated in China or the Near East and spread through the Mediterranean area with the expansion of Islam, changed little with respect to the materials, dyes, or implements used. The pile of the rug was built simply by knotting variously coloured yarns, tuft by tuft, to a warp stretched across a frame. After 1300 Persian rugs, particularly those made in Kurdistan, Khorasan, Kerman, and Feraghan during the sixteenth and seventeenth centuries, are generally considered the finest. The best ones are solidly made, having as many as four hundred knots to the square inch. In these rugs a complicated tracery—for instance, of meandering tendrils—constantly varied in colour plays over larger divisions or motifs. Ṣafavid rug makers daringly introduced overall patterns from book bindings and even from miniatures; the manner in which certain major motifs appear—particularly huge medallions, geometric compartments or borders, and floral or animal forms—frequently enables the connoisseur to place and date a rug. Turkish rugs tend to have a pile that is longer, looser, and softer than those of Persia. Many, like those of Ghiordez, employed the motifs of the 'praying dome' and the bejewelled lamp found on prayer rugs as a basic design over which delicate tendrils intertwine. Caucasian rugs are frequently smaller and narrower than Persian or Turkish rugs. Some of the most distinctive designs are those composed of small geometric shapes infinitely varied to create engaging decorative complications.

Unlike the Far Eastern and the American Indian artists, who were apparently concerned with symbolism in almost all their art forms, Muslim artists were little concerned with the meaning of the symbols they adopted. Islam was averse to the presentation of doctrine by any means other than the spoken word, and this aversion permitted Islamic artists to incorporate into their eclectic repertory the motifs of various cultural areas with little concern for the ideas originally associated with them, whereas the more self-contained and continuous traditions of the Far Eastern artists preserved the meanings of their motifs and, even in a decorative context, used them with a sense of propriety.

This lack of concern of Muslim artists with symbolism helps to explain why the most purely decorative or non-representational tradition for the enrichment of surfaces was that of Islam. Far-flung expansion had resulted in an eclectic decorative vocabulary, which was gradually chastened by the non-representational tendency of the Muslim religion. So, by the fourteenth century, Islam's decorative repertory reached a fair degree of homogeneity. The decorative treatment of the surfaces of objects or of the walls of buildings depended on the rhythmic intertwining of plant motifs or the rational inter-lacing of bands and geometric motifs. Plant motifs were more frequently used for pottery and textile designs, and geometric motifs for the surfaces of archi-tecture or furniture, but they were also combined. This limited decorative vocabulary, although subject to infinite variations in detail and colour, was usually arranged according to a few simple schemes. Motifs were repeated or alternated along a scrolling stem, or a strap interlace was continued in a band or extended endlessly in all directions to form a trellis-like structure. Another favourite arrangement on a two-dimensional surface centred around a 'star of fruition' from which strap-like projections extended and interlaced, creating geometric areas between them.

The expansive surfaces that make up the geometric shapes of Islamic architecture, as well as the poor building materials, invited decorative treat-ment. Bricks were frequently carved or combined with stone and arranged in lattice patterns. Mosaics and glazed tiles together with carved, inlaid and polychromed panels of wood or marble were applied over the rubble walls and the wooden framework. Far western Islam tended to emphasize geometric motifs and the complication and multiplication of uniformly small motifs to create a sense of decorative profusion rarely approached by any other orna-mental tradition, as the lavish fourteenth-century decorations of the Alhambra Palace in Granada and the mosque in Tlemcen illustrate. In Persia, partly under Arabic influence, more freely flowing plant motifs and less mechanically extended geometric designs were favoured, as in the early-fourteenth-century mosques of Veramin, Yezd, and Riza. In Cairo the mosque of the Sultan Barkūk (1384), placed amid the domed 'tombs of the caliphs', and in Con-stantinople the mosque of Suleiman (seventeenth century) testify to their architects' skill with tracery.

The technical and decorative traditions of Islam were continued in Spain by Muslim architects who remained after the Christian reconquests as Mudé-jares. They constructed palaces, castles, towers, gates, and churches whose exteriors were enriched by combinations of brick, stone, and tile long used to decorate Muslim buildings. Inside, walls, ceilings, and door and window frames were embellished with geometric motifs (sometimes combined with Christian emblems) carved in plaster or inlaid in wood and then articulated by colour. The patio of the Doncellas and that of the Muñecas in the Alcazar in Seville are prominent examples of Mudéjar decoration completed in the fourteenth century. Even as late as the sixteenth century Christian designers modelled the *cimborios*, or crossing vaults, of the Burgos Cathedral and La Seo of Zaragosa on the parallel-rib constructions of Islamic architecture.

The resourceful, universal use of calligraphic design was the most distinc-tive triumph of Islamic art. Styles of writing were cultivated for every possible purpose. *Kūfic* lettering was employed for stateliness or for masculine vigour, *naskhī* for an evenly smooth rhythm, *nasta'līq* for a flowing and some-times almost ethereal elegance. Fine books were inscribed in rich materials

by calligraphers, normally accorded a higher regard than miniaturists. Sometimes a few lines, marvellously refined, sufficed for a page. In religious architecture the most significant formulas of the faith were given monumental form
in various styles of kūfic and naskhī lettering, which were blended with and
counterpoised to the surrounding arabesque. (Pl. 63a,b.)

The furnishing of Muslim homes displayed a luxury and richness of taste
that had greatly impressed the Crusaders, who came from European homes
which before 1300 were much drabber than they were later to become. Tables
and chests were the chief home furnishings which Islamic artisans were called
upon to make of wood, for the Muslim used fewer articles of furniture than
the Christian. These tables and chests were beautifully carved and inlaid and
went along with luxurious rugs and ornamental panels for the doors and
shutters. The *minbar*, or pulpit, was the outstanding piece of elaborately
decorated furniture needed in the hypostyle mosque. While metal objects
were also less common in mosque than in church, Mosul in Mesopotamia was
famous for bronze lamps and ceremonial vessels handsomely decorated with
silver inlay.

Vases and bowls might give finishing touches to a Muslim interior. Among
the most decorative pottery types of our period was the lustreware of Islam.
It was characterized by a metallic sheen obtained by coating the already
decorated surface with a glaze containing gold, silver, or copper and then
firing the glaze with moderate heat. Perhaps the technique was developed
originally in Egypt and Syria, but during the late Middle Ages Persia and
Turkey were its most important Middle Eastern centres. Multicoloured and
lustrous bowls, dishes, pear-shaped bottles, tiles, and mosque lamps were
ornamented with narrative scenes or with plant, flower, and bird motifs. The
quality of the enamelled glass made in the Near East declined during the
fifteenth century, but excellent pots and bottles of blue and green glass were
still made in Persia from the sixteenth to the eighteenth century.

The Muslim lady or gentleman was likely to be strikingly clothed and
bejewelled. While Europe had learned to make good silk, during the sixteenth
and seventeenth centuries some of the Asian countries regained an important
place even in the European textile market. Persian weavers, under the
patronage of the Ṣafavid dynasty, produced brocades, damasks, and other rich
fabrics of the finest quality at Yezd, Kashan, and Isfahan. (Pl. 62b.) Stained
and printed cottons were highly prized fabrics, imported from India. Striking
jewellery was worn by Muslims in at least the sixteenth century. Earrings,
rings, belt plaques, diadems, and turban pieces were made in silver filigree,
enamelled or set with precious stones—pearls, torquoises, rubies, cats-eyes,
and carnelians.

Indo-Muslim architecture

The Muslim conquests in India brought about the development of a type
of Islamic art best described as Indo-Muslim. It flourished under the patron-

age of Islamic rulers, and from the Mogul period on, it dominated the palaces, villas, mosques, temples, tombs, towers, fortresses, schools, and other buildings of most of India. It was produced largely by Hindu craftsmen and artists, who, naturally imparting to their works some of their own artistic tradition, gave them a subtle Hindu quality not found in other Islamic art. This Indo-Muslim style produced some excellent painting and some of the world's most beautiful architecture.

The earliest buildings of the Muslim conquerors were laid out according to traditional Islamic requirements, but the Hindu builders, being unacquainted with the pointed arch and other features of Islamic architecture, often achieved the desired effect by an adaptation of Hindu architectural principles. Also, in many cases, parts of Hindu buildings were bodily incorporated into mosques, or decorated stones from demolished Hindu temples were, with some re-working, fitted into Islamic structures. The Hindu builders were expert sculptors, and they inevitably introduced sculpturesque qualities into their columns, capitals, beams, and decorative designs, joining Hindu with Islamic decorative motifs. Thus Hindu and Islamic architectural features gradually were fused into a composite style.

Several features of this architecture reveal its Indo-Muslim ancestry. They include (1) a dome which was basically Muslim in style but often employed Indian structural features, especially an octagonal arrangement of the supporting pillars; (2) pointed arches of the Persian variety, topped by a true keystone but also often formed by the Indian pyramid technique of successive inward-projecting layers of masonry; (3) stone lintels and bracketed capitals of the Indian type; (4) slender turrets, decorative kiosks in an Indian style, and minarets; (5) halls, arcades, and colonnades supported by decorated columns reflecting the influence of Indian sculpture; (6) an Indo-Saracenic gate in the form of a large semi-dome located in the front wall though the actual opening was a small door under the arch; (7) open courts surrounded by buildings or colonnades, which were characteristic of both Hindu and Islamic architecture, but with spacious and better lighted interiors in a distinctly Muslim fashion; (8) enamel tiles, mosaics, and inlays of both Saracenic and Indian design; and (9) considerable, often sculpturesque, decoration in the form of surface design or low relief in which traditional Islamic geometric figures, calligraphic lettering, arabesques, and conventional foliage patterns were fused with Jain and Hindu flowers, wreaths, baskets, and (sometimes) animals to give a much more exuberant and exotic appearance than was characteristic of purely Islamic decoration. Formal gardens, laid out in geometric patterns with pavilions, fountains, canals, terraces, walks, flowers, and trees, were a distinctly Islamic contribution to the Indian scene.

The sultans of Delhi built some magnificent structures. 'Alā-ud-dīn (1296–1316), of the Khaljī dynasty, was especially active, his greatest triumph being the 'Alāi Darwāza at the Quṭb Minār (the south gateway to the Great Mosque of Delhi), erected in 1310 and renowned for its exquisite proportions and surface decorations. (Pl. 64a.) 'Alā-ud-dīn's own tomb stands out for its calligraphic ornamentation. The architecture of the succeeding dynasty, the Tughluqs (1320–1414), was prosaic and formal and had a 'deadening effect'.[39] Its massive severity was typified in the tomb of Ghiyās-ud-dīn, an austere sandstone structure with marble dome, and in the citadel-like Kalan Mosque with its domed bastions, completed in 1387. The Sayyids (1414–51) and the Lodis (1451–1526) attempted to revive the splendour of the Khaljīs. The domes and tombs of the Sayyids were distinguished by their Hindu features.

While the architecture of Delhi set the prevailing tone, several of the finest works of the period were in somewhat variant provincial styles. In the fifteenth century Jaunpur developed an architecture well illustrated in the Jāmi' Mosque (1438–78); it was characterized by high platforms, massive sloping walls, square pillars, lofty gates in front of vaulted porches, storied cloisters, and mosques with minarets of an unconventional type—features that were for the most part distinctly Hindu. (Pl. 65a.) Bengal produced a unique architecture that is well represented at Gaur and in the many-domed Ādina Mosque at Pāndu; it used brick with subsidiary stone, pointed arches on short bracketed columns, curved cornices, roofs reflecting the influence of northern Hindu curvilinear temple towers, and carved Hindu symbols such as the lotus. A beautiful type of architecture flourished in Gujarat, where the indigenous Hindu and Jain styles prevailed, using predominantly Hindu wood-carvings and delicate stone lattices and Indian arches and domes, although the Muslim pointed arch was also in evidence. The capital city of Gujarat, Ahmadabad, was famed for its palaces, its Jāmi' Mosque (begun in 1411 with two hundred and sixty pillars supporting fifteen stone domes constructed of projecting courses of stone in the Hindu style), the Mosque of Mahafiz Khan (built toward the end of the fifteenth century), and the tomb of Abū Turab (built a century later). In nearby Māndū, the capital of Malwa, Muslim tradition dominated, with massive fifteenth-century marble and sandstone mosques, palaces, and tombs, such as that of Hüshing Shāh (1405–35). In the Deccan, the Bahmani kings (1347–1527) and their successors were great builders, and their fortresses, mosques, and tombs showed direct Indian, Turkish, Egyptian, and Persian influences. Notable among several older structures was the Jāmi' Mosque at Gulbarga, built by a Persian architect. In the sixteenth century Bijāpur emerged as the architectural centre of the Deccan, and Hindu architects and craftsmen strongly reasserted themselves. Purely ornamental minarets, rich cornices, and lotus domes distinguished their style, seen in the unique Rawda Mosque of Ibrāhīm II (d. 1626). (Pl. 64b.) The stately Gūl Gumbaz, or tomb of Muḥammad (d. 1673), was unique for its Chinese-pagoda-like turrets at the four corners. The Golconda (1512–1687) style, as illustrated in the tomb of Quli Quṭb Shāh, erected in 1625, was identifiable by its lofty windows, its bulbous domes reminiscent of Russian churches, and the plaster decorations on its minarets.

The Indo-Muslim style became more homogeneous, if perhaps slightly more Muslim, under the Moguls. Although neither Bābur nor Humāyun were in India long enough to leave monuments of special note, they definitely encouraged Persian influences and may also have introduced Ottoman ideas through pupils of Sinān. The Afghan reign of Sher Shāh (1538–45) is commemorated by two distinguished monuments—the Qil'a-i Kuhna Mosque near Delhi, with recessed portals and small minarets around the dome, and his own dignified mausoleum, built on a high terrace in a lake at Sasarām in Bihar.

Under the patronage of Akbar and his immediate successors Hindu and Muslim architects, builders, and artists worked in harmony to perfect the Indo-Muslim style, and it reached its apogee during the century 1556–1667. White marble and coloured sandstone were favourite building materials, and relief carving, mosaic, inlay, and glazed enamel tile were highly cultivated as decorative devices. Persian influence was strong at the beginning, as illustrated in the tomb of Humāyūn at Delhi (1569), but Hindu ideas, especially in decoration, reasserted themselves as Akbar's reign advanced. At Allahābād the Palace of Forty Pillars had a projecting veranda-roof supported by rows of Hindu pillars. At Agra the Jāhāngīrī Palace with its square pillars and bracketed capitals revealed rows of Hindu arches (Pl. 65b), and the Great Mosque (Jāmi' Masjid) was reared in red sandstone, rose stone, and white marble, with three large bulbous domes, ornamental minarets, and Jain-like cupolas. Akbar's greatest architectural triumph was his capital city of Fathpūr-Sīkrī (near Agra), 'a romance in stone', largely constructed between 1569 and 1574 (now partly in ruins). Its numerous carved and ornamented buildings represented an almost perfect fusion of the Iranian and Hindu styles. Among the most salient structures were the Emperor's Office (of Hindu design, with a projecting veranda roof over a colonnade), the Panch Mahal (Pl. 66a) (a five-storied pavilion, each storey smaller than the one below, on the style of the Buddhist *vihāra*, or assembly hall), the Great Mosque (with its sanctuary copied from an Iranian model but constructed of white marble), and the massive Buland Darwāza (a triumphal arch, 176 feet in height, built in 1601–2 of white marble and pink sandstone to memorialize Akbar's conquest of Gujarat). (Pl. 66b.)

Two magnificent buildings were erected during Jahāngīr's reign. Akbar's Mausoleum at Sikandara, designed during his lifetime but complete in 1613, was a fitting resting place for a great emperor. Constructed of polychrome stone and marble, it had five superimposed terraces, impressive balustrades and kiosks, and a pyramid of buildings, 'which some have thought fit to compare with certain Buddhist *vihāras*'.[40] The tomb of I'timād-ud-daulah at Agra was built in white marble by his daughter, the Empress Nūr Jahān in 1628. It was one of the earliest Indo-Muslim buildings to employ *pietra dura* inlay as decoration. Subsequently, under Jahāngīr's successor, Shāh Jahān, inlay tended to supersede mosaic.

With Shāh Jahān Indo-Muslim architecture experienced a new wave of Iranian influence, attaining a certain feminine elegance that has led to its being described as 'jewellery on a bigger scale'. The tomb of Jahāngīr at Shāhdara, Lahore, with high pagoda-like towers at the four corners and with kiosks at the top, went up early in the reign. The palace at Delhi, begun in 1638, included the majestic and highly decorated Halls for Public and Private Audience. In the white marble galleries of the Private Hall (Dīwān-i-Khās), Shāh Jahān's 'paradise on earth', the ceilings were of silver, and the pillars, arches, and ribs were encrusted with Persian designs of jaspar, onyx, and cornelian. (Pl. 67a.) In it stood the famous Peacock Throne with a glittering array of rubies, pearls, and diamonds, the most celebrated creation of the Indian lapidaries' and jewellers' skill. The Great Mosque of Delhi, designed on the outside 'to attract the eye of the faithful from afar and proclaim the glory of Islam',[41] had an austere and simple interior. The Moti Masjid (or Pearl Mosque) of Agra, put up between 1646 and 1693, was perfect in simplicity and proportion. And the Tāj Mahal of Agra (1631–53) arose in all its exalting majesty in order that beneath its marble dome, amidst gardens of incomparable magnificence, Shāh Jahān's beloved empress, Mumtāz Mahal, might sleep in eternal peace. (Pl. 67b.) The Tāj seems to have been the joint product of Muslim, Hindu, and possibly even European designers, but the master architect probably was the Turk Ustād 'Isā.

With Aurangzīb the architecture of Mogul India began to decline. His intolerance and puritanical scruples discouraged Muslim art and led to the destruction of Hindu temples and statues. The best of his few buildings, the Lahore Mosque, completed in 1674, though having a distinct merit of its own, did not match earlier masterpieces. The comparative good will, however, that had prevailed from the reign of Akbar through that of Shāh Jahān had facilitated the spread of the Indo-Muslim style among the Hindus. It was noticeable in secular architecture such as Rajput palaces and civil buildings from Madras south to Tanjore and Madura. It was even accepted by Hindu temple builders in the north, where the Jugat Kishor at Brindāban (1629) and the Jain temples of Sonogarth in Bundelkhand testify to its vigour in the seventeenth century, and Bengal temples in the eighteenth. In fact, by 1775 a decaying Indo-Muslim style was in use almost everywhere; only Hindu temple architecture in the extreme south escaped its influence.

Indo-Muslim painting

Since Islam definitely discouraged sculpture and was not unconditionally favourable to painting, those arts did not flourish in Islamic India before the sixteenth century. Nonetheless, with the Timurids and their successors after the Mongol conquest there emerged the Persian school of painting, of which we have already noted that probably the greatest representative was Bihzād of Herat. Under the patronage of the early Mogul emperors an Indo-Persian style developed. About 1550, Humāyūn brought to India Mīr Sayyid 'Ali and Khwāja 'Abdus-Samād, at least one of whom was a pupil of Bihzād.

Akbar supported a large group of court painters, both Persian and Hindu, and under his patronage and pressure the Sino-Persian and native Hindu styles gradually blended to create the Indo-Persian-Mogul style. It reached its apogee under the inspiration and patronage of Jahāngīr. The chief characteristics of this style were: (1) calligraphic line, inherited from the Sino-Persian and Jain traditions; (2) brilliant colours, which reflected both the Persian and the Hindu heritage; (3) realism and conformity to nature, borrowed particularly from Hindu portraiture, landscapes, and representations of animals and plants; (4) character portrayal, revealed in a remarkable capacity to bring out the subject's psychological traits; and (5) its courtly nature, attributable to patrons who were sultans and nobles interested in commemorating their exploits on the battlefield, in the hunt, at court, or in the harem. Rembrandt studied Mogul paintings brought to Holland by the Dutch East India Company.[42] The wide gap between his broad chiaroscuro art and the decorative and bright colour areas of Mogul painting suggests why the art of these two areas made little impression at that time on each other.

Persian painting, we have indicated, was associated with calligraphy, book illustration, and miniatures, and in India these media were likewise highly cultivated. Full page (or larger) paintings were done on paper, at first imported from Persia but later manufactured in India. The murals, painted in palaces and tombs, in particular reflected an Indian tradition. Few murals have survived, but many illustrated books and albums have. Despite the realisms of the psychological studies and the excellence of the faces, the human anatomy was not well represented, but from Jahāngīr's time onward other techniques of the painter, such as perspective, foreshortening, modelling, and shading, steadily improved. The subjects of pictures varied—emperors, nobles, ladies, or holy men; landscapes (most often only as backgrounds to portraits or divan, durbar, and hunting episodes); battles and hunting; court life (audiences, receptions, picnics, etc.); love scenes; pastimes and activities in the harem (in which the semi-nudity borrowed by Muslim ladies from the Hindus was often evident); religious and mythological stories; plants and flowers; birds; larger animals like horses, elephants, tigers, and gazelles. (Pl. 68a.)

Akbar's patronage attracted many artists and stimulated the various Hindu schools of painting. A host of artists were employed for many years in decorating the fabulous buildings at Fathpūr-Sīkrī with murals. Of the seventeen most famous painters at Akbar's court, thirteen are said to have been Hindus. Perhaps the two best-known Hindus were students of 'Abdus-Samād — Basavān, who was noted for his portraits and backgrounds (Pl. 68b), and Daswanth (d. 1584), of the palanquin-bearer caste, who won distinction under Akbar for his treatment of Indian subjects in a Persian manner. Three Hindu painters continued as important figures into Jahāngīr's time—Lāl Kesu,

Manohar (honoured for his divan scenes and animals), and the portraitist Bhagvati. Abu'l-Faḍl said of the Hindus: 'Their pictures surpass our conception of things. Few indeed in the whole world are found equal to them.'⁴³ Among the Persian painters, besides Sayyid 'Ali and 'Abdus-Samād, were Khursau Quli and Jamshed. Farrukh Beg, a Kalmuck, remained prominent during Jahāngīr's reign, especially for his hunting scenes.

Jahāngīr was himself an excellent connoisseur and art critic. He collected the best of Hindu and Islamic paintings, as well as paintings by Italian artists and engravings by Dürer and Holbein. Under his critical eye, the eye of a lover of nature, the Mogul school reached its highest level in the intensity of its three-quarters-portrait studies of character and in the naturalism of its landscapes and plant and animal pictures, which often represented rare specimens. Abul-Ḥasan, whose father was a painter of Herat, was Jahāngīr's favourite portrait painter. Ustād Manṣūr was noted for his animals, birds, and flowers; Muḥammad Murād of Samark for his gazelles; and Shāfī 'Abbāsī of Persia for his flowers. Among the Hindus, Bisham Dās was unequalled as a portraitist.

Shāh Jahān reduced the number of court painters. Among the newer artists realism now began to give way to decorativeness, and innovation to tradition. Muḥammad Nādir, a Samarkandi hold-over from Jahāngīr's time, was an eminent portrait painter. Mīr Muḥammad Hāshim rose to fame with his drawings of Mogul court figures. Shāh Jahān's eldest son, Dārā Shikūh, Aurangzīb's brother and doomed rival, was a liberal patron of Hindu artists and left a priceless album of works dated 1603–34. His preferred portraitist was Anūpchātar.

With Aurangzīb courtly painting, like architecture, declined. He discontinued patronage of painters and probably even had some murals defaced Under Shāh Jahān many artists had already become commercial or had shifted to the patronage of local nobles, some of whom, like Āsaf Khān of Lahore, decorated their villas with murals. Under Aurangzīb and his successors the dispersion of artists to local centres, such as Oudh, Hyderabad, Mysore, Bengal, Lucknow, and Patna, continued. These developments, while popularizing painting, brought with them a decline in quality, but as Mogul painting declined, Rajput painting emerged as the leading school in Hindustan (see below).

Muslim Art in Indonesia

For Indonesian art the coming of Islam spelled deterioration. Islamic opposition to sculpture discouraged native talent, and most of the subsequent Indonesian mosques had little distinction. A few, such as those at Medan in Sumatra, were constructed according to the classic Islamic style, but most of the early ones were more like pagodas, with multiple receding roofs, one above the other. The earliest ones did not have minarets. The minaret of the Koudous Mosque in Java, one of the oldest, was a square tower resting on a raised base. Christian conquest brought no greater additions to the artistic accomplishments of the Indonesians.

HINDU AND BUDDHIST ART

Hindu architecture and sculpture

Traditional Hindu art had passed its zenith before 1300, and telling blows were dealt it in the north by the Muslim conquest. Nevertheless, it continued to produce work of outstanding merit in south India. Hindu architecture was characterized by (1) massiveness, (2) a profusion of sculptured ornamentation, (3) bracketed capitals and huge stone beams and lintels, (4) elaborate pillared porches and entrance verandas (*mandapas*), and (5) enormous central towers (*shikharas*), representing the sacred mountains of Hinduism, made of horizontal rows of brick or stone receding inward to reach a peak over the square shrine which housed the god. In the northern style these towers were curvilinear; in the southern or Dravidian style they were in the form of steep, truncated pyramids; and in the Deccan style they were a mixture of the two, employing a barrel roof. In all styles the tower was heavily decorated with sculptured figures and capped with a large knob, or *āmalaka*, and crowned with further symbolic decorations. Before our period the use of the *gopura* had already begun in the south; it was a pyramid-like gate tower in the wall that surrounded a temple—a tower so gigantic that it often overshadowed the central shrine. Many of the southern temples consisted of towering gateways and other accumulations erected between 1300 and 1750 about an inconspicuous shrine of great antiquity.

Under the Vijayanagar Empire, south Indian temples became very elaborate, with pillared halls, pillared pavilions, and pillared subordinate structures, frequently added to old temples. Characteristic additions were the *kalyānamandapa*, an ornate pillared pavilion for the reception of the deity and his consort at the annual celebration of their marriage, and the 'thousand-pillared *mandapa*', a huge hall with rows upon rows of pillars. (Pl. 69a.) The variety and complexity of pillars were perhaps the most striking feature of the Vijayanagar style. Around a pillar's shaft was grouped a vast amount of huge statuary sculptured in the round, the whole carved out of a single block of stone. Often the most conspicuous element of the sculpture would be a furious horse, a rampant hippogryph, or a rearing supernatural animal.[44]

Several now ruined edifices at Vijayanagar City were representative of the style. One of them was the ornate Vitthala (Vishnu) Temple, the major portion of which was constructed in the sixteenth century under Krishnadeva Rāya. (Pl. 70a.) Its most distinctive feature was an immense hall of fifty-six pillars, each twelve feet high and forming a structural group of rearing chargers and fantastic monsters. Facing them was the chariot of the god, with movable wheels, all carved out of a single block of granite. Another representative edifice was the Hazāra Rāma Temple, whose inner walls were decorated in stone relief with scenes from the *Rāmāyana*. Still another was the King's Audience Hall, which had a hundred stone pillars arranged in ten tows of ten each. Elsewhere also—Vellore, Kanchi, or Tādpatri, for example—could be found beautiful reception pavilions, pillars with imaginative groupings of statuary, or exquisitely carved gateways. At Shrīrāngam the Horse-Court of the Ranganātha Temple had a colonnade of fighting chargers, each rearing to a height of about nine feet. (Pl. 69b.)

After the decline of Vijayanagar the Nāyak dynasty of Madura became the chief patrons of the arts, and many of the great surviving shrines of the south were completed during the late sixteenth and the seventeenth century in the so-called Madura style. This style was at the same time a flamboyant extension of the Vijayanagar style and a revival of that of Madura's old Pāndya dynasty. It was illustrated in the temple at Rāmeshvaram, which was laid out on a unitary plan with 3000 feet of pillared corridors. The Nāyaks enlarged the Shrīrāngam temple, already famous for its Horse-Court, increasing its concentric enclosures to seven and thus making its outermost dimensions 2880 feet by 2475; it contained impressive gateway towers, a Hall of a Thousand Pillars, and a golden-domed tower. (Pl. 70b.) The dual temple of Sundareshvara and Mīnākshī at Madura, erected mainly between 1623 and 1659, is perhaps the pre-eminent south Indian temple because of its systematic plan, its Tank of Golden Lilies, and its many-columned corridors, especially its Hall of a Thousand Pillars, whose sculpture is generally regarded as superior to any similar hall's. Its great gateway towers dwarf its central shrines. Outside its walls lies Tirumalai's choultry, a large open hall, the central pillars of which form life-sized statues of the Nāyak kings.

Hindu sculpture, which was done both in relief and in the round, was almost exclusively a feature of temples and public structures. Columns, capitals, cornices, niches, and the outsides of towers were covered with figures, usually of a high sculptural quality, of deities, saints, kings, and animals. During the latter part of our period stucco was used extensively. This sculpture, as well as temple construction, was the work of the superior craftsmen of the Kammālar caste, who claimed equality with the Brahmans. The south Indian bronze (largely copper) work of earlier times also continued. Pieces in the traditional style portrayed Natarāja (the dancing Shiva) and Shivaite saints, Vishnu and Lakshmī, Rāma and the young dancing Krishna, Vishnuite saints, and Kālī and Pārvatī. Life-sized figures of historic characters were also produced, like those of Krishnadeva Rāya and his two wives in the Tirupati Temple. Although highly conventionalized, Hindu sculpture was basically realist, especially in the voluptuousness of the female figures.

Hindu painting

Before the sixteenth century the Hindu tradition of fresco painting and manuscript illumination flourished in various centres. Murals probably often adorned the temples and palaces, but only few, such as the Natarāja frescoes of the Shiva Temple at Ellamānūr, have lasted. The oldest illustrated Jain manuscript of Gujarat is on palm leaf and dates from the thirteenth century, and a number on paper date from the fifteenth century. The most commonly illustrated manuscript was the *Kalpa sūtra*, dealing with the lives of the Jain saints, but a secular *Vasanta Vilāsa*, dated as of 1451, has also survived. These paintings, characterized by calligraphic line and brilliant, jewel-like colouring, preserved an ancient tradition of composition and style without showing any originality, giving elaborate detail and angular forms against a groundwork of red, gold, or yellow clouds (auspicious omens). Individual figures were given a three-quarters profile with long pointed noses and large, protruding eyes.

From the sixteenth to the nineteenth century Hindu painting underwent a renaissance in Rajputana. Under the patronage of Rajput princes, Hindu artists continued the ancient Indian tradition both in murals in the Rajput palaces and in small-scale paintings on paper. Although influenced more and more by Mogul painting as time went on, Rajput art remained distinguishable from that of contemporary artists at the Mogul courts, emphasizing colour rather than line, borrowing the technique and conception of sixth-century Ajantā fresco rather than of miniature, and drawing inspiration primarily from traditional Hindu religion and literature rather than from contemporary court life.[45] Its brilliant reds, yellows, pinks, greens, browns, and purples were relieved by white and velvet blacks (gold appearing only late in Rajput painting). It employed in the background traditional formulas packed with symbolic meaning, such as flowers, trees, plants, birds, animals, hills, moons, clouds, rain, and lightning.

Most of the extant pictures are to be found in albums or sets illustrating some ancient theme. They are generally divided into the Rājasthānī and the Pahārī (Mountain) school. The former flourished in Rajputana and Bundelkhand in the sixteenth century and after; the latter developed in the upper Punjab in the seventeenth century and continued into the nineteenth century. Both schools treated the same basic subjects, among which were: (1) the thirty-six *rāgas* and *rāginīs* (from among the musical modes to be described below) that were associated with seasons, months, days, and hours and depicted emotional situations; (2) the great epics and romances and Rajput chivalry; (3) puranic and tantric texts, especially those relating to Krishna and Rādhā; (4) the 'flavour of love' theme dealing with phases of affection and types of heroes and heroines from classical literature; (5) scenes of popular life; and (6) portraiture emphasizing personality. Both frequently combined realism with romanticism and mysticism, exhibiting *bhakti* qualities, religious eroticism, tender humility, and the sympathetic treatment of animals.

Music and Dance

Music, dance, drama, lyric poetry, and religion were inextricably intertwined in Hindu India. Much of the lyric poetry was meant to be sung; dramas employed singing, music, and dance, many of them in fact being dramatic ballets; and singing, dancing, and dramatic performances were an essential part of religion. Hindu music was highly developed both in theory and practice, both as a fine art and as a folk art. It was melody untouched by harmony, based upon a seven-tone scale with (practically) quarter-tone intervals. The numerous musical *ragas* (musical 'flavours' or melody patterns) were differentiated by their tonic, their flats and sharps, and the number of tones they used (five, six, or seven).

Although singing and the playing of various musical instruments were popular arts, particular castes specialized in professional singing, playing, and dancing. The variety of string, wind, and percussion instruments was large, differing considerably from north to south. Professional singers, musicians, and dancers were employed in many religious and court ceremonies and entertainments, and musicians were patronized by the various temples and rajas.

The early Mogul rulers and various independent sultans, especially those of Bijapur, were generous patrons of musicians, both Islamic and Hindu. The most illustrious singer at the court of Akbar was Miyan Tānsēn, originally a Hindu of Gwalior. He and the other musicians at court developed new varieties of *ragas* and a type of northern music that was a mixture of Hindu and Muslim. This Mogul school of music suffered a setback when Aurangzīb placed a ban on music, but it was not destroyed.

After the decline of Vijayanagar, Tanjore became an active centre of Hindu music and contributed considerably to the development of a style called Carnatic. In the seventeenth century Kshetrayya, under the patronage of the raja of Tanjore, wrote numerous erotic religious songs in Telugu. In the eighteenth century Tyāgarāju of Tanjore, though he shunned kings and courts, is said by some to have been the best of Hindu musicians. He wrote many chaste songs in praise of Rāma in Telugu in the Carnatic style.

The dance, occupying the important place it did in religious, court, and folk affairs in Hindu India, is often depicted in Hindu art. Almost all the leading south Indian temples and rulers employed female dancing troupes. The kings of Vijayanagar had special rooms where royal dancers practiced and performed, and the theory, meaning, and symbolism of the dance and music were set forth in elaborate treatises by Brahman pundits. Dancers normally belonged to a particular caste and were trained from childhood by dancing-masters, who knew both the theory and the practice of the dance. In general, dances told some familiar story from the rich lore of Hinduism, and some (for example the *rāsa mandala*, or circle dance of Krishna) expressed a religious eroticism. They usually required relatively little movement of the lower body (some being performed from a sitting position) but a great variety of symbolic hand and upper-body gestures (*mudrās*). Often the performers sang as they danced, richly clad. They generally wore around their ankles strings of bells which provided part of the accompaniment as they moved their feet in time with the music. Dances were commonly performed to honour some deity, ruler, or other dignitary, and consequently they took place at religious festivals, processions, marriages, births, reunions, the dedication of houses or buildings, and court ceremonies. They also played a prominent part in dramatic performances.

Nepalese, Tibetan, and Singhalese Art

Nepalese and Tibetan art grew out of the late Tantric Buddhist art of Bengal but was influenced, especially in architecture, also by Chinese ideas and techniques. Buildings were generally of stone or brick, but wood was frequently used in Nepal—for example, in the five-storey Bahavāni Temple of Bhatgāon, erected about 1703, rising one storey upon the other to form a pyramid. This temple has a projecting roof, supported by brackets and turned up at the eaves and corners in the Chinese style. Such roofs were common. The eighteenth-century temple of Patan in Nepal combined a brick structure with tiers of sloping roofs and elaborate carved-wood decorations. Another type of religious architecture encountered in Tibet and other Buddhist countries was the stupa, or pagoda; in Nepal and Tibet these tower-shrines generally consisted of a square, high base surmounted by a bulbous dome, which was crowned by a square *harmikā*, out of which rise tiers of telescoped umbrellas culminating in a spire; often the all-seeing eye of the supreme Buddha was depicted upon each of the four sides of the *harmikā*. Probably the most distinctive architectural forms of Tibet are its massive, fortress-like monasteries and palaces with inward sloping walls plastered in various colours. The most familiar of these is the seventeenth-century Potala Palace of the grand lamas at Lhasa, but other imposing monasteries are located in Lhasa and Tashilhunpo.

The justly esteemed banners (*tankas*) of Tibet are painted on cotton, canvas, or, sometimes, silk. The older ones rather rigorously perpetuate the ancient style of Bengal, but later ones, especially those of the eighteenth century, show Chinese influences, particularly in the background landscapes. The banners generally show a central figure, like the popular goddess Tārā, surrounded by many lesser figures. The subjects they depict are almost always religious episodes from the life of Shākyamuni, various Buddhas, bodhisattvas, and Shaktis (often in the nude), fierce and threatening beings, Tibetan saints and lamas, famous places, or Bön (pre-Buddhist) themes. Scenes of nativity, damnation, tantric ritual, sorcery, mysticism, magic, terror, and sexuality are common.[46]

Illuminated manuscripts and wood carvings were produced in both Nepal and Tibet, and the arts of the goldsmith and silversmith were highly developed, but perhaps the finest artistic achievements of the two countries were in bronze and brass. In fantastically bedecked figures, large and small, of the deities (often cast in the form of contorted or elongated nudes) as well as in ritual vessels, incense burners, and replicas of animals and lotuses, skilful and ingenious bronze and iron workers reproduced the style of ancient Buddhist Bengal, giving occasional evidence of borrowing also from China.

Ceylon, although its earlier achievements continued to exert an influence on Burma and to some extent Siam, was ravaged by invasions and internal conflicts throughout most of our period and produced scarcely any works of art worthy of special consideration. The chief artistic remains still stand at Kandy, dating from the late eighteenth century, when wood was used a good deal. The Temple of the Tooth Relic is well known, as are also the temples of Lankātilaka (stone and brick) and Gadalādeniya (partly in stone) near Kandy. Very good wood carvings decorate many of the temples.

Art in Southeast Asia

The artistic achievements of the Buddhist countries of the Indo-Chinese peninsula—Burma, Siam, Cambodia, and Laos—clearly reflected ancient Buddhist and Hindu ideas. This influence was evident in their stupas (which took the form of a bell-shaped dome mounted on a raised platform and from which rose a long spire), in their pyramidal *shikharas*, and in their multiple-tiered temples and monasteries with receding roofs. Local background, taste, and technique tended to develop a relatively distinctive style in each country.

The sack and ultimate abandonment of Angkor in the fourteenth century marked the end of the monumental Khmer style of Cambodia. The last significant production of this glorious tradition was the Shivaite sanctuary of Ishvarapura at Bantéai Srei. It consisted of three shrines and two edifices (probably intended as temple libraries) constructed in the early fourteenth century. Its bas-reliefs in stone and its stone sculpture in the round combined naturalism and grace with archaism; it exhibited such a profusion of decorative elements as to give rise to the expression 'Khmer flamboyant style'. The Buddhist pagodas and sculpture of the new Cambodian capitals at Lovek and Phnom Penh were on a more modest and restrained scale and, although possessed of a beauty and charm of their own, were not among the chief masterpieces. Laotian architecture was influenced by Angkor and Siam. One of its foremost examples was the pyramid-type stupa known as That Luong, built at Vien Chang shortly after 1563.

The classic (Pagan) period of Burmese art ended at the close of the thirteenth century with the Mongol and Shan invasions, and during the ensuing period Burmese art took on a folk character, 'typified at once by exuberance and poverty of expression'.[47] Although numerous royal palaces and religious edifices were built at the capitals of Ava and Pegu and elsewhere, most of the religious buildings were indifferent adaptations of two earlier styles typified by the Mingalazedi Stupa (1274) and the Anānda Temple of Pagan. The former was characterized by a square, high, pyramidal-terraced base (with stairways for access, and small stupas at the corners) on top of which was a large bell-shaped stupa tapering off into a long slender spire. The Anānda Temple, although designed as early as 1090, survives largely as a restoration of our period. It was in the form of a Greek cross; successive receding terraces, developed to a great height, gave it a cubical effect and provided space for numerous chapels and galleries, the central part capped by a golden dome-like pinnacle. The whole had the appearance of a huge white mountain. The gilded Shwedagon Pagoda of Rangoon, probably the most striking stupa of the period, generally conformed to the Mingalazedi type, but its elongated spire made it unique; it was raised to 66 feet about 1362 and to 302 by 1472. The large but simple bell-shaped pagoda of Kaunghmudaw, erected during Thalun's reign (1629–48), has no spire. The Mingun Pagoda, which rises to a height of 140 feet, was begun in the eighteenth century and was planned to reach to about three times its present height.

Brick and mortar but little stone were used in the construction of these edifices. They were abundantly decorated with relief work depicting Jātaka and other Buddhist subjects, and decorative details accumulated as time went on, as did the amount of gold, gilt, lacquer work, and elaborate wood carvings. Wood grew in importance as a building material toward the end of the period. Successive receding stories, with roofs turned up at the eaves and corners in the Chinese manner, became increasingly common.

The classic Thai, or Siamese, art of the Ayut'ia period (1350–1767) grew directly out of the Northern or Burmese style of Chiengmai and the Southern or Mon-Khmer style of Sukhotai of the thirteenth and the early fourteenth century. It also underwent Indian and Ceylonese influences, and as time went on, clear evidences of Chinese ideas appeared. In both architecture and sculpture the classic influence moved in the direction of richness of detail rather than of functional structure.[48] Although stone had been used as a structural material earlier, brick, stucco, and wood (especially in the north) were basic. The famous brick and stucco temple, Wat Chet Yot, near Chiengmai (built shortly after 1292), was a copy of the Mahābodhi (Great Temple) of Pagan (itself a copy of the Mahābodhi Temple of Bodh Gayā in India). It was an impressive pyramid on a high square base topped by a long spire. Other principal Northern-style temples were those of the Standing Buddha (P'ra Yün) at Lamp'ūn, built shortly after 1369, and the Royal Pagoda (P'rajedi Luang) at Chiengmai (completed in 1478), which once housed the famous Emerald Buddha.

The ruins at Sukhotai are numerous. The Great Pagoda (Mahā-Tāt) has a huge standing Buddha and assembly hall (*vihāra*), and the Shri Chum a huge seated Buddha and sculptured reliefs of stories from the Jātakas (c. 1350). The Singhalese-type stupa of the Chāng Lom Temple, with its long needle dome, attributed to Rama Khamheng (c. 1293), is located in nearby Sawank'alōk.

The principal ruin of Ayut'ia today is the temple of Shri Sarap'et, dating from the late fifteenth century. Its numerous bell-shaped *prachedi* (or stupas) are characteristic of the Ayut'ia style, showing greater Burmese and Singhalese than Khmer influence. Their bases were formed of a series of diminishing rings leading to a bell-shaped dome, from which rose a long spire formed by diminishing rings. They were shrines for the ashes of Buddhist holy men and Siamese kings. Ayut'ia's wooden structures employed teak columns covered with lacquer and multiple receding roofs, with slightly turned up, ornamental eaves and gables.

Amid the ruins of Ayut'ia are numerous stucco and bronze Buddhas, of which the giant seated bronze P'ra Mangala Pabitra, perhaps of the sixteenth century, is particularly noteworthy. Stucco was common for reliefs, and sculpture in the round was often done in plaster or bronze. A characteristically Siamese Buddhist figure developed, typified by the arched brows, almond eyes, oval face, sharp hooked nose, and small moulded lips of the Chiengmai figures. In the course of time stylization (emphasized by the flame-shaped topknot) set in: the faces became elongated; the figures grew stiffer and more formless; and the bodies were covered with meaningless draperies, often heavily bedecked with gold relief in imitation of embroidery.

Other vestiges of the Siamese art of the period likewise testify to its 'distinction and delicacy'. A few frescoes depicting Jātaka scenes, apparently produced during the Ayut'ia period, and some illustrated manuscripts and temple banners have survived. For a time porcelains, manufactured according to an imported Chinese technique, were produced at Sawank'alōk. In general, Siamese art was less original than that of the Kmer school. It was 'a belated flower of Buddhist art', but it had 'a fragrance of its own, . . . a supremely civilized fragrance'.[49]

Hindu and Buddhist Art in Indonesia

In Indonesia, Hindu and Buddhist art continued during the Majapahit period but showed a growing independence from Indian models and a corresponding reliance upon purely native ideas. It, too, was more ornamental than structural. The Buddhist shrine of Candi Jābung (c. 1354) and the Shivaite temple complex of Panataram (built largely between 1320 and 1370) must be counted among the superior monuments of the period. The former (a circular tower, unique in Java) stood on a high, rectangular, terraced base. The latter consisted of a group of unrelated structures built to house the ashes of the royal family. They were usually in the form of a square, terraced pyramid, supported on a high, square, and narrow base, which was decorated with relief sculpture. Though the sculptors derived their subjects from the *Rāmāyana*, their sculpture and the masks over the doorways were Indonesian in form, showing clear relationship to the puppets of the *wayang* plays. High gateways were also in evidence. This style, modified in various ways, was continued after the decline of Majapahit in Bali, where the Pura ye Ganga Temple, dating from the fourteenth and fifteenth centuries, follows the Panataram style. Later shrines were surrounded by walls with high, pyramid gateways, and the pyramid-pagoda temples were decorated with sculptures of fantastic forms in high relief. As previously remarked, Islam and Christianity brought deterioration rather than betterment to Indonesian art.

Music, Dance, and Ornament in Southeast Asia

Music and the dance were highly regarded throughout Southeast Asia. As in India, they were closely associated with religion and poetry and formed a part of most dramatic performances. Indian influence was everywhere evident, although local history and tradition gave distinctiveness to the music and dances of the several countries. Singing, dancing, and the playing of musical instruments were popular arts, but they reached their highest form in the work of professionals. Strolling bands of musicians and dancers were common, but noble or wealthy families often maintained their own troupes, and musicians, singers, and dancers were patronized by the kings. The royal ballets of Siam, Cambodia, and Java enjoyed a high repute, as did also the village dance troupes of Bali. The themes of their performance were traditional. The music included love-songs, ballads, boat-songs, lullabies, heroic songs commemorating exploits human and divine, and religious chants. The dances fell into two main categories, classic and popular. Popular dances were generally of folk origin, classic dances of Indian origin. The classic dances were usually religious in nature, performed by professional female dancers in gorgeous costumes with symbolic gestures and movements.

Personal adornment in Ceylon, Burma, and Siam was spectacular even though steadfastly traditional. Multiple strings of turquoise or amber beads and pierced pearls were used as necklaces, armlets, and anklets or draped over clothes and turbans. Gold and silver rings set with rubies, sapphires, emeralds diamonds, and pearls were worn in abundance. Turban pieces were enamelled or set with precious stones. The widespread fondness for jewellery in southern Asia resulted in great quantities of sham jewellery and mass-produced trinkets in brass and lesser materials.

*   *   *

We shall deal below with Buddhist art in China, Japan, Vietnam, and Korea.

THE ARTS IN CHINA, VIETNAM, AND KOREA

Although China's art of our period cannot be considered the greatest in her history, much of it was of high quality, and the quantity that survives vastly exceeds that for earlier and more illustrious periods. Chinese music has been treated in Chapter X and XI in connection with Chinese drama and will be so treated again below (in conjunction with Japanese music). China's sculptural products (except for ceramic figures) was of little consequence, being few in number and lacking in inspiration and technical perfection. Bronze work and jade and ivory carving were of a high technical proficiency but consciously archaic and imitative. Many architectural remains date from this period, but they were generally imitative of earlier styles, although they possessed a majestic dignity and symmetrical beauty that reflected the power and pomp of the imperial dynasties. Except in the fourteenth century (Yüan period) painters were likewise essentially imitative, although the quality of their work was high and the quantity enormous. Decadence in sculpture and imitativeness in architecture and painting were undoubtedly aggravated by the dominance during the Ming and Ch'ing periods of backward-looking, rationalistic Neo-Confucianism and by a consequent decline in the inspiration provided by the emotionalism, spiritualism, and mysticism of Buddhism and Taoism.

Some artistic achievements of the age, however, are more than imitative of traditional styles. The artists of the Yüan period at least made it one of significant creative painting. Lacquered ware and porcelain reached their apex before 1775. Textiles also attained a high artistic level. Just as sculpture was the great achievement of the pre-T'ang and early T'ang periods, and painting of the T'ang, Sung, and Yüan dynasties, so porcelain was that of the Ming and early Manchu periods; imperial patronage contributed to the perfection of the ceramic arts. And out of painting and printing came, in the sixteenth and seventeenth centuries, the popular art of the colour-print. The expansion of trade and the consequent rise of larger mercantile and artisan classes with money to spend for simple luxuries contributed to the improvement of lacquered ware, porcelain, textiles, and colour-prints. In those arts, moreover, Confucian traditionalism exerted less restraining influence.

Architecture in China

Except for the pagoda, most Chinese architecture was an extension of domestic architecture, consisting essentially of courtyards formed by detached halls. Their sloping, concave, tile roofs, often two in number in public buildings, were held up by wooden pillars, with walls filled in by panelling and brickwork. The structures of our period were numerous—domestic buildings, imperial palaces and tombs, ancestral and Confucian temples, official buildings in provincial, prefectural, and district cities, Buddhist and Taoist temples and monasteries, pagodas, relatively open rectangular, round, or polygonal pavilions in numerous gardens, memorial arches, walls, towers, bridges. The vast majority of the buildings were of comparatively light wood-and-brick construction, but stone and brick were used for the more massive edifices.

Two styles of architecture prevailed—the northern and the southern. The northern style may be distinguished from the southern by the degree of roof curvature and the amount of ornamentation on roof ridges, eaves, and pillars. In the simpler northern style, which was dominant, curvature was not extensive and ornamentation was limited. In the southern style (which was not, however, confined to the south), curvature was prolonged until the eaves turned up like horns at the corners, and carving and ornamentation were so profuse as to obscure the line of the roof.

City plans were also distinguishable, perhaps because of the varying nature of the terrain, the relative value of land, and differing defensive needs. Northern cities tended to be more symmetrical and spacious and, because invaders came from the north, were surrounded by higher and more massive walls. Most extant walls date from this period. They were made of clay and faced with brick and were narrower at the top than at the bottom. Storied, pagoda-like watch towers rose at their corners and over their gates. Broad avenues extended across the city from gate to opposite gate. At their intersections in the centre of the city rose three-storied 'drum towers', from which movement through the city was controlled and drums announced the passage of the hours. The walls and gate towers of Sian and Peking are justly admired, but all of north China, especially Shansi province, was dotted with similar walls and gate towers. Much of the Great Wall, as it now stands, with its massive gates and impressive towers, was either constructed anew or rebuilt during the Ming dynasty.

Perhaps the finest edifices of the period were the imperial palaces and temples of the Peking area and the Ming and Ch'ing tombs outside Nanking and Peking. The construction of the present city of Peking, on the remains of the celebrated Mongol capital of Khanbalak (Cambaluc) and earlier cities, was begun by the Yung-lo emperor (1403–24), who gave it its permanent form and character. It consisted essentially of three almost square walled cities, one outside the other, to the south of which another rectangular walled city ultimately developed. The innermost city, the Purple Forbidden City, defended by crenellated walls and a wide moat, contained the ceremonial halls, government offices, and imperial residential quarters, the public buildings separated from the residential quarters by walls. Next came the Imperial City, which housed officials and members of the imperial clans. The outer city was available to others. The basic pattern was similar to earlier Chinese capital cities, and the official buildings also followed tradition, being arranged symmetrically in a series of spacious courts.[50] Designed upon a monumental, although somewhat monotonous, plan for business and ceremonial purposes, they have seldom failed to impress visitors with their dignity, grace, and grandeur.

Most of the large official halls were two-roofed, wooden structures in the northern style, often built on high brick platforms. Following the distinctive Ming style of the fifteenth century, the lower roof was small and the upper roof extended downward in sweeping curves from the ridge on each of the four sides of the building (hipped roof). In later-Ming and Ch'ing structures the lower roof became larger, the upper diminished in importance, the space between the roofs became greater, and, in keeping with an earlier style, only the front and the rear of the upper roof continued uninterrupted to the eaves, while the sides were gable-ended. By the eighteenth century Chinese architecture had become conspicuously ornamental. Porticos, carved pillars and panelling, and marble terraces, staircases, and balustrades added decorativeness, and brilliant paint lent colourfulness, but a building's crowning glory was the yellow, blue, and green of its enamelled-tile roof. Yellow was reserved for the emperor.

Peking is a veritable sea of public monuments and edifices.[51] Most of the palace buildings have been restored or rebuilt (generally on the original plan) during the centuries, but the Chih-hua Temple, built in 1444, still clearly illustrates the early Ming style. The famous Wu-men, or south gate, of the Forbidden City (rebuilt in 1647) is topped with an imposing pavilion. The main ceremonial Hall of Supreme Harmony (T'ai-ho-tien, 1627), raised on three white marble terraces, contains the imperial throne. The personal palace of the emperor is the Palace of Cloudless Heaven (Ch'ien-ch'eng-kung), destroyed by fire in 1514 and rebuilt several times. The three last-named structures show the stately hipped-roof style at its best, while the Hall of Classics illustrates the eighteenth-century Ch'ien-lung style. The three-storied Drum Tower, built originally in 1273, was subsequently reconstructed. The tomb of the Yung-lo emperor, northwest of Peking, and those of K'ang-hsi, Yung-cheng, and Ch'ien-lung outside Peking are splendid examples of the tomb temples. The pavilions, galleries, temples, and pagodas around the lake in the Imperial City and at the celebrated Summer Palace outside Peking, built during the seventeenth and eighteenth centuries, were less formal buildings, well adapted to the gardens of China. Modified French styles, introduced by Jesuit architects, were evident in several Summer Palace buildings.[52]

A number of religious structures complement the majesty of Peking's civil edifices. The imperial Altar of Heaven and Temple of Agriculture in the southern city of Peking date from the Yung-lo period but were later reconstructed. Both were circular, three-level structures in white marble. The three-terraced Altar was open-topped, but the round three-storied Temple rising from the centre of the third terrace has three blue-tile roofs. The Monastery of Glory and Happiness dates from the 1450's, and the Taoist Palace of Shining Light from 1557.

There are renowned masonry structures elsewhere, mainly of Buddhist origin. The K'ai-yüan Monastery at Ch'üan-chou (1389) has unique caryatids. The Iron Pagoda of Kaifeng (completed in 1383) is a fabulous thirteen-storey polygon faced with enamelled bricks. The Monastery of the Five Towers (Wu-t'ai) was built outside Peking between 1465 and 1488, the Green Jade Cloud Monastery west of Peking between 1520 and 1580, and the great white Dagoba, a Tibetan-type stupa, in 1652. Various Tibetan-type structures were put up at the Manchu summer palace in Jehol, one in frank imitation of the Potala.

Painting in China

China's paintings, mostly on scrolls or screens, gained a three-dimensional illusion of space without the Western device of converging lines. Objects were painted in relative positions to the right or the left of a primary viewpoint or above or below it, leaving the objects isolated and independent. The Chinese artist thereby succeeded in creating an effective impression of wide landscape and panoramic view.

Chinese monochrome ink painting reached its highest point during the fourteenth century. Yüan artists perfected the old techniques and forms, giving painstaking attention to the quality of ink, brush strokes, and drawing, and combining realism with freedom of expression. They also revived the use of colour, thereby not only promoting the trend toward realism but also adding new life to painting, and linked calligraphy with painting more closely than ever before. Most of the Yüan masters, while eschewing the extreme impressionism of their predecessors, the Southern Sung painters, succeeded in recapturing their predecessors' spirit.

The painting of bamboos, plum blossoms, and horses now reached its highest level. Chao Meng-fu (1254–1322) was one of the best-known court painters. Although he continued the traditions of the Sung Academy, he used new techniques to great advantage and became the founder of a school of realistic horse-and-warrior painting. He stood out also for his calligraphy, landscapes, flowers, and bamboos. (Pl. 71a.) Another court painter, Yen Hui, was noted for his hermits and Buddhist figures. The majority of the great fourteenth-century painters, however, were gifted amateurs, men of wealth and learning who painted for themselves and friends and not for the Mongol conquerors. Among them were the so-called Four Masters: Huang Kung-wang (1269–1354), who became a Taoist recluse; a grandson of Chao, Wang Meng (d. 1385), esteemed for his waterfalls, peaks, temples, and pine trees; Wu Chen (d. c. 1354), a Taoist poet and calligrapher, prominent for his bamboo and fishermen; and the best of them, Ni Tsan (1301–74), of Wu-hsi near Soochow. Ni Tsan's simple compositions had power and austerity; by depicting a few trees or flowers, a hut, some hills, and a stretch of water he created landscapes that no one else could successfully copy. (Pl. 71b.) Ni Tsan was a master painter of plum blossoms, as was also Wang Mien. The best of all the painters of bamboo was Li K'an.

The artists of the Ming period for the most part returned to the past and copied old masters. Nevertheless, they produced pictures of marked technical proficiency, elegance, and grace, often much enlivened by colour. The Ming emperors, zealous patrons of the arts, maintained court painters, and the Hsuan-te emperor (1425–35) was himself a painter of some ability. The leading artists of this period too were gifted amateurs, the so-called 'literary-men painters'. They copied the masterpieces of earlier generations and were more interested in the history, theory, and collection of art than in original creation.[53] Among the more famous collectors were Hsiang Yüan-pien (1525–90) and Liang Ch'eng-piao (1620–91). Collection promoted the appearance of art criticism, such as *The Treatise on the Paintings and Writings of the Ten Bamboo Studies* (1633), and induced professional artists to cater to the tastes of the wealthy. The mutual interest of collector and artist contributed to the development of the colour-print (see below).

Three schools of painting may be distinguished during the Ming period: (1) a school of bird and flower painters, represented by Lü Chi (fl. 1488–1505) and some landscape painters who followed the Northern Sung Academy (Pl. 72a); (2) the Che school, which followed the impressionistic black-and-white landscapes of Ma Yüan and Hsia Kuei and other traditions of the Southern Sung Academy and was at its best in the works of Tai Chin (fl. 1430–50) and Wu Wei (1459–1508); and (3) the Wu, or Southern school, of the Soochow area, which followed the traditions of the tenth century and the Four Masters of the Yüan period but was notable for use of colour, free expression, and eclecticism.

The Wu school proved to be the most influential of the three. It was founded by the landscape painter Shen Chou (1427–1509), probably the outstanding Ming painter. (Pl. 72b.) He made a striking use of colours—blues, greyish-greens, and reddish tans—but subordinated them to brushwork in his compositions. Others associated with this school were Wen Pi (1470–1559), T'ang Yin, and Ch'iu Ying, painters of landscapes, court scenes, portraits, and pictures centred on women. With Tung Ch'i-ch'ang (1555–1636), who had a telling influence on late Ming and Ch'ing painting, the Wu school became increasingly academic and abstract. He insisted that a landscape painting could not and should not compete with nature but should rather express a landscape's inner realities, which could best be found by analysis of the masters of the past.

Most Ch'ing painters continued the academic tradition of the Wu school. They used a good deal of colour and developed the 'boneless style'—wash without line—in their landscapes, but their compositions lacked originality. The four Wangs, Wu Li (1632–1718), a landscape painter who was a convert to Christianity, and Yün Shou-p'ing, the last eminent flower painter, were generally considered the most gifted of these academic painters. The works of these six became increasingly uniform. Wang Hui (1632–1717), probably the most able of them, painted his own versions of many old masters. (Pl. 73a.)

For all that, several artists of the seventeenth century remained rather independent. Ch'en Hung-shou painted Taoist fairies, elongated women, and illustrations for wood-block prints (Pl. 73b), and Kung Hsien produced blasted and devastated landscapes. Three Buddhist monks—Chu Ta, K'un-ts'an, and Tao-chi (or Shih-ta'o)—were more original; and one of these three, Tao-chi (1630–1707), was probably unsurpassed by any other Ch'ing painter. (Pl. 74a.) Chu Ta's animals appeared to be sullen or enraged; K'un-ts'an's landscapes were sombre; Tao-chi's landscapes were more realistic than those of his contemporaries. Insisting that the spirit but not the style of the ancients should be followed, Tao-chi attacked tradition, emphasizing individualism and originality. 'I paint in my own style,' he said.54 He used colour or ink alone in some pictures and combinations of ink and colour in others.

The Wu tradition continued in the eighteenth century. Father Giuseppi Castiglione (Lang Shih-ning) and other Western court painters introduced a blend of Western naturalism and perspective with pseudo-Chinese techniques (Pl. 74b), but the Wu tradition was only slightly varied thereby; on the whole, Western painting had no appreciable influence on Chinese painters. Figure paintings, portraits, and court scenes became increasingly conspicuous in the Ch'ing period, which was noteworthy also for its collections and its art criticism. Art precepts and theories were set forth in the famous *Mustard Seed Garden Painting Manual* (*Chieh-tzu yüan-hua chuan*), a work by many hands, which reached its final form between 1679 and 1701. An *Imperial Encyclopaedia of Calligraphy and Painting* was begun in 1705. The first part of a *Catalogue of the Imperial Collections* (*Shih ch'ü pao chi*) was completed in 1745. The Ch'ing emperors were not, however, the most competent of art critics, and they often failed to make the best choice of court painters or of collection items.

The most original developments in painting after the creative Yüan period came in the decoration of porcelain and lacquered ware and in colour-prints. These developments reflected a growing commercialism, although colour-prints, despite their Chinese origins, were not popularized to the same extent as in Japan (see below). Wood-block prints in black and white came into use during the Ming period to illustrate books, novels, tales, and scientific works, and as colour technique improved, artists of reputation took more and more to drawing for woodcut illustrations. Ting Yün-p'eng's illustrations in the *Ch'eng shih mo yüan*, printed in 1606, are the oldest known Chinese colour-prints. The technique was perfected in the work of art criticism mentioned above, *The Treatise on ... the Ten Bamboo Studios* (1633), and thereafter various independent albums of colour-prints appeared. Ch'en Hung-shou, who was actively engaged in this kind of work, did the illustrations for a famous novel (*Shui hu chüan*). The art of colour-print mounted in importance in the eighteenth century.

Sculpture in China

Chinese sculpture, when not relief, was carved or cast on the assumption that it would be seen from a primary view or a limited number of views, and it was sculpturally indifferent to the surrounding space. Except for jade, ivory, and wood carvings and the sculpturesque porcelains of Fukien, the only significant Chinese sculptures of this period were the stiff, colossal stone warriors, officials, elephants, camels, and other animals at the Ming tombs near Nanking and Peking, some reliefs in the marble terraces at Peking, and the relief work on the Kü-yung Gate in the Great Wall near Nan-k'ou (1345). The colossal, free-standing statues of animals and men flanking the avenue to the tomb of the Hung-wu emperor, the founder of the Ming dynasty (d. 1398), are rigidly adjusted to the four sides of the original stone slab.

Ceramics in China

Chinese ceramics, the oldest continuous art tradition in the world, was perhaps also the most influential of all Far Eastern arts. During the T'ang and Sung periods the shapes of various types of vessels had been dignified and well-proportioned, and the variety of textures and colours in glaze had been unparalleled. Craftsmen of the Ming period produced some excellent pottery along these traditional lines, but otherwise Ming pottery was predominantly massive, simple in shape, and often broad and vigorous in decorative motif. It was frequently glazed, like Sung pottery, with a single, strong colour such as turquoise blue, dark violet, or yellow, but other prominent types were the 'three-colour vase' and the 'five-colour ware', emphasizing the sustained leaning of Chinese potters toward polychromy. Fine threads of clay standing out in relief framed the various colour areas.

The major development in pottery-making during the Ming period was a change of emphasis from the traditional stoneware to porcelain. Porcelain is produced from a clay that fires to a harder and finer consistency and results in a homogeneous, vitreous pottery. Although porcelain had been known in China since the T'ang period, it had advanced farther in Persia (see Chapter XIII), and the arrival of Persian potters at the Mongol court appears to have stimulated its manufacture among the Chinese.

Particularly good clay for porcelain was found at this time at Ching-te-chen in Kiangsi. The methods of ceramic production were crude and uncertain, but the many craftsmen who participated in them—sculptor, painter, chemist, and factory administrator—were highly organized, and each was specialized in a particular phase of the lengthy process. The translucent porcelain was first coated with a colourless glaze and then, with lead-silicate enamels, decorated in designs similar to those used on silk brocades. Monochrome Sung ware was imitated during the Yüan and much of the Ming period, but its popularity, except perhaps for the celadons, gradually declined as Ching-te-chen wares gained favour.

Under the patronage of the Ming and Ch'ing emperors Ching-te-chen became the greatest porcelain centre in China, operating an imperial porcelain factory and many private establishments besides. The basis of most of its pottery was white porcelain, but it produced a number of fine monochromes (sacrificial red, blue, turquoise, celadon, lustrous black, brown, and the famed egg-shell white of the Yung-lo period) and was distinguished during the Ming period for its blue-and-whites, tri-colours, and multi-coloured enamels. The blue-and-white ware, made by painting designs in cobalt blue on the biscuit before the glaze was applied, was outstanding during the Hsüan-te (1426–35), Cheng-te (1506–21), and Chia-ching (1522–66) periods because of a superior 'Mohammedan blue' imported from the Near East, but other colours such as green, red, and yellow were also sometimes used. The so-called 'three-colour wares' came in fact in more than three colours—dark violet, turquoise, aubergine purple, yellow, and neutral white.[55] Multicoloured enamels were formed by painting designs in liquefied coloured glass on the glaze and fixing them with a light firing. During the Wan-li period (1573–1619) enamel work on top of blue and white became especially popular as 'Wan-li polychrome'.

From China, the art of porcelain-making spread to various parts of the Far East and the Western world. After 1600 the English and the Dutch began to import Chinese porcelain. From the sixteenth century on, royal collections were common in Europe, sometimes including thousands of pieces, and by the end of the seventeenth century every house of any pretensions displayed its 'chinaware'. Chinese pottery specifically designed to please European tastes was staple in a lucrative trade that lasted into the nineteenth century. During the late-Ming and the Ch'ing period several kinds of porcelains were manufactured largely for the export market—the milk-white ware (blanc de Chine) of Te-hua, Fukien, eminent for its sculpturesque figures; the red, buff, and grey stoneware of Yi-hsing, Kiangsu, whose red tea ware influenced European pottery; the colour-glazed stoneware of Shekwan, near Canton. During the Ch'ing period Ching-te-chen porcelain was often decorated and enamelled at Canton for the European market. Chinese designs were traditionally of a floral nature; lotuses, peonies, peach blossoms, and pine trees served as setting for cranes, peacocks, tortoises, and smaller birds or for dragons, the Eight Immortals, the Eight Precious Things of Buddhism, or willowy women. As the export trade grew, however, the traditional Chinese jars, bottles, vases, and bowls were modified to meet the Western taste for tea-cups, saucers, plates, and the like.

After the disorders accompanying the fall of the Ming dynasty subsided, the Ch'ing emperors became lavish promoters of the Ching-te-chen porcelains, while Western demands for Chinese porcelains mounted. According to Father d'Entrecolles, who wrote from Ching-te-chen in 1712 and 1722 (probably with some exaggeration), it possessed about 3000 furnaces maintained by a community of nearly a million people. The industry involved almost an assembly-line technique, different workers specializing in different aspects of manufacture and decoration.

Able men placed in charge of the imperial kilns at Ching-te-chen developed new techniques and ingenious forms, designs, and colours to please their imperial masters. Ts'ang Ying-hsüan was in charge after 1682, and T'ang Ying, who left several treatises on porcelain manufacture, was the guiding light from 1728 until 1749. The K'ang-hsi period (1662–1722) was noted for its blue-and-white ware (featuring a sapphire blue), its sleek and transparent tri-colour glazes (in green, yellow, and aubergine), and its enamelled ware in soft, vivid greens (*famille verte*) and lustrous blacks (*famille noire*) supported by yellow, coral red, aubergine, and violet. Many of the enamels were painted directly on the unglazed biscuit. Among its more famous monochromes were various reds, peach-blossom pinks, powder-blues, pale lavenders, Mazarin blues, apple greens, and crackled mustard yellows. During the Ch'ien-lung

CC*

period (1736–95) new coloured enamels were elaborated—among them, the various rose colours (*famille rose*), decorated with delicate, effeminate, miniature-like designs. In monochromes new colours were tea-dust, iron-rust, and bronze. Metals, shells, birds' eggs, grained wood, jade, and ivory were accurately copied. Ingenious forms and intricate lace-work and rice-grain designs were also fashioned. By this time Chinese ceramics had reached its summit of technical perfection, but it had already begun to decline as art: 'At its best the decoration is more ingenious than original, and more pretty than artistic.'[56]

Other Decorative Arts in China

During this period some other Chinese decorative arts, such as cloisonné, silk weaving, and carpet making, likewise attained unprecedented heights. If the extensive decorative repertory of China is one of the most stable in the world, its stability perhaps results from the specific nature of the meanings associated with specific motifs. The plant, animal, bird, and human forms that comprise the greater part of the Chinese repertory were in most instances symbols associated with the emperor or with Buddhist or Taoist beliefs. Some motifs embody several references, and not only the representational motifs but also the relatively abstract ones were meaningful. The symbolic character of Chinese ornament probably contributed to the stabilizing of motifs in a readily identifiable form and certainly restricted their use and governed the way in which they were combined. Chinese motifs are generally asymmetrical and irregular in silhouette and rhythmically linear in form, with little suggestion of the sculptural relief or tectonic stability which at times characterized European ornament.

During the Ming and Ch'ing periods, the decorators of textiles, as well as of pottery, frequently imitated paintings. The basically calligraphic nature of Chinese painting and the relatively episodic treatment of space was not disturbing to the surfaces and shapes of the decorated objects in the way that the light modelled figures and the deep homogeneous space of European painting was. The ground colour was usually maintained in Chinese ornament as a continuous surface on which isolated motifs float like vignettes. None of the arts of China was under the pressure of style changes comparable to those of Europe, and for that reason artists had time to elaborate and refine the traditional techniques, motifs, and arrangements of the decorative arts. During the Ming and particularly the Ch'ing period, they frequently became virtuosos producing *tours de force* unequalled in previous eras.

Luxury in articles of ceremonial or daily use, demanded and supplied in the Sung period beyond anything known in contemporary Europe, continued to be supplied by Ming and Ch'ing craftsmen. After the mid-thirteenth century China produced rugs, for example, that though not so firm as those of Persia, were admired for the especially fine sheen of the long, soft yarn of wool, silk, and camels' hair used for the pile. Unusual geometric shapes in yellow, blue, and red with golden and reddish tans predominating in the ground are characteristic of Chinese rugs. Ming craftsmen (and their contemporaries in Japan) embroidered multicoloured floral designs on ceremonial and ritual robes which are among the finest examples of this art. Ming goldsmiths, among the most accomplished in China's long history, made delicate and elaborate pieces in foliate, floral, animal, or fantastic forms. Chinese filigree silver was equal to any. Precious stones were not faceted as they were in Europe but cut *en cabochon*, or in a rounded form, and strings of jewels were frequently interspersed with plaques of carved jade to form necklaces. Chinese craftsmen continued to make traditional ceremonial vessels, although Ming bronzes are not now so highly regarded as the earlier work on which they were modelled.

Champlevé and painted enamel processes were known to Chinese (and other Asian) craftsmen, and they also developed the technique of cloisonné. In the making of cloisonné, small cells are formed by soldering thin, flat wire on a copper surface and then are filled with enamel powder or paste, which then is fired. Chinese cloisonné was brought to a point of unparalleled refinement by Ming craftsmen, who frequently designed on a dark-blue ground. In Japan, where the technique was introduced only in the seventeenth century, a dark-green background was preferred; and at Jaipur, Pertubghur, and Ratan in India, an opalescent effect was gained from a gold ground.

Art in Vietnam

The art of Vietnam, like other elements of its civilization reflected its close cultural relationship with China. It added something, however, to what it borrowed, and the resulting product had a distinctly national character. The chief Vietnamese achievements were in the field of architecture. Buddhist pagodas and monasteries, Confucian temples, civil buildings, and tombs were constructed of wood. In general, the buildings of Hanoi, Hué, and the few other cities that were among the architectural centres reflected the southern (the more ornate) Chinese style. Perhaps the finest architectural monument was the Confucian temple complex at Hanoi. A good deal of wood carving was fashioned, but painting seems to have been little developed.

Art in Korea

Korea likewise borrowed from China but gave its borrowings a national character. Korea has a long and imposing art history, and during the Yi dynasty (1392–1910), its achievements in architecture, painting, and ceramics were in accord with its tradition. The dominance of Confucianism discouraged Buddhist sculpture and the erection of elaborate monasteries and pagodas. The Floating Stone Monastery (Pu-sŏk-sa) near Yŏngtju (*c.* 1350) contained some noteworthy mural paintings and was a good example of the wood-style monasteries of Korea, generally constructed in scenic, out of-the-way places. One of the few wooden pagodas was the five-storied Pŏp-tju-sa at Chung-chŏngto (fifteenth century). Of the many stone pagodas the square, marble edifices at Songto and Seoul (each of ten stories counting the three-storey base) were striking examples.

The most laudable achievements of the period, however, were neither monasteries nor pagodas but Confucian temples, royal palaces, and city walls. Generally they followed the northern style of China in their pavilions, two-storied halls, colonnades, gates, and towers. The two-storied, hipped-roof pavilion on the East Gate of Seoul, first built in 1392, was an august and stately structure, while the dignified Confucian temple of Seoul, constructed immediately after the founding of the Yi dynasty and rebuilt in 1601, served as a model on a more splendid scale for many structures in other towns. Within a century of the founding of the dynasty, three royal palaces were constructed at Seoul, upon designs similar to, though less elaborate than, those of Peking. These and many other wooden buildings were destroyed during Hideyoshi's invasion of 1593, but two of them were reconstructed during the seventeenth century. The king's private apartments, the gardens, and the majestic two-storied throne-room of the reconstructed Palace of Ample Virtue (Chang-tŏk-kung) are especially striking.

A large number of gifted artists of the Yi period reflected the trend toward painting in ink and colour. The panels and walls, both inside and outside, of Buddhist temples and monasteries were decorated with Buddhist paintings, and Confucian scholars promoted the Chinese ideal of the literary-man's painting. Wood-block engraving in black and white also engaged some able artists. Pottery and porcelain reached a lofty standard before the invasion of Hideyoshi, when many Korean potters were taken to Japan.

THE ARTS IN JAPAN

Upon casual examination, most Japanese art seems to reveal an enormous indebtedness to China. Yet careful study shows how non-Chinese or, better, how Japanese it is. Although the Japanese have borrowed many of their basic artistic forms, concepts, and techniques from China, they have always altered them in spirit or execution to conform to their own esthetic ideals. In general, Japanese artistic products give the impression of being somewhat more delicate and ornate, somewhat less vast and sublime in conception, than Chinese.

Our period, which covers that part of the feudal epoch which extends from the decline of the Kamakura Shogunate to the beginning of the decline of the Tokugawa Shogunate, was an era of significant productivity. Japanese paint-ing reached its highest plane, the plebeian colour-print rose to prominence, the Japanese garden became famous, Japanese porcelain acquired an independent character, and although religious architecture declined, military and civil architecture burgeoned. During the early part of the epoch the martial spirit dominated, exerting a profound influence on native Japanese art, while intuitive Zen Buddhism arose and spread, introducing Chinese architecture and the impressionistic landscape-painting of the Sung dynasty. Later Japanese art was deeply affected by the middle-class culture that emerged during 'the great peace' inaugurated by the Tokugawas.

Architecture

At the beginning of our period Japanese architects built temples in a native style, predominantly in wood. That style had developed during the Heian period (794–1185) by adaptations of Chinese models. When the Sung Chinese architecture was introduced by Zen Buddhism, it differed from the native style in its general lay-out, in the shape of its pillars, brackets, eaves, doors, and windows, and in its either plain or simple coloured interiors. In general, the Japanese gables of our period are considered to have been much more artistically handled than the Chinese. Thatch was often used instead of tile for roofing.

Zen monasteries were arranged after the Chinese manner in a series of courts facing the main gate to the south. (Fig. 5.) The main halls (Buddha hall, preaching hall, residential halls, etc.), one behind the other, formed the north and south sides of the courts; the lesser halls, belfry, sutra depository, meditation quarters, bath house, and toilet formed the other sides. Inside the main gate came a pond with a stone bridge over it, and then a two-storied gate in front of the first of the main halls. The chief surviving example of the Zen-Chinese style is the two-storied Shari-den of the Engaku-ji Monastery of Kamakura (1282).

In the early fourteenth century appeared a third style, a single-storey (setchūyō) hybrid of the other two styles. The main temple of the Kwanshin-ji, Osaka Prefecture, an early Ashikaga structure, is one of its most impressive examples. Low proportions, verandas, graceful curves, and tastefully decorated gables impart to this temple an air of simple dignity. (Pl. 75a.)

During the Ashikaga (or Muromachi) period (1334–1573), when Kyoto, the traditional cultural centre, was once again the political seat of the shoguns, numerous monasteries were built in all three styles, but the Zen-Chinese was perhaps the most common. It was adapted for the three-storied, octagonal pagoda of the Anraku-ji Monastery of Bessho, Nagano Prefecture, and for the Main Hall (1314) of the Eihō-ji Monastery at Tajimi near Nagoya.

In its earlier stages military architecture meant wooden stockades and ramparts, solid gates, and substantial quarters for the guards. The residence of the lord inside the stockade was at first built in a luxurious fashion imitative of the imperial residences at Kyoto, but during the Ashikaga period, in keeping with the rusticity and simplicity of the tea-cult (see below), a more simple yet elegant residential architecture, called the shoin-zukuri (study-style), emerged.

FIG. 5. Plan of the Zen Monasteries at Tojoku-ji Temple, Kyoto.

It used sliding panels or screen partitions, decorated with paintings, as walls, the upper part of the outside panels being covered with transparent paper to let in light. (Pl. 75b.) One of its basic features was a low, elevated room (*jōdan-no-ma*) with an alcove (for flowers, incense burner, and a painting), ornamental shelves, and a desk ledge. This room was designed to open up so as to become essentially a part of the garden and thus appropriate for guests, ceremonials, and receptions.

Much elaborated, study-style architecture became the palatial architecture of the nobles of the Momoyama and Tokugawa periods and the prototype for later residential architecture. Another earlier development in residential architecture also reached its culmination in the Momoyama period. That was the *chaseki*, or tea-ceremony room or building. It usually was plain, yet refined, but at times elegant.

The two pre-eminent civil buildings of Kyoto during the Ashikaga period embodied most of the architectural trends of the time. The Golden Pavilion (built *c.* 1397, burned down in 1950, reconstructed in 1955), had three stories, a hipped roof, and a veranda and overlooked a pond in a magnificent garden. (Pl. 75c.) The lowest storey contained living rooms in the old residential style, the second was in a mixed style, and the third was a Zen-styled single room, decorated in gold leaf. The Silver Pavilion (1480) also had a veranda and overlooked a pond in a magnificent garden, but it was two-storied and square and not so ornate, reflecting the simplicity of the tea-cult. The lower storey was in the new study-style architecture, while the second, in the Zen style, was lacquered inside and out and was intended to be overlaid in silver leaf. It was used at first as a retiring place and art treasury by the shogun, but both buildings ultimately became Buddhist temples.

The Momoyama period (1574–1614) is the time of the three great military leaders Nobunaga, Hideyoshi, and Ieyasu. Under Hideyoshi military and civil architecture prevailed over monastic architecture, bringing a flamboyance, gorgeousness of colour, and grandiosity of design that reflected his personality and the expansive mood of the military. Momoyama architecture was characterized by massive castles surrounded by deep moats and stone walls provided with corner and gate towers. Inside the walls on high foundations stood strong, elaborate, storied, wooden residences, built in the study-style, with numerous gables and other decorative features. A high central tower or *donjon* loomed above the other buildings to add to the grandeur and to serve as a look-out.

The first grand castle of this description was that of Adzuchi, no longer extant, erected (1576–79) by Nobunaga on the shores of Lake Biwa. Its central tower was seven stories high, and its rooms were elaborately decorated with paintings and carvings in gilt and gold by the most honoured artists of the day. The largest, strongest, and most elaborate was Hideyoshi's castle at Osaka (1583–85). Destroyed after 1615, it was partly restored in recent times. Hideyoshi also erected (1593) the palatial and highly decorated residential castle of Momoyama at Fushimi, near Kyoto. It, too, was destroyed (in the 1630's), but some of its buildings—superb examples of study-style architecture—were transferred to other places. The Nishi-Hongwan-ji Monastery of Kyoto has six of the halls, including a matchless *jōdan-no-ma* room and a magnificent Karamon Gate, and also the unique Hiun-kaku, a residential pavilion from Hideyoshi's residence at Fushimi. Of the castles of the Momoyama period, that of Himeji, in the Hyōgo Prefecture, with a five-storied *donjon*, alone survives. (P. 76a.)

The monuments of Tokugawa Ieyasu's time (d. 1616) have had a better fate. He completed (1610) one of Japan's noblest castles, that of Nagoya, also with a five-storied *donjon*, constructed under the direction of the warrior-architect Kātō Kiyomasa. (This castle was burned down in an air-raid in World War II; it has since been reconstructed of reinforced concrete on an iron frame.) Ieyasu also built (Kyoto, 1603) the Nijo castle-palace of the shoguns, illustrious for its well-proportioned corner towers and gates, the Karamon Gate, its four great halls (Waiting, Audience, Black, and White), and its garden. (Fig. 6.) The Shōnan-tei of the Sāihō-ji Monastery, Kyoto, a tea-ceremony house, was another notable monument of his day. When, however, Ieyasu established the Tokugawa military capital at Edo (Tokyo), the castle buildings he erected there were uninspired copies of the Momoyama style. Furthermore, Lord Masamune Daté put up at Sendai in 1607 the Shinto shrine of Ōsaki Hachiman, the first fully elaborated example of the ornate *gongen* style, generally used for mausoleums. It involved a complicated system of roofs, much carving and lacquer work, and the joining of the main shrine or mausoleum with the hall of prayer by a lobby. (Pl 76b.)

After Ieyasu, Tokugawa architecture steadily deteriorated. The Tokugawas banned the building of castles, and Buddhism, controlled and declining, showed no creative enthusiasm, repairing or rebuilding numerous monasteries in their original style. A few new monasteries erected under the patronage of the shoguns were in the *gongen* style, which was often used by Buddhists as well as Shintoists. A complete Ming Chinese style was followed in the Mampuku-ji Monastery near Kyoto, an establishment of the new Ōbaku sect of Zen introduced from China in 1655. The most important buildings of the later Tokugawas were the mausoleums of shoguns and great feudal lords, the principal ones being Ieyasu's (1636) and the third shogun's (1653) at Nikko, the second shogun's at Shiba Park (1635, destroyed in an air-raid in 1945), and Lord Daté's at Sendai (1637). The shrine and the five-storied pagoda to Ieyasu erected (*c.* 1639) in Ueno Park, Edo, were good examples of the uninspired style of the time. The more pretentious new structures, especially after the seventeenth century, whether in the *gongen* style or some other, and whether built by shogun, noble, priest, or rich merchant, were overly ornamental and lavish in colour, putting a sort of Rococo end to traditional Japanese architecture. Garden architecture, however, retained its superb qualities throughout the whole of our period.

Shiro Shoin (White Hall)

Kuro Shoin (Black Hall)

Sotetsu-no-ma (Cycads Hall)

Ō-hiroma (Audience Hall)

Shikidai (Anteroom)

Scale
0 10   50   100 ft

Tōsaburai (Waiting Hall)

Kurumayose (Entrance Room)

Fig. 6. Plan of the Ninomaru Goten (Music Halls) of Nijo
castle-palace, Kyoto.

Painting

At the beginning of the fourteenth century painting in Japan was a courtly art centred in Kyoto and dominated by various native schools patronized by the emperor, the court nobles, and the monasteries. These schools tended to pass on their tradition from father to son or to a gifted pupil adopted as a son. The leading painter of the day was Takashina Takakane, who started as a representative of one native school, the Kasuga, but ended as a representative of another, the Tosa. Paintings were relatively realistic, using a great deal of colour. They were done on walls, fans, and screens or on paper, which was often mounted on panels or rolled into long scrolls known as *emakimono*. Their main subjects were Buddhas (especially Amida), portraits of monks and well-known persons, court scenes, and historical episodes, but some were didactic illustrations of Buddhist doctrines. Murals decorated both temples and the houses of nobles, and both monasteries and aristocrats collected scrolls. One of Takakane's most famous scrolls was 'The Miracle Record of the Kasuga Shrine'. (Pl. 77.)

The native schools of painting had begun to yield supremacy to the Chinese school during the Kamakura period (1185–1333). The impressionistic ink landscapes, in black and white, of Sung China had been brought to Japan by nature-loving Zenists, who went to China to study the Sung masters and imitated their style. Minchō (1352–1431), who was both an official of the Tōfuku-ji Monastery in Kyoto and a painter of Buddhist and Taoist figures, promoted the Chinese landscape style, but the first to begin a clearly traceable Chinese tradition was Josetsu (early fifteenth century). Though only one of Josetsu's works, 'Man Catching a Catfish', painted for the shogun Yoshimitsu, is fully authenticated (Pl. 78a), he was a teacher of Shūbun (*c.* 1414–65), who became an official painter of the shogun and by the many landscapes attributed to him assured the Chinese school's popularity. Several famous painters of that school studied under Shūbun. Among them were Dasoku (fl. 1452–83), Oguri Sōtan (d. 1481), and Nōami (1397–1476). All three were reputed as painters, gardeners, tea-ceremony experts, poets, and connoisseurs. They served the shogun Yoshimasa (1449–74) and were arbiters of taste in Kyoto. Nōami was the first of the so-called Three Ami, the other two being his son Geiami and his grandson Sōami (1472–1523).

The greatest of Japanese landscapists, perhaps of Japanese painters altogether, was the monk Sesshū (1420–1506), who studied the style of both Josetsu and Shūbun. He was in China from 1467 to 1469 but, being already a painter of great power and originality, found no one there from whom he could learn. Several of his landscapes and scrolls have been preserved, and they reveal a forceful style independent of and distinct from earlier Chinese landscape masters. His landscapes 'Winter' and 'Autumn' are especially impressive. (Pl. 78b.)

Most of the landscapists were monks and not painters by profession, but in the late fifteenth century a group of professional painters, employed by the shoguns and known as the Kanō school arose, and it remained dominant for the next two centuries. It was founded by Kanō Masanobu (1453–90) and developed by his son Kanō Motonobu (1476–1559). While continuing to paint landscapes in the Chinese monochrome style, these masters applied suitable modifications of Chinese techniques to the traditional subjects of the native Tosa school and reintroduced the use of colour. Motonobu, the most illustrious painter of the period after Sesshū, was a master in both ink and colour. Meanwhile an older contemporary, Tosa Mitsunobu (1434–1525), was breathing new life into the Tosa school of imperial painters with the fine colour and design of his historical scrolls, although he also worked in ink. When Motonobu married the daughter of Mitsunobu, the marriage symbolied the union of the traditional Japanese school with the Chinese school.

Certain trends evident in the late Ashikaga period, such as the revival of colour and of native tradition, culminated in the flamboyant art of the Momoyama period. The enthusiasm for colour and bigness went hand in hand with a penchant for gold leaf and a preference for the animated and the heroic. Walls, sliding panels, folding screens, and scrolls were now decorated with huge pictures in resplendent hues on gilt and gold backgrounds and in gold lacquer. For contrast, paintings were done also in black and white. Among the most able masters of the flamboyant art were Kanō Eitoku (1543–90), grandson of Mononobu, and Kanō Sanraku (1559–1635), a favourite of Hideyoshi adopted by the Kanōs. Both of them were employed by Hideyoshi to decorate his castles. Eitoku worked with brilliant tints, a heroic style, and vigorous brush strokes to portray giant pine and plum trees, lions, rocks, mountains, and flowers and to tell Japanese tales. (Pl. 79a.) Sanraku's paintings resembled those of his master Eitoku.

The leadership of the Kanōs, however, was not uncontested. Kaiho Yūshō (1533–1615), who studied under Kanō Eitoku, later founded a school of his own and won distinction particularly for his screens depicting Chinese legends, pine trees in black and white, and fish nets. Hasegawa Tōhaku (1539–1610) also studied under the Kanō school, but then, for a time, he devoted himself to the Sesshū style and, still later, adopted also the Chinese painting styles of the Sung and Yüan dynasties, finally establishing a style of his own. Another distinguished contemporary was Unkoku Tōgan (1547–1618), who contended with Tōhaku for recognition as the rightful successor to Sesshu. Meanwhile Tosa Mitsuyoshi (1539–1613) continued in gold and rich colour the epic tradition of the Tosa school, with detailed pictures of horsemen, battles, and scenes from Buddhist lore.

Honnami Kōetsu (1569–1637), an independent genius, was the first of a new group of 'decorative painters'. They were highly regarded for their lacquer work, especially in gold, for their skill in the several styles of the time, for their use of ink on gold backgrounds, and for the wide range of their subjects. Master of the techniques of pottery, gold lacquer, and calligraphy as well as of painting, Kōetsu was outstanding for his use of lead on lacquered screens and for his portraits of priests. The approximately contemporary artist Sōtatsu further developed the decorative technique of Kōetsu, with boldly conceived screen pictures in colour. His *suiboku* paintings (monochrome, done in *sumi*, or ink) also showed a high degree of specifically Japanese composition and technique, easily distinguishable from those of the Chinese style.

In the early Tokugawa period the Kanō, Tosa, and decorative schools kept up the flamboyant Momoyama style, though on a somewhat moderated scale. A host of Kanō masters were official painters to the shoguns at Edo in the seventeenth century and, as time wore on, they became increasingly bureaucratic. Kanō Tannyū (1602–74) and his two brothers were the best known of them; Tannyū himself was an original genius who modified accepted canons. To suit the Confucian interests of the bureaucracy the Kanō school turned to Chinese subjects such as Confucius, the Seven Wise Men of the Bamboo Grove, Chinese rulers and their loyal subjects, and sacred animals such as dragons, tigers, lions, *ch'i-lins*, cranes, and phoenixes, along with landscapes, trees, and flowers. Kanō Sansetsu (1589–1651), an adopted son of Sanraku, adopted the black and white technique; he established a branch of the school at Kyoto. Kanō Tsunenobu (1636–1713), son of one of Tannyū's brothers, was also an accomplished painter. Meanwhile, Tosa Mitsunari (1583–1638) carried the Tosa classical tradition into the Tokugawa period; later Tosas continued as court painters at Kyoto. The decorative painters could also boast several able exponents, of whom Ogata Kōrin (1658–1716) is sometimes considered the most able because of the exceptional beauty of his decorated screens, figures, landscapes, flowers, and birds; he used gold and silver paste or ink mixed with gold paste to obtain decorative effects. (Pl. 79b.)

Ogata Korin flourished at a time—the Genroku Era (1688–1703)—when the superior elements of the old tradition were being combined with a rising graphic medium, the *ukiyoe* (or genre picture), to create a memorable period in art. The *ukiyoe* prints and pictures had attracted the middle-class townsmen, who demanded a relatively cheap art in large quantities. The artists of this group were the same sort of townsmen and renegade samurai that, turning their backs on the sumarai art of the older schools and looking to the life of the town for inspiration, cultivated *chonin* literature (see Chapter XI). Among their favourite pictorial subjects were courtesans and actors; they leaned toward love scenes, street scenes, scenes of everyday life, and, as time went on, landscapes; and they had a penchant for pictures that poked fun at sacred figures. Some of the *ukiyoe* were painted by hand, others were printed from wood-blocks. The Chinese wood-block print certainly helped to bring on this development, but the colour-print went much further in Japan than in China.

The new genre painting had developed in three stages. It was born in the early Tokugawa period with the works of Iwasa Matahei (1568–1650) of the Tosa school, who was noted for his 'Thirty-six Poets'. During the second stage (*c.* 1650–1740), hand-painted pictures in various colours and black and white prints were characteristic. The chief figures of this stage were Hishi-kawa Moronobu (1688–1703), whose subjects were courtesans, often with a landscape background, and who introduced picture books, and Torii Kiyonobu (1664–1729), founder of the Torii school, who specialized in theatre signs and actors. During the third stage (1740–1843) the genuine colour-print emerged, the combined work of painter, engraver, and printer, in which a basic pink was contrasted with green, yellow, and other colours. Okumura Masanobu (1690–1768) and Ishikawa Toyonobu (1711–85) were pioneers of the colour-print. Masanobu portrayed actors, courtesans, legend-ary scenes, and popular heroes against a background of elegance, luxury, and eroticism. Suzuki Harunobu (1718–70) elaborated the brocade or many-coloured print and was the leading *ukiyoe* master of our period. (Pl. 80.) He painted highly idealized tea-house beauties, daughters of merchants, and lovers, generally with a landscape background.

In the eighteenth century, as the *ukiyoe* won prominence, the aristocratic schools of the old tradition lost vitality. Confucian scholars became interested in the abstract, literary-man's painting exemplified by the Wu or Southern School of China. In Japan they were known as the Nanga School, and Ike-no Taiga (1723–76) was their most eminent representative. On the other hand, Maruyama Ōkyo (1738–95), having been somewhat influenced by a relatively unknown Chinese painter, Shen Nan-p'in, who visited Nagasaki in 1731–33, established a very realistic school of landscape painting, which also became popular among townsmen.

Other arts

During the Tokugawa period, the ceramic arts made noteworthy strides. Their advance was attributable to the growing popularity of the tea-cult and to Hideyoshi's importation of Korean potters. Especially favoured wares were Imari and Arita polychromes along with Hirado whites. Some realistic portraiture in wood of Buddhist monks was still done in the fourteenth century, but sculpture was less emphasized in later centuries than pottery and porcelain. It survived, too, in the decorative arts—in the fashioning of ornaments for the interiors or exteriors of buildings, in the carving of puppets and *nō* masks, and in ivory-carvings. A variety of other decorative arts— among them, tray-landscapes, potted dwarfed trees, fans, dolls, lacquer ware, screens, and flower arrangements—produced masterpieces of their own, and the craftsmanship of Japanese swords and armour won a well deserved repu-tation.

In Japan as in China music and the dance (other than the court music, continued from earlier centuries) were particularly associated with dramatic performances (see Chapter XI). Although Confucian scholars considered music an important means of social control, it was not highly developed as a public art. Composers were unknown as such. In both Japan and China a variety of chants and popular airs grew up in connection with dramatic performances and with entertainment by geishas and sing-song girls, but they were considered lewd (as often they were) by scholars, who favoured only certain kinds of solemn and traditional music associated with sacrifices, coronations, and other important ceremonial occasions.

In both countries likewise, the solemn classical dances associated with religious events and ceremonies were approved by Confucian moralists, while dramatic or popular dances were not, with the exception of those in the symbolic and esoteric *nō* dramas (which were generally regarded, however, as belonging in the classic group). Hence popular dances (other than folk dances) were, like popular music, associated with the dramas and geisha entertainment. Symbolic gestures had to be carefully studied, and some of the military and sword dances required fast movement and extreme dexterity. Gorgeous costuming was essential to all kinds of dancing, which was a much more highly developed art in Japan than in China.

In both countries instrument making had been carefully practiced since an early date. The Chinese had devised a seven-string zither or lute (*ch'in*), other string instruments (*se* and *p'i-p'a*), and various wind instruments (*hsiao*, *sheng*, *ti*), around which an abundant lore accumulated. Performers of all classes from scholars to sing-song girls played them, both for private and semi-private entertainment. In the early sixteenth century the Chinese musician Wei Liang-fu adapted native tunes to operatic scores and enlarged and improved the orchestras that accompanied the *k'un-ch'ü* songs and dramas (see Chapter XI). Chinese instrumentation came to include the flute, the guitar, the reed-organ (*sheng*), the drum, and castenets, lending a new emphasis to the musical and acoustical values of *k'un ch'ü* drama. At the beginning of the eighteenth century the Japanese introduced into their *jōruri* plays the three-stringed guitar (*samisen*) of the Ryukyu Islands.

THE ARTS OUTSIDE EURASIA

African Sculpture

Before Eurasian influences began to affect other continents, several peoples of Africa and the Americas had developed an independent art tradition of a high order. In Africa the artists of Benin achieved an impressive type of sculpture free from imitation of contemporary Mediterranean art but perhaps indebted to ancient Greek or oriental art. Before 1500 they had a knowledge of bronze casting that was surpassed only by the better craftsmen of Florence, Germany, India, and the Far East. Benin was the capital of the Beni of the Niger region, one of the most highly organized of the Sudanic peoples of our period. Its culture probably was originally derived from Ifé, the holy city of the nearby Yoruba people. Benin's technical tradition appears to have originated about 1300 and to have reached its climax about the sixteenth century, when Portuguese traders, then establishing trade relationships with that area, were depicted on some of the Beni reliefs.[57] The subtle surfaces of Ifé portraits and the intricate details of Benin masks were magnificently done, even if they did not reach the complexities or the exquisite finish of Florentine workmanship or match the long technical tradition of bronze casting in China and Japan. (Pl. 81.)

The bronze and terra cotta heads of Ifé are unusual in the African tradition both for their naturalism and the material of which they are made. Most other African sculpture was done in wood, usually small and compactly held within the original block. While the human body was the primary subject of Negro sculpture, as it was in European art, animals too were often represented. Also sensitive to the contrast of sculptural volumes and spatial penetrations, the African artist tended to confine his sculpture to the shape of the block, suggesting little concern for the surrounding space or for the viewer's angle of vision.

The Arts in Pre-Columbian America

In the Americas, the most significant art traditions of the fourteenth and fifteenth centuries were those of the Incas in Peru and the Aztecs in Mexico. Highly conventionalized animals, birds, fish, and human figures and various abstract forms not readily identifiable comprise most of the decorative vocabulary. The floral and foliate motifs prominent in the Far East, India, the Middle East, and Europe were noticeably lacking in the Americas. Definite meanings were apparently associated with even such abstract forms as the fret and the wave. Inca and Aztec designs seldom suggest sculptural relief or depth. Most motifs are flat, occupying the same plane as the ground. A tendency toward angular, triangular, and rectangular shaping of parts, particularly characteristic of Inca ornament, may reflect the textile origin of a number of them. The arrival of the Europeans played havoc with the leading decorative arts, but some of them have survived in the form of folk arts.

Before the European conquerors rechannelled the course of the Amerindians' culture, it had developed various architectural traditions. Along the Andean highlands, the Incas built mountain cities and fortified places with cyclopean stones, cut and fitted together without mortar or metal tools but with a precision and skill that evokes admiration to this day. In Central America, numerous and often gigantic pyramidal platforms for small temples with tall, ornamental crests rose slowly from the plains, still causing wonder at the immensity of the planning and labour they required and at the forcefulness and fantasy of the sculpture which covered and enriched them. In the area that was to become the southwest of the United States, the many-celled communal dwellings of the Pueblo Indians clung to the protective ledges of rocky cliffs. The architects of the Amerindians had not discovered a true arch and were therefore limited in their interiors to variations of column and lintel construction (the so-called 'false arch'), attaining only the most meagre, low corridor-space inside their often enormous structures.

Aztec sculpture along with the earlier Mayan, stands out as part of one of the finest pre-Columbian art traditions in the Americas. Mayan sculpture had seen its best days before 1300 (see *History of Mankind*, Vol. III), and the culture which the Spaniards found in Mexico was dominated by the Aztecs. Aztec sculpture, while greatly varied, was often characterized by compactness of form with little interplay between the sculptural mass and the surrounding space. The huge stone Coatlicue, or serpent goddess, now in the Mexican Archaeological Museum, is richly carved on all sides but with reliefs that respect the planes of the original stone block. Occasionally small works such as the spiralled arrangements of the feathered serpent deity, Quetzalcoatl, take on a distinct life-in-the-round, but Aztec sculpture is rarely designed to provide interesting views from all possible angles. (Pl. 82a, b.)

*   *   *

Many areas of the world outside Europe during this period employed a decorative, polychrome sculpture, particularly those areas in which wood was the predominant medium, such as Africa and the islands of Polynesia and Melanesia in the Pacific Ocean. Though in stone, most Aztec sculpture, whether round or in relief, was enriched by vivid areas of colour. The Americas, Africa, and Oceania, however, during this period do not appear to have demanded a great amount or variety of decorative architectural devices or of decorative furniture, whether for ceremonial or for domestic purposes, in the interiors of their structures.

On the other hand, the early Americas produced many unique pieces of ceremonial jewellery. From Peru to Mexico the Spaniards encountered fabulous objects in gold, silver, jadeite, turquoise, shell, and rock crystal. Delicately wrought gold ornaments were sewn on ceremonial robes. The Amerindian goldsmiths fashioned pendants, earrings, oar plugs, pectoral plates, headdresses, bracelets, rings, necklaces. Burial masks, wrought of thin sheets of beaten gold, and other funerary objects were among their most impressive work. Spanish and Portuguese conquerors admired many of these objects, but the ready currency value of the materials apparently overruled admiration for design and workmanship, for many were melted down before they left America. In consequence, European artisans probably saw few products of the American Indian's craftsmanship in jewellery.

Among the Incas of South America a highly ornamental effect was achieved in cloth. During the fourteenth and fifteenth centuries they were the only cultural group in the Americas to make intricately woven and richly decorated textiles of cotton-and-wool yarn. Despite their relatively simple implements, they attained an amazing refinement in the spinning of cotton and wool, and their weaving methods included almost all those contemporaneously known elsewhere. Their knowledge of dyeing permitted a wide range of colours, and they distributed colour so freely and fitted their small conventional figures and symbols so closely together as to suggest infinite variety and complication in their designs.

The Arts in Post-Columbian America

Christian missionaries transformed the art and architecture of the Amerindians. The abrupt change of religion in Latin America resulted in the interruption of most of the major arts that previously had in any way served the indigenous religious ceremonies. It also resulted in Mexico in the formation of a new kind of monastery, distinguished from its European predecessors by an immense atrium with a centrally located stone cross, around which the Indians, accustomed to outdoor congregations, could gather for services in great numbers.

In the Christian art of Mexico the emphasis on the passion of Jesus and on His blood may stem from an attempt of the clergy to capitalize on the Aztec cult of blood sacrifices. Spain and Portugal shipped their realistic polychrome sculpture in great quantities to the New World, and it formed the basis for seventeenth-century and especially eighteenth-century sculpture in Central and South America. Polychrome wooden crucifixes, showing a writhing Jesus with gaping, bleeding wounds, pain-racked eyes, and fevered, open mouth, rose in the many cathedrals, churches, and missions that soon dotted the vast Spanish and Portuguese empires in America.

Wherever American buildings rose beyond the dimensions of temporary shelter or log cabin, the architecture was influenced by that of the mother countries. In Anglo–America churches and schools were usually Georgian. The missionary role of Spain and Portugal led to building activity on a scale not even considered by England or France in North America, bringing a complete interruption of native traditions in Central and South America. A few edifices like the Cathedral of Santo Domingo in Hispaniola or the early-sixteenth-century monastery churches in Mexico belatedly introduced Gothic into the Americas, but most of the major monuments—e.g. the cathedrals of Mexico City, Puebla, and Guadalajara in Mexico and of Lima and Cuzco in Peru—were in the ornamental 'Plateresque' style or, in the later sixteenth century, in the more severe 'Herreresque'. (Pl. 45a, b.) The prevalence of earthquakes in many parts of Central America and along the Andes Mountain range encouraged the use of thick walls, heavy buttresses, low interiors, flexible rib vaults, and light vaulting materials to assure the maximum stability of their structures.[58]

The Iberian Baroque style was likewise carried to South and Central America, where it achieved some of its most exuberant and marvellous ensembles. The carved rose-coloured stone exterior and the painted and gilded interior of the Church of Guanajuato and the carved white plaster and red-tile façade of the Sanctuary of Ocotlan near Tlaxcala are examples of the ornate, polychrome creations typical of Mexico's Baroque. In the Hispano–American areas generally the eighteenth-century interest in the exotic was expressed by reminiscences of Islamic and Pre-Columbian Indian motifs. While the tiled and undulated church façades of Brazil revealed a continued dependence on Portugal, the Hispanic colonies developed a growing individuality of architecture.[59] In the New World, where, it is sometimes said, European styles go to die, a robust Baroque lived on into the nineteenth century, demonstrating an amazing creative vitality.

In contrast to the success of the Spaniards in transplanting their architectural tradition in the New World, their pictorial forms and techniques were not readily transferred. Despite the emergence of autonomous regional schools in the seventeenth and eightenth centuries, Hispanic America remained dependent on the art market of Seville for it finer paintings for church or home.[60] Not so for its pottery, however, which likewise was successfully transplanted. In the early sixteenth century, Spanish Dominican friars took the low-fire process of making majolica ware to Mexico, and through the eighteenth century, Mexico, like Spain, remained an important producer of majolica dishes, bowls, apothecary jars, and glazed tiles.

European Town Planning Overseas

Usually having no previous town plan (or lack of plan) to counteract in the rising settlements, the European architect could lay out cities freely. All over America, North and South, and at strategic points elsewhere (Manila and Cape-town, for example), new cities or additions to native cities took on a gridiron appearance. (Pl. 83). In colonial capitals a large square bordered by the cathedral and the governor's mansion would become the centre, and the other streets would branch out in perpendicular fashion, cutting the city into rectangular 'blocks' of houses.[61] Lesser cities, usually connected with the capital by a single road, would follow the same grid-system of town planning. Thus the new cities in the wilderness demonstrated, as did the rising settlements in so many other regards, the interplay of European tradition with frontier opportunities and obstacles.

NOTES TO CHAPTER XII

1. Professor A. Chastel believes that the periodic 'return to the Gothic' form after each phase of plastic consolidation in style is a characteristic of the Renaissance period in certain milieux both north and south of the Alps. This is what happens in Tuscany and Lombardy in the mid-fourteenth century on the basis of 'giottism'. The northern miniaturists had already evolved the gracious 'minor' version of monumental Gothic found in the work of Jean Lucelle and the Parisian illuminators, who lie at the origin of the precious, courtly style popular in the last quarter of the fifteenth century known as 'international Gothic', the main centres of which were in Sienna, Prague, and Paris, with ramifications throughout Europe. Highly evolved painters such as the Master of the Hours of Boucicaut and the Limbourg brothers represent the final transcending of this style by strict composition and formal precision directly preparing the advent of Van Eyck's realism. This is clearly established in the studies of Messrs Meiss and E. Panofsky.

2. Professor André Chastel stresses that towards the middle of the fifteenth century, Italian methods of composition began to become known in northern Europe, and the potentialities of oil painting were assimilated by the Italian masters, probably on the basis of examples coming from southern Italy. Antonello da Messina, who ended his career in Venice in 1475, was a key figure in this evolution, which also influenced the art of Piero della Francesca. The evolution of Italian art is not restricted to the expansion of Tuscan forms. In Flanders as in Italy, from 1480 on, we observe a renunciation of hard outline and a softening of style, a phase of so-called "relaxation" noticeable in the work of Memling as well as in that of Perugino.

3. Professor André Chastel notes that engraving spread both in Italy and in Germany from 1460 onwards, becoming at the beginning of the sixteenth century the most powerful means of artistic interchange between the various centres: Dürer drew inspiration from Mantegna and Marc-Antonio, Raphael's official engraver, and spread knowledge of the great 'Roman' style throughout the West.

Conversely, through the intermediary of engraving, the fantastic and expressionist art of the North was to stimulate the work not only of certain Lombard and Venetian artists, but, even though only episodically, that of a Tuscan like Pontormo.

4. Professor André Chastel feels that while the art of Tintoretto, by its intense expressivity and breadth of composition, is very far from the stilted precision and intellectual ambiguity of the first generation of 'mannerists', this artist nevertheless exploits certain virtualities by means of distortion of form, a quest for washed-out tones of colour, and a taste for long perspectives and 'telescoped' effects.

5. Professor A. Chastel points out that at about the same time, there was spreading through the North, and flourishing particularly in Antwerp and sophisticated centres such as Prague, a neo-mannerist trend culminating in Goltzius, Spranger, and the brilliant and ingenious painters of the court of Rudolph II. In Central Italy, too, a taste for complex and delicate forms was in evidence during the last quarter of the sixteenth century. The early-seventeenth-century innovators reacted against this taste, some, like Caravaggio (see below), by means of a return to 'nature' and striking simplification.

6. For Professor A. Chastel the expression *grande manière* is not generally applied to the decorative triumphs of Baroque art but to the preoccupation with the noble and majestic grandeur peculiar to French art at the time of the Académie and under the leadership of Lebrun, as shown above.

7. In Professor A. Chastel's opinion Poussin's treatment of landscape 'construction' can scarcely be said to be derived from Italian models but is rather the result of a personal evolution originally based on classical examples and accompanied, in his latest period, by a powerful concentration of effects, the personal character of which was clearly demonstrated during the Poussin colloquy in Paris in 1958.

8. Professor A. Chastel feels that recourse to contemporary human types, to vulgar and even provocative details, accounts for a large part of the success of 'Caravaggism'. This trend, opposed to landscape, gave renewed life both to 'scenes from daily life' and to still-life painting. Artists such as Honthurst and Terbruggen were to serve as intermediaries between Rome and the Low Countries both as regards realist inspiration and vigor of execution.

9. In Professor A. Chastel's opinion the art of Velasquez soars above the usual qualities of Spanish painting. Thanks to his Sevillian origins, he was conversant with the 'tenebrism' of Zurbarán. His direct knowledge of the Venetian style, acquired from the royal art collections, was completed by a long stay in Italy. Exquisite workmanship and formal dignity make him one of the leaders of what may be called 'total painting', but, as in the case of Vermeer, these qualities had to await the nineteenth century for full appreciation.

10. To Professor A. Chastel the gap between the robust sculpture of Giovanni Pisano— the only master to try to produce in Italy an equivalent to the statue-covered cathedral façade—and the precious art of Andréa Pisano seems of the same order as that between the 'plastic' style of Giotto himself and the compositions of those of his successors not far removed from Gothic mannerism

1. Professor A. Chastel stresses that the erection of the equestrian statue to the memory of Gattamelata on the Campo Santo of Padua (Pl. 30b) marked a vital date in the history of monumental bronze sculpture, while the altar for the Basilica of St. Antonio in the same city opened up new perspectives by the technique of grouping of the statues under a kind of aedicule. The whole of the activity of the north Italian bronze founders in Padua and Venice was influenced by these great examples, despite a tendency towards 'bibelots' and the ornamental plaquette much in vogue about 1500.

12. The model supplied by Leonardo, executed in clay and larger than life, was designed for the statue of Francesco Sforza. (André Chastel).

13. Professor A. Chastel points out that Michaelangelo's original projects (1505) for the tomb of Pope Julius II, of which only the Moses and the 'Slaves' remain, indicate a triumphal setting for the statues which were not conceived as separate figures. The *loggetta* of the Campanile of Saint Mark, with its four bronze statues and dating from thirty years later (1537–40), is a graceful construction very different in inspiration. Renaissance sculpture is closely linked to its architectural and decorative setting.

14. While there is a certain continuity in contacts between France and Italy before, during, and after the French invasions (1494–1554) the following distinctions are possible: (1) certain sporadic links towards the middle of the fifteenth century: Fouquet in Rome, F. Laurana in southern France; (2) the multiplication of orders and invitations during the French occupation of the duchy of Milan: Leonardo, Solario, Andréa del Sarto . . . ; and (3) the eventual creation of a real Franco-Italian centre at Fontainebleau, with the arrival of Rosso and Primaticcio, followed first by Serlio and Cellini and subsequently by Niccolo dell'Abbate. (André Chastel).

15. Professor A. Chastel emphasizes that the art of Bernini is characterized by multiplicity and richness of profile, by an intensification of the play of light produced by the drapery and sculpting of the limbs, and by the forceful appropriation of surrounding space obtained by the dominating effects of his obliques. As R. Witkover has clearly shown, this is where the sculpture of complex monuments requiring a regular mise en scène (as, for example, in the equestrian statue of Constantine in the atrium of St Peter's) becomes very close to the architect.

16. Marqués de Lozaya, *Historia del Arte Hispanico* (Barcelona, 1934), II, 496.

17. Professor A. Chastel sees in Normandy, more clearly than anywhere else in the West, an evolution of the 'flamboyant' style, which, by the fragmentation of space-interior screens, pendant knob-bosses, and display of decorative elements, facilitated the adoption of the rich ornamental motifs of the Lombard Renaissance at the beginning of the sixteenth century. The same is true of the Portuguese 'Manueline' style; and it is French (for the most part Norman) master-builders whom we find at this period at Coïmbra and Lisbon.

18. Professor A. Chastel feels that if the compositions of Brunelleschi at San Lorenzo, for example, and those of Alberti on the façade of Santa Maria Novella, are not unrelated to the main lines of Romano-Tuscan art, it is because, relying on the simplicity of form of such art, as opposed to the irregular Gothic lines, they were able to integrate into the new architectural style a growing number of elements borrowed from Antiquity. A similar phenomenon, leading to a very different result—that of decorative profusion—is found in Lombardy, where the circular or polygonal cupolas of Bramante and his school recall the baptisteries and exterior open arcading of Romanesque art.

19. In the opinion of Professor A. Chastel, however, Alberti was primarily the theoretician of the new architecture: his definition of the 'harmonious' building is not especially applicable to the example of Brunelleschi but aims at an anticipatory definition of the art of the future.

20. Saint Sebastian is designed on a central plan which was not often followed. The problem of a structure planned round a unified central space, with symmetrical elements, was broached all over Italy at the end of the fifteenth and beginning of the sixteenth century, but by means of widely differing formulas.

Almost all are votive churches, enlivened both internally and externally by the articulation of the architectural elements and strict play of orders, except in Lombardy (Lodi, Brescia), where the ornamentation is more profuse. (André Chastel.)

21. Professor A. Chastel stresses the influence of Sanmichele on the evolution of the Venetian palace, which, moreover, thanks to his constructions, determined the general effect of the Square of St Mark and of the Palace of the Doge.

22. Professor A. Chastel maintains that the modifications foreseen by Michaelangelo, known to us mainly from an engraving by Lafrèrie, certainly aimed at creating a kind of axial perspective through the body of the place. These were, however, never executed. The trapezoidal Campidoglio, with its monumental stairway opening out onto the city, reveals much more clearly Michaelangelo's architectural dynamism and its effect on urban design, not fully appreciated until the Baroque period.

23. For Professor A. Chastel the sweeping conceptions of Bernini are noticeable both in the powerful interior of the Church of St Andrew on the Quirinal and in the spectacular treatment of St Peter's Square, the culmination of a century and a half of efforts to provide a monumental setting for the Holy See.

24. In the opinion of Professor A. Chastel the general development is indubitably marked by a dual tendency: one to raise the intellectual and social status of the arts, the other to leave functional production to the artisan and, before long, to industry. In most cases, however, this distinction remained somewhat illusory. The Renaissance masters, insisting with theoreticians such as Vasari on the universal value of *disegno*, aimed not at isolating the painter but at making demands on his multiple capacities and directing his interest towards the ornamental arts as well as towards major compositions.

25. Professor A. Chastel indicates that armorial bearings and devices belong to a very old aristocratic and city tradition. The *impresa*, or emblem, on the contrary, representing a virtue or ideal in pictorial form, with or without a *motto*, is a Renaissance creation leading to a large output of illustrated collections (Alciati, etc.) which served to spread the fashion very widely.

26. Professor A. Chastel emphasizes that marquetry is not a matter of furniture only. The utilization of wood for decorative ensembles—choir stalls, room panelling, etc.—was a new departure at the end of the Middle Ages. It gave rise to some remarkable creations which, in the domain of church art continued to increase down to the Baroque period. In the decoration of 'studioli' or work cabinets, special mention must be made of those of Urbino and Gubbio (*c.* 1470–80), comprising a tier of marquetry panelling surmounted by a series of pictures; stone panelling makes its appearance in the 'studiolo' of Eleanor of Toledo (Palazzo Vecchio, Florence); luxuriously decorated cabinets, in which mythological or allegorical paintings are combined on the decor, are everywhere numerous during the same period.

27. Professor A. Chastel points out that to each new stylistic phase corresponds a new decorative development. This is true up to the end of the eighteenth century. Piero della Francesca supplied models for 'intarsia' marquetry, Raphael produced tapestry cartoons, Lebrun made models for furniture and even locks at Versailles. Western art was characterized by an increasing interchange between the arts, leading often to the promotion of the artisan. The history of motifs and patterns common to various decorative forms is an excellent illustration of this interdependence: the creation and development of 'grottesques', launched by Raphael's circle, gave rise in the mannerist period to the most extravagant inventions; exploited in the noble style in every conceivable subject of classical art, these 'grottesques' also form the basis of the fantasies of 'rococo' art and of eighteenth century 'chinoiseries'.

28. The new element consisted in the development of technical methods, the use of silver white and of coloured glass—enlarging the possibilities of picturesque effect—and in increased use of the bay, leading, as in the churches of St Urbain de Troyes, St Ouen de Rouen, and Sainte Gudule de Bruxelles, to compositions extending over several elements of a window.
This resulted in greater boldness and a heightening of colour, and the creation of such

masterpieces as Engrand le Prince's Tree of Jesse in St Etienne de Beauvais (c. 1522). Renaissance stained glass in northern Europe is an often underestimated branch of the major arts, at least of monumental painting. (André Chastel).

29. Professor A. Chastel points out that prior to the Renaissance, and indeed scarcely prior to the eighteenth century, the philosophy of art, that it to say, reflection on aesthetics, did not exist. In its table of activities, Scolasticism recognized only the artisan, and theoretical expositions of optics or anatomy were accessible only to scholars. Such was the situation which underwent modification when certain artistic milieux adapted scientific knowledge to their own needs and thereby entered into competition with the official scholars of the University.

This is what E. Panofsky has called the 'decompartmentalization' of disciplines, which was to prove fruitful to the extent that the draughtsman alone was in a position to develop the new concrete knowledge of nature.

The most typical case is that of anatomy, the study of which opened up in a new direction with the publication of the collections of plates by Vesalius, *Humani corporis fabrica (1542)*. (Pl. 93c.)

30. Senior clergy, themselves of princely rank and fortune, were often the most active propagandists for new styles and new cultures in Catholic countries. Among innumerable examples may be cited Cardinal Georges d'Amboise, prime minister of Louis XII, Cardinals d'Armagnac and du Bellay, ambassadors of Francis I to Italy, Cardinal Ippolito d'Este, etc. Among church dignitaries profane interests long continued to dominate, and it was from among their ranks that the great connoisseurs were recruited. (André Chastel).

31. In the opinion of Professor A. Chastel the regulations of the Council of Trent were designed to react against an excess of profane spirit in religious art, insofar as this provided arguments in favour of the policy of the Reformation. Apart from a few manifestations of severity, however, the importance of which should not be exaggerated, the clearest result of the Council was firstly to inspire an art which 'spoke' to the masses (for instance that inspired by Carlo Borroméo in Milan) and subsequently (when the Jesuit tendency triumphed) a noble and dignified art soon to lend itself to fatuous display designed to celebrate the glory of God.

32. The theoretical writings of Leonardo were almost unknown prior to the nineteenth century; a compilation published by Fréart de Chambray (seventeenth century) alone gave some idea of the scientific reflections of the Florentine artist. His studies of 'physiognomy' were spread to a certain extent by the engravings of Wenceslas Hollar. Lomasso, in particular, incorporated Leonardo's advice to painters in his own treatise on painting (1584).

The authors assume that some of Leonardo's ideas were expressed in conversations and also that the notebooks left to the Melzi family were not completely unknown. Most important, Leonardo formulated ideas on expression already found in the sculpture of Donatello and suggested in the writings of Alberti.

33. Professor A. Chastel, however, remarks that the Academic systematization of 'categories of expression' and of types stems from Poussin, basing himself on Antiquity, and not from Descartes. (For the influence of Poussin on Lebrun and the Académie Royale, see above, page 664).

34. *Principes de la littèrature* (Paris, 1764), quoted in K. E. Gilbert, *A History of Esthetics* (New York, 1939), p. 216.

35. Diderot's article 'Beau' in the *Encyclopédie*, quoted *ibid.*, p. 281.

36. His *Vite de' piu eccellenti pittori, scultori, e architettori, etc.* (1st edition 1550, 2nd edition 1568) was the first and most important treatise on the history of art, comprising both a series of biographies and an overall perspective.

37. Professor A. Chastel calls attention to the important rôle of court ceremonies, increasing in number particularly under the last of the Valois, and reaching extraordinary brilliance under Henry III. These associated dancing, music, *tableaux vivants*, and poetry in spectacles illustrating fabular themes supplied by poets and humanists.

THE VISUAL ARTS AND MUSIC 787

38. The great extension of the domed mosque—that is the mosque on a central plan—derived from the Byzantine prototype, coincides with the revival of the central plan in the monastic churches of the Renaissance in the West, in particular in St Peter's in Rome. (André Chastel).

39. R. C. Majumdar, H. C. Raychaudhuri, and Kalikinkar Datta, *An Advanced History of India* (London, 1950), p. 417.

40. René Grousset, *The Civilization of India* (New York, 1931), p. 360.

41. Ishwari Prasad, *A Short History of Muslim Rule in India* (Indian Press, Ltd., Allahabad, 1939), p. 530.

42. Professor A. Chastel points out that Rembrandt had been attracted, as Delacroix was to be in Morocco, by the exotic profiles and rich costumes of the figures in Mogul paintings. Mainly miniatures, these were small gouache drawings, based on elegance of outline and charm of costumes and animal coats.

In this context, they may be compared to the most delicate phase of miniature painting in the West about 1400, then also a precious and courtly art, sensitively fresh in tone and exploiting a rich animal repertory. The interest shown by Hindu princes and connoisseurs in engraving stems from similar affinities.

It should not be forgotten that engraving was one of the great vehicles of artistic 'zoology' and of princely portraiture.

43. Quoted by Ishwari Prasad, *op. cit.*, p. 534.

44. See K. A. Nilakanta Sastri, *A History of South India* (London, 1955), pp. 462–63.

45. Professor A. Chastel suggests that in the evolution of Indian art, it is possible to distinguish cycles and recurrences comparable to those encountered in the West.
See Benjamin Rowland, *The Art and Architecture of India* (London, 1953), p. 2020.

46. For Professor A. Chastel the dominant characteristic of these compositions is the accumulation of figures disposed in varying sizes and according to geometrical formulas, which gives them an emblematic and ritual aspect resulting in an art which is popular in character.

47. Rowland, *op. cit.*, p. 253.

48. *Ibid.*

49. Grousset, pp. 341–43.

50. Professor A. Chastel wonders how far the faithful reproduction of 'traditional' plans corresponds to a deep appreciation of the symbolic value of these compositions, as well as of their essentially ritual role. The buildings seem to correspond to the diversity of provinces, seasons, and functions.

51. Professor A. Chastel stresses that most of the buildings are shown in relation to ceremonial considerations: a long, terraced route dominates broad vistas of pathways; a monumental stairway bordered with ornamental balustrades leads to a portico sheltering the ceremonial throne itself in the form of an edifice.

52. Professor A. Chastel writes: 'Thanks to one of those Jesuits leaving a subsequently well-known description of China, we know that it is the "rococo" models characteristic of princely dwellings in the West which were used in Pekin.'

53. In Professor A. Chastel's view China also presents a parallel with the renaissance of classical forms in the West. A series of concerted 'revivals' of the formulas of past centuries associated with the prestige of great styles and of great legends, a certain snobbish regard for painting considered as one of the noble professions, a taste for 'collecting', the appearance of theoretical compendiums are all phenomena comparable with those observed in France or in Italy during the seventeenth and eighteenth centuries.

54. Tao-chi's *Hua yü lu*, quoted in Lawrence Sickman and Alexander Soper, *The Art and Architecture of China* (London, 1956), p. 201.

55. See R. L. Hobson, 'Pottery and Porcelain', *The Romance of Chinese Art* (New York, 1929), p. 129.

56. R. L. Hobson, *Chinese Pottery and Porcelain* (London, 1915), II, 247.

57. See H. Baumann and D. Westermann, *Les Peuples et les Civilisations de l'Afrique*, trans. by L. Homburger (Paris, 1946), pp. 349–352; Paul Wingert, *The Sculpture of Negro Africa* (New York, 1950), pp. 35–36; and Dietrich Westermann, 'Cultural History of Negro Africa', *Journal of World History*, III (1957), 991.

58. See D. Angulo Iñiguez, 'Caracteristicas generales en el arte hispano-americano', *Journal of World History*, IV (1957), p. 59–82.

59. *Ibid.*

60. The workshops of Zurbaran or Murillo thus came, in practice, to work for export. (André Chastel).

61. Professor A. Chastel points out that thus the formulas for the 'ideal city' which, with the exception of few fortified towns, remained in the West as unfulfilled urbanistic dreams were occasionally actually put into effect in the New World. (See above pp. 689-90.)

CHAPTER XIII

SCIENCE AND TECHNOLOGY BETWEEN
c. 1300 AND *c*. 1530

GENERAL CHARACTERISTICS

Some of the technological implications of art, music, architecture, printing, and other forms of cultural activity have been presented in the chapters above (especially Chapter XII).[1] We have already had occasion to see that Renaissance figures—Michelangelo is an apt example—might in some instances combine painting and sculpture with architecture and engineering. Leonardo de Vinci engaged in similar artistic and technological enterprises and was a man of letters and of science besides. In the several chapters that follow we shall be more expressly concerned with the inter-relations of technology and scientific investigation.

Before 1300, the level of Christendom's scientific and technological achievements in many respects was lower than that of the great civilizations of China, India, and the Islamic world. In those civilizations science had flourished during the so-called 'Dark Ages' of the West. As early as the sixth century, however, Aristotelian rationalism had gained respect in certain Christian circles, and western Europe's contacts with the Muslims in Spain were reflected from the tenth century on in a rising interest in Islamic science, itself largely dependent upon Aristotle.

For Western science, the so-called 'twelfth-century Renaissance' was in some ways more meaningful than the later revival of Classical Antiquity in Italy. In the earlier renaissance not only Aristotle's writings on logic, general science, and metaphysics, but also Galen's medical works were translated from Arabic, freeing the bolder scholars from the 'halter' (to use the figure of a contemporary, Adelard of Bath) of clerical authority by means of the new rationalism that they learned from the Greeks through the Arabs. When the commentaries on Aristotle by Averroes became available to western Europe, they further freed the inquiring mind of the twelfth and thirteenth centuries from that 'halter', but only to make Aristotelianism itself a rarely questioned authority. Aristotelian Scholasticism, nevertheless, was to help a Western spirit of rational investigation slowly to emerge. Despite the subtleties and unrealities of the Scholastic method, its long reliance on inward logic en-couraged analytical and deductive thinking, for continual disputations—in the faculties of letters perhaps more critical than in the faculties of theology—sharpened the dialectical powers and led eventually to the examination of the very processes of reasoning.

Some universities became centres of the new scientific ideas and methods. Efforts at suppression may have delayed the acceptance of new ideas to some extent, but suppression also roused curiosity, interest, and inquiry. Moderate conservatives preferred to fight fire with fire; Thomas Aquinas and his teacher, Albertus Magnus, accepted the scientific subject matter and methods of Classical and Islamic writers, rationalizing them into the framework of orthodox Scholastic theology. Since Aquinas's complete orthodoxy was taken for granted—at least during his lifetime—it was possible for him and his followers to reason on matters of scientific detail with comparatively little interference. Albertus Magnus's casual references to his own fixed habit of checking the assertions of 'the Ancients', 'Aristotle', and 'living philosophers' by personal investigation, and his high evaluation of 'experience, the best teacher', and of natural science, which he defined as 'the investigation of causes in natural phenomena', illustrate that the new trend was well begun before 1300—certainly earlier than Roger Bacon (1214–94), who flourished a half century after Albert.

The roots of scientific thinking, observation, and experiment in the West thus lay in deeper soil than Roger Bacon's much publicized and perhaps overvalued innovations in scientific method. Bacon did not claim for himself the epoch-making significance that has been assigned to him by some modern admirers. He appears to have most enthusiastically and effectively expounded the achievements and methods of his predecessors and contemporaries and to have been no less praiseworthy for his work as an encyclopedist, propagandist, and popularizer of their experimental undertakings than for his own original research. He hoped their results would be improved upon by their successors and produce the marvels that he prophesied. His enthusiasm and voluminous writings, even his quarrelsomeness, served to focus attention on the experimental method as never before and to speed its acceptance in scientific circles.

In short, before 1300 the West had cautiously begun to modify the subject matter of its science and at times to use some modern scientific methods. Inquiry into the truth, to be sure, still was likely to be deductive, starting with points of theological dogma, but when reason was found to conflict with authority, the Scholastics now appealed also to Aristotelian logic, and some might even add the voice of experience, careful observation, and occasionally experimentation. Furthermore, these methods might now be applied not only to the traditional problems of Christian theology but also to the new subject matter derived from acquaintance with Classical and Muslim lore. The medieval revival of science thus had already begun to accelerate the broadening of the Western mind, and thus the 'renascence' of the fourteenth and fifteenth centuries, for all its recovery of lost texts and its new interpretations of some long known, did not constitute a resurgence *de novo* of the science of Classical Antiquity. Much of the scientific knowledge of the Ancients had been available before that era, though not necessarily put to the best scientific use.

Science continued, in fact, for a long time on its thirteenth-century foundation with little basic modification. In Italy for about two centuries, science received much less attention than Classical literature. In the north theological interests still monopolized the energies of Scholastic thinkers. A curve of Western achievement in basic science would show a sharp upward ascent in the twelfth and thirteenth centuries, largely due to the absorption of Islamic knowledge, which would then level off for the two ensuing centuries; an upward swing (this time essentially independent) would not again be very noticeable until the sixteenth century. During this scientific interregnum, steadier progress was made in the applied sciences by artists, architects, miners, anatomists, navigators, and craft and industrial technicians than in the realm of abstract science.

The Scientific 'Plateau' of the Fourteenth and Fifteenth Centuries

Having caught up with other advanced cultures in science around 1300, why did not the West immediately make the great scientific strides that it later showed itself capable of making? Several explanations of the centuries-long plateau between the absorption of oriental knowledge and an independent Western science are possible, though perhaps not wholly satisfactory either separately or collectively. For one thing, the great appeal of Classical art and literature distracted some, although certainly not all, of the best minds of western Europe, especially Italy, from pure science. Renaissance humanism did not always cultivate the respect for new and independent research that characterizes scientific thinking. Although the humanists often rejected the inhibiting authority of the church, many of them substituted for it the authority of Antiquity. For another thing, Scholasticism persisted in scholarly circles during these centuries, fixing learned men's attention upon theological discussion and esoteric logical exercise and making them somewhat indifferent to scientific activity. Scholastic theology, even though its appeal was waning, retained a firm grip and prevented men of science, for the most part still quite orthodox, from welcoming innovations of theory or method. Consequently they worked over the old problems (e.g. realism versus nominalism) with results that, generally speaking, were useful but not startling (see Chapter VI).

The 'cake of custom' provided still another possible explanation of the long delay after 1300 in the arrival of 'the scientific revolution'. With saving exceptions, the scholarly world preferred, on the whole, to speculate rather than to experiment, to work with the brain alone rather than with eyes and hands as well, to pay little regard to the objective reality of their premises so long as their syllogisms were rigorously logical. In that way they continued their debates with the customary reliance on divine authority and Aristotelian reason, where generally prestige was sure and careers were safe, but failed to exploit the possibilities of observation of and experimentation with natural phenomena, where troublesome doubts, disapproval, and even danger might lurk. The more venturesome and active spirits often preferred to seek new geographical rather than new scientific frontiers. Nevertheless, the accumulation of new knowledge and debates about the old in art, literature, theology, logic, and geography were among the special circumstances that permitted Western science, once it had caught up, to surpass the science of other cultures rapidly (see Chapter XIV).

The troubled spirit induced in the scientific mind of the later Middle Ages by theological considerations was in a way well exemplified by the career of William of Ockham. He was convinced of the inadequacy of human reason to answer the eternal questions (see Chapter VI), thus contributing to mystic faith (for the devout) or to doubt (for the sceptical) rather than to the encouragement of objective experimental science. Nevertheless, his own interest in scientific speculation (see below) and his brilliant argumentative skill set a high standard for the university men who followed him. Later medieval science was distinguished by a number of men whom we have already discussed as philosophers (see Chapter VI). Among them was the brilliant group at Paris in the fourteenth century that included Buridan, Oresme, and Albert of Saxony. In their commentaries on some of Aristotle's scientific works, they paved the way for subsequent elucidation of certain scientific principles. For example, Buridan's revolutionary ideas on motion (that is, the theory of impetus which we shall soon describe) had an indirect influence on subsequent Italian physicists, including Galileo, and pointed the way to modern dynamics; Oresme, struggling to pierce the veil of superficial phenomena and find the meaning of ultimate reality (for example, in his explanation of impetus in the spheres), advanced a lengthy astronomical tradition; and Albert of Saxony's studies of trajectory inspired Da Vinci's thinking on certain problems of physics.

For all that, pure science in the West remained, in the fourteenth and fifteenth centuries, inextricably interwoven with theology, almost but not quite to the same degree as in the Far East and in Muslim lands. In the East, during those centuries and beyond, science had lost its former vitality, for no distinction had yet successfully been made between science and other forms of knowledge, and therefore all knowledge was subordinated to God and related to theology. In the West, on practical levels at least, the church-approved ideology was cracking under the impact of urban secularization and the conflicts of popes and ecumenical councils, and so technology and applied science, as long as they worked, were relatively unrestricted. On pedagogic levels, still dominated by the clergy, scientific knowledge remained hard to separate from theology. Since the ultimate source of knowledge is God, the conservative-minded asked, is not knowledge indivisible, like the seamless robe of Christ? A broad-minded churchman like Nicholas of Cusa found a solution for the logical impasse in a mystical 'wisdom of ignorance'. Even in the mundane atmosphere of Renaissance Italy, men such as Pomponazzi had to resort to the subterfuge of 'double truth', Christian and philosophical, in order to avoid punishment (see Chapter VI).

Neither theological nor humanistic subtleties seemed to resolve wholly the apparent conflict between revealed ('Christian') truth and scientific ('philosophical') method. Thirteenth-century Scholastics succeeded in reconciling Aristotelianism with orthodox Christianity, but some of their successors, finding reconciliation more difficult, either muffled their orthodoxy and courted a brand of heresy, as did Nicholas d'Autrecourt, or repudiated Aristotelianism and embraced an intuitive mysticism, as did Eckhart and Suso (see Chapter VI). Fifteenth-century humanists, having re-discovered Plato, succeeded in reconciling Neoplatonism with Renaissance intellectualism but were less successful with science and rank-and-file Christianity. Nevertheless, amid the several competing isms, science, under the mothering of technological, industrial, and military necessity, resorted from time to time to practical experimentation and in an increasingly secular world was able to make steady progress. Thus the three centuries between the two great Bacons were noteworthy for advances in technological practice and applied science more than in abstract science, and for the decline of the Aristotelian system of thought more than for the rise of a new scientific method.[2]

Inadequacies of Scientific Methods and Equipment

In Chapter VI we traced the changes during the fourteenth and fifteenth centuries in the dominant theories of knowledge. The major change was that the Thomists' reliance on reason as a buttress of faith was reversed at the hands of the Ockhamist nominalists, and Ockhamism was hailed as a new system of logic. Yet its attack on the validity of human reason was concerned with theological method and did not help scientific thinking directly. Even the keenly analytical Oresme failed to work out a systematic scientific theory. Although he rejected superstition and searched for reasonable explanations of natural phenomena, he was primarily a vigilant critic within the Ockhamist school, denying the validity of universal terms or propositions if applied to specific things and hence claiming that general truths must be accepted on faith. The same can be said of his contemporary Buridan.

Nicholas of Cusa in one way at least seemed more capable of modern experimental procedure. He had been educated at Deventer and the University of Padua. Padua was perhaps the most advanced intellectual centre of the fifteenth century, and by the sixteenth century its university was to eclipse every other in scientific achievement, becoming so well known that Shakespeare referred to Padua as the 'nursery of arts', where one went to 'institute a course of learning and ingenious studies' (*Taming of the Shrew*, Act I, Scene I). Well versed in mathematics, astronomy, and physics, Nicholas placed a reliance on mensuration in experimentation that was remarkable for his day; in *De Staticis Experimentis* he proposed a method of determining the weights of the materials involved, for example, in investigating the role of water and earth in the growing of plants. Few scientists were to regard experimentation as equally basic in scientific investigations until Leonardo da Vinci a century later.

In that regard Cusa was a forerunner of the modern empirical scientist. In addition, however, he had a wide-ranging Platonic spirit that led him to speculate upon the significance of the entire universe. His breath-taking concept of a plurality of worlds of which the Earth was not the supreme centre and in which each world pursued its own course was so far beyond the comprehension of most of his contemporaries that it might perhaps never have reached posterity had it not been adopted over a century later by Bruno. Cusa's zeal for experiment, however, did not induce him to try to prove or disprove this lofty concept by empirical data. Exalted by the wonders of his universe, which 'is not infinite, yet cannot be conceived as finite',[3] he was representative of the medieval metaphysician. His advocacy of the experimental method got lost in the partly speculative, partly mystical wonderment over divine magnificence which was characteristic of the science of his day.

In short, those who dealt with the subject matter of science in the fourteenth and fifteenth centuries failed to create an effective laboratory method. Abstract science, or what passed for it, went one way, mostly by speculation outside of laboratories, and empirical knowledge went another, mostly among the crafts and professions and the seekers after the occult. In this period we shall find few daring experimenters, few promising germs of later discoveries, few engaging expositions of important problems, and few striking examples of the assaying of scientific evidence. The rapidity with which the new science was accepted even among the learned can easily be exaggerated.

Such acceptance as science received was largely a result, but also to some extent a cause, of the changing technology and the growing secular spirit. Science, technology, and secularism continually reacted one upon the other. In the thirteenth century, a number of technological inventions laid the foundations for subsequent improvements. Among them were spectacles, mechanical clocks, and more effective war engines, not to mention proposals for machines of perpetual motion. By the fourteenth century people were being portrayed wearing eyeglasses, cast iron was gradually replacing bronze, and mechanical clocks—with weight-driven wheels and oscillating escapement—were being constructed in increasing numbers and improved quality. In 1352 the first of three famous astronomical clocks was set up (at Strasbourg Cathedral), to be followed by an improved model about 1574. The key to accuracy in keeping time, the pendulum, was known to the Muslims and in the West in the fifteenth century, though not yet applied to clocks. Small house clocks did not become common until the sixteenth century, and pocket watches only a century later. The pendulum for clocks was to be developed only in the seventeenth century (see Chapter XIV). The urban mind, usually being the source or at least the witness of these wonders, became somewhat disposed to accept innovation if it actually worked—that is, innovation in applied science if not yet in basic science. Yet the age 1300–1500 falls short of substained progress even in technology and applied science, especially in the fifteenth century.[4]

MATHEMATICS IN EUROPE

Before 1200 the Hindus and the Muslims were generally ahead of the Europeans in mathematical knowledge, as in several other scientific achievements. Whereas, however, men like Bháscara (b. 1114) marked a twilight, however brilliant, of development farther east, in Europe men like Leonardo Fibonacci of Pisa (fl. 1225) marked a dawn. Thereafter, in western Europe all fields of mathematics rose above their ancient levels. It has been suggested that while all contemporary civilized communities for the most part conformed to a fairly common pattern about 1200, after that time the West, freed from the unsettlement of 'barbarian invasions', began to diverge from the others, and one of the reasons for this divergence was that Western thinkers proved more ready to think in abstract generalizations.[5] Perhaps no systematic form of thought is more abstract or generalized than mathematics, even if, as the science of numbers, it is also a tool of precise knowledge and detailed measurement.

In the twelfth and thirteenth centuries western Europe began to use the Hindu–Arabic system of numerals. This system was at first primarily employed as a major aid to progress in Western commercial arithmetic. Until the cumbersome Greek, Roman, or Hebrew letter symbols were replaced by the zero-decimal symbols, mensuration and computation could rarely proceed faster than finger action on different kinds of abacuses. Fast and accurate though this method might be in the hands of an expert, it had definite limitations. It was frequently based on counting by fives (as befitted a five-fingered animal) in a sexagesimal system. Whether the Hindus invented the zero-decimal system and passed it on to the Muslims or both peoples worked it out independently and simultaneously, the arithmetic based upon it became known in the West in the tenth century as *algorism*, from the name of al-Khwārizmī, who had expounded the new method of calculation to the ninth-century Muslim world, using the term 'Hindi' to designate it (see Volume III).

In the thirteenth century western Europe witnessed the beginning of a three-hundred-year war of words between die-hard abacists and devout 'algorists', as the proponents of the new Hindu–Arabic numerical system and arithmetic were called. A few encouraging signs indicated, nevertheless, that a scientific theory of numbers was slowly emerging. For one thing, by 1300 western Europe had known the Hindu–Arabic tools for a long time, though it had just begun to apply them.

The mathematical heritage of medieval Europe included, besides, a mass of Classical and Islamic treatises, mostly in Latin translations. While Greco-Roman methods of numeration eventually gave way to the Hindu–Arabic system, Classical influences continued to dominate the study of geometry, the investigation of magnitudes such as lines, surfaces, and solids in space. Euclid's name remained virtually a synonym for geometry until the late nineteenth century. In both Islam and Christendom before 1300, commentaries on Euclid were numerous, but the West had begun seriously to study Euclidian geometry only during the twelfth century, about three centuries later than the Muslims. Within another century, Westerners were writing their own geometrical treatises but were still relying heavily on Euclid. A pace or so behind geometry went trigonometry, the measurement of the sides and angles of triangles. The older trigonometric work of Greeks, Indians, and Arabs had been systematized in the thirteenth century by Naṣīr-al-Din Ṭūsī, and from the Muslims it passed to Europe. Another field of mathematics, algebra, was, as its Arabic name indicates, an Islamic contribution, and from the twelfth century Latin translations made available to Westerners the achievements of the Muslims in that field, too. By 1300 Western mathematical research included the solving of such advanced problems as quadratic and cube roots, recurrent series of numbers, divisors and multiples of perfect or 'abundant' numbers, and linear and quadratic equations.[6]

While the scientific achievement of the fourteenth and fifteenth centuries seems generally disappointing in comparison with that of the preceding centuries, in mathematics some sporadic, localized advances were made. Even though Renaissance classicism diverted some of the best minds and the most exalted patronage to literature and the arts, the accompanying growth of the local languages led to the publication of explanations of the Hindu–Arabic numerals and the 'new arithmetic' in the vernacular. These publications for obvious reasons had no great popular impact, but among the learned in the universities they gradually achieved greater success. Progress was especially noteworthy at the recently founded (1264) Merton College of Oxford, sometimes referred to as the earliest school of mathematics in the West. In the fourteenth century, Johann von Gmunden was the first of several eminent mathematicians to make the University of Vienna likewise famous in this field. Meanwhile, at Paris Jean de Murs became illustrious for his mathematical as well as his musical writings. Both Johann von Gmunden and Jean de Murs used decimal fractions in combination with the common sexagesimal ones in equations for extracting square roots. By the fifteenth century algorism was accepted rather widely in scientific circles, and Hindu–Arabic numbers had come into common use also in merchants' ledgers. As late as 1482, at least one Medici merchant still employed the awkward Roman numerals, but by 1494 all the Medici account books were kept in Arabic numerals.

The versatility of the scholars of those centuries is astonishing. Many of them touched on several branches of mathematics and often, in addition, on astronomy, physics, and medicine, and the number of physicians who were also philosophers and scientists is striking, although only rarely was their work of critical significance and some of them were charlatans. While, for the sake of clarity, we shall deal with their achievements in these respective branches of learning separately, they themselves did not necessarily make the same distinctions among the specialists or compartmentalize their work in the same way as modern scientists are prone to do. Scholars of high renown in several fields were found nearly everywhere in western Europe, with the possible exception of Spain, where scholarship, after Raymond Lull died (1314) and until the sixteenth century, was unimpressive.

In fourteenth-century England specialists at Merton took the lead in mathematical work. Shortly after 1300 John Mauduith, a fellow at Merton College, published tables of trigonometry. His treatise *Super Quattuor Tabulis Mirabiliter Inventis in Civitate Oxon, MCCCX,* inspired the writing by a later Oxonian, Richard Wallingford, of the *Quadripartitum,* which laid the foundation for Western trigonometry. Another Merton-trained scholar, Thomas Bradwardine, who later became archbishop of Canterbury, examined favourably the arithmetic of the tradition laid down by the sixth-century Roman philosopher Boethius and also wrote on geometry, both plane and solid.

France's reputation in science during the fourteenth century rested chiefly on Oresme, Pierre d'Ailly, and Buridan, who comprised a scholarly trio probably unmatched anywhere in contemporary Christendom. Of this trio Buridan was perhaps the most original logician and physicist; Oresme was the most illustrious mathematician and was eminent in other fields, such as astronomy, as well. Oresme was much interested in graphs and worked out a process which to a degree corresponds to that of coordinates. He wrote on arithmetic, contributing, in connection with his study of motion, particularly celestial motion, some important ideas that led to the use of fractional exponents. A century after Oresme, Nicolas Chuquet in *Tryparty en la science de nombres* (1484) introduced expressions like *million* and *billion* (up to *nonillion*), though he gave them values nowhere accepted today. He also suggested the modern exponential system. The painful growth of a universally accepted vocabulary and set of symbols was only gradually to remove a serious impediment to mathematical progress.

Germany produced several mathematicians of note in the fourteenth and fifteenth centuries. The astronomer John of Saxony (1323–61) adopted the Alfonsine Tables of the stars (*c.* 1252) to the meridian of Paris and improved the reckoning of time. Nicholas of Cusa was Germany's leading scientist of this period. We have already mentioned his methods of weighing materials in order to obtain mathematically accurate checks on certain of his experiments. For Cusa, as for Oresme, breadth of interests perhaps made impossible the sort of concentration that achievement in specialized fields generally requires. Later in the same century, Regiomontanus (Johann Müller, 1436–76), pupil and associate of Georg Purbach (1423–61) at the University of Vienna, not only contributed to the fame of that university, recently become a mathe-

DD*

matical centre, but also brought to fruition certain of the earlier Oxford ideas on trigonometry. Regiomontanus' *De Triangulis* marked the birth of trigonometry as a distinct science related to both mathematics and astronomy. It also furnished a good example of intercultural exchange; it was, in part at least, based upon earlier works, one of which seems to have been a Latin translation of a treatise on religions by the Avignonese Hebrew Levi ben Gerson,7 who presented, among other things, a summary of the astronomy known to the Arabs. Johann Widmann (*c.* 1489) added to mathematics symbols (+ and −) that eventually simplified the process of addition and subtraction, though he did not himself use them in the modern fashion.

Italy's achievements in mathematics before 1500 did not quite live up to its earlier promise. In the fourteenth century Dominicus de Clavasio wrote a popular treatise on geometry and trigonometry and numerous practical works on commercial arithmetic. Lucas Pacioli's *Summa de Arithmetica* (1494) was one of the first comprehensive presentations of arithmetic, algebra, and trigonometry. He used the term *million* and *cero* (*zero*) with their modern connotation but still used other terms like *billion* and *trillion* to designate far larger numbers than are now designated by such terms.

THE PHYSICAL SCIENCES IN EUROPE

Astrology and the Birth of Astronomy

Throughout medieval times astronomy was closely related to mathematics, which provided its working tools, and with astrology, which provided astronomers with a livelihood. Astrologers were in great demand not only by laymen but also by physicians and other professional men. During the twelfth and thirteenth centuries, while striking development was taking place in the West in arithmetic, algebra, and geometry, Western astronomical ideas were likewise undergoing change through the triumph of Ptolemy's astronomical views over Aristotle's.

Until the middle of the thirteenth century most Scholastics had held to the Aristotelian cosmography, which pictured a finite universe with the earth at its centre, surrounded successively and concentrically by a layer of air, a layer of fire, seven revolving spheres (one for each of the known planets), an eighth sphere of fixed stars, and a ninth occupied by God, the prime mover of all. The theory expounded in Ptolemy's much translated and discussed *Almagest* differed from Aristotle's principally in its effort to explain those movements of the planets which were apparently irregular. It posited a system of eccentric circular orbits and epicycles as opposed to the Aristotelian system of concentric layers and spheres, though both assumed a finite universe. Ptolemy's explanation seemed to suit the apparent course of the heavens better than Aristotle's, and by the end of the thirteenth century, the Ptolemaic cosmology and astronomy was ascendant in the West. In the late thirteenth and early fourteenth century Aristotelian science was widely under attack, and these attacks contributed further to the contemporary triumph of Ptolemaic over Aristotelian cosmography and astronomy.

Although not essential to the Ptolemaic ideology, another error was adopted by Ptolemaists as well as other astronomers. It will bear repeating that that error was not that the Earth was flat; throughout the Middle Ages, whatever lay opinion might have been, the sphericity of the earth was taken for granted by astronomers. On another question, however, confusion continued. In the ninth century a Muslim astronomer Thābit ibn-Qurra had revived the erroneous Hellenistic idea that the accumulative lagging of the solar year behind the sidereal year, known as 'the procession of the equinoxes', was to be explained by an oscillation of the highest spheres, and this theory of the variation in the size of the precessions of the equinoxes was transmitted to the West by the twelfth-century Spanish Muslim Al-Bitruji (or Alpetrajius).

Medieval astronomy, in short, involved the Aristotelian view of the physical cosmos and the Ptolemaic hypothesis of planetary motion. It was based on the idea of perfect motion of the heavenly bodies, which were themselves perfect and unchangeable, and of imperfect motion of the sublunary bodies, which were subject to corruption and decay. Obviously, in such a universe one set of physical laws regulated terrestrial bodies and another celestial bodies. Aristotelian physics and Ptolemaic epicycles and eccentrics, however, only lamely explained the apparently irregular motions of the heavenly bodies; the medieval astronomer was constrained to posit a system involving eighty wheels, all operating in crystalline spheres—which was sometimes an awkward postulate. In addition, the assumptions that the Earth was immovable and that the universe was finite and thus closed, though not beyond question by a few, were long accepted by most thinkers.

Despite the errors in underlying assumptions, the West, following Islamic precedents, had in recent centuries introduced some improved observational methods in astronomy. Since the eleventh century, the astrolabe had been used in viewing lunar eclipses. The eleventh-century 'Toledo Tables' of celestial data, a Muslim achievement, were superseded two centuries later by the 'Alfonsine Tables', which, in a Latin version, were much used in the West during the succeeding century and were finally made available in print in 1483. The 'Alfonsine Tables' were, to be sure, more important as tokens of royal and scholarly interest in practical astronomy than of progress in science. Yet by 1300, both scholarly and popular curiosity over the order of the universe was keen. Dante's *Banquet* and *Divine Comedy* vividly reflect the general public interest, and there had been stored up an accumulation of knowledge that in several regards was on the right track.

For all that, scholars, with few exceptions, still relied on astrology. The widespread concern with the stars prevailed not only because of idle curiosity regarding everyday phenomena or justifiable alarm over startling astronomical events, and not only because of the need to fix the calendar and to compute the movable feasts. If the Earth and all thereon were surrounded by circling spheres, the outermost of which was the home of the moving Spirit, the Prime Cause, of the universe, the movements of the stars must affect and might reveal the future of life on the Earth, which was the centre of the entire system; the heavenly bodies must radiate an ethereal fluid and other substances or influences that helped to shape human destinies, and the position of the celestial bodies at any given moment would therefore be of the utmost significance in determining human affairs. Hence the twelve signs of the zodiac (i.e. the fanciful figures that symbolize the changing position of the sun in relation to the planets) were considered to be an excellent means of forecasting one's future. The casting of horoscopes was a common practice not only at a child's birth but also for more widely important events, and 'experts' made a profitable business of it. Physicians relied on medical astrology, including the age-old belief in 'critical days' for bloodletting and other treatments.

The recurring terrors of the Black Death undoubtedly accentuated the trend, and the revival of Classical Antiquity provided no cure for it. Popes and princes had their official astrologers. Professors in the universities accepted astrology, even exploited it. When Lorenzo de' Medici established a university at Pisa, the demand of the students persuaded him to set up a professorship of astrology. One humanist, Pico della Mirandola, raised his voice against the current practice, but contemporaries, even his fellow-Platonist Ficino, generally defended it.

Astrology nevertheless had other critics as well. Petrarch and John of Vicenza, a Dominican monk, both roundly condemned the practice as fraud, and Petrarch also condemned as charlatans physicians who relied on astrologers. Churchmen often were hostile to astrology. Augustinus Triumphus of Ancona, a contemporary of Dante, denounced it and other occult practices as weapons of the enemies of the Christian faith and warned Pope Clement V against them. Despite their faults in other regards, the Avignon popes opposed superstitions of this sort and gave serious attention to calendar reform. In France Oresme, Ailly, and Buridan, all good churchmen, condemned astrology, as did their German disciple Heinrich von Langenstein. In the sixteenth century Guicciardini attacked it on grounds of common sense, pointing out that in the public eye a single correct guess by an astrologer justified a hundred errors on his part, whereas a non-astrologer was discredited by a single error among a hundred correct guesses. Despite such denunciations, astrology has retained a certain hold on the popular mind to this day.

As in other fields of science, after 1300 progress in astronomy seemed for a long time almost to level off. Dante's cosmography accurately reflects the general understanding, not only for his own generation but also for the ensuing century or more. His was a geocentric Earth surrounded by heavenly spheres and containing various nether regions. During the fourteenth and fifteenth centuries no serious criticism of the Ptolemaic cosmology and astronomy arose in Europe, although otherwise the age was noted for its keen attacks on Aristotelian science and although during the same period the Islamic world was subjecting the Ptolemaic theory to modifications.

No ground was lost, however, and indeed some progress was recorded. For example, demand for calendar reform recurred. In the year 1318 a scheme for a perpetual calendar was proposed to Pope John XXII. Yet not until Regiomontanus's attempt (c. 1474) was any noteworthy effort made to change the calendar, and it was frustrated (see Chapter XV). Also, new catalogues of stars were compiled. The 'Alfonsine Tables' were supplemented and corrected for local meridians by careful observations made and recorded in several scientific centres of the West, greatly increasing the accuracy of astronomy and navigation. Weather records were kept over a period of seven years (1337–44) by an English priest, William Morley, who also wrote a treatise on weather forecasting, based, to be sure, on Classical works and everyday lore but presented in a remarkably objective fashion.

Advances in the study of astronomy were largely dependent upon improvements in observational instruments. Instrument makers of the Middle Ages, especially in Islamic lands, had worked out noteworthy refinements in the astrolabe—a full-circle, graduated instrument for sighting the sun, moon, or stars. (Pl. 86.) From this was developed the quadrant—a quarter-circle instrument. Muslims of the fourteenth and fifteenth centuries wrote about variants on the quadrant, among them the 'universal quadrant', the sine-quadrant, and the 'datur quadrant', which was a full-circle astrolabe with one quadrant delineated in precise detail. The term 'sextant'—one sixth of a full circle—is generally restricted to a later instrument of greater precision, used by Tycho Brahe and his seventeenth-century successors.

Prior to the sixteenth century the West generally followed in the path of the superior Muslim scientists. In southern France early in the fourteenth century, however, Levi ben Gerson invented the 'cross staff'—sometimes attributed to Regiomontanus. This instrument consisted of a long, graduated, nearly horizontal staff with a shorter perpendicular crosspiece, which was movable. The observer adjusted the crosspiece until he could sight the horizon beyond the lower end and the desired heavenly body beyond the upper end. During the fifteenth century the astrolabe, the quadrant, and the cross-staff were in common use by Western mariners.

Noteworthy astronomical speculation (without much resort to instruments) was carried on at Paris by Oresme and Ailly in the fourteenth century. Oresme, generally considered the more brilliant of the two, had some potentially fruitful ideas concerning planetary motions and the plurality of worlds,[8] but his respect for the Bible and perhaps his multifarious interests kept him from following them through. He also did much to spread existing astronomical ideas by translating into the French vernacular (with a commentary) Aristotle's treatise *On the Heavens and the Earth* (under the title *Le Livre du Ciel et du Monde*) and by writing a treatise on the subject in French (*On the*

Sphere). In these works he cast doubt on Aristotle's view that the idea of a plurality of worlds must be erroneous. Whereas Oreme tended to criticize Ptolemaic astronomy, Ailly popularized it.

It is sometimes thought that Oresme, and later Albert of Saxony, derived their ideas concerning the rotation of the earth from Buridan. Buridan was familiar with both Ptolemaic and Aristotelian astronomy and questioned the validity of some of his great predecessors' theories, notably the Ptolemaic system of eccentric spheres and epicycles. His most noteworthy achievement, however, was his application of terrestrial mechanics to celestial bodies. He expressed the idea, novel for its day, that although the initial notion of all bodies had indeed come originally from God, it had continued thereafter without any additional miraculous intervention.[9] Speculations on this theory continued over two centuries, and it was further elaborated by Tartaglia, Galileo, Kepler, and Newton (see Chapter XIV).

Parisian scientific influences were spread to Vienna by Albert of Saxony and Heinrich von Langenstein. Both men, after studying and teaching at Paris, had gone to the newly founded University of Vienna. There Albert continued to investigate the problems of mechanics that Buridan had posed. Like most of the Parisian astronomers, Albert inclined toward Ptolemy, though with modifications. Langenstein's rational bent not only made him a bitter opponent of astrology but also led him to experiment in various scientific fields. He was responsible for the establishment of an astronomical observatory at Vienna. In the fifteenth century Purbach, after an impressive career as royal astronomer in Hungary, continued this scientific activity at the University of Vienna, whose reputation in the sciences now eclipsed that of Paris, where decline had set in.

Purbach's pupil Regiomontanus carried this scientific spirit to Germany. He built perhaps the best equipped astronomical observatory of the age at Nuremberg and also set up a printing press from which he published astronomical works and improved calendars. The Florentine cosmographer Paolo de Pozzo Toscanelli (1397–1482) had already observed the phenomenon in 1456 later to be known as Halley's Comet (see Chapter XIV), and Regiomontanus himself made some careful observations of the Great Comet of 1472. From the available data he was able to lay the basis for a modern astronomy of comets.

All of the Paris-inspired astronomers accepted Ptolemy to a greater or lesser extent but were troubled by the inconsistencies of the Ptolemaic system. As observatories like those at Vienna and Nuremberg accumulated factual data, scholars pondered over the conflict between observed fact and tradition as well as between Ptolemy and Aristotle. When young Nicolas Copernicus (1473–1543) went to Italy to study at Bologna and Padua, he encountered a lengthy background of speculation on the motion of the Earth. Questioning of the Aristotelian–Ptolemaic cosmography since the twelfth century, along with the concomitant progress in mathematics and astronomy, had encouraged doubts in the minds of several scientists. A partly heliostatic theory had found some adherents since the fourth century BC, when Heraclides of Pontus had suggested that some of the planets revolved around the sun. Copernicus added to the solar satellites the remaining planets, including the Earth, in 'a great orbit around the Sun, which is the centre of the world'. The full implications of this hypothesis and its detailed complications were not to be worked out completely until Newton's day (see Chapter XIV).

The Attack upon Aristotelian Physics

In the twelfth and thirteenth centuries, as Greek scientific works became available to the West in Latin translations of Arabic translations of the original Greek, a veritable renaissance of physics, comparable to that of mathematics, began. In physics, the authority of Aristotle was not eclipsed by some other authority as it was in astronomy. In expurgated editions Aristotle's *Physics*, along with the *Metaphysics*, by the third quarter of the thirteenth century was widely used and, in fact, became assignments at the University of Paris, the unexpurgated materialism of Averroes replacing Aristotle as the forbidden reading. Thus Robert Grosseteste, Roger Bacon, William of Auvergne, Albertus Magnus, and Thomas Aquinas had had no qualms about using some of Aristotle's ideas.

Thirteenth-century Christendom was well provided also with other Classical and Muslim works of physics. Ancient Greek thought about light and vision was well summed up in Euclid's *Optics*. The Greeks knew that a ray of light travels in a straight line, that it takes the shortest path from its source via a mirror to the eye, and that the angles of its incidence and reflection are equal. Euclid and Ptolemy had thought that light emanated from the eye, and not until the eleventh century did the Arab scientist Alhazen (Ibn al-Haitham) present the idea that the form of the object perceived passes from the object into the eye and is transmuted by the ocular lens. Alhazen's *Treasury of Optics* remained until the seventeenth century the basic work on light and optics. Of somewhat less influence was William of Moerbeke's translation (*c.* 1260) from Greek into Latin of Hero's *Catoptrica* (mistakenly attributed to Ptolemy), with its theory concerning light rays.

Roger Bacon (d. 1294) had been one of the most original thinker-experimenters in physics in the Europe of his day. His experiments with lenses and mirrors, however, had little immediate influence, and his writings on optics (largely based on Muslim findings) were less often consulted than those of now more obscure contemporaries. More general and still less influential for contemporaries were his theories of mechanics and of the practical application of theoretical science. Ramon Lull (d. 1315), in his several works on physics, mathematics, medicine, and navigation, also helped to transmit Islamic erudition to the West.

Until the fifteenth century the study of mechanics advanced little beyond

Archimedes, and the Aristotelian theory of mechanics remained relatively intact. That theory posited that all terrestrial objects (made up of the four elements—earth, water, air, and fire) had a 'natural' tendency to move towards or away from the centre of the universe, which was considered to be the centre of the earth; any other motion was 'violent' motion. Motion was dependent upon a mover; God was the cause of motion, the Unmoved Mover. An object was assumed to move only so long as it was in contact with a 'mover', and without variation of force its motion was assumed to be uniform and without acceleration. All objects were regarded as inherently light or heavy by nature, tending to fall with a speed varying in accordance with their relative mass. The so-called Merton Theorem of Uniform Acceleration, set forth about 1330 at Merton College, held that a uniform acceleration could be measured in terms of its medial, or mid-point, velocity, but, although a free fall was recognized as a pat example of uniform acceleration, it was still believed that bodies of different masses, if dropped from the same height at the same moment, would fall to the ground at different velocities, the heavier mass reaching the ground first.

The development of an anti-Aristotelian physics after 1300 was closely related to the nominalists' attack on the Aristotelian Scholasticism of Aquinas and his following (see Chapter VI). Ockham in England and Nicolas d'Autre-court and Buridan at the University of Paris, taking up the physical problems over which thirteenth-century Franciscans such as Bacon had pondered, raised serious doubts about the fundamental Aristotelian principles under-lying them. In his speculations Ockham came close to the modern concept of the tendency of a moving body to keep moving, and Autrecourt inferred an atomistic theory of matter, space, and motion that was Epicurean rather than Aristotelian. Buridan, adopting the anti-Aristotelian, Classical theories which Jordanus Nemorarius had revived a century earlier, further developed the idea of *impetus*—i.e. of a motive quantity imparted to a mass by a propelling force, much as a quantity of heat might be imparted by a heating source. While Buridan's most daring idea probably was that earthly mechanics could and should be applied to celestial bodies, perhaps the best example of his speculative acumen is found in his explanation of the motion of a terrestrial object thrown by hand. The capacity to receive impetus, he reasoned, would be proportional to the density and volume (i.e. the quantity of *materia prima*) of the projectile; that was why a stone could be thrown farther than a feather. The impetus of any projected object, however, would gradually be dimin-ished by air resistance and the object's own gravity, which inclines it to move in a different direction. He explained the acceleration of falling bodies by positing an increase in impetus impressed by its own gravity.[10] Buridan thus altered the Aristotelian explanation of motion as due to a 'mover' in contact with a mass; for him impetus might be present in a mass without constant contact with its original source. If that was a step toward modern concepts of motion, it still was in one essential different from the Newtonian view of motion as a form of inertia—i.e. as continuing without a cause of motion. The thoroughness and persuasiveness of Buridan's presentation rather than the originality of his ideas (for they were not wholly new) made him influential in the new universities of the West.

Oresme, though primarily a mathematician, also examined problems of physics. While he was more abstract in his thinking than Buridan, he too urged constant analysis and criticism of surface appearances and of generalizations based on inadequate evidence. He presented some concrete ideas on physics in his mathematical treatises and in his commentaries on Aristotle. He pondered the problems of motion, gravity, and impetus, vaguely anticipating the theories of Copernicus and Galileo. He questioned the Aristotelian concept of four elements, suggesting that there might be others (e.g. light and motion) that were more fundamental.

While the nominalists were thus hammering at Aristotelian physics from the speculative and philosophical point of view, other mathematician-physicists were likewise examining the Aristotelian ideas of mechanics. The Merton College mathematician Bradwardine did some significant work in physics. He worked out new explanations (not always accurate) concerning velocity of rotation and resistance to speed. He applied mathematical precision to problems such as infinity and the relative influence of gravity on liquid surfaces at different distances from the earth's centre.

The diminishing but persistent importance of Aristotelian science is well illustrated by the investigation of the cause of rainbows. Theodoric (Dietrich) of Freiburg (d. 1311), a Dominican mystic, philosopher, and physicist, derived much of his treatise on light, colours, and rainbows from Aristotle and Averroes, but his theory of rainbows reveals a high quality of independent research and reasoning. Earlier Western physicists had studied the rainbow and had suggested an explanation of it based on refraction and reflection, but none of them had worked out so convincing an explanation as Theodoric. Late in the thirteenth century a Persian, Quṭb al-Dīn Shīrāzī, had pursued the problem along similar lines and with similar results as those later obtained by Theodoric, but Shīrāzī's conclusions probably had not yet been transmitted to the West. Thus a similar theory was doubtless hit upon independently by both Western and Islamic scientists.

Theodoric began by summarizing the data drawn from Aristotle's *Meteorology* (through early commentaries thereon) and Ibn al-Haitham's *Optics*, but he was not content to rest there. He went on to formulate some novel conclusions, using results obtained by his own experiments on the refraction of light. His explanation of the primary rainbow invoked a double refraction of the sun's rays in drops of water and a single reflection. For a second rainbow, he invoked a second reflection, dimmer than the first. His explanation was generally accepted in western Europe, and was amplified by Descartes, without basic modifications until the Newtonian era (see Chapter XIV). Theodoric used Aristotle as a good but not the sole source of scientific theory.

Less theoretical problems than those of motion and light, of course, engaged the physicist's attention. From an early date magnetism and electricity had fascinated man, although understanding of their properties was meagre. Lightning was a familiar phenomenon, and the properties of lodestones were often referred to in both Greek and Latin literature. The Chinese are supposed to have long known that a freely suspended magnet will point north and south, but only around the year 1100 did this fact become known in the West. About that time magnetic compasses were first mentioned in Europe, but in the thirteenth and fourteenth centuries the compass needle and its properties were much discussed by Lull among others, and increased use of the compass brought on more numerous and safer voyages from the Mediterranean to the English Channel and more shipping in the wintertime in the Mediterranean itself. By the end of the fifteenth century the magnetic declination of the compass needle was better understood, largely because of Columbus's observations, raising the problem of properly determining the variations of the compass and giving hope that the solution of that problem might help to fix longitudes at sea. In the same century the dip or inclination to the horizontal of a freely suspended magnetized needle was observed, opening up yet another prospect of solving the problem of longitude at sea (see Chapter XIV).

Alchemy and the Birth of Chemistry

The development of chemistry during the intervening centuries, less like physics and mathematics but more like astronomy, was complicated by magical and religious considerations. Thirteenth-century alchemy, like astrology, was deeply rooted in Babylonian, Egyptian, and Greek lore, which had come to the West largely by way of Islamic writings. Scientists everywhere usually assumed with Aristotle that the basic chemical elements were earth, air, fire, and water, and delved into the relationship of these elements to one another and to the supposed primal matter ('substance' or 'essence') of all material things. Islamic alchemical treatises held that the six major metals, though of the same essence, were correctly arranged in an ascending scale—tin, lead, iron, copper, silver, and gold. Man's natural inquisitiveness joined with his natural acquisitiveness to suggest that the commoner metals might be transmuted into the more precious ones if only the right 'tincture' (philosopher's stone or elixir) and the right method of purifying the baser metals were discovered. The proper combination of the 'principles' of sulphur and mercury (as expounded by the eighth-century Muslim alchemist Jābir ibn Hayyān) was considered decisive in this process.

Popes and princes were no less wholehearted in their support of this science than of astrology. Islamic alchemical ideas were translated into Latin by twelfth- and thirteenth-century scholars, and along with Aristotle's *Meteorology*, they were known to Albertus Magnus, Roger Bacon, and other thirteenth-century scientists. Although Albertus, Bacon, Lull, and some other Christian scholars were not convinced of the essential unity of all matter and had suspicions concerning some alchemists, they were willing to grant the possibility of the transmutation of metals and wrote treatises concerning that and other aspects of alchemy. Bacon sent the pope one of his alchemical works; Michael Scot was encouraged at Emperor Frederick II's court; and the physician Arnaldus de Villa Nova (d. 1313) was patronized by Pope Clement V.

Since alchemy offered lucrative possibilities to the unscrupulous, charlatanry flourished. The church, even the none too squeamish Avignon popes, disapproved of false alchemy. In 1317 Pope John XXII forbade the sort of alchemy that encouraged men to expect to gain riches through the transmutation of metals, and he also condemned other forms of magic. Yet, if no tin was magically transmuted into gold, primitive chemistry served some constructive purposes. Alongside the charlatanry, a well-intentioned, empirical chemical technique also throve. Knowledge of the properties of alcohol, acids, and alloys accumulated, and chemical apparatus improved. Even before a well-based chemical method had begun to develop (sixteenth century), the metal-refiner, the physician, the brewer, the soap manufacturer, and other technicians hit upon chemical ways and means that brought improvements in pigments, glass making, smelting, tanning, paper manufacture (from rags), pharmaceutical compounds, gunpowder, and other chemical processes and products. An unproductive but no less interesting experiment was that of the English physician John of Gaddesden, who attempted to distil fresh water from sea water.

The continuing doubts about the authorship of several alchemical treatises produced in western Europe reflects the sometimes clandestine, 'hermetical' nature of their work. Some of them were ascribed erroneously, or perhaps with deliberate effort to deceive, to authors of high standing. A few of the best were attributed to the great Jābir (called in Europe Geber) but perhaps were written by a European no earlier than the thirteenth century. In the early fourteenth century an Italian named Pietro Buono compiled from various Classical and Islamic sources a work entitled *The Precious Pearl*, a massive, encyclopedic collection on the subject of alchemy. Writings ascribed to Arnaldus de Villa Nova and Raimon Lull were also often cited by later alchemists. During the first half of the century the Catalonian John of Rupescissa manifested an interest in medical alchemy, considering the philosopher's elixir important for the prevention of internal corruption. He wrote a treatise on the quintessences, part of which was arranged under medical headings. Later fourteenth-century works by an otherwise unidentifiable Frenchman called Ortolanus, by the Englishman John Dombelay, and by the German Wimandus Rothschild, though not of impressive quality, give some indication of the quantity of alchemical compilations. In the fifteenth century appeared a plethora of treatises, most of which were inferior compilations of earlier materials, with descriptions of vain experiments with the transmutation of metals. Occasional condemnations of all professional alchemists indiscriminately as charlatans indicate the wide prevalence of their practices.

THE BIOLOGICAL SCIENCES IN EUROPE

Early Botany, Physiology, and Medicine

Biological knowledge can be divided roughly into that of plant life (botany), of animal life (zoology), and of human life (physiology and anatomy). During the period with which we are here concerned (1300–1530) these fields were not sciences either as systematically organized bodies of knowledge or as sets of laws based upon observed regularities. While menageries, aviaries, and botanical gardens had been made available in several Western centres by rulers and wealthy noblemen, the relevant data were chiefly derived directly or indirectly from Aristotle's treatises and certain other Classical and Islamic works.

By 1300 scholars of both the Islamic lands and Christian Europe had access to a considerable number of treatises on the various aspects of biology. Pliny's *Natural History*, with its detailed information on minerals, animals, and related matters had been immensely popular in the West throughout the Middle Ages. Various works of Aristotle on animals and other naturalia had been translated during the thirteenth century from Arabic into Latin, and a new translation of his *Historia Animalium* had been made directly from the Greek by William of Moerbeke. Botany was based largely on Dioscorides' *Materia Medica* (first century AD). Western Scholastics, notably Albertus Magnus, had written excellent treatises on various aspects of biology, revealing therein not only a wide knowledge of the earlier literature on the subject but also a keenly critical attitude toward their sources. Such studies should not, though they easily can, be lost to view amid the more numerous and popular but less admirable illustrated bestiaries.

In Europe as elsewhere botanical investigation was largely motivated by a quest for pharmaceutical herbs. In this connection, Westerners relied not only on Dioscorides (in abbreviated and alphabetized versions) but more often on a condensed medical botany attributed to Apuleius Platonicus (c. 400 AD), which sometimes was accompanied by an equally unimpressive book on animals and their uses for medicine attributed to Sextus Placitus Papiriensis (c. AD 400). The sections on plants (usually with shorter ones on minerals and animals) were similarly condensed in several thirteenth-century encyclopedias. One of the most noteworthy of the herbals still largely in use in 1300 was that of the thirteenth-century Rufinus. It was a compendium of herbal lore from Dioscorides, other non-Islamic Latin sources, and perhaps, in small part, the author's own observations.[11] A surprising amount of the available knowledge was found in alphabetically arranged medical or pharmaceutical manuscripts. One such alphabetical listing, notable for its quality and influence, was the *Synonyma Medicinae*, a dictionary of about six hundred items (chiefly herbs), compiled by Dr Simon of Genoa about 1300 from late Classical and Islamic sources.

The gradual increase of naturalism in contemporary art was reflected in the rich, even lavish miniatures with which, from about 1300 on, an increasing number not only of religious but also of secular manuscripts were illustrated. In Europe during the fourteenth and fifteenth centuries illustrated compendia both of general natural history and of specific fields became more common. Conrad of Megenberg's *Buch der Natur* (*c.* 1350) was a vernacular translation of a thirteenth-century encyclopedia. Matthaeus Sylvaticus' *Pandectae* of materia medica treated botanical items more intensively than previous compilations. Thomas of Breslau produced a herbal based to a certain extent on his own observations. Benedetto Rinio's album contained almost five hundred naturalistic illustrations of plants; the original manuscript is today one of the treasures of the Library of San Marco in his native city, Venice.

Late medieval manuscripts contain occasional illustrated treatises also on both the anatomy and the optics of sight. Available evidence points to late-thirteenth-century Italy—Pisa or Florence—as the setting for the invention of eyeglasses as distinct from single-lens reading or burning glasses; no valid ground exists for attributing it to Roger Bacon. That spectacles were common during the fourteenth century is evidenced by mention of them by several contemporaries including Guy de Chauliac and Petrarch. Furthermore, a mid-century portrait of a cardinal at Trevise depicts him wearing glasses. Until the beginning of the sixteenth century it seems that most spectacles consisted of convex lenses. Later in the same century concave lenses, for shortsightedness, were developed along with other minor mechanical improvements. Progress was slow, but soon spectacles were being manufactured in the Netherlands as well as in northern Italy.[12]

Until well into modern times physicians were torn between the humoral tradition of the Hippocratics and the 'specifics' tradition of the rival Cnidians. The authority of Hippocrates and Galen supported the humoralist doctrines, and throughout Ancient and medieval times the most widely accepted theories of physiology were derived from their ideas of the four qualities and the four humors. The qualities were hot, cold, dry, and moist, and the humors were blood, phlegm, yellow bile, and black bile. Health was believed to be brought about by the proper interaction of the humors and the qualities, and illness by a lack of balance among them. Medical treatments (bleeding, for example) were designed to redress an unbalanced condition.

Supporters of the 'specifics' tradition held that different kinds of disease might have different causes, basing their argument on the fact that certain 'specifics' were effective in only certain cases. A 'doctrine of signatures' was clearly propounded by Paracelsus (see Chapter XIV) but was traceable to older naturalists like Pliny and Dioscorides. It held that certain plants and minerals were marked by some sign or trait suggesting a particular medicinal use—thus leading to the naming of certain plants—e.g. the pulmonaria, or lungwart. Not, however, until the discovery of cinchona as a 'specific' for malaria—during the seventeenth century—did the 'specifics' tradition begin to be predominant.[13]

Plague, it was assumed, had to have a more general explanation than either of these schools could give. The Black Death in the fourteenth century and, centuries later, the plague of 1665 were attributed variously to the wrath of God, vapours carried in the air, and astrological phenomena. Oresme in the fourteenth century attempted to explain illness in quasi-chemical terms, though still mixed with magic and mysticism, and Paracelsus and some other physicians of the sixteenth century initiated iatrochemistry, or chemiatrics, attributing disease to chemical disarrangements in the body and attempting cures through chemical prescriptions, but these iatrochemists wrought little change in the persistent humoral pathology of their times. Nor did they greatly advance the practice of medicine. Blood-letting continued as a major treatment for disease, in accordance with the theory that the body must be purged of noxious matter. Methods of blood-letting varied, and several are illustrated in contemporary manuscripts and books:[14] (1) puncturing a vein at a specific point for a specific ailment; (2) cupping—i.e. drawing the blood by the application of a heated cup so as to provide suction as the air within it cooled and contracted, and (3) placing leeches on the skin.

Some Early Advances in Biological Research

In contrast, the progress of anatomical investigation in the West during the early fourteenth century was impressive. Salernitan surgeons, though obliged to restrict dissection to pigs, had engaged in anatomical research by that method as early as the eleventh century. Two centuries later dissection of human bodies was formally permitted in certain universities, notably Bologna and Montpellier; the much misinterpreted bull of Pope Boniface VIII (1299) was not intended to prohibit anatomical dissection but rather the cutting-up and boiling of bodies for other reasons. In any event, by the beginning of the fourteenth century the science of internal anatomy had achieved marked advances through dissection, with the result that Italy led the West in the field of anatomy, and despite Ibn-al-Nafīs' significant work of the previous century the West now led the Islamic countries. Surgeons such as Mondino da' Luzzi and Gentile de Foligno were among the many Italian pioneers in this field. Mondino's *Anatomy* (1316) has been called (perhaps too favourably) 'the first modern work' on that subject. The amazing achievements of his contemporaries Lanfranc and Mondeville will claim our attention when we come to discuss the practice of surgery (Chapter XV). As in some of the other fields of science, comparison with the remarkable advances of the thirteenth and the early fourteenth century, particularly in anatomy, makes it appear as if the biological sciences made little advance, though they held their own, for about two centuries thereafter.

The anatomical sketches of Jacopo Berengaria Da Carpi (*c.* 1460–1530) and of Da Vinci and Vesalius' admirably illustrated *Seven Books on the Structure of the Human Body* were to mark a new era of constant progress in the science of anatomy (see Chapter XIV). (Pl. 93b, c.) The rapid expansion of printing and illustration was a significant factor in that progress. New illustrated editions and commentaries on Dioscorides and other ancient authorities on plants, animals, and minerals appeared, and even before 1530 more and more scholars who had made first-hand observations compiled specialized treatises on quadrupeds, fishes, birds, and plants. Some of their works replaced the treatises of Aristotle, Pliny, and Dioscorides as authoritative sources in certain fields of biology.

The independence from the spirit of the past was not always for the best, to be sure, since earlier works of merit, such as Rufinus' herbal, now were neglected and unknown.[15] Nevertheless, much new information was set forth. The enthusiasm of scholars for fresh data led them to observe nature more closely, to exchange first-hand observations with one another, and generally to increase the bounds of their knowledge beyond the manuscript or printed page. Even though many of their treatises were written for the purpose merely of providing encyclopedic minutiae or of making philological contributions, their intensive activity inspired further investigation, including the identification of unfamiliar items and the more accurate description of flora and fauna. The discovery and the colonization of distant lands in Asia and the New World provided knowledge of many strange species besides (see Chapter XV). The zeal for novel information sometimes dulled the edge of critical analysis or meaningful synthesis, permitting inaccurate or meaningless details sometimes to be repeated by successive compilers. Some of the most reputable scholars of the day were credulous of wonders resembling the monsters, miracles, and barnacle-geese usually attributed to the 'Dark Ages'. Nevertheless, they conscientiously gathered together stores of data useful to later scientists.

SCIENCE AND TECHNOLOGY OUTSIDE EUROPE

The technological skill and the scientific knowledge of the Aztecs and Incas that roused the admiration of the conquistadores has been referred to above (see Chapters I and XII). Since it did not, for the most part, enter the stream of world culture, it need not detain us here.

Prior to 1500, except perhaps in anatomy, the accomplishments of Europe were not noticeably more significant than those of other Eurasian cultures, for only after 1500 was Europe to forge rapidly ahead. A fortunate juxtaposition of several series of events favoured the development of western European science and technology. After 1200 western Europe was remarkably free of 'barbarian' intruders, whereas eastern Europe, Africa, and Asia were disrupted by Mongols, Timur and the Timurids, Ottoman Turks, and other invaders, giving Europe a chance to catch up with Muslim learning, acquired particularly through the Spanish Moors; interest in Islamic technology and science (themselves a combination of Greek, Hebrew, Indian, Persian, and Arabic ideas) was reinforced during the Renaissance by the revival of the learning and abstract thought of the Greeks and Romans; the growth of European trade and town life was concomitant and interrelated with the growth of a secular atmosphere and of willingness on the part of educated men to use their hands; and the rise of the spirit of humane learning during the Renaissance coincided with the questioning of traditional authority in the Conciliar Movement and the Reformation and with the increase in the patronage of national enterprise by royal dynasties. This interplay of events helped to provide for the West a set of circumstances that permitted the Renaissance absorption with Classical art and letters to make possible, even to stimulate, the eventual development of an independent scientific frame of mind and an experimental method among the learned few and the relatively rapid acceptance of technological and scientific innovation among the less learned many. In contrast, with notable exceptions, both the learned and the populace in other great centres of civilization remained bound to their traditional cultures and, when confronted with either home-grown or imported achievements, tended as a general rule to look upon innovation as undesirable or even dangerous. Yet, despite their preference for the ways of their ancestors and their unfavourable attitude toward originality, these more conservative cultures accomplished some scientific work of distinction.

Islamic Science and Technology

For several centuries after 1300, western Europe and the Middle East went their separate scientific ways, becoming more independent of and indifferent to each other's findings than before. If the work being done in Europe was barely known in Islamic lands, that of Islamic scientists seems to have been equally unknown in Europe. The probable unfamiliarity with Shīrāzī's optics in the West (and vice versa) has already been mentioned; his scientific methods led him not only to depart from Aristotle in optics but, in addition, to consider the possibility of the earth's rotation. A fourteenth-century Persian alchemist, al-Kāshani, produced an able study of ceramic chemistry (dealing especially with the manufacture of faience ware), which was not equalled in the West until the sixteenth century. Of similarly high quality were the treatises of the Egyptian al-Jildaki, likewise unknown to Westerners.

Outstanding scientific and technological achievements, however, were few during the fourteenth and fifteenth centuries in Islamic lands, and scholarly interests other than in grammar, religion, and administration generally found no great encouragement. If natural science still attracted creative men like those mentioned above in the generations around 1300, it was mostly as an intellectual luxury. Much of that luxury was devoted in the 1300's to the continuation of Muslim scholarship in biology, particularly in Egypt and Spain. Ibn-al-Khatīb and Ibn-Khātima of Spain corresponded on such matters as the Black Death and produced skilful analyses of it. The Egyptian scholar Al-Damīri's late-fourteenth-century compendium on animal life described, in alphabetical order, over a thousand animals. More popular than scholarly and exemplifying the failure to develop a true science of zoology, it was nevertheless comparable to earlier compendia. In both Egypt and Spain of the early fourteenth century, books on horses appeared, and in Egypt an excellent presentation of veterinary medicine was written by Ibn-al-Mundhir, master of the royal stables. Egypt also maintained, though less eminently, its remarkable tradition of achievement in the physiology and surgery of the human eye.

A little was done during this period in Islamic lands also to further the science of astronomy. The most notable of those responsible for that little were the circle of astronomers around Prince Ulūgh Beg (1394–1449) in Samarkand. Qādīzāde-i Rūmī became director of an elaborate observatory, built there in 1428, which produced significantly improved astronomical data. He wrote extensive theoretical studies, and several members of his staff, notably 'Alī Qūshjī (d. 1474), were, like him, independent mathematical thinkers.

Another scientific advance came in the growing knowledge of geography. We shall speak of the contributions in the fourteenth century of such scholars as Ibn-Baṭṭūta and Ibn-Khaldūn in the next section, where the major theme is the growing knowledge of the Mediterranean and Atlantic areas. In the fifteenth century Muslim navigation made significant additions to the knowledge of the geography of the Indian Ocean as well. Like their Christian confreres in the Mediterranean, Muslim sea-captains in the Indian Ocean improved their detailed knowledge of the coasts, but not until the Turkish navigators of the fifteenth century did their observations succeed in breaking down the Ptolemaic conceptions of that ocean's contours. The new knowledge was embodied in the treatises and charts of two sea-captains in particular. One of them, Aḥmad Ibn-Mājid, who wrote about 1489, combined the fruits of extensive personal experience with the whole geographical and astronomical culture of medieval Islam. He served as pilot across the Indian Ocean to Da Gama (see below), and the early Portuguese sea-guides show a close relationship to his work. The other, Al-Mahrī, who wrote about 1511, had a more extensive knowledge of the Malaysian area than Ibn-Mājid.

In the burgeoning Ottoman state, Sultan Mehmet II (1430–81) encouraged the transformation of what had been intellectually a frontier area into an eager centre of medical and mathematical study by favouring the immigration of learned Persians. In his time, scholars were able to insist, by joint action, on considerable academic freedom; yet the scientific tradition went deep only in a handful of men. 'Alī Qushjī migrated from Samarkand to Anatolia and founded the fruitful astronomical tradition of Ulūgh Beg in the Ottoman state. A fine observatory in that tradition was kept going by Luṭfī Toqadi (executed for heresy in 1494 despite the protests of many savants) and Mīrim

Chelebi (a descendent of 'Alī Qushjī, d. 1525). Turkish admirals took up the geographical work of the fifteenth-century Arabs—particularly Pīrī Re'īs, who wrote in 1513 and 1523 careful studies of the Mediterranean coasts, freely introducing West-European findings, including data derived from the discoveries of Columbus.

For all of this list of illustrious names, by the 1300's Islamic natural science had already reached its pinnacle and had also ceased to be an actively fertilizing element abroad, whether in China or in the West. For the two centuries considered in this chapter the course of Islamic science paralleled that of the West: although the preceding scientific level was maintained, relatively little was done to advance it. After 1300 geography as a general basic discipline advanced little in Islamic lands. On the other hand, government administration motivated a fact-finding trend toward particulars. The *Tables of Countries*, compiled by a Syrian prince named Abu-al-Fidā about 1320, is typical of the period. He described the various countries of the known world in the usual manner, listing the chief cities and locating them by their coordinates. Early in the fourteenth century, the Mamlūk ruler of Egypt ordered a survey of the soil, income, taxes, and other conditions of every village in Egypt. The Ottoman administrators at the height of the empire kept careful statistical records of population and the like.

Indian Science and Scholarship

The major Indian contributions to science and scholarship likewise were made before our period, but some work of considerable merit still went on. Competent studies in lexicography, grammar, and logic continued up to the beginning of the eighteenth century. Important Sanskrit dictionaries were produced in the fourteenth century, and Sanskrit grammars of scholarly value until 1700. Grammars and dictionaries of Tamil, Telugu, Kanarese, and other vernacular languages appeared throughout the period. Indian astronomy and mathematics were expounded in Sanskrit works during the early part of our period, while Sanskrit treatises on mathematics were translated into various vernaculars. The significant astronomical tables of Makaranda came out about 1478, and astronomical works by Ganesha as late as 1520, but the traditional system of Hindu mathematics and astronomy changed little and was essentially unaffected by Arabic and Persian writings. Descriptive works of genuine significance in biology—on plants and horses, elephants, and other animals—were written until the seventeenth century. Despite several works on nosology, including that of plant diseases, Hindu medicine in many particulars remained similar to that of the ancient Greeks and showed no marked advance. The celebrated medical treatises by Tisata in the fourteenth century, Bhāva Mishra in the sixteenth, and Lolimbarāja in the seventeenth were essentially expositions or expansions of earlier classics. A great Indian dictionary of materia medica, the *Madanavino-danighantu* by

Madanapāla, was completed about 1374. Indian anatomy suffered, as did anatomy almost everywhere, from the absence of dissection.

Chinese Science and Technology

In 1300, China was probably as far advanced in the field of science and practical technology as any other country. The Mongol conquests and policy had brought scientists and technicians to China from all parts of the world. The magnetic compass was familiar and was used for navigational purposes. Block-printing had long been in use, and movable type had also developed, although extensive use of it came only in Korea in the early fifteenth century. Gunpowder had long been known and was used not only for fireworks but also for bombs and the propelling of missiles. Chinese (as well as Indian and East Indian) shipbuilding was probably further advanced than European. The large seagoing junks were bigger and more seaworthy in many ways than European vessels, although they were slower and less manoeuvrable, and they incorporated compartments in the hold that could be closed off to keep the whole vessel from flooding when the hull was damaged,[16] a system not adopted in Europe until the nineteenth century. Francis Bacon said of printing, gunpowder, and the magnet: 'These three have changed the whole face and state of things throughout the world, the first in literature, the second in warfare, the third in navigation; whence have come innumerable changes; insomuch that no empire, no sect, no star, seems to have exerted greater power and influence in human affairs than these mechanical discoveries.'[17] If he was right, it is to Chinese technology that the world owes this debt.

In addition, Chinese alchemists, potters, doctors, and herbologists had developed extensive knowledge about a wide range of chemicals, drugs, herbs, and plants. Chinese medical and pharmaceutical knowledge was so respected outside China that a famous Persian physician and minister of the Mongol ruler of Persia caused (c. 1313) an encyclopedia of Chinese medicine, the *Tanksuq-nāmah-i Ilkhan dar funūn-i 'ulūm-i Khitāi*, to be prepared. It dealt with the pulse, anatomy, embryology, gynecology, pharmacology, and other medical subjects.[18] The arts of distillation and sugar refining, and such products as sorghum, carrots, kidney beans, pistachio, almonds, grape vines, and the drug chaulmoogra oil also seem to have been introduced into China during the Mongol period. A son of the founder of the Ming dynasty, after over eighteen years of careful investigation and with the assistance of a collaborator, completed (1406) a *Herbal for Relief from Famine*. Illustrated with woodcuts, it described the cultivation of types of plant that could be grown or eaten in times of flood and drought.

Chinese knowledge of geometry was probably inferior to that of the Arabic world. Nevertheless, the Chinese had, even before 1300, mastered sufficient mathematics to enable the astronomer and hydraulic engineer Kuo Shou-ching, presumably with the aid of scientists and technicians assembled by the Mongols at Cambaluc, to construct (1276–79) probably the finest set of astronomical instruments then known. Of his sixteen instruments several were new inventions, including a sighting tube with equatorial mounting. Some scholars think Kuo discovered for himself the basic principles of spherical trigonometry. In the thirteenth and the early fourteenth century, probably in part through inspiration from Islamic sources, several Chinese mathematicians developed an elaborate theoretical algebra. Pre-eminent among them was Chu Shi-chieh, whose major works appeared in 1299 and 1303. These promising developments were not continued under the Ming dynasty.[19]

Chinese engineering skill was also impressive. Clock-drives operated by water-power, various mechanical devices for raising water, suspension bridges with iron chains, and segmental arch bridges were all known in China by this time. The great atlas of Chu Ssu-pen, compiled between 1311 and 1321, employed the use of squares to plot distances on maps.

The Mongols did not keep up their programme of importing technicians, and once the conquerors were expelled, the Chinese tended to slough off things associated with them. The dominance of Neo-Confucian philosophy in the new Ming regime, with its emphasis on abstract philosophy, moral and ethical conduct, and the past did not provide a climate conducive to the advance of theoretical science. Still, during the period of Mongol decline and the first half-century of expansion under the Mings some technological advances were made in weapons and shipbuilding. Small cannon and a sort of proto-hand-gun seem to have developed, and Chinese ship architecture reached probably its highest level. Big vessels were constructed for the far-reaching voyages of Cheng Ho into the Indian Ocean and to the coast of Africa (1405–31). No technological insufficiency would have kept Chinese navigators from pushing westward around the tip of Africa, thus anticipating Vasco da Gama (though in reverse), had the responsible Confucian administrators or traders considered such distant voyages economically or otherwise worth while.

Chinese medicine was impeded by certain erroneous theories concerning the cause of disease—such as evil spirits or an imbalance between *yin* and *yang*—and the absence of dissection. Even so, it had accumulated and under the Mings continued to accumulate empirical knowledge about diagnosis and the use of drugs, diets, and other remedies. Numerous large general medical treatises and accounts of the symptoms and treatment of specific diseases were written, including works on leprosy, smallpox, syphilis (which first appeared in China about the time of the arrival of the Portuguese), obstetrics, gynecology, eye diseases, and parasitology. Treatises also discussed acupuncture, a method of therapeutics peculiar to China, and medical systems derived from it. Acupuncture—the relief of pain by sticking needles into prescribed points of the body—has been practised for centuries, the punctures being supposed to release a surplus of either *yin* or *yang*. Among the various medical schools competing with one another and engaging in acrimonious debate, the most celebrated physician of the Mongol period was Chu Tan-ch'i (1281–1358), and a famous physician of the early Ming period was Chang Chieh-pin. The former emphasized malnutrition as a basic source of disease; the latter wrote many works, including treatises on the pulse, fevers, midwifery, children's diseases, and smallpox.

Japanese Medicine

During the Ashikaga period Japanese science and medicine were very largely derived from Chinese sources. The writings of Li Tung-yüan (of the Chin period) and Chu Tan-ch'i (of the Mongol period) were especially in vogue (the Li-Chu School). Japanese physicians also wrote numerous treatises on general medicine and the treatment of specific diseases.

THE BEGINNINGS OF WORLD GEOGRAPHY

The thirteenth century had been a golden age for Christian, Muslim, and Far Eastern travellers, and therefore for the accumulation in all civilized lands of geographical data concerning distant regions. The far-flung Mongol empire, especially under enlightened khans such as Kublai, had made possible travel from Europe to and from China by way of the mid-Asiatic land routes. Europeans also might go via the Persian Gulf or the Red Sea to India, the Spice Islands, and as far as China. Chinese travellers, explorers, and scholarly geographers were especially enterprising. Thirteenth-century emissaries from the khans to India, Persia, and the Near East wrote of the 'barbarian peoples' visited—even of certain far regions in the West. During the time that Marco Polo was in China, having voyaged in the opposite direction a Christian Nestorian priest of Chinese birth, Bar Sauma, was sent in 1287 from the khan to the pope to arrange an alliance against the Muslims. He visited Constantinople and Rome and travelled in France and England also. His was not the only embassy exchanged between the khans and the popes, though probably the most interesting one.

The Christian and the Mongol world of the thirteenth century were perhaps better acquainted with each other than with the Muslim Near East. Yet the Chinese knew comparatively little about western Europe and Africa, and the Europeans knew little about China and almost nothing about the other regions of Asia or about Africa south of the Mediterranean coastal countries. Learned men in Muslim and Christian lands had a world view roughly comparable to the Ptolemaic maps, in which little beyond the lands bordering on the Mediterranean Sea and the Indian Ocean was clearly portrayed.

For the generation or two before 1300 geographical knowledge began rapidly to expand. In Europe diplomatic expeditions (e.g. those of Giovanni da Piano di Carpini, William de Rubruquis, Buscarello de Ghizolfi, and Bar Sauma), religious missions (e.g. those of Giovanni di Monte Corvino and Odoric de Pordenone), and commercial ventures (e.g. those of the Polos) contributed immeasurably to interest in and knowledge of the rich and highly cultured peoples of Asia. Meanwhile, seafaring Westerners were renewing the efforts of the Ancients to sail around Africa to the Orient. In the thirteenth century cartography also made great progress. The medieval *mappae mundi* had generally showed only the lands along the central waterways that stretched from the Atlantic through the Mediterranean, the Persian Gulf or the Red Sea, to the Indian Ocean and the Spice Islands. For example, the Hereford *Mappa Mundi* (about 1280) was centred on Jerusalem and showed nothing of detail concerning Mongolia and China. Eventually central and eastern Asia were shown more clearly, though still vaguely, on world maps; and detailed maps, such as those giving itineraries to Italy, Palestine, or England, noticeably improved. Roger Bacon's *Opus Major* contained the only important geographical treatise produced in the West before 1300. Familiar with the Asiatic travel accounts of his contemporaries, he believed that the southern hemisphere was inhabited and that India might possibly be reached by sailing westward.

Islamic geography from the ninth to the fourteenth century was dominated by the work of al-Khwārizmī. Whereas Christian maps of the Middle Ages often were centred on Jerusalem, his Muslim successors represented the universe as a cupola centred on Arin (the corrupted name of Ujjain in India, a major centre of astronomical study). Dictionaries by Muslim traveller-geographers of the thirteenth century were available, describing in alphabetical order cities, mountains, islands, and other features of physical and political geography; and thirteenth-century Persian, Spanish, and other Muslim travellers wrote intelligently of lands as far distant as Mongolia, northern Europe, Iceland, and the Senegal River region in Africa.

Abu 'Abdullāh Mohammed Ibn-Baṭṭūta (1304–78) was in some ways the most astonishing of Muslim travellers. Born in Tangiers, he travelled on several separate voyages as far north as the khanate of the Kipchaks (in modern Russia), as far east as Cambaluc (Peking) and Amoy Harbour, as far south as Timbuktu, and as far west as Spain. Altogether he covered about 75,000 miles and wrote of his experiences with interest and urbanity, giving information about peoples unfamiliar even to the Muslims of the time. His writings, unknown in the West until the nineteenth century, still provide a rare, if not unique, source of information on the peoples of Africa in his day, as well as of some other areas.

Several efforts were made by Muslims, especially in the Mamlūk regions, to collect miscellaneous information concerning local conditions at home and abroad. One of the most important of the theoretical geographical discussions of our period was contained in the history compiled in the late fourteenth century by Ibn-Khaldūn, of Tunis and Egypt. For our present purpose (but see also Chapter VIII) the most interesting part of his vast history is Volume I, *Muqaddamah fit-tarīkh* (*Prolegomena to History*), one chapter of which contains an introductory survey of geography in which he displayed his usual critical acumen. The use of geography as a handmaiden of history and of other subjects was characteristic of Muslim compilers, but Ibn-Khaldūn made far more of it, attempting to base on geography and other natural sciences a remarkable analysis of historical dynamics.

Fourteenth-Century Geographical Ideas in Europe

As missionaries, merchants, and ambassadors extended Europe's religious, commercial, diplomatic, and intellectual frontiers throughout the Near East, across Asia, and into the Far East, they made Asia Minor and the Black Sea into a veritable bridge between Europe and Asia, while the Red Sea, the Persian Gulf, and the Indian Ocean became active seaways to the Far East. The increasing geographical knowledge resulting from the more frequent occidental contacts with the Orient entered many Western encyclopedias in their articles dealing with geography. In his *Imago Mundi*, Ailly presented a sort of encyclopedia, or compendium, of geographical knowledge. It mentioned some little known lands in the Atlantic and indicated that the world was round but gave the impression that it was much smaller and contained less ocean than actually proved to be the case. A copy of it was eventually to come to the attention of Christopher Columbus and to lead him to conclude that Spain was much closer to India than it really was.

The new geographical knowledge was put to use in the travel of pilgrims to the Holy Land (then as now a popular centre of tourism) and in the work of missionaries in Asia. After 1328 the Franciscans, following in the footsteps of Giovanni di Monte Corvino, monopolized the Chinese missions, while the Dominicans were more active in the Near East (see Chapter V). These religious ambassadors, in turn, made possible a more regular and sometimes more reliable flow of information from Asia. Meanwhile a different kind of information came through commercial channels. A descriptive treatise concerning Palestine (accompanied by maps) was written about 1313 by a Venetian named Marino Sanudo, who had spent many years in the Near East. Pietro Vesconte collaborated with Sanudo and eventually moved to Venice, commercial rival of his native Genoa. Shortly thereafter, a Florentine, Francesco Pegalotti, also a long-time resident of the Near East, wrote his *Practica della Mercatura*, an economic geography of the trading world. In 1346 the Genoese created the first company for the exploitation of a colony, a joint-stock company to administer the island of Chios.[20]

For all that, fourteenth-century geographical ideas were still frequently based on second-hand reports and speculation rather than actual exploration. While the best minds accepted the notion of the sphericity of the earth, vast stretches of the globe were *terra incognita*. No one could be certain of what lay across the Atlantic in a westerly direction (for the lore of the few who had already stumbled upon the Western Hemisphere never became common). No European knew that Africa was circumnavigable. By the end of the fourteenth century, Novgorod's trappers and fur traders had amassed a fairly good sum of information about the coasts of the White Sea and the Arctic Ocean and about some Arctic islands, and Russian trappers settled on Spitsbergen as early as the fifteenth century. Nevertheless, although the possibility of a northern sea route to Asia had suggested itself to some of the well-informed, no actual search for it was to be undertaken before the sixteenth century. As a rule, European ships of the 1300's hugged the coasts and except to a few Russian trappers, Irish monks, Viking seafarers, English sailors, and French fishermen, the vast expanse of the uncharted oceans was a barrier rather than a thoroughfare. What was needed, if it was to be penetrated, was not only the development of sturdier ships but also better training in seamanship, better instruments of navigation, and a more systematic acquisition and compilation of nautical and geographical knowledge.

Pre-Columbian Cartography and Explorations

If geographical myopia was still obscuring the finest fourteenth-century vision, a lengthy process of cure had nevertheless begun. Coastal charts (*portolani*) had been produced and used before 1300, but now they were being much improved by Genoese and Venetian cartographers. Pietro Vesconte of Genoa produced the earliest dated (though not the oldest surviving) portolan; it is dated 1311. Later *portolani* by him and other Italians showed more accurate coastal data, corrected old locations, and added new ones for newly explored regions not only along the Mediterranean coasts but also in the Atlantic area and the Far East. The marked advance in the number and dependability of details and in the knowledge of outlying regions was revealed in a new type of book—sheets of maps of limited areas bound together into a *portolani*-atlas. The Laurentian Portolano (or *Medicean Atlas*) of 1351 showed not only the basic Mediterranean lands but also, with relative accuracy, the Atlantic coast from Spain to Scandinavia, the Caspian Sea, the Black Sea, India, and north Africa, including the Nile River. A Catalan map (*c.* 1375) of similar scope gave still more accurate details, notably for the regions of India and 'Cathay', probably on the basis of information provided by Marco Polo and other travellers. A Genoese map of the next century, however, showed little advance in knowledge, and meanwhile some cartographers had reverted to the old arrangement of maps with Jerusalem at the centre. This reversion was due in part to the renewed interest in crusades to check the Turkish advance and recover the Holy Land (see Chapter III).

The making of maps again received a fillip from the translation of Ptolemy's *Geography* into Latin in 1410 and its publication in print in 1475. Not the least among the numerous achievements of Nicolas of Cusa was his cartography of Germany. In the fifteenth century Greenland appeared on a map, and charts were drawn on rectangular projections showing meridians. A map painted by a German cartographer living in Italy, Henricus Martellus, indicated knowledge of Diaz's African voyage of 1488 and showed a location for the island of 'Cipango' (Japan). (Pl. 104a.) A similar chart, by the Florentine Toscanelli, went with Columbus on his first voyage to America. The invention of printing had by that time made printed maps available to geographers and navigators for study and correction. As the Mauro and the Vienna–Klosterneuburg circular maps and the globe of Martin Behaim (1492) reveal, by the end of the century the informed geographer knew vastly more about the world's surface than Ptolemy had known.

The widening of Christendom's horizon after 1300 stimulated curiosity about Africa as well as Asia. Could Asia be reached by sailing around Africa? The interest in 'the Dark Continent' increased in intensity during the fourteenth century. It was expressed chiefly by Genoese seafaring men searching for a sea route to the Far East. About 1300 the Vivaldi brothers were lost at sea in an effort to round the southern cape. Unverifiable legend has it that a later search party reached the east coast of Africa.

The uncertain advance of the Italians induced Frenchmen, Spaniards, and Portuguese as well as Italians to become interested in the Atlantic coast of Africa. In the fourteenth century Europe's leading school of cartographers and navigators was located at Majorca and staffed with Majorcan and Catalan experts. Trade and Christianization seem to have provided sufficiently strong motivation for a few occidentals to penetrate inland via the Niger River. One striking instance was a Frenchman who had lived among the natives along the Niger for eleven years and returned home with a Negro wife, half-caste children, and some Negro servants. But most of the explorers continued to hug the coast, staying away from the interior, and so the islands off northwest Africa were the first to be colonized. The Canaries, rediscovered in 1341 by Genoese sailors in Portuguese employ, were fought over by French, Spanish, and Portuguese forces until 1495, when the Spanish finally won out.

Meanwhile at least one man had understood the need for accumulative, systematic exploration, and he put his tremendous energy and personal fortune behind an attempt to provide it. He was a scholarly, crusading cartographer, the Portuguese prince Don Henrique (who later became known as 'the Navigator' although he himself hardly ever went to sea). He borrowed information and talent from the Majorcan school. Under his direction Portuguese seamen began a step-by-step exploration to the south and southwest of Portugal and added significantly to the development of marine science and navigational technology. Equipped with better ships and marine instruments, the best available astronomical data, and more detailed maps, and trained to exploit their improved knowledge and techniques, Don Henrique's men engaged in a deliberate and methodical effort to discover new lands.

Don Henrique's major purpose is not clear. He was a scholar, a colonizer, and an ardent Christian. At the outset crusading against the Muslims provided perhaps his strongest motive. Eventually he became interested in a sea route to the east, perhaps as an extension of his efforts to get to those African areas with which the Moroccan Arabs traded by land. He also had a desire to find the Christians who under a Prester John were supposed to inhabit one of the several unknown lands somewhere in Africa[21] and might establish a second front against the relentlessly advancing Turks.

In any case, Don Henrique directed the efforts of his captains southward along the coast of Africa. After the conquest of the Muslim port of Ceuta, across the straits from Gibraltar (in 1415), he prosecuted his crusade against the Muslims in northwest Africa. While still contending also for the Canaries against French and Spanish, the Portuguese acquired the Azores (1427–31) and made it a stepping stone for further explorations. Arguin Bay was reached in 1442. By that time a lively trade with the African west coast had developed, engaging a fleet that averaged twenty-five caravels annually. It brought back ivory, gold, salt, tropical plants, oils, spices, exotic animals, and (despite Don Henrique's vigorous objections) slaves. Once Arguin was passed, exploration, conversion, conquest, and exploitation progressed rapidly not only along the Atlantic coast of Africa but also inland and on off-shore islands. The Senegal River was reached also in 1442, and one year later the rounding of Cape Verde crowned thirty years of strenuous effort. Sierra Leone was claimed in 1446, Tangiers in 1471, and Rio del Oro in 1476. The papal bull *Romanus Pontifex* of 1454 discouraged competition from other Iberian princes by giving Portugal a monopoly over African territory.

During the second half of the century, the search for a water route to India was added to the incentives for Don Henrique's driving activity. He lived long enough to see the India project get under way but not to see it completed. By 1460 he had carried the programme of Portuguese conquest far down the African coast and had organized the navigational system that laid the foundation for Portugal's astounding colonial success. His mariners sailed a new type of ship, the three-masted caravel, which had a heavier keel and greater manoeuvrability than the galley still in common use. All the information that they acquired was sifted and transferred to maps and *portolani*, thus forming a systematic store of information for other discoverers trained in Don Henrique's school for seafarers at Sagres (Cape St Vincent). These men made daring use of the cross-staff and the compass. They improved the astrolabe and by careful observation set up and corrected tables giving the solar declinations and the varying altitudes of the polestar.

When Don Henrique died (1460), the Portuguese drive slackened, until (c. 1481) King John II caused it to be resumed. Three years later, almost seventy years after Henry's efforts had begun, it reached the Congo estuary. By then the search for a cheap route to India had become the chief stimulus for probing the African coast. In 1487 John sent Pedro de Covilha by the

Cairo–Aden route across northeast Africa and the Red Sea to India, and on the return voyage Covilha, testing the possibilities of reaching the East by the Indian Ocean, reached the Zambesi River on Africa's east coast. Almost at the same time Bartolomew Diaz was blown around the Cape of Good Hope from the west and advanced northward to the seaport now known as Mossel Bay. Africa thus was shown to be circumnavigable, and a sea voyage to the East feasible. Yet it took another ten years to reach India by the route around the southern tip of Africa, and meanwhile the most dramatic events of the entire era of discovery took place.

Columbus, Da Gama and Their Successors

A common belief notwithstanding, European mariners were not impelled to new ventures by the Turkish conquest of Constantinople and the need to counteract the supposed cutting-off of trade between the Mediterranean and the Far East. The fact is that the victorious Turks did not cut off that trade; it passed mostly through Alexandria, not then in Ottoman hands, and since it was profitable for them, too, they preferred to cooperate with the Venetian merchants to exploit it. About 1490, however, the possibility loomed that the Portuguese might find a cheap, all-water route to India, thus short-circuiting the Mediterranean and killing what had become a Turkish–Venetian monopoly. Moreover, the prospects of still another route that would rival the real or potential ones then known held obvious attractions for competitors of Turkey, Venetia, and Portugal.

A Genoese sailor named Christopher Columbus, after much delay, pleading, and frustration, succeeded in persuading Queen Isabella of Castile to finance a scheme for sailing westward to discover new lands in the Atlantic and perhaps an easy route to India. The boldness of his proposal had already frightened off other possible sponsors. No one, at least in southern Europe, really knew what lay west of the Azores, how vast the ocean was, or how much truth there might be in the old fable of a sunken continent Atlantis or in the island of Antilia shown on some maps. No one knew how long a ship would have to sail west until it might reach land, how much food, water, and other provisions would be needed, what winds or currents might prevail, or even what stars could serve for navigation. Probably no one anticipated that the deviation of the compass needle might vary as one moved westward. Among the common sailors all kinds of fantasies prevailed about sea monsters, fatal winds, gigantic eddies, and resistless currents.

Columbus, however, was no ordinary mariner; he was a cartographer and a student of geography as well. He was not exclusively intent on finding a route to the Far East, although that was one of his purposes. He was actuated also by accounts of Atlantic voyages and maps showing islands such as 'Antilia' and the Portuguese discoveries of lands for exploitation and Christianization. The Spanish sovereigns were, furthermore, anxious to match the Portuguese in crusading and missionary colonization. Reaching the Orient by sailing westward seemed possible to Columbus since he knew that the earth was round and since he believed Asia larger and the Atlantic smaller than it was. Some *portolani* and reports of experienced sailors gave evidence of island stopping-places in western waters. Iceland and Greenland were known to be in these waters though far to the North.

Columbus sailed westward for his royal Spanish sponsor in 1492 and returned in 1493 with the belief that he had found a shorter sea-route to the East. For all that, his voyage contributed greatly to the contemporary geographical revolution. It was a first step in the recognition of how large the earth was, and along with later voyages it added new continents to maps and globes. Without realizing that they were not islands of the East, Columbus discovered on this voyage and a series of subsequent ones the Bahamas, Cuba, Haiti, Puerto Rico, and Jamaica, as well as the Orinco coast of South America and the coast of Central America. He had proved that the ocean west of Europe was not an impassable and unknowable barrier but was a finite and navigable waterway. Observations he made on his trips, such as the deviations of the magnetic needle, proved to be of inestimable value to those who followed him.

The rival claims of Spain and Portugal were settled by papal arbitration (1493 and 1494), giving Spain the new lands to the west and Portugal those to the east of a given line (see Chapter I). In 1497, a year after Columbus returned from his second westward voyage without having found more than a few unpromising islands, the Portuguese resumed the eastward search. Vasco da Gama sailed around the Cape of Good Hope and northward along the east African coast, where he picked up the distinguished Arab navigator Ibn-Mājid (see above), who piloted his vessels along the monsoon route until they finally reached the Malabar coast of India. Vasco da Gama was thus the first European to go all the way to India by water. While another, with genius but mistaken assumptions, had happened upon a new western world for his Spanish masters, the Portuguese navigators, with systematic tenacity, actually found the long-sought and cheaper southern route to that region from which Europeans obtained much of their supply of spices, rare gems, precious metals, and other luxuries.

In subsequent years the Portuguese took the lead in exploiting the eastern trade. They established themselves on the coast of India, and under two great viceroys, Almeida and Albuquerque, they began to explore the Moluccas systematically. These islands produced the Malays' greatest treasure for European traders—spices. When some shipwrecked Portuguese landed on the coast of Japan in 1543, Europeans had reached all the glamorous places of the East—Cathay, India, Cipango—places known before chiefly from Arab sources and the travellers of the Mongol era.

When Columbus returned from his fourth and last voyage in 1504, he was still convinced that the islands and the coast of the continent that he had found were the eastern extremities of Asia. He was to die, involved in miserable quarrels with fellow captains and the Spanish authorities, without ever realizing that he had been blocked by an unknown hemisphere. What he had really discovered was a part, though only a small part, of a vast new world. The actual exploration even of its coastlines remained for others.

Other explorers, following in the wakes of Columbus and Da Gama, added to the world's rapidly accumulating cartographical knowledge. Pedro Alvares Cabral, sailing the Portuguese route around Africa, pushed far enough westward into the south Atlantic to sight the Brazilian coast and to claim it for Portugal (1500). Amerigo Vespuci, a Florentine who had accompanied several expeditions, notably along the South American coast, publicized the 'New World' so successfully that in 1507 the name 'America' was adopted by certain European scholars for the area that he now established to be a separate hemisphere. And in 1513 Vasco Nuñez de Balboa glimpsed the Pacific, the biggest of all oceans, on which no European vessel had previously sailed.

These explorations, along with several lesser ones, made obvious that Columbus and Da Gama had reached two separate parts of the world, which most likely were not connected by land with one another, and Europeans began to speculate about the respective location of the two strange regions. A Portuguese seaman, Fernando Magellan, who had served in the Indian Ocean, had there learned about the South Seas (which were the same that Balboa had already seen from the Isthmus of Panama). Upon his return to Europe, he combined his vague knowledge of the South Seas with reports of an east-west passage through the southern tip of South America and became convinced that the Moluccas, the source of fabulous fortunes in spices, could be reached by sailing westward after all. Like Columbus he persuaded the Spanish crown to subsidize his venture. With three ships he set out for South America in 1519, sailed up the Rio de la Plata estuary (mistaking it for his east-west passage), finally found the straits ever since named after him, and despite innumerable hardships managed to cross the vast Pacific. Eventually he reached the Philippines, which he claimed for Spain. He himself was killed there, but one of his captains, Juan Sebastian del Cano, sailed the one remaining ship, appropriately called 'Vittoria', back to Spain by way of the Moluccas and the Cape of Good Hope. For the first time man had completely circumnavigated the Earth, learning the relation of the hemispheres and the oceans to one another and providing an empirical proof of its sphericity.

The belief that Asia could be reached by sailing westward, which underlay the ventures of Columbus and his successors, also played a part in the discovery of northern America and the long search for a northwest passage to India. Although the New World had much earlier been reached by Europeans from Scandinavia using the north Atlantic routes, the knowledge acquired by previous discoverers had no significant influence on the explorations of the fifteenth and sixteenth centuries. Greenland's colony of Norsemen lost contact with Europe in the fifteenth century and disintegrated soon afterward, and nothing but the vaguest rumours about the Viking discoveries seems to have been known to the great explorers of the later period.

Untouched by the Vikings' fate, some of the later explorers set out to find a route to Asia that was not already preempted by the Spanish or the Portuguese. In 1497 another Italian navigator, John Cabot, in the service of King Henry VII left England for a northerly crossing of the Atlantic. He reached shores now known to have been those of Prince Edward Island and Newfoundland, which, sharing Columbus' error, he believed to be islands off the coast of Cathay. On a second voyage he went up the straits between Greenland and Labrador looking in vain for a westward passage until he was finally forced back by icebergs. Subsequently (1534) a French explorer, Jacques Cartier, resumed the northwestward explorations, sailing far up the Saint Lawrence River and south along the Atlantic coast, until he encountered the Spaniards, who were pushing north from Florida. In this and subsequent voyages, though he found no way to the Far East, he discovered more about the North American continent. By then it was generally accepted that none of the new lands belonged to the Asian continent, but the search for a northwest passage to Cathay around North America went on (see Chapter XIV).

The epoch-making voyages of Columbus, Da Gama, Vespucci, Magellan, Cabot, Cartier, and their successors were quickly reflected in geographical writings and cartography. Francesco Berlinghiere's *Geographia*, the first book, so far as is known, for which all the maps (31 in this instance) were copperplate engravings, was printed at Florence in 1482, but the maps were still based on previous 'Ptolemies'.[22] During the sixteenth century, with the new knowledge gained from the explorers, cartographical leadership shifted from Italy to the north, and especially to the Netherlands. Waldseemüller (d. 1521) was the first to picture a large ocean between America and Asia. (Pl. 104b.) Detailed accuracy, however, was conspicuously absent from early-sixteenth-century delineations of the outlying sections and the interiors of the new continents.

Nonetheless, during the hundred years centring roughly upon 1500 western Europe executed a slow geographical about-face. Instead of looking mostly eastward from the Mediterranean it now looked more and more southward and westward from the Atlantic seaboard. Dramatic though the explorations of a Columbus or a Magellan were, the new outlook, the so-called 'geographical revolution', was not a sudden awakening but rather the outcome of a slow cultural development, the culmination of several centuries of empirical observation, scientific experiment, technological ingenuity, critical analysis, and imaginative theorizing, which had themselves been deeply rooted in Classical and medieval, occidental and oriental knowledge and lore.

NOTES TO CHAPTER XIII

1. Dr Bertrand Gille feels that despite the title of this chapter, technology occupies only a very limited place. By better situating the two great technical systems of the period, that established during the second half of the twelfth century, concurrently with the great demographic expansion, and that appearing in the second half of the fifteenth century, the authors might have demonstrated better the links which clearly exist between technology and pure science, as well as the many zones of mutual interference between these two domains of human knowledge.

   The authors, however, reply: 'As the first paragraph of the text of this chapter points out, much that falls under the heading of technology is dealt with in other chapters; to do so again would be repetitious. A contrast of scientific and technological developments before 1300 and around 1500 is attempted below; the second half of the twelfth century comes before the chronological limits of this volume.'

2. Dr Bertrand Gille stresses that the end of the fifteenth and the beginning of the sixteenth century mark a turning point. Having abandoned Aristotle, science henceforward appears as no more than an assemblage of fractionalized problems, whose very isolation from one another perhaps made possible deeper study of certain concepts, though not yet warranting the construction of a new scientific system.

3. *De docta ignorantia*, Bk. II, Ch. II, quoted in Alexandre Koyré *From the Closed World to the Infinite Universe* (Baltimore, 1957), p. 11.

4. See Lynn Thorndike, *A History of Magic and Experimental Science*, IV (New York, 1934), 612–15.

5. See J. M. Romein, 'The Common Human Pattern', *Journal of World History*, IV (1958), 449–63, and J. J. Saunders, 'The Problem of Islamic Decadence', *ibid.*, VII (1963), 701–20.

6. See George Sarton, *Introduction to the History of Science* (3 vols. in 5; Baltimore, 1927–1948) Vol. II, pt. 2, pp. 611–12.

7. A. C. Crombie, *Augustine to Galilee, the History of Science A.D. 400–1600* (London, 1952), pp. 68 and 267, and Sarton, I, 601.

8. It is frequently said that Oresme suspected the *diurnal* rotation of the Earth (see Crombie, pp. 256–57), but see R. Hooykaas, 'Science and Theology in the Middle Ages', *Free University Quarterly* (Amsterdam), III (1957), 121–25. On the possibility of other worlds, see *ibid.*, p. 113 and n. 88.

9. Buridan's *Questiones super Octo Physicorum Libros*, Bk. VIII, Question 12, quoted in Crombie, p. 253.

10. *Ibid.*, pp. 251–53.

11. See *The Herbal of Rufinus*, ed. Lynn Thorndike (Chicago, 1947) and the review of this work by L. C. MacKinney in *Journal of the History of Medicine and Allied Sciences*, II (1947), 138–140.

12. See Edward Rosen, 'The Invention of Eyeglasses', *Journal of the History of Medicine and Allied Sciences*, XI (1956), 13–46 and 183–218.

13. Thorndike, Vol. VIII: *The Seventeenth Century* (1958), p. 366 and Agnes Arber, *Herbals, Their Origin and Evolution, a Chapter in the History of Botany, 1470–1670* (Cambridge, 1938), pp. 250–255. See Richard H. Shryock, 'The Interplay of Social and Internal Factors in Modern Medicine', *Centaurus*, III (1953), 113–15.

14. Before his death L. C. MacKinney had collected about 4000 microfilm frames of miniatures from medical, botanical, anatomical, and bestiary manuscripts.

15. Thorndike, IV, 190–91.

16. J. J. L. Duyvendak, *China's Discovery of Africa*, (London, 1949), p. 18 and Radhakumud Mookerji, *Indian Shipping* (London, 1912), pp. 192–99.

17. *Novum Organum*, Bk. I, Aphorism 129, quoted in Joseph Needham, *Science and Civilization in China*, I (Cambridge, 1954), 19.

18. *Ibid.*, p. 218.

19. *Ibid.*, III (1959), 40–52, esp. 41.

20. See Charles Verlinden, 'Les origines coloniales de la civilisation atlantique, antécédents et types de structure', *Journal of World History*, I (1953), 387 and *Precédénts médiévaux de la colonie en Amérique* (Mexico City, 1954), p. 21.

21. See Armando Cortesão, *The Nautical Chart of 1424* (Coimbra, 1954), esp. pp. 54–56.

22. See 'Rare Books', *Library of Congress Quarterly Journal of Current Acquisitions*, II (1954), 180.

CHAPTER XIV

SCIENCE (c. 1530–c. 1775)

SCIENTIFIC EPISTEMOLOGY AND METHODOLOGY

THE extraordinary advances in basic science that have enriched and radically changed the life of modern man have come for the most part since 1530. To explain this advance as due from the very beginning to a conscious alliance of science with technology would be to read the experience of more recent times into earlier centuries. To begin with, no separate and well-defined fields of endeavour called respectively science and technology existed for most of the period here under consideration. Furthermore, although Galileo's acquaintance with the mechanical arts at the Venetian Arsenal suggests that theoretical ideas sometimes arose from some pattern of experience with empirical techniques and tools and although much of the work of the new scientific academies, we shall soon discover, had practical objectives in view, yet a central fact of the so-called 'scientific revolution' of the seventeenth century was that it was in conspicuous instances carried on by men with a non-utilitarian purpose. Regardless of their sources of knowledge and inspiration, they frequently went in pursuit of truth for and of itself, seeking more satisfactory answers to old theoretical questions, answers whose utility was obscure.

In contrast, modern technology is a rationalized, systematized body of differentiated knowledge directed toward getting things done on a mass basis and is often in close and carefully cultivated alliance with science. In its earlier stages, however, for the most part technology grew independently of scientific theory, and where it did grow out of abstract science, it did so in many cases by later adaptations of scientific principles independently discovered rather than by a deliberate preliminary search for them. The planned and direct alliance of the scientist with the industrialist and the engineer is of comparatively recent development, although the initial stages of it occur in our period of study. In these initial stages alliance was more likely to occur in the less 'academic' fields such as applied physics, industrial chemistry, agriculture, botany, and metallurgy, which had no regular place in university curricula, than in 'academic' fields like astronomy and mathematics, where speculative minds could still obtain satisfying results by abstract reasoning. Some examples of the alliance of science and technology will be mentioned in this chapter, but technological developments will receive greater attention in the next.

EE*

The alliance of science and technology, today taken for granted, had to be preceded by a separation of science from speculative philosophy, especially when speculation was based on unexamined and perhaps unrealistic premises. Previous times and other societies had made inquiries into the operations of nature and had systematically observed them, but the idea of a rational science of nature based on controlled observation and experiment, a science that deliberately limited its area of inquiry to the material realm, was essentially unique to the modern West. No longer concerned, at least as scientists, with final cause, modern scientists posit a mechanistic world conforming to natural laws; they do not regard moral or theological considerations as falling within the framework of their science.

This attitude meant, among other things, a shift from a qualitative to a quantitative, or mathematical, picture of the universe. It was well expressed by Galileo Galilei (1546–1642) in his *Il Saggiatore*:

'*I feel myself impelled by the necessity, as soon as I conceive a piece of matter or corporeal substance, of conceiving that in its own nature it is bounded and figured in such and such a figure, that in relation to others it is large or small, that it is in this or that place, in this or that time, that it is in motion or remains at rest, that it touches or does not touch another body, that it is single, few, or many; . . . but that it must be white or red, bitter or sweet, sounding or mute, of a pleasant or unpleasant odour, I do not perceive my mind forced to acknowledge.*'

Galileo's statement assumed a differentiation between primary (essentially measurable) qualities and secondary (essentially esthetic) qualities—that is, between, on the one hand, those that he believed to be in the object observed and quantitative and, on the other, those that he believed to be in the judgment of the observer and qualitative. Such a differentiation did not mean that scientists were not to be interested in esthetic considerations; it meant only that esthetic considerations did not lend themselves to quantitative methods readily, if at all. As Galileo further said:

'*Philosophy is written in that vast book which stands ever open before our eyes, I mean the universe; but it cannot be read until we have learnt the language and become familiar with the characters in which it is written. It is written in mathematical language.*'

In this remark Galileo used the word *philosophy* where we would use the word *science*. Even at the end of his century science was still called philosophy, although generally divided into natural philosophy (science), speculative philosophy, and moral philosophy.

Aristotelian Science Challenged

The work which is traditionally held to mark the opening of the movement commonly referred to as 'the scientific revolution' was *De Revolutionibus*

Orbium Coelestium by Copernicus. Virtually completed in 1530, it was not published until 1543. It put forth an unfamiliar but not wholly unknown system of astronomy, one which itself was not based on observation and experiment but rather on a relatively unsuspected conceptual scheme—a heliostatic and heliocentric theory of the universe. Copernicus's theory went contrary to the Biblical geostatic and geocentric implications; it also raised doubts about the symbolic importance of man as lord of nature and God's chief creature. If Copernicus was right, man would, of course, appear a mere speck in the universe. This argument was not new or strange, for as early as the sixth century the view had been put forth that 'the whole earth compared with the universe is no greater than a point'.[1] The shattering statement in Copernicus' work for a later generation of thinkers was not that the sun stood still and was the centre of the universe but rather that the universe was thousands of times greater than had been supposed. Though he himself seemed to believe in a finite world, he implied, whether he intended to or not, that the material world might be so large as to have no centre at all and, hence, that the universe might be infinite.

Copernicus, a canon of the Frauenburg Cathedral, had no desire to be un-Christian. Nor was Thomas Digges, an English Puritan who was perhaps the first Copernican to depict an infinite universe explicitly, any more ready to propound heresy. In *A Perfit Description of the Caelestiall Orbes* (1576), he nevertheless presented a chart showing the six then known planets of the solar system, which in turn he enclosed within an 'orbe of starres fixed infinitely up'.[2] Digges' work, however, was ignored by contemporaries and became known only in the twentieth century. For Digges the infinite starry orb was still the Christian heaven, where God, the angels, and the elect dwelt "devoyd of greefe and replenished with perfite endless joye."

Giordano Bruno who combined within his own person the qualities of poet and savant, in some ways better illustrates the transition from earlier theology to modern science. Though upset by the undermining of Scholastic rationalism and Ptolemaic cosmology, he could not take refuge, as had Nicholas of Cusa, in 'learned ignorance', since he was not content to accept on faith what was hard for his reason to believe. Nor was his age sufficiently informed in science for him to work out a theory of a mechanistic universe run entirely by natural law. Hence he felt constrained to resort to pantheistic infinity. While doubtless drawing in part upon Cusa, Bruno did not use his predecessor's Christian symbolism in explaining the infinity of the universe but expounded it in a rhapsody of Classical and Old Testament phrases: 'The One Infinite is perfect, in simplicity, of itself, absolutely, nor can aught be greater or better. This is the One Whole God, universal Nature, occupying all space, of whom naught but infinity can give the perfect image or semblance.'[3] He supported his mystical pantheism not only with extensive Scholastic argumentation but also with carefully organized data based on scientific observations. Thus he exemplified the sixteenth-century rebellion against

Scholastic ideology and at the same time the inability of contemporary minds to arrive at a world view by scientific methods alone.

This dilemma underlines the philosophical conflicts of Bruno's day. The supremacy of Aristotelianism had been challenged in science, but no good champion had yet come to take 'the Philosopher's' place. In fact, with the Counter-Reformation Aristotle—made more correctly and more fully available by Renaissance humanists than he had previously been—was widely reinstated in his thirteenth-century primacy in the Roman Catholic study of physics, and, in general, scientific discourse showed little progress beyond the Scholastics. Even those who in the sixteenth century rejected Aristotelianism provided no satisfying substitute for it. Telesio, a bitter critic of Scholasticism and Aristotle's theory of the four fundamental elements (fire, air, earth, and water), attempted to replace it with a theory of two (heavenly heat and earthly cold), which, he taught, could alone, without divine intervention, account for all the modifications of matter, whose quantity was fixed (see Chapter VII). The mystical naturalism of the physicians Paracelsus and Girolamo Cardano or Cardan (1501–76) combined empirical observation in fields like medicine or mathematics with the occult methods of astrology and alchemy in an effort to found a universal scientific system, propounding a kind of self-directed materialism as the explanation of change. Patrizzi and Campanella, better known as the author of the utopian *Civitas Solis*, both were avowed disciples of Telesio, even if Patrizzi doubted that all phenomena could come from heat and cold alone. These men's rationalism was perhaps more empirical and certainly more materialistic than that of their Aristotelian and Neoplatonic contemporaries, but it was hardly more acceptable to the authorities than Bruno's pantheistic naturalism, and the essentially speculative and teleological structure of their theories distinguished their thought no better than his from modern scientific thought.

New Methods and Reasoning in Science

A decisive departure in scientific method had to wait until new approaches (like that of Galileo quoted above) to the nature of thought itself were published (see Chapter VII). Sometimes they were expressed in terms of materialism, as by Hobbes, and sometimes in terms of mechanism, as by Descartes; and questions regarding human understanding furthered the empiricism of English and French Lockeans. Materialists, mechanists, and empiricists, no matter how much they might differ among themselves regarding epistemology, all helped to advance the development of a 'natural theology' (that is, one with emphasis on the Book of Nature as the handiwork of God and hence as a source of revelation). Thereby they raised some serious religious questions. Little doubt arose as to whether God had created the universe, or was First Cause, but some thinkers (the Deists were a prominent example) seriously doubted that God had since Creation continued to guide the universe, and others queried whether scientific reason could adjust God's governance and miracles to a system of immutable laws of nature. As we have seen (Chapter VII), the debate led to scepticism, and scepticism to various degrees of agnosticism. Voltaire believed that God would have to be invented if he did not exist, but LaPlace, according to legend (*ben trovato* if not *vero*), claimed to have no need of God as a hypothesis.

Yet it would be a mistake to consider the European scientists of the seventeenth and eighteenth centuries for the most part sceptics, agnostics, or atheists. Far from it, the majority of them were Christians, though with varying degrees of orthodoxy. Descartes thought of science as God's handiwork, expressible in mathematical terms and intelligible to human reason.[4] Robert Boyle (1627–91) was a devout man who wished to counteract free-thought and would have recoiled in horror at the thought of destroying the Christian edifice. Isaac Newton (1642–1727) had little difficulty in accommodating his scientific findings to his belief in God's sovereignty over His universe.

Still, the spiritual domination of the various Christian churches, though continuing strong, was ebbing in their day. They had been enfeebled by a lengthy series of 'religious' wars and assailed by new doubts regarding revealed truth with the discovery of the New World and Eastern philosophy. The interference of Protestants in the affairs of Catholic countries and of Catholics in the affairs of Protestant countries tended to make disputants take vigorous stands, and not on the basis of faith alone. In an age of absolute monarchy, Erastianism was a source of power to the state, leaving less room for defiance of the state by the church and making religion a branch, and the church a tool, of politics. On the other hand, the state, frequently under the control of enlightened rulers supported by middle-class patrons of learning, was often less hostile to new knowledge than the older and relatively independent church had been.

One of the most illustrious of the champions of the new knowledge was Francis Bacon. In the early seventeenth century his many writings outlined his view of the proper way to interrogate nature. He expounded a system of induction and instances, and while it may not be the best approach to science, his criticism of the deductive method of rigid Aristotelian thought and his emphasis on observation and experiment as the road to scientific truth were to provide a new approach for those who questioned the validity of Scholastic methods. He boldly proclaimed, moreover, that science could be used to serve man. This prophecy was not unique with him; among others, Descartes had already indicated that science might help man to control nature. But Bacon spelled the idea out well, even if science was not to be assiduously joined with technology for another two hundred years.

Notwithstanding, Bacon's reputation as a prophet cannot be justly derived from any critique on his part of medieval attitudes. He did little to improve upon the speculative system of medieval man and a good deal to buttress it. He was ignorant of the number of experiments already performed relating to impetus and of the continuing tradition of dissection; and other instances of his ignorance of the experimental science of his day indicate that, whatever the change in scientific thought he wrought, it was something less abrupt than a switch from a speculative to an empirical approach. For all his criticism of Aristotelianism, he still worked within the Aristotelian qualitative framework. While he did not completely ignore the importance of mathematics, he did not find such a system of thought compatible, and as a result he missed the true significance of the change in contemporary scientific thought—that is, its mathematical aspect. Bacon himself was not conspicuously successful as a scientist; he was an anti-Copernican, holding that the rival system of Tycho Brahe (1546–1601) was correct (a position not held by him alone, however). Like that of his famous namesake, Roger Bacon, Francis Bacon's activity as an anti-Scholastic polemicist and propagandist rather than his own scientific accomplishments explain why he is remembered as a prophet of modern science.[5]

In contrast with Bacon was Descartes. Descartes' approach was not only rational but also mathematical, based on a well-worked-out deductive process. His essays, such as *Regulae ad Directionem Ingenii* (esp. Rules XII–XXI), *La géométrie*, annexed (along with *Météores* and *La dioptrique*) to his *Discours de la méthode*, and his *Secundae Responsiones*, emphasized the method of mathematical reasoning as a tool of scientific and philosophical thought.

Galileo, a contemporary of Descartes and Bacon, was also to be largely responsible for the great innovations in day-to-day methods in science that came in the seventeenth century. Galileo used experiment in addition to reasoning and mathematics, though several of his putative experiments are now considered legendary. He was, of course, not the first to employ the experimental method. We shall soon examine the contributions of men like William Gilbert (who worked with an experimental model in the field of magnetism and electricity, to which Galileo gave small attention) and like Benedetti and Stevin (who anticipated and laid the foundation for some of Galileo's work).[6] Moreover, in several regards (for example, in refusing to accept Kepler's conclusions) Galileo lagged behind some of his contemporaries.

Nevertheless, more perhaps than to Bacon or Descartes, the role of innovator belonged to the Italian scientist. Much more than they Galileo was stimulated by the technology of his day. His study of mechanics, as his writings disclose, was affected by the work he observed going on in the Venetian Arsenal. He was not content, however, with observation alone or even with philosophical speculation and mathematical interpretation of the study of nature. His method in last analysis was composed of three sometimes overlapping phases—rational intuition, laboratory experiment, and mathematical demonstration. He realized the importance of intuitively deriving the right kind of questions from the known data, for only certain types of questions were susceptible to his method. Then he tried to find the answers by further experiment, recognizing, however, that in any experiment departure from the concrete elements in favour of abstract reasoning might at some points be desirable. For example, brilliant speculations on Euclidean space enabled him to carry out his work toward a law of inertia (see below). But, departing from the Scholastics, he preferred to limit his speculation to strictly logical deductions proceeding from premises based upon those aspects of the sensible world that he could submit to experiment. Finally, he expressed his results in mathematical terms wherever he could, using Socratic argument where mathematics alone did not enable him to demonstrate his conclusions.

Although Galileo was in every sense a polemicist (not to mention his skill as a publicist), he was not the self-conscious system builder that his contemporaries Bacon and Descartes were. He too recognized, however, the importance of eliminating Final Cause and teleology from natural science, not because he thought that the universe had no purpose but because he recognized the limits of his method and of the task at hand. The domain of philosophy was thus disintegrated; the conscious rejection of metaphysics by the natural scientist was ultimately to separate natural philosophy not only from theology but also from speculative philosophy.

New Scientific Instruments

In those days instruments were relatively new in scientific work, for only gradually were scientists deserting the study for the laboratory and supplementing speculation with manual work. They now asked less often *why* things happened, and more often *how* they happened; and *how* could be answered sometimes by repeating the process. We shall find great scientists making their own instruments, inventing new ones, and adapting old ones to new uses. We shall find them also striving for a uniform system of measurement of heat, space, weight, time, and other physical characteristics, though as yet usually without striking success. We shall find governments as well as individual scientists creating laboratories and observatories *de novo*. Only in the century or so that ran roughly from Galileo to Newton were the telescope, microscope, pendulum clock, barometer, and thermometer developed, permitting greater precision and new experiments. The wonders they and their contemporaries achieved often were sheer feats of intellect performed with what today appear to be the barest essentials of laboratory equipment.

For certain instruments to be conveniently usable as tools of science precise and generally accepted units of measurement are desirable. Medieval alchemy and medicine had had several systems of weights and measures, largely derived from Antiquity, but they had been inaccurate and not easily interchangeable. In the sixteenth century Agricola re-examined these systems in a five-book treatise *De Mensuris et Ponderibus Romanorum atque Graecorum*. In 1514 at Vienna Henricus Scriptor compiled a set of rules for measuring the contents of vessels. While these events furnished instances of progress toward precision, they also indicated the lack of a good, uniform system of measuring scientific data.

Agreement on units of measurement, however, was hard to get, as is illustrated by the early history of precision instruments. The measurement of heat, for example, required not only a widely acceptable unit of measure but also some device for counting units. Borrowing the specifications of Greek scientists and probably also the clinical apparatus of his friend Santorio Santorii (Sanctorius) (1561–1636), Galileo is believed to have constructed an air thermoscope, a crude predecessor of the thermometer and barometer. The productive though short-lived Accademia del Cimento experimented (c. 1654) with the so-called Florentine thermometer—a sealed glass bulb holding a liquid and opening into a thin tube, the degree of heat being deduced by the height of the column of liquid in the tube as the liquid expanded or contracted when exposed to changes of temperature. Further steps on the same principle were taken by Daniel Gabriel Fahrenheit (1686–1736). A German by birth, he became a lecturer, inventor, and leading instrument maker at Amsterdam. By 1721 he had developed a mercury thermometer to determine the boiling points of various liquids, such as oil of vitriol, alcohol, and water, and had devised the scale of temperatures that still bears his name; with zero fixed at the temperature of a given mixture of ice, water, and salt and with body temperature arbitrarily fixed at about 96° it put the normal freezing point of water at 32° and the boiling point at 212°. Ignorant of Fahrenheit's work, René Antoine de Réaumur (1683–1757), a French naturalist, developed a thermometer on different lines. He preferred alcohol to mercury as the liquid for the measurement of temperature, and devised a thermometric scale (80 degrees between the freezing and boiling points of water) that likewise still bears its inventor's name. A third scientist, Anders Celsius (1701–44), of Sweden, elaborated a mercury thermometer with yet a different scale (putting the temperature of melting snow at 100° and of boiling water at zero). With variations introduced by Christin of Lyons in 1743, including the reversal of Celsius's scale, this thermometer is known today as the centigrade thermometer. It is now generally used for scientific work and is the common one in countries that have adopted the metric system of weights and measures.

The early history of another precision instrument, the telescope, is shrouded in mystery. Apparently the first ones were put in use in Holland and Italy at the end of the sixteenth century. In 1608 a Dutchman named Hans Lippershey applied for a patent on a process for combining several lenses to form a telescope. Galileo, learning of the Dutch models, constructed the telescope of thirty magnification with which he made his epochal astronomical discoveries. (Pl. 87a.) Johannes Kepler (1571–1630) in *Dioptrice* (1611) suggested (among other things) that the proper placing of convex and concave lenses would give larger and more distinct images. The first Keplerian or 'astronomical' telescope was constructed by the Jesuit astronomer Christoph Scheiner (1575-1650).

Microscopes likewise seem to have been experimented with first by Dutch craftsmen. Their models were duplicated in Italy but without noteworthy improvements until after the Thirty Years War. The earliest compound microscopes were unsatisfactory in some ways, and several scientists preferred to use the simple microscope. (Pl. 84a.) Not until the nineteenth century, with the introduction of the improved achromatic microscope, would the compound microscope make its greatest contributions. Important research in the biological sciences was meanwhile done with the simple microscope.

Another tool now considered indispensible for precise experimentation—the pendulum clock—was also effectively developed in the seventeenth century. Only crude methods of measuring time, such as by oral counting, by the oscillations of a swinging object, by the quantity of dripping water, by the flow of sand in an hour glass, or by a water clock, had been available previously, and, therefore, exact time measurements, particularly of speedy actions, had been difficult. Galileo sketched a plan for a pendulum clock but died before one could be made. Tycho Brahe and Kepler had available some kind of clock that enabled them to time their observations more accurately than had previously been possible. Only in 1656, however, did Christiaan Huygens (1629-95) successfully combine the pendulum with gears and escapement to make an accurate timepiece. In 1657 he patented a pendulum clock, which he described in his *Horologium* (1658); and in *Horologium Oscillatorium* (1673), along with many other original contributions, he presented a mathematical analysis of the operation of an improved model. (Pl. 89a, b.) By experiments with a seconds' pendulum he was able to measure acceleration due to gravity and to present with greater certainty other conclusions requiring accurate time measurements. He also invented the balance spring for timepieces. Improvements on the Huygens models by William Clement (c. 1685) and others ultimately enabled scientists to time experiments precisely in terms of seconds.

The determination of longitude on shipboard long defied solution. The Portuguese voyages of discovery and the establishment of Don Henrique's nautical centre at Sagres in the early fifteenth century speeded the development of navigational instruments. We have already noted (Chapter XIII) certain early sixteenth-century improvements in cartography. About the same time there originated the basic idea in the present method of finding longitude by calculations based upon the difference in time between shipboard and the zero meridian. Huygens was able to devise a special pendulum clock for use at sea, and his improvement inspired efforts to make timepieces that would be still more accurate than his on shipboard. The problem was finally solved with the invention of the chronometer (c. 1761) by John Harrison; its reliability was proved by Captain James Cook, who took a duplicate of it along on his voyages of the 1770's.

Meanwhile other astronomical and navigational instruments had evolved that, together with the steadily growing comprehension of pole-star altitudes and solar declinations, made possible a more accurate determination of latitude as well. An English seafaring man of the sixteenth century made an improved model of the cross staff. This was the 'back staff', which was widely used until the development of reflecting instruments. Studies by Hooke and Wren (1665), Jean Picard (1669), and Newton (c. 1700) gave designs for reflecting instruments (used in connection with telescopes), but they were never actually built. John Hadley (1682–1744) and Thomas Godfrey (of Philadelphia, d. 1749) share the honours for inventing the instrument (1731) from which the modern marine sextant derives.

The means of weighing minute particles became more and more important as chemistry advanced to the stage of precise analysis. The problem was rendered difficult not only by differences in units of weight measurement, which varied from region to region and from language to language, but also by the relative crudeness and inaccuracy of weighing machines. The problem of an international nomenclature for weights was to be solved only after the scientists of the First French Republic in 1793 laid the foundation for the metric system, but the quest for a weighing machine capable of detecting tiny differences of mass ended earlier in the eighteenth century. A knife-edge balance was invented, based on the principle that the centre of gravity of a uniform bar is at its midpoint. Very slight differences in weight, causing a uniform lever placed on a knife-edge fulcrum to swing out of equilibrium, can be easily measured by means of an indicator showing the distance of swing. The accuracy of weighing that Lavoisier, for example, needed for his experiments would have been impossible without the knife-edge balance.

The very number of famous men of science who invented or helped to invent these precision instruments (and others that will be mentioned in due course below) has a significance of its own. It is an indication not only of their ingenuity but also of their need. Though the scientist usually had the help of mechanics and professional instrument-makers, he often had to improvise his instruments as he went along, since instrument-making was still in the hands of small-scale technicians who made their instruments to order one by one. In our period interchangeability of standard parts had not yet come to instrument-making or other industries, though it was beginning (see Chapter XV). The amazing thing is how much cooperation the scientists of the 'scientific revolution' were able to achieve despite lack of uniformity of instrumentation or nomenclature or norm for weighing and measuring.

The Role of the Universities and the Scientific Academies

At least partly—but only partly—because of the persistence of Aristotelian science in the universities, much of the new important scientific work of our period (with notable exceptions like Padua, Cracow, and Oxford) was done outside their walls, and not until the nineteenth century would university laboratories be commonly established to interrogate nature. In the sixteenth century the University of Padua, patronized by the Venetian republic, was perhaps the outstanding exception to the rule of general scientific conservatism in university circles. It was anti-Aristotelian. It had the rare distinction of admitting professors and students without doctrinal tests and prerequisites. Here men such as Copernicus, Andreas Vesalius (1514–64), and William Harvey (1578–1657) studied, were inspired, and themselves inspired younger men. The newer University of Leiden in the sixteenth and seventeenth centuries established a botanical garden, an anatomical theatre and museum, an observatory, a hospital, and physics and chemistry laboratories. Most scientists, however, worked as lone and independent scholars, notable examples being Leonardo da Vinci, Paracelsus, and Gilbert. Furthermore, many of them fell far short of the modern ideal of the scientist free from prejudice and superstition and engaged in the disinterested, objective pursuit of truth. For one thing, magical 'experimenta' continued well into our period, especially the efforts of alchemists to transmute metals. Yet 'experimenta' were not solely survivals of medieval superstition; they were also the signs of pioneer effort and the means of slow progress in early modern science. The scientist of the period 1530–1775—especially of the seventeenth century, the so-called 'century of genius'—was sometimes an autodidact and often a polymath. The knowledge of science in that day was still so limited that men like Descartes, Galileo, Kepler, Boyle, Huygens, Pascal, Leibniz, Newton, Lomonosov, and Franklin could make significant contributions in several fields and will be considered below under more than one heading.

The cooperation of men of science was aided by the growth of scientific societies, which provided meeting places for the best minds. They served also as a means of disseminating knowledge through their learned journals, eagerly acquired by contemporary scientists. The Accademia dei Lincei (1603–30) and the Accademia del Cimento (1657–67) each lasted only for decades, but they provided fruitful and encouraging precedents; the Royal Society of London (founded 1662), the Académie des Sciences (founded 1666), the Societas Regia Scientiarum (founded 1700; later the Prussian Academy), and the St Petersburg Academy (founded 1725) were among the more illustrious of the great academies that endured. They provided libraries, laboratories, stipends, expensive instruments, collaborators, and interested audiences and served as national clearing-houses for both the scientist and the dilettante. Thanks to the scientific societies and their learned journals, communication among working scientists became much easier than it would have been at an earlier date. The contemporary improvement of postal sources—the London penny post, for example, was established in 1680—helped to make them good correspondents.

For all their revolutionary discoveries in mechanics, mathematics, astronomy, and biology, the seventeenth-century scientists did little more than scratch the surface of their fields of study. That century was one of great promise, but the eighteenth was one of conscious fulfilment. By the end of the eighteenth century (to enumerate only a few achievements) chemistry was established as an independent field of study, geology was beginning to come into its own, the first faltering steps in the study of electricity, hyponotism, and aeronautics had been taken, and a theory of biological evolution was being dimly formulated.

MATHEMATICS IN EUROPE

Until about 1500 mathematical knowledge for the most part had advanced no further than the stage at which the Greeks and the Muslims had left it. Then humanistic research uncovered Classical texts that did much to stimulate mathematical thought; an edition of the work of Archimedes, for example, was published at Basel in 1544, making his findings, not previously unknown, more accurately, fully, and readily available. In the mid-sixteenth century Europe developed the field of algebra beyond its Hindu and Islamic sources, turning it into something European. Purbach's posthumously published *Opus Algorithmi Jucundissimum* (1492) became a leading manual of the sixteenth century.

Algebra afforded methods of solving equations previously solved, if at all, only by Greek geometrical procedures. The largely autodidact Niccolo Tartaglia (1500–57) is usually given credit for unravelling the problems long assumed to be fundamental to the solution of cubic equations, but modern scholarship indicates that the credit probably belongs rather to his colleague Scipione dal Ferro.[7] Cardan, another of the group, answered certain posers concerning negative and imaginary roots. Ludovico Ferrari (1522–c. 1560), originally a servant of Cardan, showed how to solve biquadratic equations. Rafael Bombelli's *Algebra* (c. 1550, in manuscript form) systematized and carried to higher steps the algebraic findings of the Italian school.

A notorious feud broke out between Tartaglia and Cardan, both of whom, apparently without complete justification, sought credit for solving cubic equations. Their contest centred in Cardan's having published in *Ars Magna* (1545), a summation of the known algebra of the day, a set of formulae that he had confidentially been given by Tartaglia (as well as Ferrari's). It illustrates the importance that a mathematical subject might assume in north Italian learned circles of the Renaissance. The personal bitterness displayed by the contestants was characteristic of Italian intellectuals of that age, and especially of the versatile, fiery Cardan. The dispute was not wholly unconnected with the rivalry between the non-academic and the university savants.

Disputes like this quickly made plain that a set of commonly understood mathematical symbols would permit an economy of words, simplify the steps toward the solving of equations, and save much confusion. A French lawyer-mathematician, François Viète (1540–1603), was the first to inaugurate in algebra generally acceptable letter symbols. The signs for *plus* ($+$) and *minus* ($-$), introduced as early as 1489 (see Chapter XIII), came finally to signify *addition* and *subtraction*, and that for *equality* ($=$) was introduced in 1557, but not until the seventeenth century did they become common. A German reformer and mystic, Michael Stifel (1487 ?–1567), instituted the symbol for *root* ($\sqrt{}$) and dealt with negative numbers, and Descartes (in *La géométrie*, 1637) made use of a modern exponential system (e.g. a^2, a^3). The symbol for *multiplication* ($\times$) appeared in the posthumous edition (1619) of *Mirifici Logarithmorum Cononis Constructio* of the Scottish mathematician John Napier (1550–1617), and Leibniz later introduced the dot as a symbol for the same operation. The symbol for *division* ($\div$) and those for *greater than* ($>$) and *less than* ($<$) also first occurred in print in the seventeenth century.

Simon Stevin of Bruges (1548–1620) greatly simplified arithmetical calculation when he suggested (1586) the use of decimal fractions in place of the then usual sexagesimal fractions. He urged that the new scheme be employed in coinage and weights and measures. His notational system for fractions remained quite awkward, however, and decimal calculation was simplified only when Edward Wright in an English translation (published in 1616) of Napier's *Mirifici Logarithmorum Cononis Descriptio* (1614) introduced the simple decimal point, about the same time that the Continent adopted the comma for the same purpose. The decimal system of weights and measures had to await general acceptance, however, until the nineteenth century in Europe, and until the twentieth in the United States.

Another device propounded early in the seventeenth century, logarithms, facilitated arduous calculations without demanding an understanding of the mathematical operations involved. It was based on a principle, previously examined by Stifel (in *Arithmetica Integra*, 1545), concerning the correspondence between the geometric and the arithmetic progression of numbers. Logarithms reduced multiplication and division to addition and subtraction, and the extraction of roots to simple division. The underlying assumptions of logarithms were arrived at independently by Napier (in the two works mentioned above) and Joost Bürgi, a Swiss astronomer, who thus provided another illustration of the thesis that when sufficient knowledge is available, the next step in a scientific process may occur to more than one mind about the same time. Logarithms made excellent use of the decimal system introduced by Stevin.

Meanwhile progress came also in the study of trigonometry. Copernicus wrote a treatise on spherical trigonometry in connection with his astronomical research, but his work was published separately (1542) by Georg Joachim von Lauchen, called Rheticus. Rheticus also wrote a treatise of his own (published posthumously, 1596) containing tables of sines, tangents, secants, and other trigonometrical functions. By the beginning of the seventeenth century trigonometry was well on the way to becoming a scientific partner of astronomy.

Meanwhile other high points of mathematical understanding were reached and expressed in formulae. The earliest known calculation of probabilities came in a hardly respectable enterprise: how to divide the stakes in an unfinished gambling game was described in an Italian treatise of 1494 (by Luca di Pacioli). Cardan, an inveterate gambler, also calculated some of the probabilities in games of chance and published his conclusions in a work entitled *De Ludo Aleae*; in the seventeenth century Fermat, Pascal, and Huygens did some more generalized work on the subject, placing the calculus of probabilities on a scientific basis. At the end of the 1600's Newton set forth the solution of another problem, the binomial theorem, simplifying the calculation to the *n*th power of the sum of two quantities. Yet from a certain point of view perhaps the most significant mathematical achievements of the century were in the direct application of mathematical calculation to physical phenomena, for on such calculation depended the mathematical verification and statement of the laws of physics.

Since Omar Khayyám's time (*c.* 1100) it had been recognized that a host of geometrical and other quantitative problems could well be studied by means of algebraic (i.e. analytic) methods. Thomas Harriot (1560–1621) and Pierre de Fermat (1601–65) worked with the problem of graphically representing a function (i.e. a quantity that varies because of interdependence with other variables) by using rectangular co-ordinates, thus laying the foundations of analytic geometry. Finally Descartes' *La géométrie* put forward the concept of a co-ordinate geometry, which would permit a problem in mechanics (the effects of forces upon bodies at rest or in motion) to be stated in a geometrical form and then analyzed with the aid of algebraic functions. The architect Girard Desargues' *Brouillon project d'une atteinte aux événements des rencontres du cône avec un plan* (1639) laid the foundation of projective geometry, the mathematical study of perspective. One of his fruitful suggestions was that parallel lines and planes may be conceived as meeting at an infinitely distant point and thus forming a cone. His book dealt with the question how to derive the properties of a conic section from the simpler properties of the circle forming its base.

We shall consider later the concurrent developments in the field of mechanics. The resulting study of curves of fall and other forms of motion indicated the desirability of a formula for the rise and fall of a curve—that is, for the direction of a given motion at any instant or point. The solution of problems concerned with the measurement of the length and area of closed curves had been approximated by the Ancients through an ingenious process sometimes known as the 'method of exhaustion'; it consisted of 'exhausting' step by step the margin between a curve's smallest and its largest possible length and area by calculating the perimeter and area of a polygon inscribed within it and another circumscribing it, increasing the number of each of the polygons' sides at each step. This method of exhaustion indicated the desirability of calculating any otherwise precisely immensurable quantity by translating it approximately into a curve and estimating the margin between its lowest possible maximum (approximated by the 'exhausted' circumscribed polygon) and its highest possible minimum (approximated by the 'exhausted' inscribed polygon).

The seventeenth-century scientist, faced with the problem of the measurement of variable motions (falling bodies, projectiles, celestial orbits, the pendulum, vibrating strings, beams with varying loads, etc.) had to construct a new mathematics that would enable him to tell the value of one variable (like rate of speed) at a given value (like a point of time or position) of another variable. A number of scientists made contributions toward the solution of this problem. The appearance in the 1540's of the revised edition of Archimedes made available a work of his that dealt with the method of exhaustion. Stevin, the Italian mathematician Luca Valerio (c. 1552–1618), and others devised the 'method of indivisibles', breaking lines up into constituent 'indivisible' points, planes into 'indivisible' lines, and solids into 'indivisible' planes. The work of these men threw more light on, and improved the symbols employable in, the solution of the problem of constructing a tangent to a curve and of calculating maximum and minimum values until, finally, Kepler and others recognized that the increments of a function become negligible as it approaches the neighbourhood of a maximum or a minimum (i.e. its mathematical limits). The concurrent development of analytic geometry permitted geometric problems to be expressed as algebraic equations, and algebraic equations to be projected graphically as points, lines, curves, and other geometric figures. Further speculation on the value of a variable quantity as it approaches its maximum or minimum led to the concept that mathematical quantities are better described as 'fluxions' or continued motion (a line, for example, as the continued motion of a point) than as very small parts in unbroken contiguity.

This reasoning finally led Newton and Leibniz to propound the differential calculus, a method of computing differentials in a continuously varying quantity or motion. An unfortunate squabble arose regarding the priority of discovery of this marvellous tool, but the truth seems to be that each of the two men arrived at the discovery independently, although Newton seems to have been the first to communicate it to others. Almost contemporaneously the reversing of the differential process and thereby the calculation of larger units of a curve from a differential (integral calculus) was expounded by John Wallis (1616–1703) and Isaac Barrow (1630–77). The first complete calculus textbook was published by G. F. A. L'Hôpital (*Analyse des infiniment petits*, 1696). With this new tool problems could be solved that had been nearly intractable before. Though Newton relied chiefly upon a logical demonstration, his use of the calculus at several crucial points made the mechanical theory of the universe put forward in the *Principia* (see below) seem mathematically demonstrable, and his work suggested that all other measurable phenomena might be unified by mathematics. The study of mechanics thus became more and more theoretical, since its problems could be stated mathematically, and mathematics seemed to 'prove' and generalize what observation, reason, and experiment might only suggest.

In the eighteenth century, because of the close correspondence of mathematics and theoretical physics, important advances were made in the field of analysis. Speculation on the concept of a variable as a motion approaching a limit led to debate among English philosophers and mathematicians like Berkeley, Benjamin Robins, Brook Taylor, and Thomas Simpson, and doubts arose about the validity of using infinitesimal (and therefore presumed to be negligible) quantities in careful scientific work.

Meanwhile, Continental mathematicians were more productively employed. D'Alembert's *Mémoire sur le calcul intégral* (1739) and relevant articles in the *Encyclopédie* championed the concept of the limit. The Swiss-born Leonhard Euler (1707–83), who did most of his work as a member of the St Petersburg and Berlin academies, made outstanding contributions to almost every field of mathematics. He established the calculus of variations (roughly speaking, the calculus of the variables of variables) as a separate branch of higher analysis; he was the first to convey a distinct notion of a mathematical function; he revolutionized spherical trigonometry; his method of solving simultaneous linear equations became standard. The Bernoulli family of Basel, which produced a number of skilled mathematicians, was closely associated with Euler in St Petersburg as well as Basel. Jacob Bernoulli (1654–1705) systematized Leibniz's calculus and applied it to the field of differential geometry and also placed the theory of probability on a sound mathematical basis. His brother Johann (1667–1748) helped to establish analytical trigonometry and to solve several problems involving maxima and minima. One of Johann's sons, Daniel (1700–82), not only contributed to mathematical physics but also furnished some dramatic applications of the theory of probability to insurance, statistics, and games of chance. The findings of the Bernoullis in trigonometry and probabilities were supplemented by Abraham de Moivre (1667–1754), a Huguenot refugee in England, who in the process elaborated the theory of permutations and combinations.

Perhaps the century's greatest mathematician was the Italo–French savant Joseph Louis Lagrange (1736–1813)—whose most important work, however, falls outside the chronological limits of this volume. Continuing in Euler's footsteps, he provided a nomenclature for the calculus of variations, and substituting analytical for geometrical methods, he was one of several scientists who advanced toward Euler's objective of a shift from the synthetic to the analytical in mathematical procedures (see Volume V). Several other mathematical contributions fit more appropriately within our period. D'Alembert in his *Traité de dynamique* (1743) studied the pendulum and came to the conclusion ('D'Alembert's principle') that the internal actions and reactions of any system of rigid bodies in motion tend to balance, thus permitting the reduction of the complex problems of dynamics to a generalized statistical method. Alexis Claude Clairault (1713–65) applied the analytical method to non-planar curves in space, thereby laying the foundation for solid analytic geometry. Gaspard Monge (1746–1818) seems to have conceived the major principles of his descriptive geometry (the graphical solution of problems involving space relationships) as early as 1770, but the development and publication of his discovery did not come until 1795.

Newton's prestige was so great that his notational system in the calculus was continued in England, although it was much clumsier than the system of Leibniz, used on the Continent. This divergence of notation was not to be corrected until the nineteenth century. Along with the resentment engendered among the contemporaries of Newton and Leibniz by the dispute over the calculus and the debates on the utility of the concept of the limit, notational clumsiness undoubtedly had something to do with the decline of mathematics in eighteenth-century England. Among the few English mathematicians of note after Newton was Colin Maclaurin (1698–1746), who, though he rejected both infinite and infinitesimal quantities, produced a work which no less an authority than Lagrange compared favourably with the best work of Archimedes; this was the *Treatise of Fluxions* (1742), the most complete survey of that branch of mathematics up to that time.

THE PHYSICAL SCIENCES IN EUROPE

The publication of Copernicus' *De Revolutionibus Orbium Coelestium* (1543) marks a now easily recognized milestone in the development of science. Nevertheless, the book wrought no sudden and drastic 'Copernican Revolution'; what actually happened was much more gradual, complex, and undramatic.

About 1530 Copernicus had privately circulated a briefer statement of his theory. It was based chiefly upon abstract speculation, and even in its final form the inadequacy of existing scientific knowledge and equipment prevented him from giving satisfactory, empirical evidence of his theory from specific observations. He nevertheless provided not only a text but a chart presenting the thesis that the planets circle around the centre of the Earth's orbit, approximately where the Sun is located. He did not question the perfect circular motions of the planets, retaining the Ptolemaic idea of epicycles and eccentric circles; and he mistakenly introduced an additional rotation, a conical motion, to account for the fact that the Earth's planetary axis continually points toward the pole star. Nevertheless, he introduced the principle that the Earth annually revolved about the Sun (*De Revolutionibus*, Bk. I, Ch. 10). And, indeed, Copernicus' system, by allowing the earth to move, provided a simpler explanation of planetary motion than Ptolemy's sluggish machine, reducing the number of wheels in the crystalline spheres from 80 to 34.[8]

The Lutheran preacher and mathematician Andreas Osiander, who saw

Copernicus' treatise through the press in Nuremburg, in an anonymous and deliberately cautious preface supplemented the author's. Here he claimed that basically the book presented only a purely mathematical hypothesis, intended to facilitate certain computations in astronomy, without objective significance and without prejudice to Scripture. This preface was long assumed to be by Copernicus himself, and so the full impact of the 'Copernican Revolution' was cushioned. Dedicated by the dying scientist to Pope Paul III, the book at first appeared to be acceptable to the Roman Catholic Church. Controversy developed only slowly, taking some seventy years to mature.

Copernicus found some enthusiastic disciples and supporters—notably Rheticus and Erasmus Reinhold, who calculated the *Prussian Tables* (1551) upon the Copernican system. Most people, however, finding *De Revolutionibus* difficult, remained indifferent to its implications. Martin Luther is reported to have said of Copernicus, even before *De Revolutionibus* was published: 'The fool will overturn the whole science of astronomy.'⁹ Later Melanchthon explicitly and Calvin by implication repudiated the Copernican theory. Among the arguments against it, in addition to the passages in the Bible that attributed motion to the Sun, one seemed particularly persuasive. Wasn't it more in keeping with the known facts to believe that the Earth stands still and the heavenly bodies rotate around it? If one were to accept Copernicus's modifications of Ptolemy, one would have to develop an entirely new physics.

Nevertheless, the Copernican system slowly won adherents. The observation of several professors of the University of Cracow when a conjunction of Saturn and Jupiter took place in 1563 seemed to confirm Copernicus, and the Copernican system was favourably received and taught there. Even in the popular mind, and certainly in a trained mind like that of Tycho Brahe, doubts about the pre-Copernican scheme arose when a new star appeared in 1572, for a new star was difficult to explain in a perfect and unchanging heaven. The problem arose again with the appearance of a comet in 1577, which was definitely not in the sublunary regions subject to change and decay.¹⁰

Tycho Brahe spent most of his career in observations that did much both to clarify and to compound the confusion. He worked at first in an observatory in Denmark subsidized by the Danish court and later in another in Bohemia subsidized by Emperor Rudolph II. He carefully improved the quadrant, the theodolite, and other available instruments (but had no slide rule, telescope, or pendulum clock, for they had not yet been invented); and he carefully made allowances for the possible inaccuracy of his instruments, removing the haphazardness that had been common among his predecessors. He was thus the outstanding observational astronomer of the pre-telescopic age. His greatest contribution, published in a star catalogue in 1602, was his exact measurement of the positions of about a thousand celestial bodies. In 1588 he published his own theory of astronomy in *De Mundi Aetherii Recentioribus*

Phaenomenis. He concluded that, while the other planets revolved around the Sun, the Sun and Moon in turn revolved around a fixed Earth, for, he pointed out, astronomy had no way of knowing whether the Earth moved, while the evidence of the senses tended to support the belief that it stood still.

Temporarily Tycho's system seemed to answer all astronomical problems, and without the risk of heresy. Interest in the Copernican theory, however, increased in the final years of the sixteenth century in non-scientific quarters. Bruno was burned at the stake in 1600 for holding, among other heresies, the idea of the infinity of the universe. The idea of a plurality of worlds had been discussed pro and con in earlier generations (see Chapter XIII). Copernicus, while still believing in a 'sphere of fixed stars which contains everything',[11] had given a picture of a single universe, though one that was larger than medieval astronomy had allowed, and his disciple Digges, as we have noted, had extrapolated the Copernican immensity into infinity rather than plurality. Bruno's idea, no longer a plurality of worlds but of a single infinite universe, seemed to have the authority of Copernicus and the Copernicans behind it and so was more compelling to some and more alarming to others than it might otherwise have been.

Bruno was a mystic rather than a scientist, and on empirical and other grounds his metaphysics was repudiated by Kepler, the brilliant assistant of Tycho Brahe. Kepler fell heir to the post and the mountain of astronomical data left by Tycho Brahe. Yet he never adhered to his predecessor's system and from the beginning was an ardent Copernican. Driven by a mystical fervour and highly influenced by Pythagorean–Platonic doctrine, he offers a picture of one who was part medieval and part modern at the same time. He lived in an age when it was possible for his mother to be accused of witchcraft, and she escaped conviction only by a terrifying margin. He was the first to apply mathematics to empirical methods in order to derive laws of celestial motion. For example, in his Rudolphine Tables (1617), listing over one thousand star places, he used the recently invented logarithms.

Not content with mere description, Kepler applied a stern logic to an explanation of his observations. In the year 1604 a new luminous body appeared in the constellation Serpentarius, and Kepler noted that the new body was without parallax (i.e. unlike some hitherto known astronomical bodies, it did not seem to change position when observed from different points). It had then to be at approximately the same distance from the observer as the bodies in the region of the fixed stars. Even less than the new star of 1572 could this one be explained in the Ptolemaic framework, in which the phenomena of the outer distances were supposed to be changeless. Kepler also made repeated observations of the planet Mars, which resulted in a book that, as its title indicated, gave an etiological explanation of celestial physics; this was the *Astronomica Nova* αἰτιολογητός, *seu Physica Coelestis, tradita commentariis de motibus stellae Martis* (1609). Here he set forth the first two of his laws of planetary motion: (1) Planets move about the Sun in ellipses, not circles, the

Sun being one of their foci, and (2) planets do not move uniformly but rather in such a way that if a line (or radius vector) were drawn from any one of them to the Sun, that line would sweep through equal areas within the ellipse in equal periods of time. In his *Harmonice mundi* (1619), he enunciated his third law of planetary motion: The square of the period of time that it takes a planet to complete its revolution around the sun (its periodic time) is proportional to the cube of its mean distance from the sun. These laws knocked the remaining props from under the Aristotelian theory of perfect circular motion of the heavenly bodies and at the same time brought about a correction of the Ptolemaic epicyclical astronomy.

Galileo, different in temperament, background, and religion from the German Kepler, contemporaneously aided in bringing about a decisive change in astronomical thought. Galileo's work in physics (which we shall examine below) by disproving Aristotle's ideas of motion made Copernicus seem more plausible. In addition, Galileo made highly dramatic contributions in the field of observational astronomy. By the year 1609, the telescope had become known in Italy, and Galileo was one of the first to recognize its importance to the astronomer. (Pl. 87a.) Through the telescope, he found, the moon seemed far from perfect, being mountainous and rough in many places and not smooth and polished as one might suppose. Far more telling, however, were the observations of the satellites of Jupiter, which were plainly seen to revolve around their planet. Since they seemed to form a system similar to that of the Sun, they reinforced Galileo's belief in the Copernican system. He later observed that Venus went through phases, just as the Moon did. In 1610 he published some of his observations in a booklet entitled *Sidereus Nuntius* (*Messenger of the Stars*). Several other observers, particularly Johann Fabricius and Christoph Scheiner, had independently observed what today we call 'sun spots' when, in 1612, Galileo announced his observations of that phenomenon. Was it possible then that the sun itself was corruptible?

The combination of these discoveries with the general intellectual ferment of the age made Galileo's ideas distasteful to many. Strong forces within the Roman Catholic Church were alarmed, particularly after the publication of his *Dialogo . . . sopra i due massimi sistemi del munde Tolemaico e Copernicano* (1632), which decried the Ptolemaic system and upheld the Copernican. This work involved Galileo in a bitter battle, more over his disregard of clerical injunction than over scientific principle. It ended only when, at the age of seventy, he was forced by the Roman Inquisition to recant, at least publicly, 'the false opinion that the Sun is the centre of the world and immovable, and that the Earth is not the centre of the world and moves.'[12] To be sure, some of Galileo's opponents were guided by personal resentment of his barbed tongue. Nevertheless, men of good will also differed with him, and thus with Copernicus, for they refused to abandon the great Scholastic design of the past. Some of Galileo's adversaries sincerely argued away even the visual evidence and, on the ground that the use of an instrument blunted the senses, refused to look through his telescope.

Nevertheless, the combined impact of the recent achievements in mechanics (which we shall soon consider) and astronomy completed the wrecking of Aristotelian physics. After Kepler and Galileo, the validity of the Copernican hypothesis was more generally accepted, but over two centuries had to pass before it could be thoroughly proved. Meanwhile Descartes put forth an attractive theory to account for the motion of the planets. He posited a world in which all space (*extension* in his vocabulary) was matter; hence all space was filled with a viscous fluid, and motion of any particle in this viscous plenum set up an eddy (or *vortex*), moving all other particles including the planets themselves.

Born in the year in which Galileo died, Newton was able to build upon the contributions of a number of predecessors. Copernicus had removed the Earth from its position of priority; Bruno had proclaimed an infinite universe; Kepler had explained the movement of the heavenly bodies according to mathematical principles; Descartes had explained it as due to vortices; and Galileo and others had not only laid the foundation of observational astronomy but had also developed a system of terrestrial mechanics. Newton owed to his predecessors besides their scientific contributions a widespread readiness to receive scientific innovation. Galileo had been disciplined for his beliefs; Newton carried on no conscious battle with entrenched opinion and was widely proclaimed in his own day. This marked change of attitude toward the scientist between Galileo's generation and Newton's was a correlative of the impact that the burgeoning of science had had upon public opinion.

Newton in clearly enunciated principles of his own connected Galileo's work with Kepler's three laws of planetary motion. Newton's importance lies less in his originality than in his own method—avoiding unnecessarily complex hypotheses, seeking propositions gathered by induction, testing the propositions by experiment, and reducing experience to mathematical abstraction. This method led him to the conclusion that heavenly bodies and terrestrial phenomena were subject to the same effects and causes, the same physical laws. Robert Hooke (1635–1703) was perhaps partly justified in claiming to have stated the now well-known law of gravitation before Newton, but Hooke seems not only to have been more interested in terrestrial gravitation alone but also never to have proved the law experimentally or mathematically.[13] The relationship between the terrestrial and the celestial was for Newton no mere incidental similarity; it was identity. His *Philosophiae Naturalis Principia Mathematica* was published in 1687. Thereafter Hellenistic astronomy, whether Aristotelian or Ptolemaic, was outdated; it was not necessary to know the *Almagest* in order to understand the *Principia*. Newton for the first time defined some fundamental terms and carefully set down his own rigid method.

We shall review Newton's laws of motion later. The principle that won him his best claim to immortality was that of universal gravitation, already vaguely broached by Kepler, Hooke, and others. Starting from Kepler's laws of planetary motion, Newton assumed that every particle of matter attracted every other particle, the power of the attraction varying in direct proportion to the product of the attracting masses (i.e. quantities of matter) and in inverse proportion to the square of the distance between them. This principle and Newton's discussion of viscosity contradicted Descartes' theory that the motion of the planets was due to vortices in a viscous fluid that filled all space, but the Cartesians were to take a long time to be convinced of their error.

Huygens' genius was in many ways second only to Newton's, who expressed great admiration for him. His invention of the pendulum clock was due to his need to measure time exactly in his astronomical observations. He also improved the telescope and introduced a type of micrometer (1658) for measuring planet diameters more precisely. With one of his improved telescopes he recognized in 1655–56 that the peculiar appearance of the planet Saturn was due to its now familiar rings, and he was the first to discover one of the several satellites of that planet.

Having already made significant contributions to astronomy, Huygens was invited to join the new French Académie des Sciences and worked at the recently established Paris Observatory. (Pl. 88a.) That observatory was an offshoot of the Académie des Sciences. Formally inaugurated in 1672 under the protection of Colbert and the patronage of Louis XIV, it brought together several famous astronomers. One of them was Jean Picard (1620–82), inventor and one of the most noted astronomers of his day. With the aid of his colleague Adrien Auzout (d. 1691), he invented the filar micrometer, independently building on a principle discovered by William Gascoyne in 1639; when mounted on a telescope it made possible the measurement of smaller astronomical distances. Ole Roemer (1644–1710), a Danish astronomer, worked at Paris with Picard and, after his return to his native land, developed some splendid instruments, the most famous being the transit-circle, which attached to a telescope permitted the measurement of astronomical angles.

Gian Domenico Cassini (1625–1712) was the dominant figure at the Observatory. Even though at that late date he was still an anti-Copernican, he became a member in 1644 and director in 1671 of the Observatory, having previously been professor of astronomy at Bologna. Work carried on under his direction led him to the mistaken belief that the Earth is flat at the equator and so to the beginning of a fruitful controversy (see below). He also measured the parallax of Mars and attempted from it to estimate the distance between the Earth and the Sun. His estimate was better than any available until that time, although we now know that he was in error about 7 per cent. A Cassini dynasty developed at the Observatory, continuing as directors beyond Domenico for three generations (son succeeding father until the French Revolution temporarily closed it).

As transoceanic travel became common in the seventeenth century, the need to calculate longitude at sea became more urgent. The English astronomer John Flamsteed (1646–1719) recognized that without accurate knowledge of the position of the fixed stars, such calculations would be impossible. With this need in mind, in 1675 King Charles II authorized the building of the Greenwich Observatory, with Flamsteed as 'astronomer royal'. Flamsteed installed the instruments in the new observatory (opened in 1676), his great triumph being the installation in 1689 of a mural arc of 140 degrees. (Pl. 88b.) Between 1676 and 1689 he determined the position of some twenty thousand fixed stars; and his star catalogue, rendering all previous ones obsolete, has remained the basis of modern astronomical calculation. His anxiety to postpone publishing his findings until he could perfect them led to conflict with Newton and Edmund Halley (1656–1742), who wanted prompter publication for their own purposes.

At Flamsteed's death Halley was appointed astronomer royal. As a young man Halley had been the first to make a study of the stars in the southern hemisphere, establishing the position of about 341 stars (1678). It was he who, puzzled (along with Hooke and others) about the mathematics of the motion of a planet, put crucial questions to Newton and, having persuaded him to make public his mathematical deduction of the law of gravitation, arranged for the publication of the *Principia*. Halley is noted chiefly for his studies of comets, particularly of the one that bears his name. He observed that the orbital elements of the Comet of 1682 were quite similar to those recorded for the comets of 1456, 1531, and 1607 and, correctly assuming that they were the same comet, predicted that it would return about every seventy-five years.[14]

In the eighteenth century astronomers continued along the parallel and supplementing lines of mathematical and observational astronomy. Frequently the same men engaged in both observation and the relevant mathematics, but mathematical calculation more than observation engaged the attention of some outstanding Continental astronomers—Euler, Clairault, and d'Alembert among others. Newton having solved the problem of reciprocal attraction for two celestial bodies, these men studied the motion of three mutually gravitating bodies. Although they were not successful in solving it in general, they did arrive at approximate solutions for particular cases—that of the Moon, the Sun, and the Earth, and that of the Sun and two other planets. Their solutions improved both the lunar and the solar theory as well as the tables based on them. With some notable exceptions (e.g. Nicolas Louis de Lacaille, who helped calculate the lunar and solar parallaxes) observational astronomy was almost monopolized by the English. James Bradley (1693–1762) endeavoured to find an annual parallax in the stars, which would provide the final link in the evidence necessary to prove the Copernican hypothesis. He was unable to do so, but his studies contributed to astronomy two important concepts—the discovery and explanation of the aberration of light from the stars (1729) and (1748) the nutation of the Earth's axis (the approximately nineteen-year period of oscillation in the Earth's precession due to the pull of the Sun and the Moon on the equatorial bulge).

During the eighteenth century the astronomer's equipment was greatly improved. New observatories arose; longer, more accurate star catalogues became available for both northern and southern skies; and solar and lunar tables were revised. In 1720 John Hadley constructed the first practical reflecting telescope, and subsequently improvements of telescope mountings permitted wider sweeps of observation. (Pl. 87b, c.) In 1733, Chester Moor Hall invented the achromatic lens (see p. 859 below), and in 1755 John Dollond the heliometer.

Meanwhile the Newtonian theory of universal gravitation continued to gain adherents. Pierre Charles Lemonnier in 1746 and Euler in 1748 were able to show that the disturbances in the movements of Jupiter and Saturn could be explained by the law of gravitation, thus suggesting that the whole solar system was subject to the same gravitational pull that Pierre Bouguer (1698–1758) had recently shown (see below) applied to the Earth's mountains. The return of Halley's comet, as he had predicted, in 1758 was additional and even more convincing evidence of the validity of the Newtonian calculations. In 1770 the American astronomer David Rittenhouse constructed his orrery, a machine that reproduced the workings of the solar system for pedagogical purposes. It was not the first orrery—the name is derived from the Earl of Orrery's (c. 1713)—but it was probably the most accurate one that had yet been constructed, revealing the scientific world's readiness and ability to reduce the movement of the planets to clockwork.

The major accomplishments of Frederick William Herschel (1738–1822), of Hanover and England, will be considered in Volume V, but before our period ended, he had begun the investigations that were to make him the greatest of all eighteenth-century observational astronomers. He was able to construct huge telescopes, one with a 40-foot length and a 48-inch mirror (1789). He was the first in modern times to discover a new planet—Uranus (1781), and he demonstrated (1802) that some double stars circle each other. Subsequent research showed that, in so doing, they follow the Newtonian law of gravitation, thus disposing beyond question of the Aristotelian view that Earth and the heavens were subject to different physical laws.

Attempts were made in the eighteenth century to deduce the origin of the solar system. The first notable one was by Immanuel Kant in his *Allgemeine Naturgeschichte und Theorie des Himmels* (1755). Kant believed that matter was initially distributed throughout space in a finely divided condition, that gravitational force had formed central bodies and nuclei about which the adjoining matter had condensed, and that the mutual interaction of the nuclei and the central bodies accounted for the revolution of all planets around the sun in the same sense and on nearly the same plane. This theory was advanced some forty years before Laplace's more satisfactory nebular hypothesis (see Volume V).

By the middle of the eighteenth century scientific cooperation on an international scale among learned societies and governments reached the point where they could pool their resources for the study of extraordinary celestial events. Such events came in 1761 and 1769 with separate occurrences of otherwise rare passages of Venus across the Sun's disc. Since the seventeenth century astronomical observations had permitted approximations of the relative positions of the members of the solar system but not of its actual scalor dimensions. Transit instruments and methods which permitted the measurement of the ascensions of stars by timing their transits had been devised and improved in that century and the next by Römer, Halley (or perhaps, more accurately, Hooke), Joseph-Nicolas Delisle (1688–1768), and others. Multiple observations of the parallax of Venus during the transits of the 1760's were made possible by sending out several expeditions for that purpose and using the instruments and methods already devised. The second set of observations (1769) permitted a check upon the first (1761), leading to some important astronomical deductions. Lomonosov ventured the hypothesis that there was an atmosphere around the planet Venus. But the most important finding by far was a fairly approximate calculation by means of the solar parallax of the mean distance of the Earth from the Sun. Since the solar parallax was taken to be a constant, it was thought possible at last to ascertain the size of the solar system. The Newtonian world now seemed practically completely measured. Only in the nineteenth century was it shown that the solar parallax is not an independent constant, but, for all that, a great and wonderful international scientific effort has not lost its meed of glory.

Advances in Mechanics and Dynamics

The Aristotelian system of terrestrial mechanics was dependent upon common observation; its overthrow demanded the highest type of conceptual reorientation. In the late sixteenth century several men initiated such a reorientation.

One of them was Stevin, the proponent of decimal fractions, who was primarily interested in statics (that is the mechanics of bodies at rest or in equilibrium and of the forces holding them in balance). He established (or, perhaps more accurately, reconfirmed) 'the law of the inclined plane': two counter-balancing weights lying on the inclined planes of a triangle will be in equilibrium when their masses are proportional to the length of their supporting planes. From this law he deduced that of 'the parallelogram of forces' for machines in which more than two forces are involved: if the magnitude and direction of two forces acting on a single point are represented by two sides of a parallelogram, the diagonal from that point will represent their resultant. Stevin's experiments in the statics of liquids (hydrostatics) led him to conclude, anticipating Pascal, that water pressure is independent of the shape of the containing vessel but depends upon the height and surface of the column exerting the pressure. Stevin did not limit himself to statics, however. Anticipating Galileo, too—and by several years—he experimented with falling objects (1586), finding that when a light object and a heavy object are released at the same instant they take the same length of time to reach the ground, a direct contradiction of Aristotelian mechanics. As an engineer and eventually a high technical adviser to Maurice of Orange, Stevin made some extraordinary practical inventions besides.

The ambivalence of the Aristotelian tradition in science, especially in Roman Catholic countries, where the Scholastic method was still strong, especially in theological matters, is reflected in the work of several sixteenth-century scientists. The Venetian Giovanni Battista Benedetti (c. 1530–90) was a mathematician concerned with mechanics, perspective, and astronomy who professed great admiration for Aristotle. At the same time he repudiated some of Aristotle's physical and astronomical ideas, inducing some modern scholars to consider him perhaps more important as a forerunner of Galileo than is justifiable. One of Benedetti's criticisms of traditional science concerned falling bodies. In avowed contradiction of Aristotle and in anticipation of Galileo, he reasoned that two bodies of the same material but of different gross weights falling in the same medium would maintain the same velocity. In his earlier work Tartaglia also exemplified the persistence of Aristotelianism, but with his later experiments in ballistics—a science which he was the first to set forth in a printed book (*Nuova scienza*, 1537)—he came to recognize that a projectile was subject to both 'violent' and 'natural' forces at once and not, as the Aristotelians thought, successively.

Galileo's most noteworthy scientific contributions lie in the field of dynamics (that is, the branch of mechanics which deals with motion and with the action of forces that produce or change motion) and, more particularly, in the field of kinematics (the study of motion without reference to causal factors). Although the familiar story of his dropping objects from the tower of Pisa is dubious, and although some of the verifications he reported were mentally rather than experimentally derived, his skill as a stylist made his reports classics of scientific literature. He carried on experiments, like that of Stevin, with metal balls rolling down a grooved board. His reports of them indicated that he considered something radically wrong in Aristotelian mechanics, for he held not only (what had long been suspected) that the rate of increase in the velocity (acceleration) of different objects falling in a vacuum would increase uniformly as they fell but also that they would fall at the same velocity. He concluded, therefore, with a mathematical formula, that for any falling body the distance of fall was in fixed ratio to the square of the time consumed by its fall ($s = \frac{1}{2}at^2$).

Something approaching this was discerned by Stevin and other contemporaries of Galileo—among them Dominico Soto (1494–1570) and Isaac Beeckman (1588–1637)—but they had not appreciated its full significance.

Accepting the medieval notion of impetus (see Chapter XIII), as had Galileo also in his early years, they had thought of it merely as a description of a simple fact—that bodies travel faster as they fall closer to the earth. Its full meaning as the fundamental law of dynamics could come only when the theory of impetus (that a force imparts to an object a property of motion which in time expends itself) was displaced by the theory of inertia (that an object will maintain its state of uniform motion or of rest unless force is applied). This Galileo began to do. His experiments with balls and boards permitted him to observe that a ball released at a given level on one side of a dip formed by two inclined planes tended to run up to that level on the other side, no matter how long the other side. He concluded that a body moving on a horizontal plane would remain unchanged in the velocity and direction of its motion if left to itself, loss or gain of motion being attributable to some external cause of retardation or acceleration. Thus Galileo came close to enunciating the modern concept of inertia. While holding to the theory that matter is essentially spatial extension, Descartes enunciated a speciously accurate generalized expression of the inertia principle in 1644, but it was meant to apply to a system of dynamics that, as Newton was to show, was faulty: 'When a body is at rest, it has the power of remaining at rest and of resisting everything which could make it change. Similarly when it is in motion, it has the power of continuing in motion with the same velocity and in the same direction.'[15] This statement may be considered correct only if Descartes' erroneous concepts of relevant terms like *body* and *resisting* impact are disregarded.

Descartes, basing his physics on corporeal vortices operating in a plenum, could not accept Galileo's laws *in toto*, since they posited a vacuum and an incorporeal force, gravitation. He was ready to use them, however, as a roughly useful tool for computation. Yet in the course of the seventeenth century, the dichotomy between computation and philosophy grew less sharp. In Galileo's method, empirical observation was crucial, notably in his experiments with inclined planes (which provided verification not so easily available from falling bodies, since motion on inclined planes was sufficiently slow to permit measurements and comparisons); yet empirical observation, intuitive concept, mathematical generalization, and philosophical law were all inextricably concatenated, and philosophy was regarded as neither different as a kind of knowledge from computation nor superior to or independent of it. Incidentally, Galileo performed his experiments on falling bodies without the pendulum clock. He had to measure time by the weight of water from a steady flow; only at the end of his life, when he was already blind, did he dictate his specifications for a pendulum clock based upon the principle of the isochronism of the pendulum—that the time consumed in the swing of a pendulum is independent of its displacement, or the distance traversed—a principle which he is traditionally supposed to have discovered while he was a student at Pisa.

Galileo's contemporaries, some of them his disciples, extended the study of mechanics. Evangelista Torricelli (1608–47) was outstanding in the field of the dynamics of liquids (hydrodynamics), studying the relation of such factors as the path, velocity, and pressure to the flow of liquids. Pascal advanced the study of hydrostatics by working on the principle, earlier reached by Stevin, that at any point of a fluid the pressure is the same in all directions, and he contributed to the field of pneumatics (the mechanics of gaseous bodies) the suggestion that the phenomena produced by atmospheric pressure correspond to that exerted by a liquid.

Huygens was perhaps the true founder of the science of 'dynamics' (a word coined by Leibniz). As we already have seen, Huygens continued Galileo's work with the pendulum, producing an efficient pendulum clock and elaborating the knowledge of pendular action. In the process he propounded the mathematical relationship of a centrifugal force in a circular motion to its velocity (directly as the square thereof) and to its radius (inversely as the square thereof). Along with Wren, Wallis, and Edmé Mariotte (1620 ?–84), Huygens also increased the knowledge of the elementary laws of impact (the mutual action of colliding bodies on each other), proving that the sum of the kinetic energy of two elastic balls after impact is equal to that before impact.

Newton thus had at his disposal, when he undertook his studies, a rich accumulation of suggestive material in mathematics, astronomy, and mechanics, and perhaps his greatest claim to glory lies not so much in his own original contributions as in his putting the physical science of his day into a cohesive body of knowledge. His *Principia* opens with definitions of the major concepts of mechanics with which he proposed to deal—mass (the quantity of matter in a body, the product of its density and bulk), momentum (the quantity of its motion, the product of its mass and velocity), and force (any action which changes or tends to change its state of rest or the uniformity of its motion). He then gave his attention to dynamics. Building upon or correcting the work of Galileo, Descartes, Kepler, Huygens, Hooke, and others in terrestrial and celestial mechanics, he proved that all objects are subject not only to a common law of gravity but also to common laws of motion. His laws of motion are set forth in the *Principia*, Book I. The first law ('every body continues in a state of rest or of uniform motion in a right line unless it is compelled to change that state by forces impressed upon it') was the definitive statement of the principle of inertia; it emphasized the role of force in changing either motion or rest. It gave the final touch needed to upset the Aristotelian conviction that motion rather than rest is the more 'natural' state of matter. Newton's second law of motion ('the change of motion is proportional to the motive force impressed and is made in the direction of the right line in which that force is impressed') also called attention to force; it provided a formula for the measurement of force ($F = ma$). Newton's third law of motion ('to every action there is always opposed an equal reaction') was the most original contribution of the three. It indicated that forces occur in pairs, that *equilibrium* is not necessarily synonymous with *rest*, and that the total effect of forces in the universe must even out. The implications of this law for celestial mechanics are obvious. For over two hundred years Newton's work remained the basis of the mechanical sciences.

In the eighteenth century mechanics was the work of men who were skilled mathematicians, for mathematics had grown with, and had become prerequisite to, good work in mechanics. Thus, a series of general ideas were formulated that could be applied to problems in many fields. One of these was the principle of the conservation of force. Unlike Newton, who believed that the quantity of motion in the universe needed replenishment from time to time by divine intervention, Leibniz posited a finite amount of force in a closed universe, assuming that, as one object lost force, it communicated it to others. Johann and Daniel Bernoulli, applying their mathematical skill along this line, put forth 'the great law of the conservation of *vis viva*' but, restricting their work to mechanics, did not extend it to other branches of physics. Johann Bernoulli, building on Stevin's and Galileo's observations of particular systems in equilibrium, such as balanced weights on pulleys or on inclined planes, noted the general tendency, when a small displacement takes place in such a stable system, for the equilibrium to be re-established. Calling the small displacement a *virtual velocity* and calling the product of the force times the displacement in its direction *energy*, he arrived (1717) at the principle of virtual velocities: 'In any equilibrium of forces whatsoever, in whatever manner they may be applied, and in whatever directions they may act upon one another, whether directly or indirectly, the sum of the positive energies will be equal to the sum of the negative energies taken positively.'[16] Today Bernoulli's statement has come to be called 'the principle of virtual work' (*work* having meanwhile been defined as the product of force and distance); it states that for a system in equilibrium, a very slight displacement of relative position may be regarded as effecting no change of energy. For bodies in motion an equally significant contribution came with a theorem known (after its author) as 'd'Alembert's principle'; it states that the actions and reactions of a system of free bodies cancel one another (and they are thus in what today would be called 'kinetic equilibrium'), the internal reactions being equivalent to the external or impressed forces. In 1744 Maupertuis, defining 'action' as the product of mass times velocity times distance of change within a dynamic system unaffected by outside forces, enunciated 'the principle of least action': 'Whenever any change occurs in Nature, the quantity of action employed for this change is always the least possible.'[17] Daniel Bernoulli, Euler, Lagrange, and others also worked on this principle, which was completely formulated only during later centuries as the principle of stationary action. By the end of the eighteenth century, however, Lagrange was able to combine the principles of virtual velocities and of least action to formulate equations pertaining to the motion of any system of bodies (see Volume V).

Advances in Optics

The study of optics made marked advances during these centuries. Scientists had long known that light rays bend, or are refracted, when passing from a rarer to a denser medium. Kepler attempted (1604) to arrive at a general law of refraction but reached an approximation sufficient only for an elementary theory of vision. He also, in studying the telescope, gave a geometrical explanation of it in his *Dioptrice* (1611), thereby becoming the founder of modern optics. In the study of the eye's function Kepler improved on the ideas of Alhazen. Willibrord Snell (1591–1626) of Leyden established (1621)—though only intuitively—the basic law of photometry: the intensity of light varies inversely as the square of the distance from its source. Snell also (1621) figured out the law of refraction (now stated: $\sin i = n \sin r$), which means essentially that rays of light passing from air into a denser medium are bent toward the vertical by a constant ratio (the refractive index). Snell's law remained unknown until Descartes restated it independently in 1637 in his *Dioptrique*. According to Descartes light is a sort of thrust or pressure transmitted by particle to particle from the source through the intervening plenum. It was logical for Descartes to deduce from his premiss of vortexes that light would travel more rapidly in a dense than in a light medium. Fermat questioned Descartes' view, however, basing his argument on the principle of least time (that nature does things with the greatest possible economy of time). Assuming that light would therefore move faster through the more extensive medium, air, than through water or glass and using the calculus to determine the minima and maxima involved, he showed that Snell's law held mathematically.

Later in the seventeenth century two rival hypotheses struggled for predominance in the study of light. One, the corpuscular hypothesis, leaning upon the contemporary atomism (see below), explained light as made up of particles emitted from luminous bodies; the other, the undulatory hypothesis, described it as a wave in an all-pervading medium. A series of studies of the phenomenon of diffraction (the breaking-up of light into bands of brightness and shade or of colour) by Francesco Grimaldi (1618–63), professor of mathematics at Bologna, seemed to support the wave hypothesis. In the same year (1665) that Grimaldi's findings were published, Hooke published his *Micrographia*, in which he too supported the wave theory. Hooke thought of light as spread, like eddies in a pool, by a rapid series of spherical vibrations or pulses in an all-pervading medium, each light ray thus being a radius of a sphere and each sphere normally cutting the rays at right angles. Colour occurred, he decided, whenever the pulses deviated in an oblique direction to the light rays. From his study of irridescent substances such as soap bubbles and mica flakes he concluded that when light formed colour at a given point, the colour depended on the thickness of the coloured surface at that point. Where the thickness changed gradually, he found a band of colours varying in the same order as those of the rainbow.

Although differences of velocity were implicit in Snell's law of refraction some students of light held that light travels with an infinite velocity. Roemer observed, however, that the intervals of observable time between the eclipses of Jupiter's moons were shorter when the Earth and Jupiter were approaching each other than when they were receding, and he concluded that light had a finite velocity (1675). His estimate of the velocity of light was approximately 193,000 kilometres or 120,000 miles per second, which is over 100,000 kilometres short of the now accepted figure. Although this finding was rejected by the Cartesians, Bradley's findings on the aberration of light from the stars, which we have seen came in 1726, seemed to verify Roemer's work.

Prismatic colours had long been known; dealers in diamonds, for example, tried to cut their stones in such a way as to show colour to best advantage. In 1672 Newton, who had read Kepler's *Dioptrice* while a student at Cambridge, published his first scientific paper in the *Philosophical Transactions*, the organ of the Royal Society; it was a report of his experiments with prisms. Speculating on the arrangement of the spectrum, he came to the conclusion that sunlight was a mixture of lights of all the colours of the rainbow. Hooke took exception to Newton's theory, insisting upon his own; colour is due to varying arrangements of light waves on upper and lower reflecting surfaces. Huygens, also differing with Newton, in 1678 announced his theory to the Académie des Sciences and in 1690 published it in his *Traité de la lumière*. It held that light spreads from a source through an all-pervading plenum or ether in regular spherical emissions each particle of which, in turn, emits a wavelet. His theory, he felt, explained the phenomenon of double refraction as due to the passage of light first through ether in free space and then through ether in the pores of material objects. At first Newton tried to combine the undulatory with a corpuscular theory of light but finally decided for the corpuscular theory: 'Nothing more is requisite for putting the Rays of Light into Fits of easy Reflexion and easy Transmission, than that they be small Bodies which by their attractive Powers, or some other Force, stir up Vibrations in what they act upon.'[18] Newton's study of colour had led him to abandon any hope of making an improved refracting telescope on the mistaken assumption that an achromatic telescope was impossible. Nevertheless, Hall privately made an achromatic telescope a few years after Newton's death,[19] and in 1758 Dollond independently discovered and publicly revealed how it could be done.

The overawing authority of Newton made the corpuscular theory of light dominant for another century, and several attempts were made to verify it by experimental evidence. The Dalmatian-born Italian Jesuit scholar R. G. Boscovich (1711 ?–87) taught that matter, including light corpuscles, was not continuous but was made up of minute particles surrounded by spheres of repulsion or attraction, thus permitting light to penetrate certain substances. Euler, on the other hand, was a proponent of a wave theory and put forth his arguments in popular *Lettres à une princesse d'Allemagne* (1760–62). Although he marshalled his arguments well, he submitted no fresh evidence to shake the foundation of the corpuscular hypothesis. To answer this argument, Joseph Priestley (1733–1804) published his *History and Present State of Discoveries relating to Vision, Light and Colours* (1772). Yet in the nineteenth century the Hooke–Huygens wave theory won out, only to be challenged again in the twentieth.

Kepler, Snell, Huygens, and others had studied the varying intensity of light, but precise methods of photometry came only in the eighteenth century with the Comte de Buffon (1707–88), who examined the varying intensities of different luminous bodies and experimented with sunrays. Pierre Bouguer (1698–1758) constructed the first effective photometer and showed, as Snell previously had intuitively suspected, that light intensity is inversely proportional to the square of the distance from its source. The German physicist Johann Heinrich Lambert (1728–77) summed up the photometry of his day in a work entitled *Photometria, sive de Mensura et Gradibus Luminis, Colorum et Umbrae* (1760), which discussed also many of the problems still raised today. Although Bouguer was a more careful experimenter, Lambert is generally regarded as the creator of the modern system of photometry.

The Study of Heat

No precise distinctions were made between fire, flame, light, and heat before the seventeenth century. As the quarrel over the corpuscular theory of light indicated, the theory was common, though disputed, that (to use Newton's words) 'God in the Beginning form'd matter in solid, massy, hard, impenetrable, movable Particles.'[20] An earnest student of Epicurus, Pierre Gassendi (1592–1655), tried, with some success, to adapt Epicureanism to Christian theology, and he was one of the staunchest advocates of atomism, derived from the physical theories of Democritus and the Epicureans. He applied it to heat, maintaining that heat consisted of special types of atoms, cold being produced by other, 'frigorific' ones.

In contrast, Francis Bacon, his contemporary, and some English successors to Bacon agreed with Plato that heat was a form of motion. In his *Novum Organum* Bacon put forth views that at first sound quite modern, although closer reading may suggest confusion. A series of interesting experiments in the new scientific vein later led Boyle also to the conclusion that heat was the rapid agitation of the components of a substance. Although he also talked of 'atoms of fire', he said in his work *On the Mechanical Origin of Heat and Cold* (1675): 'Heat seems principally to consist in that mechanical property of matter called motion.' He dismissed as erroneous the idea that air was necessary to produce heat—an idea that many had accepted, not differentiating between combustion and heat. Hooke went further than Boyle, maintaining that heat was 'a property of a body arising from the motion or agitation of its parts.'[21] He distinguished heat from fire and flame and held that all bodies had some degree of heat, nothing being perfectly cold.

The distinction between light and heat only gradually became clearer. For centuries mirror and lenses had been used to focus the sun's rays on combustible material to bring about fire, and Bacon in the *Novum Organum* suggested the use of burning-glasses. In a later work he speculated too whether a mirror could concentrate cold as well as heat, but the Accademia del Cimento was the first to demonstrate experimentally the reflection of cold. The French physicist Edmé Mariotte in 1679 pointed to an important difference between the sun's heat, on the one hand, and rays of a fire, on the other: when heat from the sun passed through a transparent body, it was not separated from light, but heat was separated from light in the case of rays from a fire. This difference indicated that the radiant heat of a fire was not identical with its light.

Despite the more scientific views (discussed below) of Hooke and others on combustion, for a long time the so-called 'caloric theory' of heat was considered valid. This theory maintained that heat was engendered by a material substance which was given the name *caloric*. Caloric was described as an elastic fluid that was all-pervading and imponderable; its particles were attracted by other matter but repelled by one another. If two bodies of different temperature came into contact, caloric flowed from the hotter to the colder until the two were brought into equilibrium.

The study of heat was aided by increased efficiency in the measuring of temperature. Thanks to the development of the thermometer by Fahrenheit, Réaumur, and Celsius (see above), the science of heat was gradually placed on a quantitative basis. In some circles the theory of Gassendi as modified by his critic Jean Baptiste Morin (1583–1656) prevailed—that heat and cold were different though associated entities, but Georg Wolfgang Krafft (1701–54) and Georg Wilhelm Richmann (1711–53), both members of the St Petersburg Academy, dropped units of cold from their calculations, dealing only with varying degrees of heat. Richmann devised a formula for determining the temperature of a mixture of liquids, which was based on the assumption that the intensity of a given quantity of heat would vary inversely to the mass of the heated substance or mixture of substances. Experiments by Johan Gadolin (1760–1852), a Finnish scientist, and others showed that that assumption held true only for bodies of homogeneous composition, other things being equal. Lomonosov, who began with an atomistic hypothesis, suspected the kinetic nature of heat, suggesting, for example, that heat transfer in gases was the result of elastic collisions among their particles.

Meanwhile, Boyle, John Mayow (1643 ?–79), and others were conducting the investigations of combustion that will be described below. In consequence, about 1760 Joseph Black (1728–99) was in a position to expound the distinction between heating value and temperature, that is, between the quantity and the intensity of heat. This distinction was based on the principle that each body had its own 'capacity for heat', which was in no way related to the quantity of matter it contained. This 'capacity for heat' is now known as 'specific heat'. Within several years Black was able to demonstrate that during such changes as melting and evaporation definite quantities of heat seem to be absorbed or to disappear and cannot be detected by the thermometer, but that during the reverse procedures (that is, freezing and condensation) these quantities of heat reappear. That quantity he labelled 'latent heat'. Some years later, Johann Carl Wilcke (1732–96), German–Swedish scientist, experimenting with the melting of snow at Stockholm, came independently to similar conclusions. Black's discovery was of great use to James Watt, we shall see, in developing his steam engine. Before the end of the century the studies of Benjamin Thompson (Count Rumford) and others made possible long strides in the study of heat, but the caloric theory continued to be embraced into the nineteenth century.

The Study of Acoustics

The experimental school, in attempting to determine the nature of motion, produced results that were highly suggestive also in explaining the phenomenon of sound (acoustics). The relationship of pitch to length of string had been recognized since Pythagoras, but Galileo was the first to draw attention to the rate of vibration of the string as the significant factor. Reporting Galileo's otherwise little known studies of sound, a French admirer, Marin Mersenne, in *Traité de l'harmonie universelle* (1627) and *Harmonicorum Libri* (1635), demonstrated how sound was determined by vibration. Repeating Pythagoras' experiment, Mersenne went on to show that the pitch of the note emitted by a vibrating string was inversely proportional to the square root of the density of the material composing the string and directly proportional to the square root of its tension. He inquired further why a freely vibrating string produces not only its clearest, or fundamental, tone but overtones as well and why as the fundamental tone weakens, certain other tones continue for a while. Descartes suggested that the vibration of a whole string produces its fundamental tone while the vibration of separate parts within it produce its overtones, but verification of his hypothesis did not come until later (see below).

Another problem of acoustics that contemporaneously attracted attention was the measurement of the velocity of sound. Aristotelian physics had taught that high tones were transmitted through the air more rapidly than low tones. Gassendi was one of the first to carry on significant experimental research on this problem. He had a cannon and a musket fired at the same instant and measured the time between the moment that observers at a suitable point saw the flash and the moment that they heard the report, and he found that both reports were heard simultaneously. Thus still another Aristotelian doctrine was upset. Gassendi calculated the velocity of sound to be about 1473 Paris feet per second. Throughout the century others conducted similar experiments, and all of them, including Mersenne, Borelli, Viviani, Boyle, Cassini, Huygens, Picard, and Roemer, got lower velocities.

In the early seventeenth century the Aristotelian assumption that sound is transmitted through the medium of air was still generally accepted. A few, however, believed that only certain parts of the air rather than the whole were necessary. For example, Gassendi, in keeping with his atomism, thought that special atoms in the air carried sound. To what extent the audibility of sound was correlative to the density of air could not be settled experimentally until a proper instrument became available. The invention of the air-pump by Otto von Guericke (c. 1650) supplied the needed device; it used air pressure to drive a piston in a cylinder whose air was thereby alternately exhausted and supplied. The inventor himself conducted a series of experiments which were fundamental to an understanding of the property of gases, and one of them, confirmed by the subsequent findings of Boyle, Denys Papin (1647–1712), and Francis Hauksbee (d. 1713 ?), proved not only that audibility varied with the density of air but also that sound was diffused through water and solids, thus undermining another Aristotelian teaching.

The research of these men demonstrated, in addition, that the intensity (or loudness) of sound (as distinguished from pitch) varied with the density of air. This fact suggested that sound intensity might differ with different gases. Priestley's subsequent tests showed that sound was barely audible in hydrogen, stronger in oxygen than in air, and in carbonic acid gas much stronger still. The question arose also whether varying temperatures had any influence on sound intensity. William Derham (1657–1735) conducted experiments which determined that in general sounds are stronger in winter than in summer and that the sound of firearms is not weakened in damp weather but is almost inaudible in very dry weather.

Inevitably the study of sound entered the field of music. Earlier observations had indicated that a sound resulting from two deep organ tones differing slightly in frequency would have periodic variations of intensity ('beats'). Joseph Sauveur (1653–1716) recognized that these variations must be caused by the periodic coincidence of the vibrations which produced the two initial tones. Working with two notes a semitone apart whose relative frequency was known (15 to 16), he was able to calculate their vibration frequency (90 and 96) by the number of beats (6) they produced and thus to derive a formula for the vibration frequency of any note. He was also one of those who showed, as Descartes had surmised, that the overtones of a single plucked string must be caused by oscillations of parts of it. The experimental investigation of the nature of sound permitted the scientific study of music (see Chapter XII) to begin in earnest. In his *Principes d'acoustique et de musique* (1701) Sauveur indicated the natural derivation of the major chord from the fundamental tone and established the musical doctrine of harmonics or overtones. In the course of the eighteenth century, scientists, mathematicians, and musicians (D. Bernoulli, Euler, Taylor, and Guiseppe Tartini, to mention only a few who did their principal work before 1775), advanced the understanding of tone vibrations and harmonics.

The Study of Magnetism and Electricity

Until the sixteenth century the study of magnetism and electricity was essentially undeveloped. The increasing use of compasses in navigation had led, however, to some empirical observations in the field of magnetism. Lodestone was known to be capable of re-magnetizing compass needles, and the repellent and attracting qualities of the different magnetic poles was discovered early. The changes in the magnetic declination of the compass (deviation from the true north–south line) and in its dip or inclination (angle with the horizon) had been observed (see Chapter XIII), the latter independently by George Hartmann (1544) and Robert Norman (1581), but had not yet been carefully differentiated.

To William Gilbert (1540 ?–1605), physician to Queen Elizabeth, usually goes the credit for initiating the scientific study of magnetism and electricity. He is said to have spent great sums of money in research, rejecting the traditional belief in the medicinal and occult virtues of the magnet as well as in other superstitions of the day. He devised an instrument with a metallic needle for measuring the electrification of various materials and proved that other things than amber were electrified by friction. One of the first to use an experimental procedure (only later to be made explicit by his contemporary Francis Bacon), he demonstrated the difference between electrical and magnetic influences, showing that magnets act on only iron objects or lodestones and orient them in a specific direction, while electrical forces act on a large number of other materials as well without having any effect upon their orientation. His experiences with the lodestone led him to make experiments with a small globular lodestone (later called 'a little Earth', or *terrella*) and to conclude that the Earth itself is a huge lodestone or magnet. He mistakenly attributed magnetic properties to the other planets as well and asserted that magnetism explained why the same face of the moon always was turned toward the Earth—a fruitful error, since it led to the idea of the mutual attraction of widely separated bodies.

Even if some of Gilbert's astronomy was wrong, his detailed experiments mark the beginning of the modern approach to planetary motion, magnetism, and electricity. The publication of his major book, entitled *De Magnete, Magneticisque Corporibus, et de Magno Magnete Tellure; Physiologia Nova* (1600), was a decisive step toward the understanding of physical phenomena and of the experimental method by means of models. The result of about seventeen years of study, it was the first important scientific work published by an Englishman. Most of it was devoted to his findings on magnetism, only one chapter being given to a discussion of the still less familiar phenomenon of electricity.

Little advance was made beyond Gilbert's findings in those fields for over a century and a half. Descartes attempted the first scientific explanation of magnetism in his *Principia Philosophiae* (1644). Consistent with his system, he believed magnetism to be due to vortices that, he supposed, circulated about magnetic bodies. Further observations of magnetic behaviour revealed that compass deviation changed even in the same place in the course of time. Halley looked into this problem on the several scientific expeditions that he made to various parts of the world and began the systematic collection of data on compass variations. He was also the first to recognize that the aurora borealis was related to the magnetism of the Earth. During the eighteenth century students of magnetism were aided by the increasing skill of manufacturers of artificial magnets, and Charles Augustin Coulomb (1736–1806) was able to determine the law according to which the force of a magnetic pole varies. In the 1780's he demonstrated that Newton's inverse square law (gravitational attraction varies in inverse proportion to the square of the intervening distance) held good also for magnetic attraction and repulsion (see below).

Most investigations of electricity in the seventeenth century were repetitions of Gilbert's work. The Accademia del Cimento added, however, to the slowly accumulating stock of knowledge by a study of various electrical substances, listing them in the order of their attracting power, with amber at the head of the list. That excited amber lost its charge when held close to a flame was also noted. Von Guericke succeeded (*c.* 1650) in making an electric generator and discovering electrical discharge; his generator's essential component was a ball of sulphur continuously rotated and rubbed by hand or cloth so as to produce a charge. The sulphur, it was found, then attracted various objects such as paper and feathers. Leibniz observed electric sparks (1671–72). Picard discovered murcurial phosphorescence (1675), and the phenomenon fascinated early-eighteenth-century scientists. Some attempted to explain the phosphorescence of excited mercury in a barometer tube as the action of sulphur or some special type of phosphorus in the mercury, until Hauksbee gave the correct explanation (1709): the friction of the mercury against the glass tube generated electricity.

Observations like these made clearer Gilbert's basic distinction between electric and non-electric substances. After much experimentation Stephen Gray (1729) was able to distinguish between a conducting and a non-conducting substance. He demonstrated that certain bodies could receive and transmit electrical properties whereas other bodies, such as glass and silk, could neither give nor receive electrical properties and might thus be used to preserve charges. Jean Desaguliers (1683–1744) gave the name of *conductors* to substances capable of transmitting electricity and of *supporters* to those which lacked this capacity; the latter were in the nineteenth century called *insulators*. Charles François Du Fay (1648–1734) was able to distinguish two opposing kinds of electricity, each attracting the other and repelling its own kind; he made the error of thinking that one kind was 'vitreous' and the other 'resinous'. We now prefer to call them positive and negative.

By the middle of the eighteenth century electrical machines and investigations of electricity were quite fashionable. (Pl. 95a, b, c.) One of the problems facing investigators was to find some way of preserving electric charges. Once it was established that water could be electrified and that glass was a non-conductor, the first electrical condenser (today known as the Leyden jar) became possible. It was developed by two men working independently, E. G. von Kleist[22] of Pomerania in 1745 and Pieter van Musschenbroek of Leyden in 1746. Subsequent improvements allowed fascinated people to engage in transmitting electrical shocks at a distance; William Watson (1715–87) sent one across the Thames in 1747.

Seventeenth-century investigators had explained electrical phenomena as due to quasi-material effluvia, and some attempted to show that bodies when electrified increased their weight. Their failure to do so led them to conclude not that electricity was merely a condition of charged bodies but rather that, like heat and light in the corpuscular system, it was an imponderable substance. The doctrine of imponderable substances, however, supplied no causal explanation for electricity, whereas the wave theory of light seemed to provide a simple one. Euler, for example, believed that the source of electrical processes was the ether, in which light was also propagated, electricity being due to a disturbance of the ether's equilibrium.

Benjamin Franklin thought in somewhat similar terms. His interest in electrical phenomena was first roused by some electrical apparatus sent to Philadelphia by Peter Collinson, a London merchant, member of the Royal Society. In the popular mind at least, Franklin's study of lightning as an electrical phenomenon is a most spectacular and unprecedented achievement. Yet several investigators had preceded him with similar investigations. For instance, a friend of Boyle named Dr Wall had likened certain electrical experiments to thunder and lightning (1709); so had Newton; and in 1746 the German physicist J. H. Winkler came to the same conclusion. In 1749 Franklin set forth a large body of evidence on which he based his idea that thunderstorms are electrical in nature. In 1752 he carried out his famous kite experiment, collecting an electrical charge directly from a thundercloud into a Leyden jar. He eventually deduced that a single electric fluid pervaded all bodies, though in varying quantities, and was the cause of all electrical phenomena. He was the first to talk of positive and negative electricity. A body was electrically neutral, he said, when its electric fluid was in equilibrium within and without; if it had more than its normal amount of fluid, it was positively electrified and, if less, negatively electrified. Some scholars disagreed and put forth a theory of two fluids, but Franklin was able to explain the charging of the Leyden jar in terms of one. For this theory of electricity, which he communicated to the Royal Society, he was in 1756 made a member.

Several contemporaries of Franklin also made significant contributions to electrical studies, which, however, were overshadowed by his dramatic success. In 1753 Richmann became one of the first 'martyrs of science' when struck by lightning while attempting to measure atmospheric electricity with an 'electrometer' he had devised as early as 1745. Wilcke established in 1757 the fact that when two bodies are rubbed together both negative and positive electrification are invariably produced. F. U. T. Aepinus (1724–1802), for a time professor at the Academy of Berlin and later at that of St Petersburg, where he superintended the Normal School, collaborated in some of Wilcke's investigations. Aepinus discovered the electrification of material by induction and demonstrated that the distinction between conductors and insulators is far from absolute.

The relative simplicity of Franklin's experiments evidences the primitive state of contemporary knowledge about electrical phenomena. By the close of the eighteenth century scientists were able to go further than Franklin and other pioneers and to determine a precise law for the measurement of electrical forces. The new science of electrostatics thus developed. Aepinus, whose *Testamen Theoriae Electricitatis et Magnetismi* (1759) first systematically attempted to move the study of electricity from a descriptive to a quantitative basis, recognized that the electric force between particles diminished with the increase in the distance between them. Daniel Gralath, burgomeister of Danzig, experimented with electric shocks and invented an electrometer (*c.* 1746). Priestley in *The History and Present State of Electricity* (1767) summed up and expounded the then known studies of electrical phenomena in a persuasive way that won him membership in the Royal Society. He suggested that Newton's inverse square law of gravitational attraction applied also to electrical attraction. Henry Cavendish (1731–1810) proved this application experimentally in 1771, but he did not publish his findings, and they remained unknown until 1879. It remained for Coulomb, by means of a torsion balance that he invented which was capable of measuring the force of an electric charge, to demonstrate the law experimentally. His experiment was conducted at the same time as the one (described above) by which he proved that magnetic attraction was likewise subject to the inverse square law. The usual unit of quantity of electricity is now known as a *coulomb*.

Load, Stresses, and Strains

Before the sixteenth century builders made little effort to work out a rational explanation of their craft. Vitruvius' writings on architecture, rediscovered in the fifteenth century, showed no real knowledge of what we today would call scientific principles of construction. Few working drawings by medieval builders are extant, but studies of the ground-plans of medieval buildings make quite obvious that although their builders worked out proportions with remarkable effectiveness, they did so chiefly on practical rather than theoretical principles. Craftsmen in the building tradition had long known what loads, stresses, and strains various materials and structures could bear, but they had learned such things by trial and error.

The experimental investigation of the behaviour of materials was first clearly stated in Leonardo da Vinci's writings. He expressed, for instance, what architects had practiced—namely, that an upright pillar consisting of a compact bundle of shafts could support a load much heavier than the sum of the loads which the shafts could support separately. He appears to have concluded from actual experiment that a pillar of a given height has a carrying power proportional to the cube of its diameter. His manuscripts mention still other calculations and experiments related to the strength of materials.

Little systematic study of the strength of materials is otherwise known before Galileo. Some of the questions he raised were stimulated by his conversations with craftsmen in the Venetian Arsenal and his observations of procedures there. It was already well recognized that the scale of a structure was important in determining its strength. Galileo, going further, studied the nature and measurement of the resistance of materials to fracture. He set forth some interesting propositions and proved them geometrically. One example was an elaboration of Leonardo's conclusion: 'In prisms and cylinders of equal length, but of unequal thickness, the resistance to fracture increases in the same ratio as the cube of the thickness of the base.'[23] Why then could giant fish and huge ships with slender bases survive at sea? he asked, and he answered: Only because water deprived them of their weight. He concluded that it would be impossible to increase indefinitely the dimensions of land structures.

Study of this field continued lively after Galileo. Bernard Forest de Belidor (1693-1761) brought together the various writings of the day on structural engineering, and his *La science des ingenieurs* (1729) and *Architecture hydraulique* (1737-39) have been called the first scientific textbooks on engineering. Men more noted for work in other fields also concerned themselves with the problem of the strength of materials. Mariotte took it up because of interest in hydraulics, which was growing with the increased demands for ornamental fountains. Musschenbroek, years before he began experimenting with the Leyden jar, carried out a series of comprehensive laboratory experiments with extemporized machines to test building materials under stress. The naturalist Buffon aided in inspecting and testing timber for French naval construction. The physicist Coulomb, more famous for his later work in electricity, in an essay presented to the Académie des Sciences in 1773 was the first to apply mathematical maxima and minima to measuring the strength of architectural materials; his work provided a reasoned explanation of the inclined plane which the cracks in crushed masonry often form.

Before the seventeenth century rule of thumb seems to have prevailed in the building of retaining walls. For ages man has used artificial banks or stone walls as retainers and as fortification. Late-medieval churches and castles give silent testimony of great technological skill. Italian military architects of the sixteenth century, faced with the problem of defence against artillery (see Chapter XV), abandoned the straight medieval wall, broken only by towers at suitable intervals, and favoured more complicated traces, providing frequent bastions for the defenders' artillery and at the same time presenting the besiegers with a less simple target. Despite these enduring achievements of earlier days, no record of rules or specifications to be observed in erecting walls has yet been found that can be dated before the age of Louis XIV.

Marshal de Vauban (1633–1707), the chief military engineer of the Sun-King, prepared such specifications, giving dimensions for walls between 6 and 80 feet in height. Vauban was the greatest expert of his century on fortifications. His skill made the bastion a major element of fortification until in the nineteenth century it was supplemented by the tenaille system of the Marquis de Montalembert (1714–1800). During a long military career Vauban designed or improved some 160 fortresses that were regarded as well-nigh impregnable in his day. Throughout the eighteenth century his specifications for retaining walls were gospel for the military engineer. Pierre Bullet (1639–1716) in his L'Architecture pratique (1691) gave rules for designing retaining walls and propounded a theory of earth pressure, upon which Pierre Torteaux de Bouplet (d. 1744) elaborated. Coulomb presented the first satisfactory equation for calculating the pressure of a given quantity of earth against a retaining wall.

In civil architecture the acknowledged master of the post-Gothic age was Palladio. His famous treatise on architecture (1570) dealt with such subjects as trussing materials, ancient Greek and Roman houses, and his own designs for houses, roads, bridges, piazzas, and basilicas and other temples. Though he did not allow sufficiently for the horizontal thrust of an arch, he contributed to the knowledge of the strength of abutments and of the arches which they supported. In the seventeenth century the Jesuit architect François Derrand worked out a more satisfactory arch construction by providing greater depth for the abutment as the rise of the arch was reduced. Wren, in his official reports to the government on architectural matters, indicated an interest in construction problems, and his criticism of the design of the old St Paul's Cathedral in London led to his being given, after the Great Fire of London in 1666, the task of building the new one. With the growing elaborateness of public buildings, serious studies were made of the arch and its abutments. Various methods were discussed by François Blondel, Hooke, Philippe de Lahire (d. 1719), and Coulomb (to mention only a few). The design, structure, and strength of Classical arches and domes and their supporting piers became a subject of controversy in French engineering circles with the building by Jacques Germain Soufflot (1713–80) of the Church of Sainte-Geneviève (later named the Pantheon) in Paris. The controversy lasted until the end of the century, leading to a number of serious experiments and monographs on the strength of building materials.

The Rise of the Science of Meteorology

Prior to the seventeenth century the standard treatise on meteorology was Aristotle's *Meteorologica*. The chief means of predicting weather were astrological observations, weather-lore founded on superstition, and the uncertain data of untrained observers. Descartes' *Météores* (1637), though sometimes in error, at least gave the study the dignity of a branch of physics. The discovery and improvement of certain instruments made possible a more exact examination of the atmosphere. In the seventeenth century, the thermometer was introduced (see above), and the Accademia del Cimento made a working hygroscope. Vicenzo Viviani (1621–1703), Torricelli, and Von Guericke developed the barometer (and thereby explained nature's *horror vacui* as due to atmospheric pressure). Hooke produced a wind-gauge and a weather clock, Hooke and Wren a rain-gauge. A composite weather clock was in operation by 1700. Studies were made also of the relationship of wind-currents to general atmospheric conditions; speculation was especially keen about the trade winds. During this transitional period meteorology, consisting of attempts to understand atmospheric pressure and to measure weather phenomena, was merely an offshoot, so to speak, of elementary pneumatics. Nevertheless, as early as 1660 Von Guericke had acquired enough understanding of relevant barometric principles to forecast a storm from a sudden drop of atmospheric pressure.

The contemporary study of gases led to the pronouncement of Boyle's (or Mariotte's) law (the volume of a gas varies in inverse proportion to the pressure upon it, providing the temperature remains constant). One of several important consequences of this discovery was that it prompted serious study of the Earth's atmosphere. Hooke and Mariotte both discussed the extent of that atmosphere, and Halley in 1686 made a good rough estimate of it—not over 45 miles high. This estimate was based on the assumption that air cannot be rarefied to much more than 3000 times its volume at ground level. Since the atmosphere's relation to the winds was not understood, its movements were assumed to be due to disturbances of the equilibrium governing atmospheric pressure. Inquiries into the nature of wind were also carried on, particularly by Halley, who produced the earliest meteorological chart. He at first thought that the aurora borealis was atmospheric, but (see above) he eventually decided that it was a magnetic phenomenon.

Increased contacts throughout the world gave greater opportunity for comparative observations. As early as the seventeenth century the value of synchronous meteorological observations at various places was recognized. Even before the development of the pendulum clock permitted relatively precise time allowances for such work, a concerted series of instrumental observations was undertaken. Paris, Clermont-Ferrand, and Stockholm were the scenes of the earliest meteorological investigations (1649–51) of which the records are still extant. The Grand Duke Ferdinand II of Tuscany (1610–70), scientist and patron of the Accademia del Cimento, established the first large-scale international organization, supplying its observers with instruments from his own purse; forms calling for observations of pressure, temperature, wind direction, and humidity were also provided.

Such studies not only obtained meteorological information but also tested old instruments and suggested new ones. The Hungarian scientist J. A. von Segner (1707–77), better known for his turbine (Segner's water-wheel) and his suggestion of the idea of surface tension in liquids, wrote several treatises dealing with the mathematics of thermometers and barometers. The Russian polyhistor Lomonosov showed great ingenuity in the improvement of old instruments and the invention of new ones—such as an indoor anemometer, a thermometer of 150 degrees between freezing and boiling, and a pendulum that was delicate enough to suggest the tidal motions of the earth's crust.[24] The meteorologist Jean André Deluc (1727–1817) made marked changes in the barometer and the thermometer. Experimenting with several liquids, he recommended the use of mercury for thermometers (as Fahrenheit had done before him). In the controversy already raging over the relative merits of Réaumur's and Fahrenheit's thermometric scale, Deluc proposed that each country continue to use the scale already adopted by it; for him the important thing was the construction of as accurate a thermometer as possible, graduation taking a secondary place.

The superstitious factors in weather prediction vanished only slowly, where they did so at all, and not until the late eighteenth century was meteorology firmly established as a substantive branch of science. Many pamphlets still were published in the eighteenth century to explain unusual or disastrous weather as the judgment of God. Nevertheless, the scientific study of weather also made progress. The philosopher Wolff put forth a dull though systematic discussion of the subject, but the best meteorological treatise of the century was that of Father Louis Cotte (1740–1815), published in 1774. Sponsored by the Académie des Sciences and derived to a large degree from information sent by scattered observers to Paris, Cotte's work was the first textbook of empirical meteorology.

Iatrochemistry and the Beginnings of Modern Chemistry

In the science of chemistry the most promising lines of advance appeared in the enterprise of the iatrochemists and the workers in the budding chemical industry. The iatrochemists were a school that endeavoured to make physiology a branch of chemistry. The founder of this school was Theophrastus Philipp Aureolus Bombastus von Hohenheim (1493–1541), better known as Paracelsus because, a self-taught Swiss physician, he often used the prefix *para* ('super') in the titles of his works to emphasize his superiority of knowledge. Having examined miners' diseases and metallurgy at first hand in the mines of the Tyrol, he discovered chemical problems far more intriguing than the alchemical processes he previously had studied. Curiosity led him to travel through western Europe learning the healing art from the books of nature and experience. Later, as professor of medicine and town physician at Basel, he expounded and practiced novel theories so successfully but also so tactlessly that he was driven out by the local practitioners to lead a life of wandering from city to city. Everywhere he went he angered physicians and pharmacists by publicly burning the books of Galen and other ancient physicians and by ridiculing the humors, bleedings, and purgings of the current medical practice in the Coan tradition. Insisting on a curiously empirical yet mystical approach and relying heavily on novel concoctions for healing, he broached the Cnidian theory that the processes of the human body are chemical and therefore, when out of order, can be cured by readjusting the body chemistry with specifics. He laid great stress on the *tria prima*—salt (earth, the incombustible principle), sulphur (fire, the combustible principle), and mercury (air, the volatile principle)—but he also used arsenic, opium, and iron.

For all his quarrel with his contemporaries Paracelsus was also a child of his day. He believed in transmutation, in the philosopher's stone and other alchemic wonders, in nymphs and sylphs. To him the natural and the supernatural world were equally subject to the control of the physician, but his belief in mystical, demoniacal, and magical forces made it impossible for him to arrive at natural law. His contempt for some of the healing methods of Galen and his followers was not always due to logical considerations. In place of herbal remedies and diet he advocated the use of metallic drugs that had been purified by fire and of medicines prepared by techniques familiar to alchemists. His underlying principle—that effective medicines might be prepared in the chemical laboratory—whatever its intrinsic merit, was hidden in the occult.

Nevertheless, Paracelsus and other iatrochemists, in their desire to discover and reveal the chemical nature of physiological processes, were pioneers preparing the way for a sounder chemical theory. Valerius Cordus (1515–44), better known as a botanist than as a physician or alchemist, described in scientific terms the method of obtaining ether by treating sulphuric acid with alcohol. Andreas Libavius (1550–1616), bitterly criticizing Paracelsus for relying on magical remedies and astrology, took pride in eliminating superstitious elements from his own work, and his *Alchymia* (1597), with a section on *chemia* and related techniques, is a storehouse of the chemical knowledge and laboratory methods of his day. In basic ideas, nevertheless, he differed little from Paracelsus and the late medieval alchemists, whom he often cited with approval as well as condemnation. He too believed in transmutation. He even went so far as to write a *Defensio et Declaratio Perspicua Alchymiae*

Transmutatoriae (1604) in reply to a work attacking alchemy. Johann Rudolf Glauber (1604–68) produced a number of both medicinal and industrial preparations. His fame rests today chiefly on the continued use of Glauber's salt, which he made from vitriol and common salt, not only as a cathartic but also as an alkali in the dyeing process.

The most notable of the iatrochemists was Jean Baptiste van Helmont (1577–1644). To him Paracelsus's theory of three principle elements was unacceptable, since material bodies could not be resolved into them. He put forward a novel theory—that all tangible bodies are a product of water—and sought to verify it by experiment. Having planted a small willow tree in a tub of earth, he found, about five years later, that the tree had gained 164 pounds, although none of the earth had disappeared; hence, he inferred, the solid matter of the tree must have been transmuted from the water that the tree had absorbed—a striking example of the danger of the empirical method when applied to an inflexible conceptual scheme. Helmont also showed the material character of gases and differentiated between water vapour, gas, and air. He held that digestion was a process of fermentation, and he prescribed alkalis to counteract digestive acidity. It was he who coined the term *gas*, deriving it from the Greek *Xάos*, but not until Lavoisier was the term generally used, most chemists being satisfied with *air*.

The kind of chemical knowledge that came from the nascent chemical industry was frequently less theoretical and more technological than iatrochemistry. The bleaching, dyeing, and cleaning processes all depended upon practical experience. The making of glass, pottery, and gunpowder required some empirical chemical knowledge. Mining involved the manufacture of nitric acid and other chemical processes; mining treatises (which we shall mention later) frequently contained passages relevant to chemistry; and the assayer provided much experience that chemical science was eventually to use. To cite one example, the German humanist historian Georgius Agricola (Bauer) (1494–1555), who also was well trained in medicine and physics, produced remarkable treatises on geology and minerology. From personal observations in the mining region in which he lived, he compiled (in 1556) a study entitled *De Re Metallica*. Among other things, he described the process of stirring molten cast iron (puddling) with an oxidizing substance in order to produce wrought iron.

By the 1660's something akin to a dignified science of chemistry might be said to have existed. A Scot professor of chemistry, William Davidson, was attached to the Jardin du Roi in France in 1648, and a Frenchman, Nicolas de Febure, was appointed royal professor of chemistry by Charles II of England in 1660. Yet Boyle even then could say of chemistry that 'the illiterateness, the arrogance and the impostures of too many of those that pretent skill in it' caused learned men 'to repine'. But the learned repined, he implied, for the wrong reasons. They did not like to see 'any person capable of succeeding in the study of solid philosophy' become addicted to 'sooty empirics', to 'a study which they scarce think fit for any but such as are unfit for the rational and useful parts of physiology'.[25] Boyle accepted as his own task nothing less than to examine with all his senses the natural phenomena that the despised chemical art made known. He was particularly anxious to determine the nature of the material transformations already described by Libavius and his iatrochemist followers.

Boyle did not frown on the application of chemistry to medicine but was much more interested in building a connecting link between physics and chemistry. A number of 'mechanical philosophers' of the seventeenth century had come by that time to believe that matter is not infinitely divisible but is composed of a few indivisible primary 'elements' like Paracelsus's *trio prima* —mercury, sulphur, and salt. In his *Sceptical Chymist* (1661) Boyle attacked the assumption that all things are composed of three, four, or some other small number of elements, and he also exposed the semantic difficulty arising from the use of the word *element* in different ways. Reacting too far in the opposite direction, he himself decried the current usage of *element* for conveying an erroneous concept of 'certain primitive and simple or perfectly unmingled bodies, which not being made of any other bodies, or of one another, are the ingredients of which all those called perfectly mixed bodies are immediately compounded, and into which they are ultimately resolved.' We now know that he was correct at least in doubting that elements are only a small set of unmingled 'ingredients of which all ... mixed bodies are immediately compounded.' He never drew up a list of chemical elements of his own; he seems even to have doubted whether such numerous simple substances as the modern term *element* designates existed at all, preferring to believe in corpuscles as the elementary substance of all bodies. His commitment to the corpuscular, atomistic physics of his day made it possible for him even to think that metals and certain other materials actually 'grew' in the earth. But his scepticism about the elemental quality of the substances commonly called *elements* in his day was a bold step in the right direction.

Among other things, Boyle studied combustion and realized that bodies would not ordinarily burn without air. Hooke, who had been Boyle's research assistant, put forth in his *Micrographia* the idea that combustible bodies were dissolved by a certain 'nitrous substance' in the atmosphere. This substance was discussed in greater detail by Mayow, also a disciple of Boyle. In *Five Medico-Physical Treatises* (1674), Mayow gave an excellent summary of his own work along with that of Boyle, Hooke, and Richard Lower (1631–91), showing that respiration was a process closely related to combustion. Mayow suggested that that part of the air which was indispensable for respiration and combustion was composed of certain 'nitro-aerial particles'. Boyle's school thus put forward promising concepts in chemistry and chemical methodology, but it remained for other scientists to write the textbooks. The French savant Nicolas Lémery produced the first general textbook of chemistry, *Cours de Chimie* (1657), to be widely used, and it was published in new editions (e.g.

Paris, 1756) even after it was surpassed by the *Elementa Chemiae* (1732) by Herman Boerhaave (1668–1738), brilliant teacher of medicine at the University of Leiden.

For most of the eighteenth century the study of chemistry was dominated by the phlogiston theory of combustion. Johann Joachim Becher (1635–82) had contended that solid earthy substances are composed of three constituents: fixed earth (non-combustible), oily earth (combustible), and fluid earth. These were comparable to the salt, sulphur, and mercury of the iatro-chemists. Georg Ernst Stahl (1660–1734), professor of medicine at Halle, republished some of Becher's works and candidly borrowed from his theory. According to Stahl, any body capable of combustion must contain an oily, sulphurous earth that escaped from the other earths during the process, and this combustible earth, which he chose to call by the Greek name of *phlogiston*, was the essential element of all combustible bodies such as charcoal, wood, and fats. In other words, burning meant the escape of phlogiston into the atmosphere or into a substance that would combine with it. The almost complete combustibility of charcoal was attributed to its rich phlogiston content. By this theory, when a metal was heated, the freeing of the phlogiston would leave behind a calx, and hence phlogiston + calx = metal; therefore, if charcoal were used to reheat the calx, an exchange of phlogiston would take place and the metal would be restored. (Pl. 92a.)

The theory seemed to answer many questions satisfactorily. It was accepted by leading English chemists, such as Black, Priestley, and Cavendish. Following Van Helmont in distinguishing gases from air, they began to make fruitful studies of gases, combustion, and the calcination of metals. Black identified something he called 'fixed air'; we call it carbon dioxide. Benefiting from earlier experiments by Stephen Hales (1677–1761), who developed a pneumatic trough to collect and store gases, Cavendish was able to prepare something he called 'inflammable air', or what we call hydrogen (1766). In the 1770's Karl Wilhelm Scheele (1742–86) in Sweden and Priestley in England worked on similar problems independently. Probably about 1773, Scheele arrived at the discovery of oxygen, which he called 'fire-air'; he called nitrogen 'vitiated air'. These findings he published only in 1777. Before that date Priestley had discovered and isolated several gases—among them, nitric oxide, nitrogen, carbon monoxide, and a gas which was particularly excellent for respiration and inflammation and which he called 'dephlogisticated air' (we call it oxygen). To Priestley atmospheric air was a combination of 'dephlogisticated air' (oxygen) and 'phlogisticated air' (nitrogen).

The chemical world now had much empirical data at its disposal; what was needed was a savant who, as Newton had done for physics, would give chemistry a systematic nomenclature and organization. In his 'Course on True Physical Chemistry' (1752–54), Lomonosov anticipated some of the fundamentals of modern chemistry. Drawing on Leibniz, Daniel Bernoulli, and several others who since the first decades of the seventeenth century had dealt with the problem of *vis viva* (see above) and the conservation of matter, he had as early as 1748 articulated a general conservation law. In its 1760 version it ran: 'All changes occurring in Nature are subject to the condition that, if so much is taken away from one substance, just so much is added to another.'[26] Yet the honour of being the Newton of chemistry is usually attributed to Antoine Laurent Lavoisier (1743–94).

Realizing the significance of at least his French contemporaries' and predecessors' work, Lavoisier began in the 1770's the studies that were to end in his signal contributions to chemistry. Metallurgists had long been puzzled by the fact that tin and lead increased in weight when calcined. Jean Rey (*c.* 1630) had explained this phenomenon by demonstrating that they absorbed more from the air than they lost in the process, but his work went unnoticed until 1775. Boyle (*c.* 1673) explained the weight increase as due to the absorption of fire particles. In 1772 Guyton de Morveau reported in his *Digressions* upon his experiments on the combination of metals with air, prompting Lavoisier to experiment with the combustion of phosphorous, sulphur, and metals and to report his findings to the Académie des Sciences that year. Having been enabled to use a knife-edge balance (see above) for his measurements, Lavoisier agreed with Boyle that calcination increased the weight of metals but disagreed that fire particles accounted for the increase, which he considered (without knowing Rey's similar conclusion) as due rather to air. In 1774 Priestley informed Lavoisier of his 'dephlogisticated air'. Lavoisier thereupon theorized that 'dephlogisticated air' (or 'oxygen', as he named it) probably was the factor which made combustion and calcination possible. Combustion was thus satisfactorily explained as a process of oxidation. (Lavoisier's subsequent contributions to chemical nomenclature belong to Volume V.)

With Lavoisier chemistry can be said to have become modern in spirit. He made universally acceptable the idea of chemical elements questioned by Boyle a century earlier. Like Galileo, in studying familiar phenomena he arrived at new answers from old materials. Like Newton, he incorporated a quantitative spirit into the explanation of familiar phenomena, which in turn proved capable of explaining unfamiliar phenomena. Whether he discovered or merely gave a name to oxygen is less important than that he was the first explicitly to expound the role of air in chemical change and thus overthrew the phlogiston theory, which had outlived its usefulness, substituting for it a theory that made the further growth of his science systematic and regular.

Meanwhile the ground was being prepared for the field of analytical chemistry. The work of Boyle, E. F. Geoffrey (1672–1731), A. Baumé (1728–1804), and others permitted T. O. Bergman (1735–84) to begin in 1775 the preparation of tables of 'affinity' (tendency to combine chemically) of fifty-nine substances. Leaning on the older analytical work of the iatrochemists and Boyle and on the newer work of Black, Bergman, and other contemporary chemists, Scheele discovered a large number of new organic compounds including the vegetal acids, of which only vinegar (acetic acid) had been recognized earlier. Andreas Sigismund Marggraff (1709–82) introduced the use of the microscope for chemical analysis, discovered sugar crystals in beetroot, and analyzed other compound substances. These men laid the foundation for the subsequent development of organic chemistry.

Geology, Palaeontology, and Crystallography

Before the late eighteenth century, geology had no separate existence as a science, and the word *fossil* meant 'something dug from the ground' rather than, as in its modern connotation, 'organic remains'. In 1775 the auxiliary sciences of geology, such as palaeontology, were still at a low stage, and the prevalent cosmogony made it difficult to think of the Earth in terms of a never-beginning, never-ending development. Literal interpretation of the Biblical account of Creation within six days had implanted the conviction that the Earth was only about 6,000 years old, making extremely unconvincing any explanation of the otherwise familiar changes in the Earth's crust by some process that required a near-eternity. Nevertheless, the attribution of these changes to the Flood was beginning to encounter greater questioning than before. For example, how could the ancestors of all the many animals now known to exist on the Earth's surface have found room on Noah's Ark? And what about those animals that now were to be found only oceans away from where the Ark was supposed to have landed?

Before the eighteenth century scientists interested in geological and palaeontological matters got little beyond obvious queries about common phenomena. What made salt water go up stream from the estuaries of rivers? How did springs come to be located on hill tops? How account for the varying structure of land, the gradual conversion of seaside into inland settlements? What were fossils? Several sixteenth-century thinkers attempted explanations. Agricola, Bruno, and others concluded that valleys had been sculptured by rivers, that land and sea were continually shifting, and that fossils were organic remains. Leonardo da Vinci conjectured, like the Aristotelians, that water must be more abundant on the Earth's surface than land, and that a great deal of water must be inside the Earth. His work as an engineer led him, however, to some empirical conclusions. Having observed the silting of river mouths and the strata in excavations and on both sides of river canyons, he inferred that rivers cut their way through mountains in the course of time. He doubted that the appearance of fossil shells far inland could be a result of the Deluge or of spontaneous generation. Though he recognized the gradual, agelong transformation of the earth's surface, the origin of mountains was puzzling to him: he suggested that they were built up by river silt or by the sinking of surrounding lands in subterranean cave-ins. The Persian Gulf, he thought, had once been a great Tigris lake, and the Caspian Sea must have subterranean outlets to the Black Sea (which, in fact, is higher). Guillaume de

Postel, a sixteenth-century professor at Paris and his Netherlands contemporary Nicolaus Biesius explained geological phenomena in an even more mystical and astrological manner. Still, Postel had travelled widely and his works on geography, along with some amusing errors and serious misinformation, contained a few shrewd guesses of future geographical developments, such as the discovery of an antarctic continent and the building of canals through the Panama and Suez isthmuses.

The founding of physical geology as a science was largely the work of Agricola. His *De Natura Fossilium* (1546) (*fossil* still meaning anything dug out of the earth) was the first systematic treatment of palaeontology. This work and his posthumous (1556) *De Re Metallica* (see Chapter XV) dealt more or less indirectly with the problems of physical geology, but his *De Ortu et Causis Subterraneorum* (1546) examined them directly. His method was largely descriptive, although he attempted also to explain earthquakes and volcanic eruptions. He worked out clearly the part played by the elements in the gradual formation of hills and mountains, and he was the first to present a detailed study of the contents of the Earth's crust. He also made a significant contribution to stratigraphic geology in his description of the order of strata in the Harz Mountains.

For the next century or so progress was slow. Gessner and David Frolich (1600–46) were among the earliest of mountain explorers, the former in the Alps (1555) and the latter in the Tatra Mountains (1616). With the examination by Nicolaus Steno (1638–86) of the geology of Tuscany the systematic study of the subject began. His small book *De Solido intra Solidum Naturaliter Contento* (1669), largely indebted to the findings of his Italian predecessors, formulated acceptable surmises concerned with the formation of the Earth's crust. Finally Giovanni Arduino (1714–95) set forth (1759) the principle that different families of organic bodies are to be found at different strata of the earth's crust and described the four strata with names (primary, secondary, tertiary, and quaternary) that are still used in geological terminology, though since refined, to designate the age of rocks.[27] The field of physical geology was further aided by the construction of geological maps, which Martin Lister (1638–1712), an English physician, was the first to propose.

Steno and other workers after him speculated about the occurrence of organic fossils and attempted to account for them. He also laid the foundation for the scientific study of crystallography. His *De Solido* showed that quartz crystals must have grown in liquids through the regular accretion of new layers upon a nucleus. Hooke and Huygens thought that the new layers must be made up of tiny spheroids. Domenico Guglielmini in 1706 published a work asserting that each salt crystallized in its own characteristic shape determined by the regularity of the angles made by its faces, and Linnaeus in *Systema Naturae* (1735) extended this assertion to around forty different mineral crystals. The findings of these and other crystallographers enabled

J. B. L. Romé de Lisle in an *Essai de cristallographie* (1772) to establish that
the crystals of the same substances are closely related in shape to each other,
having the same or nearly the same angles between their corresponding faces.
Subsequent work by Romé de Lisle and René Just Haüy (1743–1822) led at
the close of the eighteenth century to the definition of six systems of crystal
structure that are still considered fundamental.

The problem of the origin of the Earth, the branch of learning today called
geogeny, produced recurrent debate. Descartes in his *Principles of Philosophy*
(1644) supposed that the Earth and the other planets had originally been
glowing masses like the Sun and that as the Earth gradually cooled down,
spots similar to sun spots formed on its hardening crust. Thomas Burnet in
his *Sacred Theory of the Earth* (1681) stayed within the bounds of orthodoxy,
supposing that the Earth had been formed from a chaotic mixture of earth,
water, fire, and oil, and that the Flood accounted for the present formation
of the planet. Leibniz systematized Descartes' theory in *Protogaea*, which
was published only in 1749, decades after his death, possibly because he
dared to look upon fossils as the evidence of aeonian changes in animal
organisms. Newton, though not directly concerned with geology, suggested
that the principle of gravitation might be useful in explaining the formation
of the Earth and the heavenly bodies.

One of the moot points in the debate was the role to attribute to fossils.
Were they tricks of God (or Nature) or were they, as Leibniz had suggested,
organic remains? Throughout the eighteenth century speculation on this
subject went on. A satisfactory answer depended upon the studies that
gradually extended the presumed age of the planet. Joseph Torrubia, in one
of the earliest works on paleontology (*Aparato para la historia natural
española*, Madrid, 1754), comparing fossils found in Spain with marine
specimens he had collected in the Philippines, concluded that warm waters
must have at one time covered the mountains of Aragon. Lomonosov, having
decided that the Earth's surface was in constant flux, concluded that the
Earth had been slowly evolving and that peat, coal, and oil were of organic
origin. Buffon in his *Théorie de la terre* (1749) and *Epoques de la Nature* (1778),
making guesses as to the time it took for the original molten gas of the Earth
to cool and then to go through six other epochs, assigned to the Earth around
80,000 years, far in excess of the traditionally accepted age. Using fossils and
geological observations to back his guesses, he introduced experimentation
into geology, substituting globes of cast iron for the Earth.

Geodesy, the study of the size and shape of the Earth, had engaged
scientists since at least the days of the ancient Greeks. Simultaneous observations by Jean Richer and his colleagues of the Académie des Sciences when
Mars approached the Earth closely in 1671 led to the discovery that a pendulum swung more slowly at Cayenne than in Paris. Some maintained that the
only feasible explanation was that the pull of gravity diminished as one
neared the equator, and, if so, the Earth could not be a perfect sphere. The

shape of the Earth thus became another subject of debate, some maintaining that it must be spherical and others that it must be oblate. To settle this dispute the French Academy sent one expedition to Lapland with Maupertuis and Clairault (1736) and another to Ecuador (then part of the province of Peru) with La Condamine and Bouguer (1735–43) to measure an arc of a meridian of longitude in those two distant places north and south. Maupertuis in *Sur la figure de la terre* (1738) concluded that the earth tended to flatten out at the poles, and a comparison with the results of the Peruvian measurements supported his contention. Observations in Peru led Bouguer to recognize also that mountains exert enough gravitational pull to cause deviations in a plumb-line. Bascovitch, when, after measuring a meridian arc between Rome and Rimini (1750–53) and finding that it did not agree with the measurement of a meridian arc in France, was able to explain the discrepancy of measurements by the pull of the intervening Appenines. Eventually these and subsequent meridian arc measurements were helpful in providing a natural standard of measurement that became the basis of the 'metric' system devised during the French Revolution.

A problem that had long puzzled seafarers was that of the tides. It bothered Mediterranean sailors only a little, since the tide of the inland sea is almost imperceptible, but it became much greater with the extension of commerce and naval warfare in the other oceans. Ships were often dependent on the tide for entering and leaving harbours. Galileo believed tides to be caused by the rotation of the earth on its axis, finding in them another phenomenon explicable by the Copernican hypothesis as he saw it. Further theories were advanced by others, of which perhaps the most significant was Newton's. He was not able to give a complete explanation of tides, but in his gravitational studies he recognized that the moon had a much greater tide-generating force than the sun and that the highest tides occurred at the new and the full moon.

The Académie des Sciences conducted a series of tidal observations in French harbours that indicated the incompleteness of Newton's explanation. Thereupon (1740) it offered a prize for a better one. Among the winners were Daniel Bernoulli and Euler, who were able to estimate, among other things, the lag of high tide at the moon's transit of the meridian. Another winner was Maclaurin, who showed that tides can be viewed as homogeneous rotating fluid masses and calculated mathematically as such. Kant in his *Allgemeine Naturgeschichte und Theorie des Himmels* (1755) suggested the retarding effect that mutual tidal reaction must have upon the rotation of the Moon and the Earth. The mounting data on the subject enabled Pierre Simon Laplace (1749–1827) to inaugurate (1774) the observation of the tides that eventually led to his theories regarding oceanic oscillations and the calculation of the mass of the moon, which he set forth in his *Méchanique céleste* (1799–1825).

The interest in earthquakes and tidal waves and in their origin was greatly enhanced by the horrible disaster to Lisbon in 1755.[28] Voltaire's outburst of poetic indignation did not prevent scientific studies by others. Among the scientists two theories of geology became dominant toward the end of the century with the work of Abraham Gottlob Werner (1750–1817) and James Hutton (1726–97). Hutton's followers were known as the Vulcanists, since they maintained that the Earth had originated from volcanic action; Werner's followers were called the Neptunists, since they maintained that the sea had played the more important role (see Volume V).

WORLD GEOGRAPHY

Since the days of the Majorca and Sagres schools of navigation, geographical discovery had ceased to be mainly the accidental by-product of the activity of nomads, soldiers, sailors, merchants, crusaders, fishermen, or missionaries; by the sixteenth century it was more likely to be the calculated outcome of carefully planned expeditions of exploration. The study of geography underwent a rapid change with the discovery of the New World and the circumnavigation of the globe. These events forced map makers to adopt global concepts, and terrestrial globes became popular. The earlier examples were, as might have been expected, inaccurate. The large-scale map of Waldseemüller and the Lennox and the Schöner globe, of 1507, 1510, and 1515 respectively, reveal little knowledge of either the New World or Asia, although Waldseemüller's map of 1507 is distinguished for having first attached the name *America* to the new found hemisphere. (Pl. 104b.)

Continuously changing concepts of land masses because of the new explorations and the technical improvements made possible by the printing press caused a tremendous spurt in cartography. Plane-maps began to show more precision. Johannes Honterus (1498–1549), who established the first printing press in Transylvania, published *Rudimentorum Cosmographiae Libri Duo* (Cracow, 1530; expanded and revised in later editions), which contained a world map that showed parts of the east coasts of North and South America.[29] The outstanding map maker of the sixteenth century was Gerhard Kremer, usually called Mercator (1512–94), a Flemish-born, German-bred geographer, expert both in mathematical theory and the practical construction of maps and globes. From 1537 to the time of his death he made global and continental maps as well as instruments for observation. One of his early triumphs was a large detailed map of Europe.

Map-making involved mathematical and other complications. An especially difficult one was the representation of the spherical surface of the Earth on a plane. One of Mercator's early maps presented the world on a double heart-shaped projection. His later cylindrical projection made permanent the improvement by which equal angles on a global projection would also be equal on a plane-map. His global spheres and maps showed little detail of the new discoveries until his famous chart of 1569, which indicated continents and seas of recognizable shape and size and designated California, Florida, Chile, Japan, Delhi, and Abyssinia. This was the first map to give parallels and meridians at right angles, thus leading to the distortions top and bottom characteristic of the 'Mercator' projection. It was published 'for the use of navigators' but was not widely used until the next century, when it reappeared with extensive improvements.

The term *atlas* was probably first employed by Mercator to describe a collection of maps. He himself compiled an atlas of nine maps (later increased in number). A contemporary, Abraham Ortelius of Antwerp (1527–98), anticipated him in publishing the first modern geographical atlas, *Theatrum Orbis Terrarum* (1570). Not only did it include some fifty-three copper-plate maps, but it also gave a catalogue of the authorities consulted in editing the work, thus providing an invaluable listing of early cartographers who might otherwise have remained nameless. The work was hailed as a master-piece, and many map makers sent material to be included in later editions; the number of maps increased to over a hundred, eventually including twelve of the ancient world. By the time of Ortelius' death about twenty-eight editions of his atlas had appeared—in Spanish, Latin, Dutch, German, and French. Mercator's atlas, though earlier, was not published in full until after his death. Meanwhile Dutch seamen and pilots, the chief mariners involved in the Atlantic coastal carrying trade, helped to prepare a series of charts describing the passage from Cadiz to Zuider Zee. These charts formed the basis for the first collection of marine maps, entitled *Spiegel der Zeevaart* (*Mariners' Mirror*), which was issued in two parts by Lucas Janszon Wag-henaer at Leiden (1584–85). Within four years it appeared in English and subsequently in other languages as well. By 1600 map making was a well-established business (see Chapter XV).

Mercator and Ortelius wrote only briefly on geography, their chief work being in cartography. While the same sort of mathematical and cartographical interest dominated Peter Apian (1495–1552), who published one of the earliest maps of America, his *Cosmographicus Liber* (1524) was primarily a written text that zealously upheld the ideas of Ptolemy. Even though the information contained in Ptolemy's *Geographia* was recognized by that time as far from accurate, by 1500 that classic work had already gone through seven printings in western Europe. Apian provided still another edition of it. His authority was great, and his edition of Ptolemy remained a chief source of geographical information during the earlier phases of the great explorations.

Newer geographical ideas gained more ground with the voyages of Magellan and other discoverers. A German linguist named Sebastian Münster (1489–1552) published a *Cosmographia Universalis* (1544), which blazed a fresh trail. Compiled with the assistance of over one hundred other geographers, it was a detailed, scholarly description of the then known world. The various political divisions were treated separately, with descriptions of the manners and customs of the peoples. Thanks to the literary merit of its German translation (*Beschreibung aller Länder*), it circulated widely, popularizing the study of geography throughout the Germanies. Münster's *Cosmographia* was followed by the writings of Nathanaal Carpenter (1589–1628 ?), Bernhard Varenius (1622–50), and Torbern Bergman (1735–84), each of which supplied the general reader with a steadily increasing knowledge of the globe. Sea currents were indicated for the first time only in 1665, when the German Jesuit polymath Althanasius Kircher (1601–80) gave some of them in his *Mundus Subterraneus*. Varenius' *Geographia generalis* (1650) in an annotated Latin edition by Newton (1672) and in various translations became the standard geography manual for more than a century. Despite the author's brief life and his several false hypotheses, he is generally regarded as the founder of scientific geography.

Explorations of the Seventeenth and Eighteenth Centuries

After 1600 (roughly) the outstanding problem of European explorers was to find some way to go from Europe to Asia by sea without sailing via Cape Horn or the Cape of Good Hope. Some had hoped to discover a northwest passage by water around North America to Cathay, but this search was abandoned after the voyages of Martin Frobisher in 1576 and the several explorations of Henry Hudson in the 1620's seemed to demonstrate its hopelessness. The arduous quest, however, had meanwhile shown the European peoples north of the Iberian peninsula the routes to a part of the globe, North America, that later attracted great numbers of them.

Upon the repeated failure to find a northwest passage some explorers, almost all of whom were in English, Dutch, or Russian service, set out to discover a northeast passage around Europe and Asia to the Orient, the feasibility of which had been suspected early in the sixteenth century (see Chapter XIII). The voyages of men like Hugh Willoughby and Richard Chancellor, Stephen Burrough, and Willem Barents in the sixteenth century and of Hudson in the seventeenth, though they required high courage and great nautical skill, were of small significance in establishing closer contacts among European and Asian peoples. They did, however, add to the growing store of geographical information. Meanwhile (as we shall soon note) the Russians were pushing the overland settlement of Siberia. Stretch by stretch, they explored the great Arctic rivers, reaching the Kalyma (1644), from which Simyon Dezhnev probably sailed around the East Cape (or Cape Dezhnev) through the straits that separate Asia from America and in any case reached the Gulf of Anadyr,[30] a branch of the Pacific Ocean (1648). Almost a hundred years later (1741), Vitus Bering, a Danish-born navigator in the service of Peter the Great and his successors, sailing northward from Kamchatka, discovered (or, more accurately, rediscovered) the straits now named after him, reached the islands off Alaska from the east, and proved that Asia and America were nowhere directly connected. Bering's companion, Alexis Tchirikov, on an independent voyage, touched the Alaskan mainland. Except for the fur trade the mapping of the Arctic and a northeastern passage to Asia was of little but geographical interest up to fairly recent times. Until the opening of the Suez Canal in 1869, Vasco da Gama's lengthy and strenuous route to the East remained the only practical one for European traders and travellers who wished to avoid long overland treks, dangerous rivers, and forbidding wilderness portages.

Expanding explorations made the coastal outlines of the five great continents fairly well known, but the seaborne European explorers' knowledge of the interior of the new land masses remained sketchy. Even today the geographical picture of some parts of the Asian continent is relatively incomplete. Until 1775 (and beyond), major land explorations by Europeans were carried on in India by several rival national groups, across the endless Siberian steppes by Russian settlers and explorers, and into China through the efforts primarily of missionaries. Elsewhere European maps continued to reveal ignorance of enormous stretches of the world's largest and most populated continent and the adjacent islands. (Pl. 105a, b.)

One whole continent, Australia, remained essentially unknown to Europeans until the close of our period; and about one immense ocean, the Pacific, their information was very limited. For a long time, however, the existence of an enormous continent in the southern part of the world had been assumed; such a land, according to some, simply had to exist in order to keep the earth in proper balance. On maps it was indicated as *Terra Australis* and was thought to be connected with Antarctica, although little was known about either region. The early European explorers did not exhibit particular interest in the waters south of the Malaysian region, and the Spanish adventurers and traders who crossed the Pacific from Mexico westward to Manila and back always took a route too far to the north to enable them to sight much of Oceania.

Serious exploration of these areas began only when the latecomers in the quest for eastern treasure (the Dutch, the English, and the French) appeared on the scene. In 1606 the Spanish captain Luis Vas de Torres crossed through the straits (now named after him) between New Guinea and Australia without realizing how close he was to a continent unknown to civilized men. A decade later some Dutch merchantmen on their way to Malaysia went too far south and touched upon the west coast of the huge island subsequently named Australia. Years afterwards (1642–44) another Dutchman, Abel Tasman, discovered the island now called Tasmania, as well as the Fijis, and sailed completely around, without ever sighting, the Australian mainland. His voyages proved that the islands which others had seen south of the Indonesian archipelago were not connected with Antarctica. The English navigator William Dampier (1652–1715) explored more of the west and north coasts of Australia but failed to reach the still unknown east coast.

For another hundred years, the picture of Australia remained unclear. Only by the scientific expeditions of the French sailor Louis Antoine de Bougainville (1729–1811) and the English sailor James Cook (1728–79) was its mystery finally cleared. Cook completed two revealing voyages in the

Pacific (1767–71 and 1772–75) and was killed on the Hawaiian Islands in 1779 while on a third. On these trips Cook rounded both the continent of Australia and the islands of New Zealand (which until then had also been thought to be part of the Antarctic), sailed northward along the east coast of Australia, discovered the Great Barrier Reef and New Caledonia, and systematically charted much of the Pacific with its major island groups and its North American coast as far north as Alaska. At much the same time (1768–73) a Scot named James Bruce of Kinnaird visited Abyssinia and fairly approximately located the source of the Nile River. By the close of the period with which this volume deals almost every part of the world that man could reach by sea had been at least sighted by Europeans and fairly well mapped. Although several island groups and the interior of several continents still were largely *terra incognita* to Europe's cartographers, the educated man's picture, if not his comprehension, of the world had become global both in form and extent. Nearly all the world's cultures were to a greater or lesser degree familiar with one another.

In some instances geographic information about the hinterlands was to remain exceedingly vague until the air travel of the twentieth century made interior exploration more feasible. Africa, except for its coastline, was little touched by landborne explorations before the nineteenth century. Several regions were inhospitable and offered few incentives to explorers. China and Japan were not always favourably disposed toward foreigners and limited the freedom of movement of such Westerners as they admitted at all. In still other areas land exploration proceeded but at a slow pace, keeping only slightly ahead of the gradual penetration by settlers and colonists. From time to time advanced garrisons, isolated missionaries, solitary adventurers, marooned sailors, or lone trappers learned a good deal about remote regions, but their knowledge did not become common and so remained fruitless from an economic or scientific point of view, although like the prototype of Robinson Crusoe, they entered into folklore and literature.

A major exception to the general rule that the explorations of this period were seaborne rather than landborne was the expansion into Siberia. Around 1580 a noble Russian family, the Stroganoffs, became interested in improving their holdings across the Ural Mountains. Yermak Timofeyev and a band of about 1600 Cossacks in the Stroganoff service began to push across those mountains and, equipped with firearms, easily defeated the larger forces of the Siberian khanate, armed only with bows and arrows. They took the city of Sibir (whence the name Siberia) and advanced into the region of the Tobol River. In the next sixty years Russian explorers, traders, settlers, and Cossack bands moved into the Siberian wilderness and the Arctic waters until (see above) they reached the Pacific.

About the time that Dezhnev reached northeast Asia, the Russians, still advancing overland, also reached the Pacific farther south. They explored the intervening Asiatic coast and the shores of the Sea of Okhotsk, founding the town of Okhotsk in 1648. Vasily Poiarkov discovered the Amur River in 1644, but after a few decades the Russians were obliged by the Chinese (in the Treaty of Nerchinsk, 1689) to withdraw from that region. Meanwhile they founded Irkutsk on Lake Baikal (1651). With the discovery of Kamchatka (1697) and the occupation of the Kurile Islands (1711) Russia was well ensconced in the northern Far East. Beginning early in the seventeenth century, it sent embassies to China and made commercial and boundary treaties with the Chinese emperor (particularly at Kiachta in 1727). On the basis of an order of Tsar Ivan IV in 1552 'to measure the land and make a draft of the state' Russian explorers would draw up 'drafts' that, while not plotted like maps on coordinates, nevertheless provided a vast collection of data.[31] Such a work was S. Remezov's *Book of Drafts of Siberia* (1701), which served as a guide for future explorations.

In the eighteenth century the Russians undertook far-reaching geodetic surveys and scientific expeditions involving three continents. They mapped the Don region, the Black and Caspian Seas, Kamchatka, Siberia's Arctic and Pacific coasts, the Aleutians, Alaska, and other parts of the American northwest. Especially noteworthy were the Great Northern Expedition (1733–43) and the polar expedition of Admiral V. Y. Chichagov (1765–66). A Russian population, consisting chiefly of traders, garrisons, and peasants attracted by virgin lands was eventually superimposed upon the nomadic tribes of Siberia. When a large part of the Kalmucks east of the Volga in the 1770's retreated before the Russian advance and, with the Chinese emperor's consent, settled in Sinkiang, the epic of the invasions by Siberia's steppe peoples came to a close. Before 1775, with the exception of certain areas directly north of Persia and Afghanistan and on the borders of China (areas which were to be acquired only in the nineteenth century), Russia had extensively explored (and dominated) that immense Asian realm which she now controls (as well as Alaska and the northwest coast of America).

THE BIOLOGICAL SCIENCES IN EUROPE

The number of eminent naturalists of the sixteenth century is impressive. The preface to a treatise by Ulisse Aldrovandi (1522–1605) listed thirty-two, and his list was incomplete.

Advances in the Study of Botany

The sixteenth-century biological encyclopedists still treated animals and herbs (as well as minerals) largely as *materia medica* but sometimes were interested in something more. The wider interest was evident in the extensive commentaries of Pierandrea Mattioli (1500–77) in his Latin edition of Dioscorides (1554). Though, like other contemporary botanists, he was inspired by Antiquity, he went far beyond the Classical writers; he was able to draw on the store of new information exchanged among distant scholars by letters, sometimes accompanied by drawings of plants and animals, or found in accounts of the strange flora and fauna of the New World and Asia. Garcia da Orta published in Portuguese a treatise on the 'simples' of India, and Christopher Acosta one in Latin on the 'aromatics' and 'medicaments' of that region. Nicolaus Monardus's treatise on the 'simple medicaments' of the New World—also in Latin—did the same for the Americas. Still, these works resembled the Classical and medieval handbooks on *materia medica* in that most of the 'simples', 'aromatics', and 'medicaments' were herbs or extracts from herbs, and a large amount of wonder-lore accompanied the description of their medicinal virtues. One of the few sixteenth-century naturalists to plead for the separation of botany from medicine was the Bohemian Adam Zaluzianski (1558–1613).

The more scientific and disinterested approach was encouraged by the spread of botanical and zoological gardens. The first botanical-zoological garden seems to have been installed at Venice in 1533; Lisbon, then a leading centre for voyagers to distant lands, also inaugurated one early; Padua followed suit in 1543; and the Medici created one of the best at Pisa in 1549. During the century they sprang up not only in connection with universities and on royal or aristocratic estates but also as municipal institutions. Even though zoological specimens were brought together more often as curiosities than for scientific study, scholars such as John Gerard, in London and at Lord Burghley's country seat, and Gabriele Fallopio, Aloysius Anguillara, and Jacobus Cartusus, at Pisa and Padua, had charge of royal, university, or municipal gardens, as well as their own private collections. Such establishments permitted direct observation of many animals and plants not accounted for in extant treatises, with consequent correction of older biological data.

Contemporary art clearly testified to the growing interest in nature (see Chapter XII) and, in turn, helped to further the spread of man's knowledge. At the close of the fifteenth century, great artists like Leonardo da Vinci and Dürer turned their talents to the depicting of botanical specimens in drawings, wood-cuts, and other media. The new interest in artistic but accurate illustration was amply demonstrated in the *Herbarum Vivae Eiconos* (3 vols, 1530–36) of Otto von Brunsfels and in the *De Historia Stirpium* (1542) of Leonhard Fuchs (1501–66).

These two naturalists were perhaps even more significant for other reasons. Fuchs's work provided not only a well-illustrated herbal but also one of the earliest attempts at a scientific nomenclature. It still conformed to the prevalent interest in plants chiefly for their medicinal value as defined by Dioscorides but was one of the last herbals of that nature. The great geographical discoveries of the sixteenth century made readily apparent that many more types of plants flourished in more parts of the world than Dioscorides, Pliny, or any of the Ancients had dreamed of, and the contemporary development of printing and book publishing made possible a wide distribution of the new knowledge concerning plant usage inside and outside of Europe. A modern plant geography seems first to have been suggested by Brunsfels,

who indicated that the specimens he found in the neighbourhood of Strasbourg could not always be identified with those that Dioscordes mentioned.

Within another century, although herbals remained a happy medium for
the illustrator, a point was reached where they could contribute little to
systematic botanical knowledge. For one thing, confusion arose from the
lack of an adequate and commonly acceptable taxonomy (system of classification). Confusion over classification came largely because until the eighteenth
century two somewhat contradictory schools of naturalists, both harking back
to differently elaborated ideas of Aristotle, struggled for predominance. The
older one held to what today is called the 'artificial' or 'hierarchical' system—
that the organic species are arranged in a hierarchy with discontinuities
between them. This school classified plants in an order, more acceptable to
Christian Aristotelian logic, that put emphasis upon the differences in the
species. The other school held to the 'natural' system—the view that the
several species of plants and animals are links in a great chain of being, the
gradations having been slowly achieved in a continuous, unbroken process.
This school tried to classify plants by some scheme of kinship.

As knowledge of plants accumulated, the need for a single system of
botanical classification grew. Hieronymus Bock's *Neu Kreutterbuch* (1539)
was perhaps the earliest to attempt to provide one, but with no immediate
success. In many travels Charles de l'Ecluse (1525–1609) studied the rarer
flora of Spain, eastern Europe, the Levant, and India and, aided by Matthias
de l'Obel (1538–1616) and others, supplied information that tended to bolster
the 'natural' school of classification. Zaluzianski in his *Methodi Herbariae
Libri Tres* (Prague, 1592) and Kaspar Bauhin (1560–1624) also favoured a
'natural' classification. Finding that much of the current confusion was a
consequence of the use of different names for the same plant, Bauhin provided
(1623) a catalogue of some 6000 plants (*Pinax Theatri Botanici*), identifying
their synonyms. To avoid future confusion of similar origin, he proposed the
binominal system of nomenclature (a generic name followed by a specific
modifier—e.g. *lilium album*). Perhaps the most important early system of
'artificial' classification was that of Andrea Cesalpino (1524–1603), professor
at the University of Pisa and director of Pisa's botanical garden, who in a
treatise *De Plantis Libri XVI* (1583) set forth a scheme that gave major
attention to patent fruit and seed differentiations rather than flower structure.
Joachim Jungius of Lübeck (1587–1657) despite the prestige of Cesalpino
returned to flower structure as a basis of plant terminology, identifying the
stamen, the style, and the perianth. He used Bauhin's binominal system, and
he seems to have been the first to suggest the classification of plants by genera
and species as well.

The microscope greatly aided seventeenth century botanists to understand
the structure of plants. Among the most skilled of contemporary technicians
of microscopy were the Dutchmen Jan Swammerdam (1637–80) and Antony
van Leeuwenhoek (1632–1723). From his youth Swammerdam showed

interest in insect life rather than in plant life, collecting several thousand species. His great skill, however, in making instruments and drawings and in using scalpels, lancets, knives, scissors, and other devices so small that they had to be ground with the aid of magnifying glasses provided a model for microscopists in all fields. Exhausting himself by his work, he died relatively young, and only thanks to the editorship of Boerhaave were his writings, under the intriguing title *Bybel der Natuure* (1737), presented to the public. Like Swammerdam, Leeuwenhoek was primarily an observer, not a theoretician. He made his own lenses and, self-taught, turned his microscope on all sorts of minute objects, animal as well as plant. He preferred the simple microscope to the more common compound one of the day. (Pl. 84a–d.) Another outstanding pioneer in the new method of observing minute particles was Hooke, whose *Micrographia* (1665) was the earliest monographic treatise on microscopy. He was the first to describe cellular structure—in cork and other plants. (Pl. 85a–d.)

John Ray (1627–1705), a devout Puritan, furnishes a pat example of the school of scientists who considered the study of zoology and botany an essentially religious expression, a means of understanding God's handiwork through the Book of Nature. While he was no expert microscopist, his *Historia Generalis Plantarum* (1686–1704) carefully identified some 19,000 plants, checked and re-checked—by first-hand inspection wherever possible or against well-established authorities. Although he used descriptive phrases instead of single words for many of his plants, he helped to advance botanical classification (dividing plants into 125 sections) and made important contributions to precise nomenclature. He distinguished between the great natural groupings of plants, beginning with imperfect forms such as algae, ferns, and marine plants; and he divided flowering plants into monocotyledenous and dicotyledenous.

Floral morphology was furthered by a number of Ray's contemporaries. J. P. de Tournefort (1656–1708), a professor at the Jardin des Plantes, calling attention to differences in petals (apetelous, polypetalous, etc.), put about 8000 species into 22 classes, distinguished chiefly by the forms of their corollas; this method of classification was not superseded until Linnaeus's day (see below). Nehemiah Grew (1641–1712), secretary of the Royal Society and discoverer of Epsom salts, also made the perhaps more significant discovery of the sexuality of plants; he regarded the flower as the sexual structure of a plant, the stamen being the male organ, the pollen the seed, and the pistil the female organ. Along with Leeuwenhoek and Malpighi (see below) he was one of the founders of microscopic plant anatomy. Rudolf Jakob Camerarius (1665–1721), professor of biology at Tübingen, who was the first known to experiment with the sex of plants, in his *De Sexu Plantarum* (1694) treated the subject more fully than Grew. The hybridization of plants, now easily detected, was achieved experimentally by several of a later generation, notably by Joseph Gottlieb Koelreuter (1733–1806), who recognized (in a work published in the 1760's) the role of wind, insects, and birds in the pollination and seed distribution of plants incapable of self-fertilization.

The most significant eighteenth-century studies in the field of botany were those of Stephen Hales (1677–1761) of England and Karl von Linné or Linnaeus (1707–78) of Sweden. Hales was the father of vegetable physiology. Seeing analogies between animal and plant physiology, he enquired into the function of plants and, in so doing, influenced not only the field of botany but also of chemistry. Linnaeus occupies as the organizer of botany a position somewhat analogous to Lavoisier's in chemistry. He at first adopted the 'hierarchical' or 'artificial' system of classification. Unconvinced in his early work by the accumulating data suggestive of a theory of evolution from species to species, he at first regarded each living species as having been fixed forever at the time of the Flood, and this premise long made it difficult for him to embrace a 'natural' (i.e. evolutionary) system of classification. He nevertheless worked hard to identify botanical families, thus preparing the ground for the future recognition of the kinship of legions of plants.

Linnaeus's chief works were *Systema Naturae, sive Regna Tria Naturae Systematice Proposita per Classes, Ordines, Genera et Species* (1735), which went through twelve editions in his lifetime, and *Species Plantarum* (1753). Using the binominal terminology of Bauhin (that is, one name for the genus and another for the species), he grouped plants (and animals and minerals as well) into classes, orders, genera, and species. His taxonomy, though following a mainly 'artificial' system of classification, was based upon the number of stamens, styles, and other parts of a plant's sexual apparatus, and it provided the foundation for modern taxonomy when modified by Bernard de Jussieu (1699–1777), Jussieu's nephew Antoine Laurent de Jussieu (1748–1836), and their successors.[32] In the later editions of the *Systema Naturae* Linnaeus himself suppressed the passages that implied that cross-fertilization of the species was impossible.

Contributions to the Study of Zoology

The development of zoology paralleled that of botany, particularly in the attempt to arrive at systematic classification. In the fifteenth and sixteenth centuries, new Latin translations of the Aristotelian treatises on animals were made directly from the Greek by Theodore of Gaza, George of Trebizond, and others, nine editions being published in Venice alone between 1475 and 1575, but no new intensive zoological study appeared. This concern with Aristotle combined with the importation of curiosa from the newly discovered countries to rouse a keen interest in zoology.

In the first half of the sixteenth century several minor works were published concerning fish, and certain scholars manifested an interest also in bird life. About mid-century Guillaume Rondelet (1507–66) produced his *De Piscibus*, thought by some to have been plagiarized from the commentary on Pliny's *Natural History* of Bishop Pellicier (1490–1568). About the same time came treatises on birds by William Turner (*c.* 1508–68) and Pierre Belon (1517–64). Later Volcher Coiter (1534–76) put out his classification of birds (see below).

By the end of the century general compendia containing sections on all classes of animals were appearing. Gessner's multivolume *Historia Animalium* (1551–87) provided a very full, if unsystematic, account giving many excellent pictures of animals. His Italian contemporary Aldrovandi produced several treatises that, although not equally complete, marked a definite advance, since they considered anatomical features as a means of classification. Edward Wotton (1492–1555) worked along similar comparative lines.

Part of the parallelism of zoology with botany can be accounted for by the fact that some men worked in both fields. Ray is an especially good example. In his *Synopsis Methodica Animalium Quadrupedum* (1693), he set forth the first scheme for a systematic classification of animals. He was also the first person to expound a clear notion of a biological 'species'. Classification persisted, however, as a problem, not to be fully overcome until the concept of fixity of species was discarded. Influenced by Ray's classificatory system for animals, Linnaeus performed for zoology much the same service as for botany. Adopting the species as the unit of classification, he divided animal life into six classes, (mammals, birds, amphibians, fish, insects, and worms), putting more reliance on external morphological characteristics than on internal structure. Unlike Ray, he did not distinguish, for example, between vertebrates and invertebrates. He adopted the binominal system of class names for animals as he had for plants. The International Commission of Zoological Nomenclature, disregarding earlier works, has stipulated that the tenth (1758) edition of his *Systema Naturae* be the basis of taxonomy in the field.

Nevertheless, in its own day, the Linnaean system did not go unchallenged. Toward the end of Buffon's career as director of the Paris Jardin des Plantes, he became convinced that the species were not fixed. His *Histoire naturelle*, which ran posthumously to forty-four large volumes (thirty-six during his lifetime) and went far to popularize the study of biology, rejected the 'artificial' classification of Linnaeus, adopting instead a 'natural' system. The convenience of Linnaeus' nomenclature, however, was not affected by the shortcomings of his taxonomy.

Some of the important biological work of the seventeenth and eighteenth centuries was of a largely descriptive nature. In their anxiety to avoid speculative systems, the Italian Accademia del Cimento and the French Académie des Sciences deliberately encouraged descriptive work in the study of biology. Francesco Redi (1626–78) described the life cycle of the fly from larvae (which he called 'worms') through pupae (which he called 'eggs') to adult flies and in so doing disproved the common belief that 'worms' came by spontaneous generation from putrefaction. Réaumur made one of his several contributions to pure science in his *Mémoires pour servir à l'histoire des insectes* (1734–42), observing his subjects not only in their habitat but also under specially arranged conditions. Some of his descriptions of insects (he used the term in the broadest sense) remain standard, and his experimental methods much admired, to this day. Perhaps no biological studies of the century were more important than those of August Johann Roesel von Rosenhof (1705–84) on the hydra. For the hydra seemed to have some of the characteristics of an animal and some of a plant, and a number of students of nature became convinced that the dividing line between the animal and the plant kingdom was not clear-cut.33 The importance of this biological concept to the philosophy of the Enlightenment has already been indicated (see Chapter VII). Among other things, it led a number of the *philosophes* to speculate whether Man was not himself, in a self-propelling biology, part of an endless chain of being destined for continuous change in the direction of perfectibility.

Anatomy and Physiology

In the field of anatomy and physiology most of the creative work of the early modern period, with the notable exceptions of Ray's and Leeuwenhoek's, was done by physicians. The anatomical drawings of Leonardo da Vinci, derived from the dissection of about thirty cadavers, anticipated Vesalius, but Leonardo was interested in human anatomy for art's sake rather than for science's sake, nor were his observations contemporaneously published. The initial landmark in modern anatomy as a science was the publication of Vesalius' *De Humani Corporis Fabrica* (1543). The author, born in Brussels (1514), was at the age of twenty-two professor of anatomy at the University of Padua. His book had as great an impact in its field as Copernicus', published in the same year, had in its. Vesalius was not a revolutionary in spirit or method; dissection had been performed long before him, and he did not attack Galen in the headlong fashion of Paracelsus. He attempted, however, to give a dispassionate description, with the aid of superb illustrations, of the human body. (Pl. 93c.) He based his analysis on dissection rather than on untested authority, and he did not hesitate to correct Galen when the occasion arose. For instance, Vesalius failed to find the pores that Galen supposed the septum of the heart to have. Ironically, some critics in Vesalius' time, not realizing that Galen's anatomy was based for the most part on Barbary apes, refused in the name of orthodoxy to accept Vesalius' findings because they contradicted the master.

Vesalius was only incidentally interested in the comparison of anatomical features, but he nevertheless contributed to the study of the anatomy of lower animals also, sometimes dissecting living animals as well as dead humans. Greater interest in comparative study was manifested by several contemporary anatomists. Belon in 1555 published engravings pointing up the homologies of the skeletons of man and bird.34 The Italian Nicholas Massa compared apes and men. Girolamo Fabrizio ab Aquapendente (1537–1619) enriched his treatises on animal and human embryology with excellent illustrations. Coiter made use of experiments on the hearts and brains of animals in two treatises on comparative anatomy: one of these, *De Differentiis Avium*, with illustrations, was included as an appendix to his edition (1575) of the work of Gabriele Fallopio (1523–62) on the parts of the human body. Carlo Ruini (*c.* 1530–98) wrote a book on the horse (1598) that is a classic of veterinary anatomy.

The term 'comparative anatomy' seems to have been first used by Francis Bacon in 1623, but only to refer to comparison of variations within the same species. As anatomical knowledge advanced, the field of comparative anatomy became more comprehensive. And anatomical knowledge advanced with great strides. The celebrated surgeon and teacher Marco Aurelio Severino (1580–1656) dissected specimens of many species, introduced the term *zootomy* (1645), and showed that freezing by snow and ice might be used for anaesthetic purposes. Thomas Willis (1621–75) first reported on his study of the nerves and brain in 1664. Grew published *A Comparative Anatomy of Stomachs and Guts* in 1681. Edward Tyson (1651–1708) wrote on the tapeworm and other parasites in the 1680's. Claude Perrault (1613–88), perhaps the most productive of the seventeenth-century comparative anatomists, worked especially on fishes and birds; an architect by profession and a leading member of the Cartesian Académie des Sciences, he developed a mechanistic theory of anatomy. His mantle fell upon Guichard Joseph Duverney (1648–1730), who in 1683 made his most important contribution, an account of the anatomy of the ear. In the 1690's Martin Lister (1638–1712) published anatomical studies of marine animals and invertebrates, and in the next decade of the opossum and the orang-outang. Even without taking into account the contributions of Harvey (see below) posterity would have ample evidence of the extraordinary activity of seventeenth-century anatomists in the large number of structures of the body named after them—circle of Willis, Casserio's artery, Graafian follicles, Peyer's patches, Ruysch's tunica, etc. In the next century comparative anatomical collections and museums became more and more complete, perhaps the best of them being that of John Hunter in London.

Much of the success in the study of anatomy after the middle of the seventeenth century was due to the fuller use of the microscope. As early as 1610 Galileo had examined the eye of a small animal with a compound microscope, but he was not much interested in biology. Francisco Stelluti used a low-powered microscope or magnifying glass for his study of the bee, published in 1625. Harvey also, we shall soon see, used some kind of a magnifier. One of the first to make full use of the microscope was Marcello Malpighi (1628–94), professor of medicine at Bologna and elsewhere. In addition to working as a pioneer with microscopic plants, he discovered the role of capillaries in the circulation of the blood and made many minute observations on the development of the chick in the egg and on the anatomy of the silkworm. Swammerdam's interest in insect life (mentioned above) led him to comparative research in insect anatomy, development, and metamorphoses. He

GG *

established a 'natural' classification of insects that still is regarded as having some validity. His contemporary and compatriot Leeuwenhoek, determined to see the complete circulation of the blood, put the tadpole under his microscope. He also discovered the unicellular organisms that we today call protozoa (1674) and bacteria (1676). And skill with the microscope enabled Pierre Lyonet (1707–89) to produce an admirably illustrated monograph on the anatomy of the caterpillar.

The Study of the Circulatory System

In his *Exercitatio Anatomica de Motu Cordis et Sanguinis in Animalibus* (1628), Harvey presented a revolutionary study of the movement of the heart and the blood, derived, he said, 'not from books but from dissections; not from the positions of philosophers but from the fabric of nature'. He, too, made reference to magnifying glasses; with them he was able to confirm that almost every animal has a heart. This discovery contradicted the long generally accepted belief of Aristotle that only large, red-blooded creatures have hearts. It was but a minor point, however, in his book.

Notwithstanding its deserved fame, much of Harvey's experimental work had been anticipated by his predecessors. He was not revolutionary in his findings so much as in his methods. He was not the first, for example, to point out that the route of the venous blood to the left side of the heart was not through the septum but through the pulmonary artery; the unfortunate Servetus had described the lesser circulation of the blood in his *Christianismi Restitutio* (1553), which was subsequently suppressed, leaving its influence on his several successors up to and including Harvey a debatable matter. Harvey's discussion of the valves of the veins was more obviously based on earlier observations by his teacher, Fabrizio ab Aquapendente.

The research of Harvey's predecessors, however, had been directed toward different ends. His main contribution was, where he did not wholly refute, to raise doubts about hitherto accepted views, such as that growth, muscular activity, and nervous functions are each dependent upon a corresponding spirit (*pneuma*) distributed by the blood, that the function of the venous blood is to distribute the 'natural spirit', which is the principle of growth, that the function of the arterial blood is to distribute the 'vital spirit', which is the principle of muscular activity, and that the function of the nerves is to distribute the 'animal spirit', which is the principle of the nervous function. This view was derived from Galen. According to the Galenic system, the blood encountered the natural spirit in the liver, the vital spirit in the heart, and the animal spirit in the brain. This system involved several erroneous ideas not only with regard to the role of certain organs in blood physiology but also with regard to the method and the direction of the flow of the blood. The major significance of Harvey's work rests upon the fact that he framed a different conceptual scheme and then proceeded to test it in the best quantitative and experimental manner of the time—by 'both argument and ocular demonstration'.

'The greater circulation' of the blood from arteries to veins and thence back to the heart had already been suggested by the work of Vesalius, Servetus, and others, and their work provided Harvey with a foundation on which to build. To Harvey the lesser circulation (that is, the path by which the exhausted blood flowed from the veins through the lungs and, freshened, returned to the arterial system) was more of a mystery. A significant passage from his treatise underlines the quantitative basis of his initial hypothesis:

'For a long time I turned over in my mind such questions as, how much blood is transmitted, and how short a time does its passage take. Not deeming it possible for the digested food mass to furnish such an abundance of blood, without totally draining the veins or rupturing the arteries, unless it somehow got back to the veins from the arteries and returned to the right ventricle of the heart, I began to think there was a sort of motion in a circle.'35

By experiment and observation he then confirmed this hypothesis. He found that the valves in the vein kept the blood from flowing in more than one direction, and he also showed that the amount of blood passing through a body's heart in an hour far exceeds the weight of that body. He then concluded that he could explain the venous and arterial system only by a one-way and continuous circulation, which is 'the sole and only end of the motion and contraction of the heart'.

Later research completed the explanation of the circulation of the blood. Malpighi's discovery of the capillaries has already been mentioned; it was reported in his *De Pulmonibus* (1661). It was confirmed by Leeuwenhoek, who not only, as previously stated, traced the blood circulation of the tadpole but also probably was the first (1674) to make the red corpuscles known. The work of Harvey, Malpighi, and Leeuwenhoek in the circulation of the blood was supplemented by a growing knowledge of other organic processes. In 1651 Jean Pecquet discovered the function of the lacteals, and somewhat later (1652) Olof Rudbeck of Uppsala and Thomas Bartholin of Copenhagen discovered the lymphatic nodes. Francis Glisson in 1659 gave a detailed account of liver, stomach, and intestines, and Thomas Wharton in 1656 of the pancreas.

Iatrophysics and Mechanistic Medicine

Harvey's method and conclusions were an inspiration to those who thought that biological phenomena could be put into a quantitative and mechanical (or iatrophysical) frame. This was the period when the medical profession was becoming conscious of medical statistics (see Chapter XV). About the middle of the sixteenth century a Paris printer had published a set of figures covering about fifty-five cases of illness from 1549 to 1554, analysing the types of ailment, the patients' occupation, and other relevant data. The mechanistic-quantitative point of view was reinforced by several of Harvey's contemporaries. Descartes' philosophic dualism of mind and body made room for the interpretation of the human body in the same mechanical and quantitative terms as the physical universe; his mechanistic views were set forth in his posthumous textbook of physiology, *De Homine* (1662). A leading exponent of the quantitative approach to physiological functions was Sanctorius, Galileo's medical colleague at the University of Padua. He invented an instrument for counting the pulse, a sort of clinical thermometer, a weighing chair, and other devices for measuring physiological phenomena. These, and especially the weighing-chair, enabled him to initiate the study of what today would be called 'metabolism'. He weighed his own intake and excretion of food over a period of decades and came to the conclusion that perspiration and respiration account for more discharge than conscious evacuations. He set forth his theory in *Ars de Statica Medicina* (1614).

François de la Boë Sylvius (1614–72), one of the great teachers at the University of Leyden, was, to be sure, an iatrochemist, perhaps the first to carry out careful biochemical experiments, making significant discoveries in the physiology of the digestive processes, but he was also a firm believer in the mechanistic action of the muscles. The work of Giovanni Borelli (1608–79) in applying mechanics to the living organism is generally considered the most significant attempt to put biology into the field of mechanics. Greatly influenced by Galileo, Borelli investigated and explained circulation of the blood, respiration, and the movements of animal muscles and bones on mechanical principles, as though they were forces, weights, and levers, though he also recognized that certain physiological reactions must also be chemical. (Pl. 91a, b.) He has the distinction of being the father of the iatrophysical school of anatomy. This school perhaps reached its logical apex with Georgio Baglivi (1669–1707), who founded the medical system known as 'solidism'. He contended that sickness originates in the bodily 'solids' rather than the Galenic 'humors'. After the Leyden jar was discovered (1745), the growing use of electric shock to stimulate ailing muscles gave the iatrophysicists a new argument.

Though a certain number of researchers continued in the eighteenth century to seek the explanation of muscular, circulatory, and other anatomical movements along mechanical lines—notably the able group gathered in the St Petersburg Academy—a reaction shortly set in against Borelli's school. The German chemist Stahl, also a physician, insisted in his *Theoria Medica Vera* (1707) that 'the sensitive soul', expressing itself through body chemistry, provided a better explanation of bodily function, structure, and health than the analogy—which seemed to him oversimplified—to a machine. This theory was called *vitalism*.[36] By the end of the century noted physiologists like M. F. X. Bichat had embraced Stahl's vitalistic theories, but the high point of the vitalist-mechanist controversy was not to come until the nineteenth century.

The Empirical Study of Disease

About 1500 a new challenge to medical men appeared in the form of a disease of debated origin. Reputedly it was imported by Columbus' sailors from America to Spain and thence to France and Italy—or vice versa, for it was called 'the French disease' (*morbus gallicus*) by the Neapolitans, in whose country it became epidemic after the arrival of the invading French armies (1494), and the 'Neapolitan disease' (*mal de Naples*) in France, where it was spread by the returning French armies. Whether the disease was a *morbus americanus*, *gallicus* or *neapolitanus* or, as has also been maintained, an epidemic form of the medieval 'pox', it came to be known most widely, for a time, as the *morbus gallicus*. Girolamo Fracastoro of Verona (1483–1553), professor of logic and physician, in 1530 published a poem entitled *Syphilis sive de Morbo Gallico*, and thenceforth the disease came to be known as 'syphilis', after a shepherd in the poem on whom Apollo visited an ulcerous disease. The poem mentioned as remedies for the disease mercury and guaiacum, a wood resin used by the American Indians. In a later work (*De Contagionibus*, 1546) Fracastoro described several contagious diseases, including syphilis and typhus fever, and suggested that syphilis might be caused by *seminaria* (*seeds*), thus anticipating the germ theory of disease. Controversy still goes on regarding the origin of syphilis, with suggestions to the effect that venereal diseases have long been in existence everywhere and that the sixteenth-century pandemic in Europe was but a variation imported from America to localities that had not been conditioned to resist it in a virulent form.

Advance in physiology proved dependent on improvements in anatomy, physics, chemistry, and other related sciences. The work of such men as Sanctorius, Descartes, Harvey, and Borelli, whatever the shortcomings of their conclusions, helped the development of modern physiology. But advance came only step by step. As late as the Great Plague of 1664–65 in London (see Chapter XIII), epidemics were generally attributed to supernatural causes. Such principles and practices gave way only slowly before improved anatomical knowledge, good instruments, and empirical concepts.

By the end of the seventeenth century physiology and medicine were able to make great strides side by side with anatomy and surgery. Some of the achievements will be described in Chapter XV in connection with the practice of medicine and surgery. The chief inspiration in physiology came perhaps from Sylvius and Boerhaave, whose reputation as teachers of medicine at Leyden made their university renowned (see Chapter XVI). In their country (and largely because of their efforts), the teaching of chemistry as, among other things, basic to medicine was well developed, and anatomy and surgery too were regarded as closely related to medicine. Both men emphasized that medical training must include not only chemical and botanical knowledge but anatomical and physiological knowledge as well. Thus, long before the period here under discussion ended, the old distinctions of prestige and practice between surgery and medicine began to break down. After Boerhaave's day, surgery became associated less with barbers and more with physicians as a respectable professional skill. Select societies of surgery were formed—the Académie Royale de Chirurgie in Paris in 1731, the British Surgeon's Company in 1745.

The closer association of medicine with surgery gave practitioners of both a common interest in pathological anatomy and experimental physiology. The most outstanding student of Boerhaave was Albrecht von Haller (1708–77), who in 1756 published his *Elementa Physiologiae Corporis Humani*, which has been called the first modern manual of physiology. He not only collected information about the various organs, some of it derived from his own experiments, but also correlated their functions. Giovanni Battista Morgagni (1682–1771), an Italian physician, in *De Sedibus et Causis Morborum*, studied the relation of certain diseases (e.g. pneumonia, syphilis, meningitis) to certain parts of the body and summed up the knowledge of his day regarding the correlation between structural changes (like wounds, abscesses, gangrene, and tumors) and sickness.[32] The work of Hales with both plants and animals provided a much better understanding of respiration. Réaumur brought increased knowledge of the process of digestion (1752); without completely explaining the solvent action of the gastric juices, he recognized it and differentiated it from putrefaction. Building on the exposition by Willis of the nervous system (see above), several eighteenth century investigators—among them, Jean Astruc (1684–1766), Robert Whytt (1714–66), and J. A. Unzer (1727–99)—revealed the nature of the reflex movement as a response, not necessarily conscious, to stimulation of the nerves related to the spinal marrow, and they otherwise studied nervous diseases.[38] Some physiological background was a prerequisite for the understanding and introduction of inoculation (see below) and, later in the century, of vaccination against smallpox, the cornerstones of the science of immunology.

Conflicting Schools of Embryology

Modern embryology owes its beginnings to Harvey's *De Generatione Animalium* (1651), but Harvey got some of his inspiration from the studies of his teacher Fabrizio ab Aquapendente, who had been a pupil of Fallopius, who had been a pupil of Vesalius, and Harvey in turn lent inspiration to Malpighi's microscopic examination of the embryology of the chick. The Classical theory of reproduction, along with that of the human physique, had been based upon Aristotle's *De Generatione Animalium* on which Muslims, Christian Scholastics, and sixteenth-century humanists (e.g. Gesner) patterned their treatises concerning animal and human reproduction. Aristotle held that the male parent gave to the embryo its form, and the female parent its nourishment, and that some imperfect forms of life were spontaneously generated. At the opening of the sixteenth century the most current theory of reproduction was derived from this Aristotelian tradition.

Illustration, a noteworthy factor in all biological progress, was especially significant in the study of embryology. Medieval manuscript illustrators depicted the stages of development of the unborn child in series of as many as sixteen pictures, derived from Classical archetypes. From about 1300 onward, there was some improvement in these archetypes, and eventually additional illustrations appeared as a result of the increased use of dissection. Leonardo da Vinci's remarkable notebook sketches reveal his interest in the subject. In the sixteenth century Coiter and Aldrovandi began careful investigations of the embryological development of the chick in the hen's egg. Their work was followed up by Fabrizio ab Aquapendente in books entitled *De Formato Foetu* (1600) and *De Formatione Ovi et Pulli* (1621). His engraved illustrations of human and animal embryos, notably those of the chick, led to the development of a scientific embryology.

Having studied the embryo of the deer as well as the chick, Harvey came to the conclusion that the mammalian embryo was equivalent to the egg of the bird and other oviparous creatures and put forward the famous dictum *ex ovo omnia*. At the same time he questioned but did not wholly dismiss the possibility of lower and imperfect animals being spontaneously generated. The view that life originates from eggs was given further confirmation when Reinier de Graaf (1641–73) discovered with the aid of a microscope the resemblance between the ovarian (Graafian) follicles of several species of mammals and the egg of a bird.

Harvey's theory of embryo development was essentially unlike that of Aristotle; it was what today is called embryological epigenesis. In this theory, the germ cell is considered new, and the embryo is believed to develop its separate features by successive stages until birth. An opposing school held to a preformation or mosaic theory—viz. that the germ was a fully formed but minute model or mosaic of the adult animal. The conflict had, of course, certain religious overtones. Had not God created man in his own image? The microscope seemed at first to substantiate the preformation theory. Observing that among oviparous creatures the embryo develops inside the egg, some held that the embryo of the higher animal, too, must therefore be essentially derived from and similar to its female parent. Hence the separate parts of the embryo must be fully differentiated from the beginning, gestation being merely a swelling from a speck to full size. Malpighi and Swammerdam were the chief exponents of this theory.

Leeuwenhoek developed a different though parallel theory. In 1677 Ludwig van Ham, a student at Leyden, showed him some spermatozoa, believing them a pathological phenomenon. (Pl. 85d.) Leeuwenhoek, however, found them healthy specimens and was thus enabled to put forth the theory that the male semen formed the foetus. The resulting school of animalculists claimed, considerably more pointedly than Leeuwenhoek, that the human embryo from the very first was a complete though miniature 'homunculus'. Thus there grew up two conflicting preformation schools, ovists and animalculists, claiming respectively female and male parent as the determinant of the form of the foetus. When Charles Bonnet (1720–43) showed (1740) that some female tree lice (aphids) can produce their young without fertilization (parthenogenesis), the ovists seemed to have triumphed.

The preformation school of embryology won the support of the anatomical school of mechanists, since they too repudiated any progressive embryological change other than by the expansion of preformed parts. Until the eighteenth century the preformation theory therefore carried great weight, and so renowned an authority as the Swiss scientist and belletrist, Albert von Haller (1708–11), perhaps the most esteemed professor of physiology of his day, backed it. Nevertheless, the idea of a miniature completely preformed in seed or egg was called into question when Réaumur proved that some crustaceans and worms are able to regenerate lost bodily parts *de novo* and when Tremblay showed that polyps reproduce asexually. Caspar Friedrich Wolff (1733–94) struck at the preformationists in two signicant treatises, *Theoria Generationis* (1759), his doctoral dissertation, and *De Formatione Intestinorum Praecipua* ... *Embryonis Gallinecei* (presented in 1768 to the St Petersburg Academy, of which he was a member). His investigations showed that both plant and animal development came about by differentiation, that the chicken intestine, for example, was not a preformed structure but developed from a *simple* sheet of tissue. Wolff's argument was condemned by Haller, and so great was Haller's prestige that Wolff's pioneer work on epigenesis was not adequately appreciated until the nineteenth century.

The belief in spontaneous generation also died hard. It survived Redi's demonstration (see above) that the supposed spontaneous generation of flies from organic matter was in reality nothing more than the hatching of eggs. The most stalwart defender of spontaneous generation in the eighteenth century was John Needham (1713–81), an English Catholic priest. He sealed and corked boiling broth in flasks to exclude external influences, believing that boiling had killed any germs in the broth. On opening the flasks days later and discovering organisms, he claimed that the theory of spontaneous generation had been adequately demonstrated. Lazzaro Spallanzani (1729–99), doubting the experimental procedures of Needham, disproved his work by more carefully controlled experiments, designed to show that animalcules did not grow in infusions properly sealed and boiled. Needham remained unconvinced, however, and the Needham–Spallanzani controversy went on for years. Along with the transformation of species and the preformation of the embryo, spontaneous generation remained a debated issue during the eighteenth century.

The Beginnings of Modern Psychology

In the early modern period, the study of psychology was intertwined with speculative philosophy (see Chapter VII) as well as with medicine, biology, and related fields. Descartes, we have seen, established a system of philosophy on the basis of his famous dictum *Cogito, ergo sum*. Convinced of the existence of a mathematical world and putting great emphasis on reason as against perceptual experience, he hoped to replace medieval dogmatism with deductive procedures. His greatest contribution to psychology was his concept of a mind-body dualism—that is, a thinking substance and an extended substance. Extended substance, he maintained, behaved according to mechanical law, the body being little more than an automaton. The human being, however, was not a mere automaton since he also had a reasoning soul or mind, mind and body having a point of contact which Descartes placed in the pineal gland. Descartes also believed in innate ideas—that is, truths inherent in man's nature and therefore *a priori*, inescapable, and acceptable as a basis of further reasoning.

The existence of innate ideas, we have also seen, was debated by contemporary British empiricists. In this connection, Francis Bacon did not disagree with Descartes in any essential. Hobbes, on the other hand, was monistic, attempting to explain all activity in the thoroughly naturalistic terms of Galilean mechanics. All the content of the mind, he thought, was reducible to motion, sensations being motions in the psychological organism. Hobbes did not find many disciples, but Locke had a greater effect upon later British empiricists. Locke's epistemology was more concerned with the validity of knowledge than with the process of knowing, although the question 'How do we know?' was also of importance to him. His *Essay Concerning Human Understanding* (1690) gave his answer to that question: Knowledge comes from experience, which takes two forms of psychological expression, sensation and reflection. For Locke the mind on birth was *tabula rasa* and no ideas were innate; ideas came from sensations, combinations of sensations, and reflections upon them. Although himself a devout Christian, Locke thus seemed to be saying that the mind is the product of the external material universe. By thus breaking thought up into elemental components, Hobbes and Locke began what is sometimes called psychological atomism.

In accounting for knowledge of the external world, Locke adopted Galileo's distinction between primary and secondary qualities (i.e. between those assumed to be in the phenomenon and those assumed to be in the mind), and thus brought a reaction from Berkeley (1710). Admitting that all knowledge of the external world came through the senses, Berkeley asked whether all qualities were not equally secondary. How do we know, for instance, of extension except through touch? He denied any superiority of human knowledge of primary as opposed to secondary qualities. Hence his doctrine: We can know material substances only by their sensory qualities, and all such qualities are equally knowable or unknowable; things have reality for us only because we have been vouchsafed a share in God's perception of them. Berkeley thus repudiated all human concept of material substance outside the mind (to be is only to be perceived), but he did not question the existence of the mind itself. For him, in other words, all ideas were innate.

David Hume (1711–76), in turn, reacted against Berkeley's psychology. Dividing mental operations into the fundamentals of immediate perceptions and mediate ideas (derived from perceptions), he found that for him mind and self were themselves as difficult of perception, and thus of knowledge and proof, as material substance had been for Berkeley. The concept of cause-effect likewise had for him no objective validity other than customary association, though it was a very valuable working tool. In general, although willing to accept mathematical proof, Hume was sceptical about abstract thought and seemed to reduce human knowledge to satisfying associations.

Hume was thus one of the founders of the school of British associationists of the eighteenth century. Drawing upon the psychological atomism of Hobbes and Locke as well as upon Hume, David Hartley (1705–57) put forth the explicit doctrine of the associationist school. Hartley, a physician by training, was aware of the work that had been done on the brain and the nervous system and gave a physiological buttressing to his statements, attributing thought to vibrations of the medullary substance and to neutral processes. He maintained that there are two orders of events, the mental and the physical, which are not identical but which run parallel to each other. Change in one is therefore accompanied by change in the other. Sensations and ideas are interconnected by physiological processes, and from this interconnection comes a general law of association. Stated simply, this law assumed that if sensations are often experienced together, they will form corresponding ideas, which will usually occur to the mind together with them.

The empiricism of Locke's and Hume's day and the credo of the *philosophes*, partly attributable to it, is discussed in Chapters VII and IX above and Chapter XV below. The *Encyclopédie*, edited as it was by the scientist-philosopher-belletrist Diderot and the mathematician d'Alembert, was committed in its oft-quoted 'preliminary discourse' (by d'Alembert) to the empirical approach to knowledge and, implicitly at least, to scientific determinism. Diderot himself, with painstaking attention to accuracy and detail, wrote a number of the articles on science and technology, and a large part of the illustrations were of actual technological processes and machinery. A number of the leading scientists of the age wrote articles for the *Encyclopédie*, which thus became at the same time a compendium of the latest scientific and technological findings and a medium of propaganda against obscurantism— both in the articles on science and technology and in numerous others on humanistic, political, religious, social, and economic subjects. Its first volume appeared in 1751, and its last (XXXIV–XXXV, the indexes) in 1780. In Beaumarchais' *Barber of Seville* (1775), Dr Bartholo, representative of an uneasy older generation, heartily disapproved of the scientific and other innovations of his day. Calling it a 'barbarous century', he complains that it has produced 'every kind of foolishness'—'freedom of thought, attraction [i.e. Newton's law of gravitation], electricity, toleration, inoculation, quinine, the *Encyclopédie*, and [bourgeois] dramas.' By that time one of the schools of the Enlightenment *philosophes*, that represented by Condillac, La Mettrie, and Holbach, had by 'pure reason' achieved a thoroughly monistic and materialistic psychology, but, as his *Neveu de Rameau* revealed, Diderot was not altogether in their camp. And Kant, following Hume, though with a Pietistic touch, reacted against the rationalism of the French Enlightenment and sought to restore room for faith in a series of idealist *Kritiks*, culminating in his *Kritik der reinen Vernunft* (1781).

SCIENCE OUTSIDE EUROPE

Science in the Islamic World

Most of the significant activity in the development of pure science outside of Europe after 1500 took place in the Far East. In Africa and America (except for the sculptural and architectural techniques discussed in Chapter XII) such scientific knowledge as is known to have been accumulated after 1500 by people not directly influenced by the European and the Asiatic scientific tradition was apparently of the empirical or technological nature required for everyday needs. In the Islamic world the stock of scientific principles remained for the most part unchanged from the preceding period where no change crept in from Europe. Except perhaps in the field of architectural technology and engineering (see Chapter XII), after 1500—and especially after 1600—in all Islamic lands the natural sciences became as a rule a mere tradition, the effective standards of which probably declined.

In the course of the sixteenth century Ottoman science tended to run to encyclopedism more than to fresh monographs. Yet it often showed a high awareness of the demands of experimentation or of mathematical cogency. Among the astronomical observatories maintained at Istanbul and elsewhere the fine one run in the tradition of Ulūgh Beg and 'Alī Qūshji (see Chapter XIII) continued to do good work under Taqī-al-dīn Misrī for a few years after 1579. Many Turkish scholars, however, were content simply to translate earlier Persian or Arabic works into Turkish. The Islamic tradition of learning had hardened and independent scholarship became less and less free. For instance, in 1601 Sari 'Abd-al-Rahmān, a freethinker with his own cosmology based on natural law, was executed. Study was increasingly hampered by a ban on the ordinary importation of printed books, such as the Arabic classics then being printed in Europe.

The Ottoman experience was not wholly untypical of other Islamic centres. India under the Moguls, for example, rewarded physicians and astronomers and built well-equipped observatories, yet produced little basically new. The major difference was that the Ottomans were more closely involved intellectually with the new Occidental upsurge. We have already noted (Chapter XIII) the work of Pīrī Re'īs and his introduction of the new Western geographical knowledge into Turkey. In the seventeenth century the most significant figure in Ottoman science was Ḥajjī Khalīfa (d. 1657), an encyclopedist who mastered the Islamic scholarly tradition and also tried to introduce to Turkish readers new Occidental discoveries in several fields. His attempt bore little fruit, however. On the other hand, some Turkish medical writers could claim a certain originality. It was from Turkey that Mary Wortley Montagu brought to England the practice of inoculation for smallpox (c. 1718).

Science in India and China

For the Far East and India it is difficult to separate the science of this period from technological achievement. The high technical quality of Far Eastern textiles, porcelains, rugs, furniture, and other decorative products has already claimed our attention (Chapter XII). Another field of outstanding technology in the Far East was naval architecture. In the 1590's a Korean admiral, Yi Sunsin, perfected an iron-clad tortoise boat and wrought great havoc upon the fleet of the invading Japanese, but the secrets of the vessel's construction apparently died with him. India, too, in addition to skilful workers in textiles and other decorative arts, had highly competent shipwrights. When contacts between India and the West became frequent, Indian craftsmen built Western-type vessels for Westerners while retaining their own traditional type for compatriot traders.

Several Chinese engaged in theoretical scientific research. Chu Tsai-yü's treatise on *Resonant Tubes*, published in 1584, evidenced a certain amount of experimental investigation in the field of music; he established (well before Mersenne's exposition of the same principle in 1627) that the intervals for 'an equal tempered scale' are to be founded by mathematical measurements.[39] Progress was made in the seventeenth and eighteenth centuries toward a scientific methodology relating to linguisitc changes and the reliability of historical documents (see Chapter IX). The experimental method, however, was used only on occasion; it was not adopted as basic for the investigation of nature, and few scholars or physicians devoted their energies to such things as mathematics, astronomy, the study of disease, or the perfection of mechanical contrivances.

Chinese savants continued, rather, to devote their efforts to compiling data, with or without adding to them. The skill of the Chinese artist in illustration was well exploited in several noteworthy scientific compendia. The great illustrated encyclopedia *San-ts'ai t'u-hui* of Wang Ch'i and his son, published about 1609, contained illustrated accounts of tools, plants, animals, and other subjects. Mao Yüan-I's *Wu-pei chih*, completed in 1628, was a huge illustrated compendium on weapons, strategy, ships, defences, and other phases of warfare. Sung Ying-hsing's small compendium, the *T'ien-kung k'ai-wu*, which was published in 1637, provided an illustrated account of Chinese industrial arts of the early seventeenth century. It dealt with the manufacture of flour, clothes, dyes, ink, weapons (including gas explosives), salt, sugar, and pottery, the casting and forging of metals, the designing of ships and wheeled vehicles, the mining of coal and jade, and pearl diving.[40] Cotton cultivation and cotton cloth manufacture developed extensively during the Ming dynasty under imperial stimulation, and treatises on silk and cotton and on cloth manufacture appeared with pertinent illustrations. The *Tzu-hui* dictionary of Mei Ying-tso (1615) showed a marked superiority over earlier works in the scientific arrangement of characters, and it, in turn, was bettered by the *K'ang-hsi tzu-tien*, published in 1716.

The great Chinese encyclopedias were discussed in Chapter XI. Several compendia dealing with medicine deserve separate mention. Among the principal contributions of China to medicine was the *Pen-ts'ao kang-mu* ('Materia Medica') of Li Shih-chen, completed in 1578 after twenty-six years' work. In view of the conflict of the contemporary European iatro-chemists with the Galenists, Li Shih-chen's knowledge of specifics is particularly impressive. His book discussed 898 vegetable and about 1000 animal and mineral drugs and included 8,160 prescriptions. It commented upon inoculations for smallpox, the treatment of syphilis, and the use of such drugs as kaolin, stramonium, chaulmoogra oil, ephederine, and iodine as specifics. It went through many editions in China, was widely used in Japan, and much of it was later translated into Western languages. Wang K'en-t'ang, between 1597 and 1607, published a stupendous work in 120 volumes, the *Principles and Practice of Medicine (Cheng-chih chung-sheng)*. In 1642 appeared a small book by Wu Yiu-hsing which, though entitled *Discourse on Plague*, really dealt with epidemic fevers; he distinguished between typhoid fever and other kinds and emphasized the nose and mouth as important channels of infection. One of the best doctors of the Ch'ing period was Chang Lu, whose *I-t'ung*, compiled between 1644 and 1693, became a standard. Li's *Pen-ts'ao kang-mu* was supplemented and brought up to date in 1765 by Chao Hsüeh-min.

The Jesuits were able to introduce Western mathematics, astronomy, geography, surveying, medicine, and other branches of knowledge into China in the seventeenth century during the declining years of the Ming dynasty. The succeeding Manchu dynasty, in an effort to make itself acceptable to the Chinese, was even more determined to exalt traditional Neo-Confucian concepts and discourage innovation. Nevertheless, modern Western science at first engaged considerable interest on the part of some practical Confucian scholars, and where the Chinese saw concrete advantage to be gained by borrowing from the West without danger to sacred institutions, they were ready enough to borrow. Since native firearms were inferior, the cannon and hand guns of the Portuguese were copied in the early sixteenth century. Later in the century, Japanese imitations of Portuguese weapons and, in the seventeenth century, Dutch weapons were also copied. The Jesuits were employed by both the Mings and the Manchus to cast cannon. Agricultural products such as maize, the sweet potato, and the peanut were introduced and spread between 1573 and 1610. In addition, the use of tobacco and later of opium, though prohibited, spread also, because a popular demand for them arose. In 1628 the Grand Secretary Hsü Kuang-ch'i, a friend of the Jesuit Ricci and a long-time Christian, completed a great compendium on agriculture, the *Nung-cheng ch'üan-shu*, which, besides incorporating accumulated Chinese knowledge, added everything of practical use from Western knowledge that he was able to obtain through the missionaries.

Much of the knowledge the Christians brought was embodied in translations and ultimately copied into the great manuscript library (*Ssu-k'u ch'uan-shu*) of the Ch'ien-lung emperor in the eighteenth century. Relatively few Chinese, however, read and understood this body of information. It did not become an integral part of Chinese learning, and Western astronomy and mathematics seemed to be of interest or practical value only to the technicians associated with the Bureau of Astronomy at Peking. Because of their scientific knowledge the Jesuits were put in charge of the Bureau in 1645 with Schall as director, Verbiest following him in 1688. They reformed the calendar, introduced knowledge of the telescopic discoveries, and otherwise made themselves useful, equipping the observatory, providing technical and geographical information, and translating Western scientific treatises (without teaching the Copernican system).[41]

Though by the late eighteenth century some of the more practical aspects of Western science began to be clearly discernible, its wide application to agriculture, navigation, and other things of prime importance was not made clear to the Chinese before the nineteenth century. Moreover, Western science was suspect in general, since it was expounded by evangelists, who brought the tenets of Christianity, which the Confucian scholars and the Manchu government, after some dalliance, rejected as fundamentally disruptive of the traditional culture (see Chapter V). The few missionaries permitted to remain in China were looked upon with considerable suspicion and hence neither were asked nor volunteered to keep the Chinese scholarly world up-to-date on scientific or technological developments. The opportunity for China to grow up scientifically with the West thus was lost.

Science in Japan

In Japan the Chinese-influenced Li-Chu school of medicine remained dominant during the Momoyama and the early Tokugawa period, even though other Chinese schools claimed adherents as well. Probably the leading native physician of the Momoyama period was Dōsan Manase, who during the last quarter of the sixteenth century followed the Li-Chu school in numerous treatises on many types of disease. In the late sixteenth and seventeenth centuries the scientific and technological achievements of the West were eagerly sought, and Japanese physicians who learned surgery and other elements of Western medicine from the Jesuits founded a 'Southern Barbarian' school of surgery.

As the Tokugawa period advanced, European medical knowledge continued to enter Japan through the Dutch at Nagasaki, where European physicians gave instruction to the Japanese who were interested, introducing them to medical treatises in Dutch. Inevitably Western medical ideas began to appear in Japanese medical literature. A Dutch version of Ambroise Paré reached Japan by 1655, and parts of it appeared with illustrations in Japanese works in 1706 and 1713. The teachings of the German physician Engelbert Kämpfer, who was in residence at the Dutch factory in the 1690's, further facilitated the spread of European methods. In 1766 Kagawa Gen-etsu published his *San Ron*, the foundation of modern obstetrics in Japan, which was a fusion of Chinese and Western ideas with the author's practical experience. For the most part, however, during our period the Japanese rejected Western science and technology; what they wanted, they thought, could not be separated from Christianity, and they feared that Christianity meant not only cultural subversion but also possible political subjugation.

NOTES TO CHAPTER XIV

1. Boethius, *De Consolatione Philosophiae*, Book 2, *Prosa* vii.

2. Alexandre Koyré, *From the Closed World to the Infinite Universe*, reproduces this diagram on p. 37.

3. Quoted in Dorothea W. Singer, *Giordano Bruno; His life and Thought, with annotated translations of his work on the infinite universe and worlds* (New York, 1950), p. 86.

4. It is quite exact to say here that, according to Descartes, science is God's handiwork. The first principles of science, the 'seeds of truth' deposited by God in the human soul, then known in the philosophical tradition as 'eternal truths', are God's creatures. God 'made' the principles of human reason just as He made light, and does not contemplate them as if they were eternal ideas existing in His understanding. (Georges Canguilhem.)

5. Professor G. Canguilhem points out that these reserves concerning Bacon's modernity, his precursory genius, and the recognition of his inability to grasp that the natural sciences should take the same path as mathematics are all the more interesting and important in that Anglo–American authors generally tend towards what appears to contemporary French authors, trained in the school of Alexandre Koyré or of Robert Lenoble, to be an over-estimation.

6. To Professor G. Canguilhem the works which Alexandre Koyré has devoted to Galileo have done much to cool the ardour of historians who, taking as a starting point different ideologies (pragmatism or Marxism) have attempted to derive science from the mechanics of civil or military engineering techniques. In this connection, as Galileo himself stated in his *Discorsi*, it was questions rather than ideas that he found in the works of the technicians, mainly in the theory of the resistance of matter and hydrostatics. In his book

Les ingénieurs de la Renaissance (Paris, 1964) Betrand Gille considers the opinion of Alexandre Koyré too exclusive.
The authors here relied not so much on Koyré as upon comments directed to them personally by the late E. J. Dijksterhuis.

7. See Ettore Bortolotti, 'L'Algebra nella scuola matematica bolognese del secolo XVI' in *Studi e ricerche sulla storia della matematica in Italia* (Bologna, 1928), pp. 7 and 17–20, and Alexandre Koyré, *La science moderne (de 1450 à 1800)* in *Histoire générale des sciences*, II (Paris, 1958), pp. 37–39.

8. In Professor G. Canguilhem's opinion it is not certain that the number of circles in Ptolemaic astronomy were more than twice the number of Copernican circles. The astronomer Purbach would appear to have counted only 42. It was not so much the reduction in numbers which constituted the superiority of the Copernican explanation as the organic, systematic character of this explanation; for instance, the postulate of a relationship between the distance of a planet from the sun and the revolutionary cycle of this planet.

9. Quoted in Dorothy Stimson, *The Gradual Acceptance of the Copernican Theory of the Universe* (New York, 1917), p. 39.

10. See Ingomar Düring, 'Von Aristoteles bis Leibniz', *Antike und Abendland*, IV (1954), 152, and Ambroise Jobert, 'L'Université de Cracovie et les grands courants de pensée du XVIe siècle', *Revue d'histoire moderne et contemporaine*, I (1954), pp. 216.

11. *De Revolutionibus*, Bk. I, Ch. I.

12. Galileo's recantation, quoted in the introduction to Galileo's *Dialogue on the Great World Systems*, ed. Giorgio de Santillana (Chicago, 1955), p. xix.

13. For this and other disputes of Newton and Hooke, see Alexandre Koyré, 'An unpublished letter of Robert Hooke to Isaac Newton', *Isis*, XLIII (1952), especially pp. 333–37.

14. Professor G. Canguilhem, by way of addition, comments as follows: This is one of the most resounding events in the history of modern astronomy and in the evolution of celestial mechanics. Halley had calculated the reappearances of the comet for 1758. Clairaut fixed its passage at about April 14, 1759. In fact the comet was a month ahead of this reckoning. As an example of the influence of a scientific event of this magnitude on public opinion, Victor Hugo's poem 'The Comet', in *La légende des siècles* may be found of interest:

> 'He foretold the day the star would come again.
> What jeers! ...
>
> . . . . . .
>
> And, suddenly, with ghostly stealth
> Appeared above the wild horizon
> A flame suffusing myriad leagues,
> A monstrous flash out of the blue immensity,
> Out of the splendid, deep, and suddenly illuminated sky:
> Said the terrible star to man: Behold, here I am.'

15. Paraphrased in English by Sir James Jeans, *The Growth of Physical Science* (Cambridge, 1951, p. 148. Descartes' texts most clearly relevant to the law of inertia are to be found in *Principia Philosophiae* (1644), Part II, para. 37, page 54 and in *Le Monde ou Traité de la lumière* (1664), Chap. VII, p. 82.

16. Quoted (with slight modifications) from A. Wolf, *A History of Science, Technology, and Philosophy in the Eighteenth Century* (Macmillan Company, New York, 1939), p. 64.

17. Quoted *ibid.*, p. 68.

18. *Opticks* (1704), Query 29.

19. 'Hall, Chester Moor (1703–71)', *Dictionary of National Biography* (London, 1920–22), VIII, p. 946.

20. Quoted in A. R. Hall, *The Scientific Revolution (1500–1800), The Formation of the Modern Scientific Attitude* (Boston, 1957), p. 213.

21. Quoted in Wolf, *Sixteenth and Seventeenth centuries*, pp. 277–78.

22. A recent study attributes to Cuneaus of Leyden the invention of the famous 'jar', assigning to E. J. Von Kleist only an accessory rôle. See the article by John L. Heilbron: 'A propos de l'invention de la bouteille de Leyde', *Revue d'histoire des sciences*, XIX, n⁰ 2 (April–June, 1966). (G. Canguilhem.)

23. Wolf, *Sixteen and Seventeenth Centuries*, p. 470.

24. On Lomonosov's thermometer, see Boris N. Menshutkin, *Russia's Lomonosov* (tr. J. E. Thal and E. J. Webster; Princeton University Press, Princeton, 1952), pp. 70–72.

25. *The Works of the Honourable Robert Boyle*, ed. Thomas Birch (1772), I, 354. For a recent re-evaluation of Boyle see Marie Boas, *Robert Boyle and Seventeenth Century Chemistry* (University Press, Cambridge, 1958).

26. *Observations on the Solid and Liquid States of Substances* (1760), quoted in A. A. Morosov, *Michael Wassiljewitsch Lomonosov, 1711–65* (tr. W. Hoepp; Rutten und Loenig, Berlin, 1954), pp. 211–12; this is almost verbatim the same as Lomonosov to Euler, July 5, 1748. See also Menshutkin, pp. 116–18, and A. A. Zvorikine, 'Remarques sur l'histoire des inventions et de la pensée scientifique et technique russe des dix-septième et dix-neuvième siècles', *Journal of World History*, special number (1958), p. 186. On the wide currency of the conservation law of mass before Lomonosov and Lavoisier see Henry Guerlac, *Lavoisier, the Crucial Year: the Background and Origin of His First Experiments on Combustion in* 1772 (Cornell University Press, Ithaca, New York, 1961), p. xv.

27. Michele Gortani, 'Italian Pioneers in Geology and Mineralogy', *Journal of World History*, VII (1963), pp. 510–12, n. 8.

28. Thomas D. Kendrick, *The Lisbon Earthquake* (London, 1956), esp. pp. 57–71.

29. Oskar Netoliczka (ed.), *Johannes Honterus' ausgewählte Schriften* (Vienna, 1898), p. 152.

30. For a discussion of the thesis that Dezhnev went by land rather than by sea, see F. A. Golder, *Russian Expansion on the Pacific* (1641–1850) (Cleveland, 1914), pp. 67–95, and Raymond Fisher, 'Simon Dezhnev and Professor Golder', *Pacific Historical Review*, XXV (1956), pp. 281–92.

31. Quoted from 'Additional Materials in Connection with the Remarks of Soviet Scientists on the Plan of Volume IV' (Ms. previously cited).

32. To Professor G. Calguilhem the contribution of Bernard de Jussieu towards the establishment of a 'natural' method in botany was practical rather than speculative. The Botanical Garden planted in the grounds of Versailles during the reign of Louis XV provided the demonstration of this method. The principles of natural classification, on the other hand, were expounded and developed by Antoine-Laurent de Jussieu (1748–1836) in his work *Genera plantarum* (1789). Nor should it be forgotten that Michel Adanson, botanist, geographer, and explorer of Senegal, had divided and classified vegetable species into 58 natural families in his work entitled *Famille des plantes* (1763).

33. Arthur O. Lovejoy, *The Great Chain of Being* (Cambridge, Mass., 1936), pp. 232–33.

34. Professor G. Canguilhem cautions that the use of the term 'homology', the exact meaning of which in comparative anatomy was determined only towards the middle of the nineteenth century after the studies of Etienne Geoffroy Saint-Hilaire (1772–1844) and with those of Richard Owen (1771–1858), runs the risk of suggesting continuity of project and concept from Pierre Belon down to Cuvier and Owen, and that progress in comparative anatomy consisted in broadening the field of observation and deepening the exploration of concept. In reality, it required the introduction of a fundamental distinction between analogy, a concept symbolic and mystic rather than scientific, and homology, originally a mathematical concept, and, above all, the introduction of a dissociation between structure and function. Analogy is functional and does not imply similarity of structures. Homology is a similitude of structural relations, without its being necessary for the organs to have the same form and function.

35. William Harvey, *Exercitatio Anatomica de Motu Cardis et Sanguinis in Animalibus*, edited with an English translation by Chauncey D. Leake (Springfield, Ill., 1928), Preface and Ch. viii, p. 70.

36. The use of the term 'vitalism' does not seem either accurate or strictly applicable in describing the doctrine of De Stahl. Medical historians have always carefully distinguished between *animism* and *vitalism* (see Daremberg, *Histoire des sciences médicales* [Paris, 1870]), and the vitalists of the Montpellier school, Barthès and his disciples, always differentiated between themselves and De Stahl and animism. (G. Canguilhem.) *The authors have used the term* vitalism *broadly, as a synonym of* anti-mechanism *(as, for example, Charles Singer and Abraham Wolf sometimes do).*

37. See Oswei Temkin, 'The Role of Surgery in the Rise of Modern Medical Thought', *Bulletin of the History of Medicine*, XXV (1951), pp. 248–59.

38. Georges Canguilhem, *La formation du concept de réflexe aux XVIIe et XVIIIe siècles* (Paris, 1955), p. 131.

39. See L. Carrington Goodrich, *A Short History of the Chinese People* (New York, 1943), p. 203.

40. *Ibid.*, p. 205.

41. Joseph Needham, *Chinese Astronomy and the Jesuit Mission: an Encounter of Cultures* (London, 1958). See also P. M. d'Elia, 'La Reprise des missions catholiques en Chine à la fin des Ming (1579–1644)', *Journal of World History*, V (1960), pp. 679–99.

CHAPTER XV

TECHNOLOGY AND SOCIETY
(1300–1775)

MEASUREMENTS AND THEIR APPLICATION

FROM the thirteenth century on, man has succeeded in harnessing tools to his material needs as never before. For the earlier scientific and technological advances of this period, accurate measurement, though recognized as desirable, was difficult to achieve, but, as explained in Chapter XIV, increasing precision of calculation became a cornerstone of the seventeenth-century 'scientific revolution'—especially in the physical sciences, whether geography, astronomy, chemistry, physics, meteorology, or navigation. In the biological sciences, too, perhaps the most important discovery, that of the circulation of the blood, was in large part quantitative, and still greater strides were to come in the eighteenth century and later, with the development of an adequate classification system. The transition from arbitrary or parochial incommensurables to a universally acceptable taxonomy in the biological sciences made measurements and, therefore, counting, categories, and comparisons more uniform and precise. Moreover, the discovery of the cell gave to biology a fundamental unit to measure and quantify even while atoms and molecules were still largely a qualitative, philosophical theory in chemistry and the other physical sciences.

Mechanical clocks play a particularly significant role in the history of units of measurement. Only after the fourteenth century did Italy's clocks strike every hour. They were not only the first machines whose construction required exact scientific knowledge but also the first to be driven by stored energy, the expenditure of which was measured by determined intervals. Huygens' pendulum and balance-wheel clocks permitted still more precise measurement of time not only to scientists but to ordinary men as well. (Pl. 89a, b.) Affairs of the day could now be arranged to the minute, even the second, instead of the hour or half-hour previously marked by the wheel clocks of the public squares and monasteries, crudely regulated by means of the foliot balance or crossbar, the earliest form of clock escapement. As time became more and more susceptible to accurate calculation, the clock became a monitor not only of scientific experimentation but of social relations as well, introducing accuracy, promptness, and uniformity of timing into human activities, until, with the rise of the industrial factory, it developed into a veritable tyrant. The attitude toward time became a major criterion of differentiation among ages and peoples.

If accurate telling of time was one of the applications of science to human affairs which proved of lasting importance to the practical business of life, accurate location and measurement of space was another. The introduction of two coordinates for mapmaking permitted a noteworthy advance in cartography. Along with better maps, the application of simple mathematics to quadrants, sextants, compasses, and other early navigational instruments made ocean travel more secure even before the improvement of the telescope and the invention of the chronometer. The measurement of the meridian eliminated much of the guesswork from the calculation of global distances.

Accurate accounting was still another addition to the practical side of life. Commercial arithmetic developed rapidly in the West from about 1300 on; double-entry book-keeping was introduced probably in the fourteenth century; and Hindu-Arabic numbers came into use more and more extensively until in the sixteenth century they were regularly used. The shortcomings of eighteenth-century Russian agriculture have been attributed, along with bad management by landlords and lack of enterprise in peasants, to the backwardness of Russian accounting methods.[2] Increased commercial risk-taking led inevitably to efforts to calculate the risks taken. Marine insurance, with rates based at first on pure guesswork, had been introduced into northern Italy before 1300 but became common in Barcelona during the fourteenth century and in Bruges during the fifteenth. By 1600 the mathematical theory of games was being studied in various parts of Europe (see Chapter XIV), and the mathematics of probabilities, today indispensible to actuarial and other kinds of statistics, was to engage the attention of some of the best mathematical minds of the seventeenth century.

By that time mathematics had come to play a fashionable role in the life of the educated European. The amateur (the so-called *curioso*) as well as the scientist had begun to look for regularities behind the manifest aspects of nature, and the same sort of contemporary quest for perfect standards of excellence as was expressed by Classicism in the arts and literature gave rise also to a taste for the rigid rules of mathematics. The state encouraged this vogue as it accumulated more and more statistics and accounted more and more strictly for its income and outgo of money. Large numbers of manuals appeared for surveyors, merchants, seamen, soldiers, and others who might profit from a knowledge of simple mathematics, and the society of the commercial capitals of Europe became familiar with 'those rather mysterious figures "teachers of mathematics" who were . . . both a symptom and a cause of this process'.[3]

In the sixteenth century mathematics was applied in a signal way to an ancient problem of time-keeping. Calendar reform had been suggested by Roger Bacon and the Avignon popes because of the long observed inaccuracy in the co-ordination of the Julian calendar with the solar year. Yet no serious efforts were made to remedy the calendar until 1474, when Pope Sixtus IV invited Regiomontanus to Rome to attend to the necessary readjustments.

On account of that astronomer's untimely death, however, nothing came of this effort. Several mathematicians of the ensuing century wrote treatises which made still more clear how inaccurate the Julian calendar was: in about 1600 years since its inception its minor inaccuracy of 11 minutes and 14 seconds per year had resulted in a ten-day shift in datings. For example, the spring equinox, which in Caesar's time fell on March 21, fell on the 11th in 1582, the year reform was finally put into effect.

This reform came at the instance of Pope Gregory XIII. Aloysius Lilius, a mathematician-astronomer-physician of Naples, and after his death Christopher Clavius, a mathematician of Bamberg, worked out the details. On their recommendation, in Catholic countries ten days—October 5 to 14—were arbitrarily dropped from the calendar at once and the day after October 4, 1582, became October 15, 1582. This radical surgery restored the calendar to the solar co-ordination that had existed at the time of the Council of Nicea (AD 325). To maintain correct co-ordination thereafter, leap years were to be observed in every year divisible by 4 except for the centurial years unless they were multiples of 400. Thus 1600 was to be a leap year, but not 1700, 1800, and 1900. In spite of these careful mathematical shadings the Gregorian calendar will develop one day of solar inaccuracy every 3,323 years. Some difficulty was encountered in adjusting the 'new style' calendar to the lunar calendar, which also figured in the fixing of movable church feasts. A still more formidable obstacle was the reluctance of non-Roman Christians to follow the papal lead. The Catholic calendar was not adopted in Protestant Germany until 1700 (and then only with certain modifications), in England not until 1752, and in Russia not until the Revolution of 1917.

In the seventeenth century, though dates were still commonly given in Roman numerals, other calculations, whether in scientific research or in financial accounts, employed not only Arabic numerals but also the decimal system, and the new mathematical shorthand or symbols (see Chapter XIV). Simplified notation made easier the invention of devices for mechanical calculation. The abacus, the time-honoured calculating device used in western Europe since around AD 1000, was supplemented by 'Napier's Bones', developed around 1617 by the father of logarithms; the 'bones' were a system of numbering rods. Then, shortly after the introduction of logarithms made it possible to reduce higher arithmetical processes to lower ones (see Chapter XIV), came the slide rule, usually attributed to the English mathematicians Edmund Gunter (1581–1626) and (more accurately) William Oughtred (1575–1660). The first calculating machine known to be designed with details for its construction was that which Pascal invented in 1642, when he was only nineteen years old, to help his father add up sums of money. (Pl. 90.) Despite its intricacy dozens of useful machines were made to Pascal's design, and several still survive. Again illustrating that an invention may come to more than one mind when the culture is ripe for it,

Samuel Morland, not aware of Pascal's idea, developed his own machine for addition and substraction in 1666, and later devised another for multiplication. In the 1670's Leibniz, again independently, invented and described his calculating machine. While it, too, was intricate, at least one example, which still exists, was made. Only in the nineteenth century did any significant advance in this type of computer prove feasible.

'Political arithmetick', or what we today would call 'vital statistics', was also a product of the seventeenth century. The word *statistics* had not yet been coined. Vital statistics were kept by parish churches, but only as records of baptism, marriage, and Christian burial. In France after the Revocation of the Edict of Nantes, Huguenots could not prove birth, marriage, or death since they did not belong to legitimate parishes, and so they could not legally bequeath property. The publication of bills of mortality for London parishes in the seventeenth century indicated growing concern for a well-ordered method of calculating births, deaths, and reasons for mortality. In Holland the interest in mortality statistics and tables was shared by scientists like Huygens and statesmen like Jan de Witt, no mean mathematician himself.

With the growing power of the state, attempts were made to assess various factors affecting population. In 1662 John Graunt (1620-74) published his *Natural and Political Observations . . . made upon the Bills of Mortality*—based, that is, upon the weekly mortality announcements published by certain English parishes. Though his method of gathering data was crude by modern standards, his book was a significant step in the study of demography. Graunt's work was continued by William Petty, who used empirical measurements with self-conscious deliberation. In the preface to his *Political Arithmetick* (1691) Petty said: 'Instead of using only comparative and superlative Words, and intellectual Arguments, I have taken the Course (as a Specimen of the Political Arithmetick I have long aimed at) to express myself in terms of Number, Weight, or Measure; to use only Arguments of Sense, and to consider only such Causes as have visible Foundations in Nature; leaving those that depend upon mutable Minds, Opinions, Appetites and Passions of particular Men, to the Consideration of Others.' Gregory King (1648-1712) adopted this quantitative concept of demography in his *Natural and Political Observations and Conclusions upon the State and Condition of England* (1696). In France, where the royal intendants had frequently concerned themselves with demographic data, Abbé Jean-Joseph Expilly undertook a *Dictionnaire géographique, historique et politique des Gaules et de la France*, which, though incomplete in six volumes (1762-70), still pays off as a mine of statistics.

The use of mathematics in calculating life insurance risks seems to date from an earlier period. Until the middle of the seventeenth century, however, the buying of insurance continued to partake more of the nature of mere chance than of calculated risk. No allowance was made for differences among the insured of age, occupation, or other factors that today are given special weight in the computation of insurance premiums. Graunt's work led to the drawing up of other mortality tables after the middle of the seventeenth century, and in 1693 the astronomer Halley published a well elaborated actuarial table. Halley was critical of the techniques used by Graunt and Petty, and the first English life insurance companies, established in the early eighteenth century, preferred his computations.

Numerous instances during the seventeenth and eighteenth centuries reveal a sort of logical relationship between mathematical and technological development: the accumulated knowledge of the mathematics of relevant subjects (such as described in Chapter XIV) suggested and sometimes helped to make possible new steps toward the solution of old practical problems. Ship-building, architecture, and engineering improved with the employment of mathematics in such problems as the strength of materials, the building of arches, and tables of proportion. The advances in trigonometry and the development of logarithms made astronomical and navigational calculations easier. In surveying, the theodolite (first used in the sixteenth century) was more regularly employed for calculating angles. The volume of barrels was made subject to careful measurement (an obvious aid not only to vintners but also to customs officers). Military experts applied new developments in geometry to theories of fortification and to the study of ballistics.[4]

So long as the new knowledge held forth the promise of glory or material advantage and did not undermine tradition, governments generally befriended it. Governmental patronage was especially liberal in geographical research. After the discovery of the New World the making and printing of charts and maps became a big business, pursued by governments as well as private trading companies and commercial chart makers. With the new printing press to serve them, they put out numerous maps, sometimes by means of wood block but, as time went on, more often by engraved copper plates. The study of geography had obvious political and commercial implications (see Chapter I). As early as 1503 the king of Spain established the Casa de Contratación de las Indias, a combination of hydrographic office and board of trade. In a century and a half it gathered data from about 18,000 sailings—from 117 to 188 a year on the average during its busiest years, 1580–1620. Within five years a separate hydrographical office was established, perhaps the first in history. Geographical information about the New World became crucial to the success of further explorations and settlements by the rival colonial powers, and new information was guarded with great care, official charts sometimes being kept under a veil of secrecy. Map makers were encouraged by governments to keep pace with the growing knowledge of geography, for their charts and maps were not only of great aid to the mariner but served the merchant and the military as well. For similar reasons governments showed a friendly interest in meteorology and meteorological instruments. On the other hand, until the mid-eighteenth century, the study of the origin of the Earth often ran into difficulties with the authorities, because calculations of the time needed for geological processes were in conflict with a literal interpretation of the Book of Genesis and so smacked of heresy.

MACHINES, INDUSTRY, AND POWER

As scientists came to depend less on theoretical speculation and more on accurate observation and measurement, they became more dependent on the makers of precision instruments. Astronomers' telescopes and biologists' microscopes could be no better than the most expert lens-grinders' products, and alchemists or chemists were limited by the expertness of craftsmen in the manufacture of glass. Until about 1300 in such enterprises as the glass industry and the making of surgical instruments Western craftsmen had followed the lead of the Muslims. Then the West forged ahead slowly, and the consequent improvement of lenses and other apparatus played a major part in the great biological and astronomical achievements of the succeeding centuries.

The dependence of the scientist on well-designed apparatus and precision instruments was not evident, however, before the physicial sciences became highly organized, specialized bodies of knowledge. During the fourteenth and fifteenth centuries (as earlier), such inventions as were made were usually by craftsmen working empirically and with little theoretical knowledge; the occasional experimentalist in the ranks of theoretical science was likely to work alone in a private laboratory without employing the skill or technical advice of craftsmen. In the sixteenth and seventeenth centuries, however, empirical craftsmanship and theoretical speculation were more often found working in co-operation. Several instances of this association of practice with theory have already been noted. In the course of routine medical practice, for example, Paracelsus worked out certain of his revolutionary theories; in the mines of the Erzgebirge Agricola laid the foundations for his treatise on metallurgy; Galileo made observations in the Venetian Arsenal; Mercator was a simple map maker when he devised the Mercator projection; Fabrizio was originally a lens grinder, and Leeuwenhoek a microscope maker. Another example was Vanoccio Biringuccio of Siena (c. 1480?–540), who (as we shall soon see) combined his experiences as a miner with speculative theory. Nor is the number of other relevant instances small.

Yet, during the period here under discussion there was more talk about the need for the alliance of science and technology than actual alliance. Bacon's dream of bringing philosophy down from the empyrean inspired generations of European scientists and statesmen and kept before them always the goal of wedding science to technology, but it was prognostication rather than reality. The 'scientific revolution' of seventeenth-century Europe usually placed emphasis upon science for its own sake rather than for technological improvement.

Nevertheless, the concept of science that took hold in seventeenth-century Europe prepared the way for a mutually acceptable alliance of science and technology. The technician assumed greater importance in industry, while the importance of the craftsman diminished and, along with it, that of the guild tradition of which he was a product. Simple tools were replaced by machines and engines, and in the craftsman's place gradually came the mechanic and, later, the engineer, more theoretical in outlook than his prototype but still not a pure scientist (that is, one who considered himself a disinterested questioner of nature). The technical foundations of the eighteenth-century 'Industrial Revolution' (with some exceptions that will be noted below) were laid not by scientists but by skilled mechanics, some turned engineers, for science and industry generally went their separate ways. Only in the nineteenth century, with the development of new sources of power, new techniques and skills, and a new socio-economic situation was the dream of Bacon finally to be fulfilled; the successful marriage of science and technology, for better or for worse, brought about a lasting alliance of scientist, engineer, mechanic, and craftsman, with the sympathy and subsidy of business, society, and government.

The Increased Use of Machines

Modern man may well be characterized as a machine-making animal, but he owed much to his forerunners. The ancient Chinese, Egyptians, Greeks, and Romans are known to have borrowed or invented varied types of machines and tools—wheels, pulleys, bellows, lathes, treadles, potter's wheels, spinning and weaving mechanisms, mills, water organs and clocks, siphons, Archimedean screws, burning mirrors, and even automatic machines. During the Middle Ages the yoke for oxen, the hard horse collar, harness for animals in single file, and metal horseshoes had made the exploitation of animal power more efficient. Water power and windmills had been used East and West for centuries before our period for such tasks as grinding grain, working bellows, pumping water, processing metals, and sawing wood. During the Middle Ages western Europe also knew the ship's rudder, lateen-rigged sails, fore and aft rigging, the compass, the quadrant, clocks, buttons, forks, and improved textile machines. The thirteenth-century picture album of Villard de Honnecourt contained sketches of various types of machines, even one for perpetual motion. Some of these early machines had not been commonly applied to mankind's needs before the fifteenth or sixteenth century. For example, the crank, known in ancient China and in ninth-century Europe, was widely used only by the fifteenth century, when western Europeans applied it to the bit and brace, paddle wheels, and the hurdy-gurdy.

As a result of the abundance of machines from other regions and earlier ages the period from 1300 to 1500 in Europe was not spectacular for the invention of new mechanisms so much as for its marked improvements and wider application of older machines. Mechanisms like plows, clocks, wind-mills, and water mills are portrayed in sketchbooks of the period, such as Leonardo da Vinci's notebooks and the *Mittelalterliches Hausbuch* (c. 1480), compiled by an unknown gunmaker and belonging to a south-German family. Leonardo's prestige has led to a common assumption of the superiority of Italian technology over that of northern countries in their day, but the comparison may be somewhat unfair, since his sketches and manuscripts were a compendium not merely of the science and technology of his day but also of his own designs, some of which were only unrealized dreams.

In any case, Northern technology was far from stagnant. In the fourteenth century an astonishing proportion of Nuremberg's population were master craftsmen, and in the fifteenth century printing, metallurgy, and precision work were especially well developed in the free cities of Germany. During the next century, as astronomy shifted its basic ideas from the Earth to the Sun and Western Europe moved its maritime bases from the Mediterranean to the Atlantic, technological leadership shifted from Italy and Germany to the Netherlands. By the end of the sixteenth century the craftsmen of the Netherlands led all Europe in the manufacture of precision machines, lenses, maps, and the like; the windmill reached the height of its effectiveness in the Netherlands, where it could be put to unusually profitable use in reclaiming land from the sea by wind-powered pumps; and Dutch civil engineers and millwrights led Europe's engineering profession until the development of steam power.

The medieval millwright was in some ways the archetype of the modern engineer. He had to understand, at least empirically, the action of water and wind, wheels and treadles, cogs and pulleys, cranks and shafts, wood and metal. The water-wheel was the most common source of automatic power in the late Middle Ages. It usually was driven by an undershot wheel, but, from the fourteenth century on, the overshot wheel was used more and more, thereby adding the weight of the water to the power of the stream. The undershot wheel, however, remained the more common until the sixteenth century, and at the end of that century—around Toulouse, according to Jacques Besson's *Théâtre des instruments mathématiques et méchaniques* (Lyons, 1579)—there developed a sort of water-turbine. It was driven by a confined stream of water directed at curved blades on the periphery of a horizontal wheel. Waterpower was used to grind corn, pump water, blow bellows, saw wood, sharpen tools, crush olives, wood, or ore, and for many other purposes. (Pl. 96a, b.)

The windmill was particularly adaptable to the area of northern Europe, where wind velocity was relatively dependable. Most windmills were simple affairs—either fixed buildings facing the prevailing winds or pivoting struc-tures. The earliest form of windmill in Europe seems to have developed in the Baltic area. It was of the post type—that is, the entire structure of the mill, supported on a strong post, had to be rotated into the wind in order to be operated at the most efficient rate. As the mills became larger, this rotation required more and more physical effort. A later development was the tower mill, of which it was necessary to rotate only a cap carrying the wind-shaft on which the sails were fixed. Both post and tower types were described as early as 1568 by Agostino Ramelli in his *Diverse et Artificiose Machine.* The windmill continued to play an important role in European economy until the end of the eighteenth century and is still used in Holland, Portugal, Rhodes, America, and Australia for pumping water and other minor tasks not requiring a regular supply of power. (Pl. 97a, b)

The pump also underwent rapid development from the sixteenth century onward. Agricola, Ramelli, and other contemporaries described around a hundred types of pumps. Some of them sucked up liquids by creating a vacuum; others worked under pressure of a plunger. The water pipes and pump cylinders of this period were constructed of timber, frequently by boring holes lengthwise through logs, since the casting of metal cylinders of large diameter, though essential for guns, was still too costly for industrial purposes. Each part of a pump or other machine had to be made separately and laboriously by hand, for interchangeable parts were unknown. A great advance was made in the development of pumps in the seventeenth century because of the practical necessity for draining mines and building public waterworks. Curiosity was aroused by the fact that water could not be raised more than about 28 feet by suction, and resultant studies of the 'spring of the air' and atmospheric pressure by Torricelli, Von Guericke, and others had a remarkable impact on the development of pumps, and vice versa (see Chapter XIV).

As cities grew and the providing of public services became a matter of growing concern, water supply became one of the critical urban problems. Some of the great stone aqueducts of the Romans still stood, monuments to early ingenuity, but they were far from sufficient. The introduction of pumps to supplement the old gravity-flow system did much to increase the comfort and health of urban peoples. As early as the fifteenth century the city of Augsburg got its water by an elaborate pumping system. Around 1526, German engineers planned and built for the city of Toledo in Spain a remarkable waterworks system that used forcing pumps, but this sixteenth-century plant was short-lived. The inadequacy of contemporary plumbing defeated the engineers' skill; a local chronicler recorded that this system 'worked with great pistons, and the water hammered so furiously and was driven with such terrific force through the metal pipes, that all the mains were fractured, strong enough material out of which to cast them not being available'.5 Juanelo Turriano's ingenious but costly system of raising water by means of two interlocking, alternately rising and falling chains of wooden troughs replaced it about 1573. The piston-pump of German engineers was successfully adapted later for water supply in London, Paris, and other large cities. One of the most remarkable water systems of the period was that which supplied the palace and fountains at Versailles (installed in 1682 by a Dutch engineer named Rannequin). For all these successes, however, until the nineteenth century inhabitants of large cities were generally dependent upon neighbouring wells, hand pumps, small fountains in market places, or water brought by a gravity-flow system, unless they bought their water from a water-carrier. Not until efficient waterworks were established could much be done toward purifying the supply of water, especially before physicians properly understood the causes of disease.

For a long time machine tools advanced little beyond the state described by Hartmann Schopper in 1568 in his *Panoplia, Omnium Illiberalium Artium Genera Continens*. Wood long remained the chief construction material, plumbers, blacksmiths, and other mechanics making the metal parts by hand. Precision was difficult to obtain with such materials. To cite only one example, the lathe did not evolve before the eighteenth century into the modern iron-cutting industrial machine that we know. (Pl. 98a, b.) Long before 1300 it had been used for turning softer materials, being worked by hand by means of a string attached to a bow much like a hunter's bow, which, moved back and forth, was capable of giving only alternating motion to the revolving parts. The treadle-drive was introduced in the thirteenth century: one end of a driving cord was attached to an overhead elastic wooden pole and the other to a treadle; the wooden pole would pull the cord back after it had been rotated in the opposite direction by rapidly working the treadle; thus the craftsman's or his assistant's hands were freed. The obvious need for continuous drive in a single direction was answered no earlier than the fifteenth century, and perhaps not until the sixteenth, by means of a hand crank and wheel. By this means much of the pewterware of that period was fashioned. Leonardo da Vinci sketched a lathe with a treadle working a flywheel on a crankshaft, which, while apparently never realized, did suggest to future mechanics the workability of a lathe with a spindle mounted and driven between two bearings, thus possibly increasing its strength and therefore its load. About 1490 the 'slide rest' was introduced, a toolholder that permitted the mechanical manipulation of the cutting tool. Thus by the end of the fifteenth century the essential elements of a screw-cutting lathe were available. In 1561 Hans Spaichl of Nuremberg made a lathe that seems to have incorporated at least some of these improvements, but the guilds of his city, interested in preserving the old methods of production from competition, tried, with only limited success, to prevent him from selling it. Besson developed a screw-cutting lathe (1578) which, though apparently more cumbersome, introduced a longitudinal feed. It was now possible to build the machines that shaped the balustrades, railings, and other woodwork of Baroque houses and made wood-turning a gentlemanly hobby of the period.

Only as the clock and instrument industries grew in the eighteenth century did greater precision and tougher machines become available, and by the end of our period the machine industry could produce an all-metal lathe capable of cutting metal parts by precise, adjustable, automatic mechanisms.[6] As the lathe, and along with it grinding, boring, polishing, wood-planing, gear-cutting, and other machines improved, the manufacture of industrial machinery and especially of scientific instruments became more precise.

Interchangeable parts, taken for granted today, could come but slowly. Only the combination of (1) standard units of gauging with uniformity of design and specifications, (2) standardized machine tools, and (3) power machinery worked under a system of specialized labour enables precisely fitting parts to be mass-produced in different places and assembled into complicated machines. Such conditions were not possible in our period, but the beginnings of the process were perceptible. The movable type of the printing industry was an early form of interchangeability, though only within the same printing shop, for type was likely to differ from printer to printer. When screws were manufactured in series (at first, probably of bronze), they were interchangeable within the series, but they were expensive, and wooden or iron pegs were more common. Screws do not seem to have been used in clocks before the end of the fifteenth century or in carpentry until the sixteenth. They were relatively rarely employed by the woodworker, clock and instrument maker, or locksmith until the seventeenth. Not until the nineteenth century were screws made pointed; before that time holes had first to be bored for their entrance or they were used with nuts. These conditions did not lead to uniformity.

The idea of interchangeability was obviously in the air, nevertheless. In the eighteenth century determined efforts were made to develop large-scale manufacturing of machine tools; one of the outstanding large-scale entrepreneurs was the inventor-manufacturer John Roebuck (1718–94). Since cast iron was now more extensively used, more powerful machines could be built, and skilled mechanics were trained to build and operate them. The precision work made possible by the great improvements in metallurgy (see below) in the eighteenth century hastened the readiness of manufacturers to use movable and interchangeable parts. Early in that century Réaumur suggested (*L'art de convertir le fer forgé en acier*, pt. 2, memoir 6) the manufacture of muskets with interchangeable parts, and extraordinarily well gauged cogwheels for clocks were produced in series by the Swedish technological genius Christopher Polhem, but they seem to have had little influence on subsequent industrial processes. By the time of the great instrument-maker George Adams (d. 1773) some standard instruments with some standard component parts were available for several different experimental purposes. The wars at the end of the eighteenth century produced a demand for muskets that led Honoré Blanc, Eli Whitney, and others to put the principle of standardized movable parts into operation on a large scale, but that story belongs to Volume V of the *History of Mankind*.

The Application of Steam Power to Machinery

The earliest modern experiments with steam propulsion were carried out by scientists interested in experimental physics. In 1495 Leonardo da Vinci had suggested the use of steam to shoot a projectile. The writings of Heron of Alexandria, a Hellenistic scientist who had described an aeolipile and puppets that were made to dance by steam power, were published in translation in 1575, but it is impossible to tell how influential his ideas were. In 1606 Giambattista della Porta in *I tre libri de' spiritali* indicated that as steam condensed inside a closed vessel a vacuum would develop, and he described a steam engine that could raise a column of water; his work presented the fundamental idea on which a practical steam engine ultimately was based. Solomon de Caus in *Les raisons des forces mouvantes* (1615) described a similar machine, but whereas Porta had worked under the misapprehension that steam was to be identified with air, De Caus, recognizing that steam was evaporated water, made clear that steam pressure was of a much greater magnitude than air pressure. Several other suggestions for experimental steam engines were made during the seventeenth century.

As the depth of mines in Europe increased, a practical need for power greater than that furnished by man, animal, water, or wind arose. In earlier centuries mines had been likely to be open pits, cave extensions, or shallow shafts, but with the fifteenth-century boom in mining, shafts got deeper, sometimes extending underground a hundred feet or more, especially in precious-metal mines. In some German mines shafts went to a depth of six hundred feet to follow veins of silver, gold, or copper ore, and drainage became a formidable operation. Sturdier pumps driven by animal or water power were needed for raising the water which collected underground from seepage or floods. Soon large mines were fitted with complicated drainage machinery. Hide buckets attached to a single rope were manipulated by a winch with sufficient reliability to keep the Bohemian silver mines at Kutná Hora (Kuttenberg) free of floods though a depth of 1500 feet was reached in the fifteenth century, but in a mine at Schemnitz (now Banska Štiavnica) in Slovakia the drainage system had to be powered by ninety-six horses in three relays, working three large wheels. In order to get the horses to and from the wheels, a system of circular ramps was dug out of the side of the mine. In 1760 a Schemnitz engineer, Josef Karel Höll, reporting to the Académie des Sciences, described a machine that, working as a sort of siphon, might lift a column of water nearly a hundred feet. Complicated and expensive though they might be, such improvements were profitable in the new era of large-scale mining. The Kutná Hora mines alone produced an average of 200 hundredweight of silver per year.

A steam-driven pump for drainage purposes was first suggested in *The Elements of Water Drawing* (1659), written by either R. D'Acres or Robert Thornton. The steam engine as a practical device, however, began with their contemporary the second Marquis of Worcester, who in 1663 described an apparatus ('the water commanding engine') for raising water by means of steam. Worcester gave no diagram of this engine, and his description of it was very obscure. An engine was in fact built that raised water 40 feet, much higher than any earlier engine had attained, but whether it was worked by steam is not certain. Although Worcester was granted a ninety-nine year monopoly by Parliament, he did not form a company to develop his invention, and it never went past this trial stage.

Meanwhile Von Guericke, Boyle, and others had shown that a piston could be utilized to transform air pressure into work (see Chapter XIV), and Huygens proposed a piston machine that was driven by the alternate expansion and contraction of gas from gunpowder explosions (1680). Familiarity with the piston enabled an assistant first of Huygens and then of Boyle, the Frenchman Denis Papin (1647–1712), to make the next significant advance in the construction of the steam engine. Papin's awareness of the power of steam was demonstrated in his 'digester', a pressure cooker for extracting gelatin from bones, into which he introduced the safety valve. As a professor of mathematics at Marburg, he constructed a small experimental steam engine. It worked on the same principle as Worcester's but borrowed the cylinder and piston from Huygens': steam produced under a piston in a cylinder raised the piston; when the steam was allowed to condense, the pressure of the atmosphere drove the piston down; it was raised again by renewing the steam pressure. (Pl. 99a.) Papin's design was published in 1690, and he suggested that it could be used to remove water from mines. Later, improving on the Savery steam engine (see below), he was able to drive a model ship by means of paddles. His plans never were adopted, and he died a disappointed man.

Meanwhile English coal mines were getting deeper. By 1700 some were about 400 feet deep, and by 1750 600 feet or more. It remained for the Englishman Thomas Savery (1650–1715), possibly a military engineer, to describe a steam device that could be put to effective use in them. In 1698 he patented the first steam device that actually was used to pump water out of a mine, though a shallow one. By this time the need was greater than ever; in 1702 one mine operator alone was using 500 horses to provide the power necessary for pumping. That year Savery established in London the first steam-device factory in the world, and he advertised his product with a small book, *The Miner's Friend*. Unfortunately, Savery's device proved expensive to work because of great fuel consumption; its cycle of operation could be repeated only five times a minute; its suction and forcing lifts were very limited; and the joints in its boiler could not withstand high pressure.

A more practical engine was produced by Thomas Newcomen (1663–1729). It combined three scientific principles already known—the balance-beam, the vacuum produced by the condensation of steam, and the piston working in a cylinder—to produce a machine that successfully performed traction duties[7]. (Pl. 99b.) Newcomen's engine needed only low pressure to move its beam up and down. It had two great advantages over Savery's high pressure device: it could be operated from the surface, and it could lift water from depths so great that Savery's device in its stead would have had to be used in relays. In spite of its inefficiency for other purposes, it proved inexpensive enough to operate at coal mine pits, where the cost of fuel was low. By 1769 some 100 Newcomen engines were being used in northern England alone.

John Smeaton (1724–92), a noted civil engineer, improved the Newcomen engine by giving greater precision to its various parts, in particular its cylinder boring. He made a large engine that was sent in 1775 to pump out the dry docks of the naval base at Kronstadt, Russia. In Russia, as elsewhere, local engineers were grappling with the same problem. A Russian engineer, I. I. Polzunov, had, in fact, built an apparently practical steam engine, which was first put into operation in 1765 but which, Polzunov having died in 1765, no one could repair; it was abandoned when, after about two months' successful operation, it sprang a leak. A French engineer, Nicolas Cugnot, had in 1763 constructed a steam engine capable of propelling a carriage, and in 1769 he attached it as a tractor to cannon, but it was so slow and unstable that it too was abandoned. In contrast, Smeaton's engine at Kronstadt was successfully displacing two huge windmills, each some 100 feet high, which had been installed by Dutch engineers in 1719. Complaints, however, were common over the extravagant fuel consumption of whatever steam engines were kept in operation.

While repairing a small model of a Newcomen engine, James Watt (1736–1819), trained as an instrument maker, with contacts among prominent Glasgow scientists, noticed the enormous waste brought about by the alternate heating with steam and cooling with water of the cylinder at each stroke. This observation led him to invent a separate but connected chamber (or condenser) which was kept cool for rapid condensing of the steam while the cylinder, enclosed in a steam jacket, was kept hot continuously; an air-pump vacuum in the condensing chamber tapped the steam from the cylinder. In 1765 Watt built a model of his steam engine and by 1769 had solved his problem to the point where he obtained a patent. In 1774 John Wilkinson (1728–1808) invented a boring mill that could bore cylinders for Watt's engines with unprecedented accuracy.[8]

Watt and Matthew Boulton, a 'captain of industry', established, after great expense, a steam-engine business which prospered for years. Until 1800 this firm had the protection of patents, which it assiduously took out on Watt's inventions. Patents had first been granted in England by Edward III in the fourteenth century, but they led to such abuse that in 1623 Parliament enacted a Statute of Monopolies, intended, while forestalling harmful royal monopolies, to encourage inventors by giving them exclusive rights to the profits from their inventions for a specified period of time. Thus, as indicated above, the Marquis of Worcester was granted ninety-nine years of rights for his 'water commanding engine'.[9] Savery held a master patent for the use of steam in his device, nd this monopoly compelled Newcomen to enter into partnership with him. Obviously the patent could be an obstruction as well as an incentive to a fertile mind.

Although Watt's inventions opened a new future for the steam engine, it still had to be permanently installed where used, and its use was limited largely to pumping. Although power-driven machinery was thus employed for coal mines as early as the 1760s, the miner's pick and sledge had little real competition from more efficient machinery until the 1850s. At the urging of Boulton, Watt designed a rotative engine, which was the prime mover from the 1780's, well into the nineteenth century. After 1800 Watt's patents expired, but the firm long continued to enjoy a great success, owing to its superior workmanship and experience. By that time steam was turning the wheels of the textile industry.

Improvements in Textile Machinery

Textile machinery had been developed very early in the Near and Far East, particularly in the spinning and weaving of silk. The spinning wheel permitted the maker of yarn to turn with his left hand a wheel which twisted the fibres while his right drew out the thread. The spinning wheel was the first major improvement upon the simple spindle and distaff since pre-historic times. The earliest evidence of its use in the West is from the late thirteenth century. In England, where the textile industry flourished exceptionally well from that time onward, this mechanism came to be known as the 'bobbing wheel' or 'great wheel'. In the fifteenth century a treadle was added, thus leaving both hands of the operator free for handling the thread. A well-designed 'flyer', probably itself the result of a long development, is depicted in a late-fifteenth-century illustration.[10] The flyer allowed spinning and winding to be done mechanically in one process. Spinning wheels with these devices were called 'Saxony wheels'.

Mercantilist restrictions upon the importation of cotton into England from India came at the beginning of the eighteenth century at a time when, paradoxically, the demand for cotton goods was growing. Capital and inventive talent turned away from silk, wool, and linen toward the satisfaction of the demand for cotton goods. In 1738 an attempt to mechanize spinning fully was made by Lewis Paul when he introduced the technique of stretching carded cotton or wool between two sets of rollers running at different speeds, but this invention was not successful until reintroduced by Richard Arkwright (1732–92). When finally put into operation, it proved capable of producing a cotton yarn much stronger than thitherto available and suited not only for the weft (the transverse threads) but also for the warp (the longitudinal threads).

These improvements encouraged the growth of the cotton industry in the competition with other textiles such as silk, wool, and linen that had hitherto been preferred as richer or tougher. The demand for cotton yarn grew apace.

HH*

By 1764 James Hargraves introduced his 'spinning jenny', which made it possible for one spinner at one machine to operate a large number of spindles. This invention was an instantaneous success, lending itself to service in the cottage industry as well as in the nascent "factories". Then in 1768 Arkwright introduced the 'water frame', which, like Paul's machine, worked by rollers and had the advantage of being run by the cheap power of water wheels. The cotton yarn it produced was strong and coarse, an excellent substitute for the expensive linen thread still used by many weavers for warp. In 1774 Samuel Crompton invented his 'mule', which, combining features of both the jenny and the water frame, produced the finest yarn; it took its name from its hybrid origin. Steam power was not applied to spinning until 1785. The advanced techniques and the complicated sources of power required for textile machines suggested the consolidation of operations and encouraged the establishment of textile 'factories' in Britain.

The development of weaving machines lagged behind that of spinning machines. In many lands long before 1300, men and women had known some process or other of making cloth by interlacing threads (called the weft) with lengthwise threads (called the warp) The warp threads were attached to a frame and the weft was passed back and forth between them by means of a shuttle. Heddles had early been introduced in some regions to separate the warp threads and stretch them apart as needed for a particular pattern. The need had also been discovered for battering the weft so as to produce a tighter weave, and beams for stretching the threads and woven material so as to keep them tauter. Hence by the sixteenth century in western Europe the weaving loom was already a complicated mechanism, though it was still powered by hand and foot. The ribbon loom, which could weave a number of silk or satin ribbons simultaneously, was invented in Holland around 1621 and became known throughout western Europe in the ensuing century. In 1733 John Kay invented the 'flying shuttle', which was shot through the weft by pickers connected by cords with a stick held by the weaver. This relatively simple instrument enabled the weaver to work faster and to double the width of his cloth.

Kay's invention, for all its importance, created a set of mechanical difficulties, particularly in connection with the 'picker', a mechanism for throwing the shuttle—an operation which required considerable practice to do expertly. That problem took decades to solve, and it was not wholly solved until mechanical controls on a power loom replaced the hand of the weaver. Jacques Vaucanson, while working on the mechanisms of the silk industry, eliminated the need for an attendant at the draw loom by devising (1747) a more efficient apparatus of punched cards for the weaving of figured fabrics. In 1785 Edmund Cartwright was to introduce a power loom, capable of being driven by horses, water wheels, or steam engines, but his loom was not really practical. Power looms were not so rapidly developed as were power spinning machines, for several technical improvements had to be made before looms could readily be adapted to 'the factory system'. As late as 1813 England had no more than 2,400 power looms, but a hundred times that number of hand-operated ones.

The Bleaching and Dyeing Industry

The textile industry became closely allied with the chemical industry. Washing, bleaching, and dyeing, auxiliary techniques in the manufacture of textiles, were not readily adaptable to machinery. In the fourteenth and fifteenth centuries in Florence and other Italian textile centres, the finishing of rough woollen cloth—including the raising of the nap with 'teasels' (prickly seed balls), the shearing of the loose nap, and dyeing—called for advanced skill and was done mostly by hand. A special guild in Florence, the Calimala, dominated this branch of textile manufacture. Bleaching alone required lengthy processes—soaking in alkali, washing, drying, and heating—that had to be repeated several times, and dyeing remained a complex problem as of yore. Washing was somewhat quickened, however, by the use of fulling mills (known to have been used in England as early as the twelfth century), which pounded the cloth in the vats. Such a mill, run by a water wheel, consisted of a shaft fitted with cams for lifting the heavy wooden hammers that did the pounding.

By the eighteenth century the bleaching and dyeing of cloth had become a part of a rapidly growing chemical industry. (Pl. 92b.) In 1756 Francis Home suggested the use of vitriol (sulphuric acid) for bleaching. Supplies of the acid were readily available because the enterprising Roebuck, having developed a process of making sulphuric acid in lead chambers, had established a plant for that purpose near Edinburgh in 1749. Watt experimented with chlorine as a bleach and performed other chemical experiments. The chemistry involved in these processes, however, was still of a relatively crude sort. The modern sulphuric-acid plant and the manufacture of a bleach (from chlorine) that was efficient and of an alkali that was not injurious to cloth had to await the generations of Claude Louis Berthollet (1748–1822) and Joseph Louis Gay-Lussac (1778–1850). Such new bleaching techniques as were invented earlier worked for linen and cotton fabrics only; silk and wool continued to be bleached by the lengthy traditional methods.

The old methods of dyeing had depended upon the use of plant or animal colouring matter, into which fabrics were immersed. During the fourteenth and fifteenth centuries the need for alum as a fixative or mordant in this process had precipitated several conflicts among the cities of Italy for control of the alum mines, and Lorenzo de' Medici's diplomacy and military forces were called upon more than once to assure the Florentine textile manufacturers an adequate supply. Although numerous dyes were available, only a limited number of shades of any one colour could be produced. The Incas of Peru knew how to dye cloth, and though their secrets were lost, a number of new dye-stuffs reached Europe from America—cochineal and brazil-wood among them. Cornelius Drebbel (1572–1634), a Dutch inventor who also contributed to the understanding of the thermometer and attempted submarine navigation (see below), produced a brilliant scarlet in wool, afterwards exploited in Gobelins and other tapestries, by dipping in a bath of cochineal, tin, and other chemicals.

Subsequent improvement in the dyeing processs was brought about in large part by the efforts of the French government. In the seventeenth century Colbert took steps to encourage this aspect of the textile industry. He offered prizes for innovations and gave government support to eminent chemists. In the early eighteenth century the chemists Charles François Du Fay (1698–1739) and Jean Hellot (1685–1766) were among the early government-sponsored directors of the French dyeing industry. In keeping with the prevalence of mechanical theories of their day, they subscribed to a mechanical theory of dyeing—that is, that particles of dye enter the pores of the dyed material and thus change its color. Pierre Joseph Macquer (1718–84), who was director at mid-century, discovered new techniques that extended the range of dyes. He introduced Prussian blue, which penetrated the material rather than coloured the surface, as had some of the earlier dyes, and a fast red. Berthollet, who eventually succeeded as director, contributed to the new processes, advancing France's already leading role in the dye industry. Being primarily interested in chemistry, Macquer and Berthollet proposed a chemical theory of dyeing to replace the mechanical one.

The Glass Industry

Since it was dependent upon heat, the glass industry in the Middle Ages had been impeded by the competition for wood as fuel, in which shipbuilding and metallurgy outbid it. During the later Middle Ages the Venetians were the leaders of the glass industry in Europe, for the most part making art glass, but others threatened their leadership. Florence and Antwerp had famous glass works; in France the *gentilhomme verrier* was a highly respected artisan; and in the fifteenth century, according to Aeneus Sylvius,[11] Bohemia could boast the most splendid stained-glass windows of Europe. In England entrepreneurs in the glass industry were encouraged by royal grants of monopoly and employed both French Huguenot and Venetian workers.

Early in the seventeenth century the first technological monograph on the subject appeared—the Florentine Antonio Neri's *L'Arte vetraria* (1612). It eventually became the basis of similar works in other languages, stimulating a search for new means of producing glass of different colours and better quality. The Bohemian glass workers learned to add chalk to their product, making a potash-lime glass that had an extraordinary crystalline quality which lent itself well to engraving. Caspar Lehmann, court jeweller at Prague (d. 1620), seems to have originated cut-glass. The Bohemian works also produced exceptionally beautiful enamelled glass, and at the end of the seventeenth century Bohemian craftsmen had learned the process now known as 'sandwiching'—fitting two layers of glass together with a silver or gold etching on the inner one. The German chemist Johann Kunckel (1630–1703), whose edition of Neri's work long was standard, discovered how to make artificial ruby (red glass), and several other scientists, like Glauber and Boyle, also made contributions to the colouring of glass.

The shortages of tin and lead for pewter, the need of utensils for the increasing consumption of tea and coffee, and the Baroque and Rococo emphasis upon decorative art all conspired to make simple pewter, earthenware, and wooden utensils unfashionable and to favour more ornate glassware (as well as porcelain). In the seventeenth century Thomas Percivall perfected a coal furnace for the manufacture of glass, freeing the glass industry from dependence upon wood, increasing production, and lowering prices. By 1665 French glass makers had developed a method for casting glass that enabled them to make larger panes and mirrors, such as then went into the palace at Versailles. The Dutch, famous since the sixteenth century for their lenses and other scientific glassware, in the eighteenth century became especially proficient in ornamenting glass by scratching or stippling with a diamond point. By that time glass was a common material for drinking vessels and liquid containers (though second to porcelain for household uses), and it had made possible airier and lighter windows as well as large and bright mirrors for interior decoration. For fine glassware 'Bohemian crystal' fitted the taste of the Baroque period, and in the early eighteenth century took precedence over Venetian glass, but only to give way toward the close of the century to the heavier lead glass of England and Holland, which lent itself better to Neoclassic design.

Closely allied to glass was the optical industry. The power of glass to magnify had long been known, and, we have seen (Chapter XIII), some form of eyeglasses was invented around 1300. The increase in the number of books because of the development of printing made the need for reading glasses still greater. The growing demand for lenses for magnifying glasses, microscopes, and telescopes also provided an incentive to glass makers. The preparation of glass for lenses was in the hands of skilled craftsmen until the introduction of cast glass, the better understanding of its properties, and the growing demand for precise scientific instruments transformed the manufacture of optical glass into a mass-production industry.

The Porcelain Industry

Chapter XII described the amazing development of porcelain manufacture in China and the Islamic countries, and the efforts of Westerners to duplicate the vitrified translucent 'chinaware' of the Far East. As in the case of several other Eastern crafts, unverified tradition has attributed its introduction into the West to the Crusades. About 1500 Italian craftsmen in Venice were reported to have made porcelain, using a Muslim recipe, but throughout the sixteenth century Europeans were still importing most of their porcelain from China. The effective production of porcelain in the West seems to have begun about 1700.

The development of the porcelain industry in Europe was stimulated by the same shortage of tin and lead for pewter and the same need of utensils for the increasing consumption of tea and coffee as promoted the glass industry, as well as by a continuing desire of Europeans to duplicate the decorative 'chinaware' of the East. The improvement of both porcelain and cruder pottery in Europe took place through a process of trial and error, little use being made of scientific methods. By the late seventeenth century the secret of making hard-paste porcelain was discovered in Germany by Ehrenfried Walther von Tschirnaus and Johann Friedrich Böttger, and Meissen ware (the so-called 'Dresden china', first sold at Leipsig in 1710) became especially esteemed. In France Bernard Palissy (1510–89) had devised a technique for making superior pottery by moulding, modelling, and casting instead of turning, and in the late seventeenth century the Poterat family of Rouen was prominent among several that manufactured a soft-paste, low-temperature pottery, but then the secret of the German hard-paste process became known in Vienna, St Petersburg, and elsewhere, and the French royal faience works at Sèvres began to prefer it (c. 1769). In England the pottery industry made long strides forward with the technique of Josiah Wedgwood, who not only produced an artistic product but also was admired for his new methods. He was the first potter to use a steam engine to run his machines, and he was a model employer in a century that was placing strong emphasis upon humanitarianism.

The Printing Industry

The improvement of printing was associated with the improvement of metallurgy and textiles, providing a felicitous example of the interdependence of the several new industries. Printing required metal for type and for parts of the press, and the quantity-production of paper required cotton and linen. As early as the thirteenth century metal as well as wooden type was used effectively in the Far East, but the West seems to have come upon metal type independently. Not until the 1440s was metal type used effectively in Europe—by Gutenberg and others. Important steps in this process came with the development of the hand mould for casting uniform type and of the hand press (despite its complicated and cumbersome screw device, lever, and horizontal plate). By 1500 large printing establishments had grown up in Italy and in south Germany (see Chapter XI); a publishing firm at Nuremberg was big enough to employ twenty-four presses and a hundred type-setters, printers, correctors, and binders.

Meanwhile the manufacture of paper was also being improved. It has been asserted, with some justification, that the increased use of linen for clothing and bedding in the fourteenth and fifteenth centuries made possible the development of printing. Paper, then made for the most part from cotton, had been introduced into western Islamic lands from the Near East as early as the tenth century. By the twelfth century it was common in Muslim Spain but rare in western Christendom until the thirteenth, when paper-mills began to appear. When an abundance of linen rags made possible and profitable the manufacture of rag paper, a good medium became available for printing. A paper mill established near Nuremberg in 1389 probably had something to do with that city's later importance as a printing centre.

The effective printing of metal type requires an oily kind of ink. The manufacture of ink and colours was well developed in the Far East (See Chapter XII), but Chinese ink, made from lampblack, was not suitable for metal type. The pre-Columbian Amerindian used an ink, also unsuitable, made from the juice of the ink plant (*chauchi*). The West was forced to invent a special printers' ink, which was eventually perfected by mixing a varnish derived from resin, linseed oil, and soap with lampblack.

HEATING, MINING, AND METALLURGY

Architecture has been discussed as an art in Chapter XII; some of its implications for science have been mentioned in Chapter XIV; and it will be considered as a profession in Chapter XVI. A few words are called for here on the heating of houses.

Coal as Fuel

Social or domestic architecture was in some degree influenced by the Renaissance interest in Antiquity, although not on a wide scale until the seventeenth century. Various political, economic, and social forces brought about changes in domestic architecture from the sixteenth century on. The distribution of church lands by the king in England and elsewhere, the rise of commercial fortunes, and the growing power of the state brought new families of wealth or prestige and new demands for comfort and ostentation on the part of both old and new families. The Château of Versailles was a grandiose example of competitive ostentation. By the eighteenth century in England the drawings and works of Palladio had become a vogue, and stately homes in the Palladian style still dot the English countryside. Although comfort was sought in many instances—conspicuously, for example, in the Georgian house—the concept of comfort seems to have eluded some of the great houses (although the modern critic may be prone to forget that what may seem inconvenient to him in the way of sanitation and heating was of little concern to the eighteenth-century country gentleman.)

More and more, homes built after 1300 were likely to have built-in fireplaces with flues and chimneys, and they no longer had to depend upon moveable but unventilated braziers for heating. The Germanic countries also developed a relatively moveable stove made of tile resistant to heat. Not only were such stoves able to contain and radiate heat better than fireplaces but also their tiles, glazed in colour and ornamented in relief, often made them most decorative. Fireplaces, chimneys, and stoves were built in Gothic, Renaissance, and later period styles. As they became richer in decor, the demand for tiles, not only for stoves and chimney facings but also for wainscoting, grew, especially for the white tiles of Delft, with lively figures and landscapes painted in blue upon them.

Domestic heating took a new turn as the traditional fuels—wood and charcoal—became scarcer. Coal had been used by the Chinese for metallurgical processes as early as the T'ang dynasty. It had long been known in Europe also but before the sixteenth century had been less widely used as a fuel than wood, charcoal, lignite, or peat. After 1500, however, deforestation became a serious problem in several European countries because of the increased demand for wood as fuel and structural material, the expansion of arable land, the rise of sheep farming, and the lack of regard for what today would be called 'conservation'. When the English queen, Elizabeth, took measures for forest preservation, the resulting shortage of wood and charcoal necessitated the resort to coal as a fuel, and the coal industries in Northern England expanded. Coal from Newcastle in the Northumberland region ('the Black Indies') not only found its way into the English homes and manufacturing establishments but also was exported to the Continent. A few Continental countries gradually began to produce coal.

Newcastle's coal became proverbial. It was a fuel of poor quality, containing large amounts of iron sulphide, which gave an evil-smelling smoke. By the late seventeenth century the London housewife was already complaining of the soot, smoke, and stench from the city's chimneys. Studies began to appear on how best to construct chimneys to reduce this nuisance. The increase in the consumption of coal made the andiron, used for the domestic burning of wood, obsolete, and it was supplemented by the grate. Finally, in the eighteenth century iron coal-consuming stoves were invented. Two of the most successful were developed by men from the British North American colonies—Benjamin Thompson (later Count Rumford) and Franklin, both of whom lived for long periods in England and on the Continent. The new stoves symbolize the change that was taking place not only in architecture and related problems but also in technology in general. The age of coal and iron had slowly matured between the fourteenth and the eighteenth century.

Machine and Research in Metallurgy

Coal and iron have to be mined. In ancient and early medieval times mining, like agriculture, had been carried on by the lowest class of labourers. Before machinery was devised for surmounting natural obstacles like underground gases and water, the digging of ore and coal (and salt, too) was limited almost exclusively to surface or near-surface mining. Although sometimes a mining town—for example, silver-producing Kutná Hora (Kuttenberg) in Bohemia—

received special privileges because it was a source of income for the crown, until the thirteenth century miners were generally slaves or criminals, and the death rate among them was high. Until the nineteenth century most mine labour was manual—swinging pickaxes and sledge hammers, loading and pushing hand carts—with some of the lighter operations done by women and children. This work was usually performed under depressing and dangerous conditions—darkness, cold, damp, and suffocating dust, with only primitive drainage and ventilation (Pl. 102b.)

Mining, along with the processing of metals (or metallurgy), made slow progress in mechanization. As early as the thirteenth century writers mentioned the use of water power for ore-crushers and smelter-bellows, but the two ensuing centuries brought little advance in the application of machine power to crushing and smelting. The sixteenth century marked the beginning of a bonanza period in smelting as well as mining of metal, especially in Germany, Spain, and New Spain, partly explained by the increasing demand for arms, machines, and precious metals. Expanding capitalistic enterprise, evidenced in the world-wide activities and pyramiding fortunes of families such as the Fuggers, produced large-scale industries in which mechanization was inevitable. Metallurgy was one of these. About 1451 Johannsen Funcken introduced in Saxony an effective way to apply an old method of separating silver from argentiferous ore. This was the 'saiger' process of extracting silver by alloying crude copper containing silver with lead, melting off the lead (to which most of the silver would adhere), and then recovering the silver. The essentials of this process had been invented as early as the twelfth century by Venetian metallurgists. On the other hand, Bartholomé de Medina's 'patio' process was new, discovered in Mexico in 1557. It used mercury to form amalgams whereby to extract gold and silver from their ores. The efficiency of these processes further stimulated the tremendous expansion of silver and gold mining in the sixteenth century. In 1516 a strike of silver in Joachimsthal (Jáchymov) in Bohemia led to the coining of *Joachimsthalers* (eventually abbreviated to *thalers* or *dollars*), and somewhat later the Spanish piece-of-eight (dollar, 'eight bits') became common.

A similar boom was taking place in iron mining and processing. In the 1400s blast furnaces developed to the point where they created temperatures high enough to produce a good grade of cast iron. Cast-iron cannon had been produced for the dukes of Burgundy as early as the fourteenth century, and soon such cannon were competing with wrought-iron cannon. During the ensuing period old types of furnaces survived despite the greater efficiency of the newer ones. Several major types can be differentiated. The ancient Catalan furnace, which was not the most primitive of them, was still widely used in Spain and southern France, and the Scandinavian 'Osmund' furnace was better yet, but the later German 'Stückofen' was the most efficient. The Stückofen was normally a large brick or stone structure about ten feet high and from two to five feet wide, needing a stronger blast, which was provided by water-driven bellows. When built with a special tap for the slag, it became the *Blasofen*. It was capable of turning out fifty tons of iron a year, and under certain conditions could produce steel. Where rapid streams could be harnessed, water power was used for working tilt hammers, for drawing wire, and, from the sixteenth century on, for other metallurgical activities.

After the sixteenth century (until the eighteenth) progress in mining and metallurgy was comparatively slow. Most of the important innovations came in Germany, where the Stückofen grew in height, size, and hence productivity. The wooden box-bellows, invented by Hans Lobinger of Nuremberg (1550), replaced the less efficient leather ones. As the shafts of furnaces went higher and the blasts grew hotter, the reduced metal made better contact with the charcoal fuel, and a high-carbon iron, strong and more easily convertible into wrought iron and steel, resulted. The demand for iron ore, increasing as iron replaced wood and other materials in many uses, joined with the increasing demand for precious metals to spur the miners toward greater productivity on their part.

Books giving careful descriptions and critiques of industrial processes were in the sixteenth century becoming familiar. The first attempts to describe in some detail the problems of mining were made in two anonymous booklets, *Ein nützlich Bergbüchlein* (1505) and the *Probierbüchlein* (1510). Thirty years later appeared Biringuccio's classic, *De la pirotechnia*, which gave a systematic description of the metallurgical processes of his day. The classic *par excellence* on mining is Agricola's *De Re Metallica* (1556).

A physician by profession, Agricola had served as a doctor in Joachimsthal in 1527–33. He had early acquired an interest in mines, and the importance of his works in the early study of geology has already been noted (see Chapter XIV). His treatise on metals displays a practical approach to mining. It covered many fields and phases of the metallurgical process (such as methods of mining, assaying of ores, smelting, and the extraction of precious metals) and painstakingly described the tools and machines actually in use, including several types of hauling machines, waterpumps, and ventilation devices. (Pl. 102a). The author had little patience with methods that smacked of magic or fantasy. Of the resort to divining rods to find ore he protested: 'A miner ... if he is prudent and skilled ... understands that a forked stick is of no use to him, for ... there are the natural indications of the veins which he can see for himself without the help of twigs.'[10] Agricola's was a more empirical approach. He bore witness to the perils of mining, incidentally referring to stream pollution by the waste from metallurgical works and the destruction of agricultural land by undermining and charcoal burning.

Agricola's and Biringuccio's books were perhaps the best but not the only ones to give detailed information on the state of machinery in the sixteenth century. A number of the processes, tools, and machines they described, as older pictorial representations show, were not new, though sometimes they had recently been improved or, with the increasing demand, were more commonly employed. The two classics make obvious that by their time the techniques of mining and metallurgy were already well developed, at least in the search for precious metals.

When iron ore became one of the most profitable products of the mines, some old difficulties still plagued the metallurgical industry and even grew worse. One of the most troublesome was the lack of fuel. Until the invention of coke (see below), charcoal was preferred, but as the demand for charcoal grew, the supply diminished because of depletion of the forests, and its price rapidly went up. Mounting costs obliged the metallurgical industry to break into small parts. A blast-furnace that smelted pig iron might have to send its product either to small furnaces to be recast or to forgemasters to be converted into wrought iron or steel. In turn, wrought iron might go to slitting mills. Cast iron was used chiefly for household utensils and some types of ordnance, wrought iron for bolts, wire, common tools, nails, and spades, and steel for weapons, fine tools, and machine parts. Coarse pig-iron was still often produced at the beginning of the eighteenth century by blast furnaces that provided insufficient blast air. This process, as well as that of making steel, required large amounts of charcoal though less and less charcoal became available. The production of iron and steel was thus checked; in 1709 a typical blast furnace in England could produce only between five and ten tons of metal per week.

Furthermore, as mine shafts became deeper, they presented new and intricate mechanical problems. The hauling of ore underground, though it had been speeded up as early as 1530 by running four-wheeled cars on rails, was still cumbersome. Hoisting was done with gear operated by horse whims, or drums around which a rope was wound; even where animal power replaced human power, this was an awkward and sometimes a dangerous procedure. In 1627 gunpowder was used in the Schemnitz mines to supplement the old method of cracking rock—heating with fire and dousing with cold water—but gunpowder was not adopted in England to blast coal until 1713. The pumping of subsoil water from the mines presented another obstacle until, as already described, the development of steam-driven pumps helped to surmount it. In the early, shallow mines, ventilation had not been a crucial problem; a shaft cut in two by a vertical division was considered sufficient to permit air to pass down one side and up the other. As the mines became deeper, however, the problem of methane gas or 'fire-damp' became more pressing, and better ways of inducing circulation of air had to be found. (Pl. 102b.) The problem of illumination complicated that of ventilation, for the gases readily exploded when they came into contact with naked flame. That danger was not to be eliminated until 1815, when Humphry Davy and George Stephenson invented reliable safety-lamps. Between the close of the sixteenth and the beginning of the eighteenth century few improvements came to mining methods.

Then a veritable revolution in mining and metallurgy took place. It came as a result of at least three considerations: (1) the increase in demand for iron, (2) the introduction of steam power to hoisting and pumping in the mines, and (3) a need for high-quality fuel in metallurgy. A process of making coke by heating coal and thus driving off its volatile contents was discovered in the seventeenth century but was made economically feasible by Abraham Darby (1677–1717) and his family only in the eighteenth. Coke relieved the foundries of dependence on charcoal, and foundries and furnaces, which had tended to follow the forests, were now located near coal fields and ore deposits. The production of cast iron mounted at an amazing rate, and many objects that previously had been made from wrought iron were now made from cast iron. At first coke was used only in making pig or cast iron. But several ironmasters soon recognized that coke could be used in converting pig iron into wrought iron, and in 1784 Henry Cort was to develop the 'puddling' process—agitating the pig iron with iron poles in a reverberatory furnace until, as the carbon and other impurities burned away, it became a mass of wrought iron. The wrought iron was then put through grooved rollers that produced a finer wrought iron. Rollers had been used in Germany and Sweden (by Polhem, for example) previous to this time, but Cort's process revolutionized the production of malleable iron, and he deserves the credit of fathering the modern rolling mill.[13] The use of coke in place of charcoal as the fuel for producing pig iron and wrought iron brought a rise in the demand for coal and in the supply of cast iron and malleable iron. In 1788 61,000 tons of pig iron were produced in England.

Quality steel had been produced in India and imported by Arabs and Persians into Europe since the early Middle Ages. Europe made its own steel but only in small quantities, and it was expensive. In England a process of making steel known as 'cementation' was patented in the seventeenth century. It consisted of enclosing bars of iron together with some charcoal inside sealed pots, thus protecting the contents, when heated in a furnace, from contamination by sulphur and other volatile ingredients of the furnace fuel. The metal produced by this process was more highly carburized outside than inside, and it had to be rendered homogeneous by forging. The resultant product, known as 'shear steel', was good for cutlery but not hard enough to produce fine products like watch springs. Réaumur, one of the first scientists to deliberately apply his knowledge to industry, carefully examined the structural and other differences between iron and steel, showing that steel was something other than refined iron. He published his findings in 1722 in *L'art de convertir le fer forgé en acier*, which was subsequently translated into English and German. It lifted the process of steel manufacture from trial-and-error to an experimental level, discussing the parts played by 'sulphurs and salts' (i.e. modern carbon) and by cooling in determining the qualities of iron and steel. If his explanations were often couched in Cartesian mechanistic terms, he nevertheless explained metallic fracture in a way that was not to be bettered for well over a hundred years. Cast steel was known long before the 1740s, but then a watchmaker named Benjamin Huntsman (1704–76) succeeded in making of it the kind of steel he wanted for a successful business in high-grade watches. He found that steel could be hardened by placing it (or its components, malleable iron and charcoal) in closed crucibles inside coke furnaces; the coke provided a higher temperature for a longer period of time than coal could provide. After some hesitation because the resulting steel seemed too hard, the steel makers of Sheffield copied Huntsman's methods, making *Sheffield* almost synonymous in English with *steel*.

Before 1775 the outstanding discoverer of new chemicals was Scheele. Several new metals were among the elements and compounds discovered or put into common use for the first time by him and his contemporaries. Zinc had been known since the time of Agricola, but not until the eighteenth century were the proper fuels, retorts, and furnaces available for its extraction; the first zinc smelters were built in Germany and the Low Countries. Cobalt was discovered in 1733, platinum in 1735 (in Colombia), nickel in 1751 (Saxony becoming the centre of its production), and manganese in 1774.

The intimate relationship of coal, iron, and steam, the inventiveness of certain Englishmen, the astonishing number of skilled mechanics in England, the abundance of England's natural resources such as coal and iron, and the availability of English capital seeking investment were among the factors of the complex beginnings of the 'Industrial Revolution'. England's lead in industrial innovation did much to bring about its political predominance in the early nineteenth century. Around 1775, however, France and Belgium were also well advanced industrially and, according to one school of thought, but for the succeeding political turmoils those countries might not have fallen behind in the development of the factory system.

TRANSPORT AND NAVIGATION

Roads, Bridges, and Transportation by Land

After the decline of the Roman Empire little new highway construction was undertaken in western Europe for over 1,000 years. Outside of the Roman system (as in Germany) dirt roads were common, but they were often reinforced with fascines and timber or stones and gravel. Only few local roads of medieval times were paved, but those few seem to have been something more than 'mud tracks', as modern writers often think. Some of the ancient Roman roads served medieval man best, to be sure, not as means of communication but as quarries for neighbouring villages and cities. Nevertheless, those that were frequently used were kept passable by assiduous attention to their surfaces, side drainage, and bridges, and road maps of the late Middle Ages afford ample evidence that the arterial highways of the old Roman Empire were still well travelled.

Upkeep of roads, old or new, was a divided responsibility. Kings' high-ways were generally well tended, not only for military purposes but also as major avenues to seaports and markets. Since easy access meant commercial advantage, important urban centres also sometimes paved strategic roads (with cobble stones or slabs), levying special taxes for the purpose. For instance, a stretch of highway leading via Senlis to Paris was repaired by the practical citizens of Ghent in 1332. In England local parishes traditionally had the obligation to maintain roads; repairs were consequently haphazard until, in the eighteenth century, several turnpike acts enabled road keepers to levy tolls on travellers, thus relieving local parishes of the financial burden. In France and most other continental countries some form of *corvée* was resorted to, though not always successfully, as a means of guaranteeing road maintenance. In addition, certain religious organizations were renowned for building and maintaining bridges and causeways such as that at Glastonbury and the celebrated Holland causeway.

During the fourteenth, fifteenth, and sixteenth centuries transport in the West was a fairly well organized and highly competitive business. Whereas the Romans had moved themselves and their goods on horseback, medieval men used carts. Pack animals—even pack-humans (porters)—were used occasionally for short local trips or over difficult terrain, but for heavy long-distance haulage the two-wheeled cart (*bronnette*) and, more often, the four-wheeled wagon (*charrette*) were standard. 'Cart brokers' in large centres put merchants in touch with carters' organizations. In the fourteenth century, Alsatians and Lorrainers monopolized the transport of wool from the Low Countries to Switzerland, while the Béarnese controlled the route from Toulouse to the Atlantic ports. In some localities 'colliers' hauled small loads by neck harnesses (*ad collum*) in 'barrows' or small carts. Most trips, especially in dangerous or bandit-ridden territory, were made in slow convoys, for the safety of the highways was precarious in days when local police were either rare or unknown and when accommodations for travellers were notoriously limited and inconvenient. Occasionally, however, a special agent could make a fast solo trip; on one such the distance from Venice to Florence was covered in four days. As competition increased and com-mercial routes shifted, carters waged price wars, and merchants organized to drive sharp bargains with them. After the St Gothard route was opened by bridging the gorges of Schötten (1237), French carters and boatmen on the older routes had to lower their rates to compete with the newer one. In 1318 a Florentine textile concern paid less per mile for land transport from Paris to Marseilles than for water transport from Marseilles to Pisa. The Medici with their many branch establishments made arrangements all along the routes from Italy to the northern centres, assuring themselves of safe transport, reasonable tolls, good markets, and other conveniences.

One of the difficulties that impeded the building of new roads was the high cost. Expenses, to be sure, could be absorbed by levying tolls on travellers, but such levies were so frequent that they formed an added burden to already difficult, expensive, and slow communication, and each new levy ran the risk of killing the gold-laying goose. With the growth of centralized administration, royal governments became more and more interested in a good, centralized system of communication and transport. King Louis XI of France repaired some main roads and in 1464 reinstituted the ancient system of postal couriers. In the early sixteenth century the Holy Roman emperor granted Franz von Taxis authority to organize a postal system for the Empire, thus starting the Taxis family's rise to centuries of wealth and fame, but the Imperial postal system grew with but little significant road building. Thereafter couriers, postal services, and (later) coach service became more common and, with the London penny post (1680), cheaper.

The oldest known technical document on road-building is a police ordinance (1554) of Julich–Berg regulating the repair of roads with stones, timber, and faggots found beside them, but the French were the first modern nation to make a systematic study of road building. As early as 1622 Nicolas Bergier published his *Histoire des grands chemins de l'Empire romain*. Dedicating it to his king, he expressed the hope that work on the roads would bring employment to the poor and profit to the kingdom both in war and in peace. The book caused much discussion, but the funds needed to carry out its suggestions were not provided until Louis XIV's solicitous minister Colbert made more stalwart efforts to encourage road construction. In 1693 Hubert Gautier published his *Traité de la construction des chemins*, which advocated the building of roads on foundations of large stones rammed down on end. In 1716 the French created the first body of civil engineers maintained by a European government, the Corps des Ingénieurs des Ponts et Chaussées (see Chapter XVI). Under the direction of Pierre Trésaguet (1716–94) French engineers built the finest roads in Europe, on principles far superior to those of Gautier. By 1776 France already had some 12,000 miles of finished roads, with a comparable mileage under construction or repair, and French engineers that year planned a system of national highways. (Pl. 100.)

In England road building followed a somewhat different pattern. At first the roads, as in France, were primarily a royal responsibility, and the benevolent despotism of the Tudor monarchs brought the first significant road improvements to England; in 1555 Queen Mary appointed inspectors of roads, each answerable for designated portions of the roads. By 1663, however, a Turnpike Act permitted the collection of tolls, and thereafter English roads were often the enterprise of privately owned turnpike companies operating under a government franchise. English road builders were far more empirical than their French counterparts. The blind engineer John Metcalf (1717–1810) understood that well-drained road foundations made for good permanent highways. His younger contemporaries Thomas Telford (1757–1834) and John McAdam (1756–1836) improved upon his methods after 1775. As long as horses and wagons or coaches were the prevalent mode of transport, their type of road (crushed stone over a layer of stone chips bound with sand) served well.

Improvement of highways inevitably raised the problem of bridge construction. The usual materials for bridge building were wood and stone. Bridge builders who preferred wood adopted some of the sixteenth-century principles of Palladio. One of the problems that the bridge engineer confronted was that bridges obstructed the waterways. The French engineer Jean Rodolphe Perronet (1708–94), who built some of the outstanding stone bridges of his time, was able to reduce the amount of waterway obstructed by his piers. Whereas a Roman bridge of AD 14 at Rimini blocked about 65 per cent of the waterway and the Pont Neuf in Paris (1607) about 50 per cent, Perronet's Pont de la Concorde (1787) in Paris blocked only 35 per cent. The increasing knowledge of the strength of materials (see Chapter XIV) did much to aid construction engineers with their problems. Although French engineering theory was far ahead of English in the eighteenth century, a notable contribution to bridge construction was made in London with the completion of old Westminster Bridge by Charles Dangeau de Labelye (1705 ?–81), a Swiss engineer. Using watertight wooden caissons as cofferdams, he was able to place the bridge piers inside a watertight structure. In England, too, cast iron was introduced as material for bridges when another Abraham Darby (1750–91) and John Wilkinson (1728–1808) in 1779 built the Coalbrookdale Ironbridge over the Severn River, thus marking the start of a new era in bridge-building. (Pl. 101.)

Despite the sometimes cooperative efforts of merchants, towns, feudal lords, and benevolent governments and despite the ingenuity of road and bridge builders, land transportation remained slow and difficult. In the sixteenth century a lone mail courier might travel under favourable conditions fifty miles a day, but the ordinary traveller in a convoy might feel lucky to make fifteen, and the coaches of the eighteenth century did only a little better. Roads grew more and more congested as the population grew. With notable exceptions, they were seldom better than mire holes in the winter and dust-heaps in the summer, unless some attempt had been made to pave them with cobble-stones or other surfacings. Good or bad, the roads had to serve not only for human travel but also for herding animals and fowl to market. The Smithfield market in England, at least partly because of the improvement in roads, within a fifty-year period raised its sales from 80,000 head of cattle to some 130,000, and in the same period the number of sheep sold rose from 640,000 to almost a million.

The horse remained the chief and fastest means of transportation in Europe until the nineteenth century, although oxen, mules, donkeys, and reindeer were also used as draft animals; in Asia or Africa water buffalo, elephants, or camels were common work animals; and in the Americas until the horse was introduced by Europeans, dogs and llamas pulled the loads that men and women did not themselves carry. Horse-drawn wagons were usually uncomfortable and were hard on highways constructed for lighter vehicles. Pack-horse convoys remained common in Europe even in the seventeenth and eighteenth century, when wheeled conveyances became familiar. By the eighteenth century horse express routes for perishable foods were well established in England; for example, some 320 horses daily passed through Tonbridge laden with fish for the London market.

To the cartwrights of the Hungarian village Kocs goes the honour of devising a practical passenger vehicle, known in Hungarian as the *kocsi* (French *coche*, German *Kutsche*, English *coach*). Only slowly in the fifteenth and sixteenth centuries did they become known in France, Germany, England and elsewhere, but in 1634 over 3,400 coaches covered the English routes. At first, they provided only slightly greater comfort, since their bodies were slung in frames by leather straps rather than buoyed by springs. Not until 1670 were steel springs introduced into coaches, and not until 1750 were fast, sprung stagecoaches in general use in England. With the better paving of roads in the latter part of the eighteenth century, the era of the stagecoach reached its crest.

Various experiments were tried with steam as a means of power for four-wheeled vehicles. The French engineer Cugnot's steam-carriage, mentioned above, moved only around $2\frac{1}{2}$ miles per hour, and it proved unsteady and dangerous besides. In England William Murdock (1754–1839) constructed a very small model but abandoned the project upon instructions from Watt, his employer. The successful solution of the problem had to await Trevithick's steam locomotive (1801).

Ships, Lighthouses, Canals and Transportation by Water

Transportation by water was generally much cheaper than transportation by land, and most heavy goods still went by water wherever seas, lakes, rivers, or canals were available. Several cathedrals and castles in southern and eastern England were built of stone brought from Normandy, since it could be more cheaply ferried across the Channel than dragged from other parts of England, and timber shipped from Scandinavia cost less in English coastal regions than timber carted from the English hinterland. Until the fifteen and sixteenth centuries most sea transport was coastwise; hence, the prevalence of *portolani*. If cargoes had to be shifted to inland waters and canals, they were transferred to barges, sometimes even a double transfer being required in shallow harbours, where lighters were used to carry goods from ship to barge. Huge cranes—sometimes portrayed in contemporary paintings[14]—facilitated this work at ports and trans-shipping points. River traffic was more important to eastern Europe with its longer and slower rivers than to western Europe. The vast river systems of America and Asia provided the most frequented avenues of transport, travel, and communication for European explorers and settlers, who built their first rude communities on the banks of American and Siberian rivers, which furnished them also with water, fish, drainage, power, and recreation. In eastern Europe timber was floated down river, and other bulky goods were freighted on river rafts, a method of transportation that was not practicable on most western rivers, which flowed too rapidly. Tolls multiplied—notably in Germany—to the point where some rivers were deserted by merchants. In northern France and the Netherlands, however, internal waterways were well travelled. Barges, towed by men or draft animals, provided perhaps the cheapest form of transportation, and they handled much of the heavy short-haul goods.

Seafaring ships of the West were of two distinct types before the seventeenth century—the oared galley and the sailing vessel. (Pl. 106a.) In the Mediterranean, until about 1500 the galley with one bank of oars was supreme both as man-of-war and as merchant ship. Oars were steadily increased in length, even to fifty feet. Reaching inboard for one-third of their length, they were manipulated by as many as seven men each. The steering oar early gave way to the rudder, and man power was supplemented by masts and sails. The Venetians and the Genoese used huge galleys equipped with both oars and sails, called galleasses, and slow freighters (naves or carracks) of as much as sixteen-hundred tons' burden. In 1571, at the Battle of Lepanto, the Christian armada included six galleasses and over two hundred galleys, to say nothing of smaller auxiliary craft. Lepanto was the last significant naval battle in which the galley was considered the decisive vessel, although it continued to be used for about two centuries longer.

Meanwhile the sailing vessel had come into its own, especially on the Atlantic. The stern-post rudder, which permitted more effective steering, had probably been known to the Chinese in the eighth century, to the Byzantines in the twelfth, and in Poland in the thirteenth. It was fully developed in fourteenth-century Byzantine vessels. The fleet which the English king Henry V assembled for the invasion of France in 1413 included cogs, carracks, barges, and balingers, mostly of about five hundred tons' burden, the best known being the blunt, broad, slow-going cogs of north-western Europe. Meanwhile the Portuguese and the Spanish were developing the caravel, a small, broad, high-pooped, lateen-sailed vessel for ocean travel. This was the type of ship used by Vasco de Gama and Columbus. Columbus' Santa Maria was of only a little over two hundred tons. (Pl. 106b.) By this time rigging had improved; three-masted vessels with bowsprits were common from the fifteenth century on, and with two masts square-rigged and one lateen rigged, navigators could beat 'up the wind'. Since the winds over the Atlantic rarely die down completely (except in the equatorial doldrums), nations with Atlantic outlets were able to abandon the clumsy oar-driven galley in favour of more manoeuvrable sailing vessels. The Great Armada (1588), with only four galleasses and four galleys but around one hundred and thirty sailing vessels (the largest of 1,300 tons), exemplifies the replacement of the galley by the Atlantic type of shipping.

Improved navigational methods and larger freighters permitted freer travel on the open ocean, and longer sailings eliminated many trans-shipments. In addition to the well-known all-water route between the North Sea and Venice or Genoa via Gibraltar, the Dutch and the Germans were able to maintain a continuous sea-route between the Netherlands and the Baltic ports. The explorations of the fifteenth and sixteenth centuries gave still another impetus to water transportation. Not only did the growing commerce with the nascent colonies and the Far East augment the demands on shipping but also intra-European communications grew because of increased traffic in exotic products. Changes in social and economic conditions accelerated in the sixteenth century to a degree that induces some historians to call it a period of 'commercial revolution' (see Chapter I), due in part to the opening of new markets, the vogue of new commodities, the consumption of larger quantities of old ones, and the importation of precious metals from the New World. (Pl. 107a, b.)

In the seventeenth century, though the Dutch had to import most of their shipbuilding materials, they were perhaps the leading shipbuilders and marine carriers of Europe. Pieter J. Livorn invented (1595) a type of vessel (called in Dutch the *fluitschip* and in English the flute) of slender design, light weight, and shallow draft that was faster and cheaper to build and to run than earlier types. The flute was especially constructed to carry the bulk goods—wine, salt, grain, timber, etc.—that were the staples of northern commerce. The Dutch fishing vessels (*busses*) had long excelled in the North Sea fisheries, Dutch broad and flat-bottomed flyboats carried much of Europe's cabotage, and Dutch whalers dominated the whale oil market. (Pl. 106c.) A Dutch device known as the 'ship's camel' lifted heavy vessels over sandbars and through shallow canals. And Drebbel built a submarine that in 1620 was rowed below the surface of the Thames for several hours. The superiority of Holland's shipping was one of the major reasons for that little country's successes in the trade of the North and Baltic Seas and in the race for colonial empire against the Portuguese, Spanish, and English.

Several improvements in navigation and sailor's diet facilitated lengthy voyages for Dutch and other European crews. To the magnetic compass, known to navigators for several centuries, was added the telescope, which in the seventeenth century was quickly adapted to navigation, and finally, in the eighteenth century the ship's chronometer. The planting of vegetable gardens at ports of call (see below) helped to counteract the heavy toll of scurvy.

Larger ships made imperative larger docks and jetties, which began to appear in the early eighteenth century. Breakwaters were needed to divert rapid currents and tides at river mouths and to diminish the force of ocean waves in harbours, but the breakwaters that were built sometimes speedily collapsed, until, in the early nineteenth century, steam-power facilitated the handling and transporting of heavy stone blocks. Wet docks, which were of great aid in estuaries with a wide range of tide, were constructed in the seventeenth century. The engineering of these docks was relatively simple: great basins, excavated by pick and shovel, were connected with the tideway by a short canal with lock gates. In 1660 the Surrey Docks were begun in England, and a private dock at Blackwall was built to accommodate East India shipping. A wet dock was completed at Le Havre in 1667, and in the first quarter of the eighteenth century Liverpool began construction of another. (Pl. 103a).

The placement of warning lights for coastal and sea shipping had long been haphazard. The Romans had built beacon towers, but early medieval beacons had been mere piles of burning wood. By the fourteenth century elevated pitch pots and coal braziers began to take the place of wood fires. The entrance of the Gironde River had been marked by a lighthouse since the Moors had first erected one; the Black Prince built another about 1370; a third was begun in 1584, and that one was increased in height in 1727 to 186½ feet. In England the Guild of the Most Glorious and Undividable Trinity, founded in 1515 mainly to pray for those in peril at sea, broadened its functions, particularly after the Reformation, and the brethren of its Trinity House, among other things, erected beacon lights. A light might also be erected by a private person as a business venture, but he had to get permission from Trinity House if he wished to collect a toll from passing ships. The Eddystone Light on the dangerous rocks outside Plymouth Harbour was destroyed and reconstructed several times before John Smeaton in 1759 built an enduring structure.

Internal waterways (i.e. rivers and canals) carried a large share of the increased activity in transportation. Substantial advances were made during our period in controlling floods, changing the courses of rivers, and dredging their bottoms. Many rivers were connected by canals. Canals had been constructed in Holland and Italy in late medieval times primarily for drainage, but they also served barges and small boats. Whether the lock was first used in the West in one or the other of these two countries is debatable, but by the eighteenth century it was familiar nearly everywhere in Europe. (Pl. 103b.) In France, under Henry IV's minister, Sully, all navigable rivers were declared part of the royal domain, and five additional rivers were made navigable—the Vesle, the Vienne, the Eure, the Ourcq, and the Vilaine. Louis XIV's minister Colbert furthered this policy. His dream to connect the Atlantic and the Mediterranean by canals and rivers, avoiding the long and hazardous trip via Gibraltar, was realized in 1681 with the opening of the Languedoc Canal (148 miles long, 119 locks) connecting the Rhône and the Garonne. This project required a huge dam, a long tunnel, and, to avoid additional locks, several aqueducts. It was the engineering marvel of its age. In northern Europe during the seventeenth century Gustavus Adolphus of Sweden, the Great Elector of Brandenburg, and Peter the Great of Russia also encouraged the construction of canals.

In Britain waterways were developed not by the government but by private investors, and large-scale canal building was delayed until the eighteenth century. Earlier, however, Parliament had encouraged the improvement of rivers, and in the seventeenth century locks were built on the Thames between London and Oxford. The first ambitious canal project in the British Isles was the Newry Canal in northern Ireland, completed in 1742 by Thomas Steers, a Liverpool dock engineer. In the 1750s another Liverpool dock engineer, Henry Berry, built the Sankey Canal to carry cargoes from the Lancashire coalfields and salt workings to the turnpikes toward Liverpool, but it was only about ten miles long. Both Steers' and Berry's canals were, besides, deadwater navigations. The first serious attempt to build a lengthy canal in England in other than relatively flat country, where ordinary locks would not do, was financed by the Duke of Bridgewater (1736–1803) and engineered by James Brindley (1716–72). In the 1760s Brindley, a self-trained engineer, began construction of a series of canals connecting Bridge-water's coal pits with the open sea. The earliest of these canals caused great controversy because Brindley abandoned the use of locks, preferring a constant water level, which required the building of an aqueduct some ninety-nine feet high over the Irwell. It is doubtful whether he knew that similar feats had been successfully accomplished in building the Languedoc Canal in France about a hundred years earlier. After Brindley completed his design, England became laced with canals, some of which still serve well.

Attempts were made in the eighteenth century, particularly after Watt's engine provided rotary motion, to construct ships powered by steam. The major problem was how to construct an engine big enough to furnish the requisite power but small enough to leave room for passengers, cargo, and fuel. Papin in 1707 proposed to demonstrate the feasibility of pulling barges by means of steam-driven towboats, but he never obtained permission to do so. In the 1760s and 1770s William Henry of Pennsylvania and Jacques Perier and the Marquis de Jouffroy of France tried out steam-driven ships without practicable results. The problem was to be partly solved only in 1790, when John Fitch put the finishing touches on a vessel 60 feet long that made a speed of 8 miles per hour and was used for several thousand miles of commercial service but left so little space for passengers and cargo that it was not a financial success. Not until the early nineteenth century did a steam-powered vessel prove commercially profitable.

Experiments with Air Transportation

Fascinated by the idea of transportation through the air, would-be aeronauts of various ages have attached birdlike wings to their arms and boldly glided or flapped from great heights, generally with tragic results. Leonardo da Vinci speculated about machines that would fly and carry men, but his ideas were not known to his contemporaries, and until the seventeenth century human flight was generally conceived as feasible, if at all, only by the imitation of birds. In the seventeenth century Hooke experimented with models of flying machines, as did also Borelli. These costly experiments convincingly demonstrated that neither the human arm nor the machine of that day could support the human body in the air.

In the seventeenth century a more fruitful prospect for inventive ingenuity—the lighter-than-air craft—opened up. Von Guericke's new air-pump made it possible to suck air out of a container and create an artificial vacuum, and in 1670 the Jesuit Francesco de Lana Terzi suggested that several thin-copper spheres if completely evacuated might be able to lift a small cart; Hooke, Borelli, and Leibniz pointed out, however, that these thin and empty globes would collapse under the pressure of the external air. In 1755 Joseph Galien published *L'art de naviguer dans les airs*, in which he suggested that men could be carried aloft in a high ship filled with enough air from the upper regions to withstand external air pressure. In 1766 Cavendish demonstrated the low density of hydrogen (or 'inflammable air', as he called it), but human flight was not to be achieved until the 1780s—first by 'hot air balloons' and only later, by globes filled with 'inflammable air'.

THE TECHNOLOGY OF WARFARE

Before the Hundred Years' War the armies of western Europe had relied heavily on the crossbow, despite ecclesiastical prohibitions against it because of its lethal power. During the Crusades it had proved itself in competition with the Muslim horse archers, and by the end of the thirteenth century it was a favourite infantry weapon of the Italians. Mercenary crossbowmen were in great demand, as was evidenced by their presence in the French army at the Battle of Crécy (1346).

The longbow, however, proved a better weapon. Having probably originated in eleventh-century Wales, it had done well in several thirteenth-century battles of the English against the Scots, and it achieved decisive results against the French in the Hundred Years' War. From the naval battle of Sluys (1340), during which bowmen rained arrows on the French from the rigging and decks of the English ships, through the land battles of Crécy, Poitiers, and Agincourt, and until the very end of the sixteenth century, the longbow was the principal weapon of English armies. Though its impact was probably less overwhelming than the crossbow's, it was deadly at a hundred yards and when drawn by a trained archer could reach to about three hundred; it could be shot more speedily than a crossbow, required less training, being lighter and less complicated, and was wieldy at closer quarters. At the climax of the Hundred Years' War, over half of the English infantrymen were longbowmen, the remainder being armed with bills (spears with a scythed cutting head and spikes at the side and top). Longbowmen completely outclassed crossbowmen, who in consequence were not employed in large numbers in Continental armies after the fifteenth century. In the next century the longbow, in turn, gave way, though only slowly, to small firearms.

Other close-quarter weapons were also rendered obsolete about the same time. Some were variations of the spear, like the bills just described. Somewhat similar to halberds, they were used by both infantry and cavalry during the fourteenth and fifteenth centuries. They were superseded by the pike. The length of the pikestaff, extended by the Swiss to 20 feet, made the pike a formidable weapon, which until the sixteenth century enjoyed supremacy. It could be used to defend a square against cavalry or to attack dismounted men.

Vehicular weapons were not unknown. Tanks and other curiously modern devices were sketched by Da Vinci, but most of these sketches were of greater biographical interest to us than of practical military importance to his contemporaries. Of real effect in the fifteenth century were the wagon stockades—mobile fortresses—employed with tactical success by the Hussite armies.

The origin of gunpowder is still somewhat of a mystery. Its employment as an explosive for military purposes progressed in a roughly parallel fashion in different parts of the world. Probably the first use of it in warfare came, at least in the West, at the time of the triumph of the longbow in Europe. Sometime between 1319 and 1346, and somewhere between Andalusia and Scotland or between Italy and England firearms were employed for the first time in western Europe. An Oxford manuscript dated 1327 pictures a pot-bellied cannon (*pot de fer*) being touched off. In 1345 Edward III ordered the preparation of guns and ammunition for his invasion of France. A document at Tournai in Belgium records the testing of a cannon in 1346, during which a two-pound projectile, after penetrating the wall of a house, killed a man. According to Froissart, cannon were used that year at Crécy and later in the siege of Calais. In the same century the Chinese (who had long been familiar with pyrotechnics) also began to employ gunpowder in warfare. Russian artillery, too, made its first appearance in the second half of the fourteenth century. The various Islamic peoples seem to have learned the use of firearms about the same time.

The arms race was now on. England, France, the Netherlands, northern Italy (with its famous 'Lombards'), the Turks, and others all vied with one another in the production of bigger and better guns. Of the earliest extant cannon, the largest—'Mad Meg' at Ghent—is a little over 16 feet in length and 25 inches in calibre. Fourteenth-century cannon were few, inaccurate, and hard to fire. Their more telling effect in the ensuing centuries was largely an outcome of the improvements in metallurgy and gunpowder. Better casting explains how the English could produce four hundred cannon for the siege of St Malo (1378). Four years later a Londoner turned out seventy-three cast-iron guns, one of them multibarrelled. 'Greek fire', probably invented in the seventh-century Byzantine Empire, was highly effective in the defence of Constantinople in the 1450s; it was a liquid or paste (sometimes considered an ancestor of gunpowder) which broke into flame on contact with water. For all that, the city fell in 1453, doomed in large part by the Turks' battering of its old fortifications with the new cannon.

The western Europeans perhaps lagged in adopting gunpowder, but once started, they took the lead. Military theory changed with the new weapons. In the early fourteenth century the military theories of Marino Sanudo of Venice and Guido da Vigevano (born in Pavia, c. 1280), based on Italian tactics of an era before explosives were common, had been considered standard; in the late fourteenth century they began to yield precedence to treatises concerning the manufacture and use of firearms—as well as other types of war-machines. Among the authors of later works were Konrad Keyser of Franconia, Giovanni da Fontana of Padua, and several anonymous Germans. The increasing use of firearms in the fifteenth and sixteenth centuries brought new military treatises, often with elaborate illustrations concerning cannon and small arms, fortifications, and siege engines.

Firearms meanwhile grew more varied. In the fifteenth century the hand grenade became a standard military weapon, and special battalions of 'grenadiers' were trained to throw bombs. The most noteworthy innovation of the century in weapons was an ancestor of the modern rifle, which began as the German *Hackenbüchse* in the early fifteenth century and became the French *harquebus* or *arquebus*. It was a hand gun—something in appearance like the modern bazooka. At first too awkward and ineffective to have significant tactical value, the arquebus progressively improved until during the sixteenth-century wars of the French and the Spanish it became an effective weapon. Italy was the proving ground for early modern warfare. Though its own armies had lost their reputation (largely because the Italian city-state no longer produced a warlike officer class), Italy remained the place to go for study and practice of strategy, tactics, and fortification. There the Spanish worked out their tactics of infantry fire power.

The heavier, longer (six feet or over), more deadly, and farther reaching musket had meanwhile come into use. The early musket needed two men and a support stuck in the ground for proper manipulation and aiming, but it gradually grew shorter and more wieldy, and in the hands of an expert gunner it could reach a target at five hundred yards—two hundred beyond the range of the longbow. By the 1550s the musketeer had become the pride, and the source of the superiority, of the Spanish army. Even though a good archer could fire several arrows in the time it took to load a musket and the English continued to use longbowmen until the seventeenth century, the English army, and other armies still more rapidly, were forced to follow suit. The process was speeded up when the dangerous and inefficient match-lock, an attachment for priming and firing both arquebus and musket, began (at the opening of the sixteenth century) to yield to the more satisfactory wheel-lock.

The effectiveness of small arms and cannon, though modest by modern standards, thereafter increased steadily. Rifling was introduced in 1520 (though not generally before the end of the eighteenth century), and improved hand-grenades in 1536. The pistol was invented in Spain about 1540, and the wheel-lock pistol in 1543. Paper cartridges came in 1560, hot shells in 1575, fixed cartridges in 1590, rifled pistols in 1592, and the percussion fuse in 1596. The bayonet, which seems to have originated as a dagger at Bayonne in the fifteenth century, became, when attached to a wooden haft and plugged into the muzzle of a musket, a common battle weapon in the seventeenth, and early in the eighteenth Vauban made it a standard battle weapon. By that time the rifled, flintlock fusil, lighter (about ten pounds in weight), simpler, and more wieldly than the musket, rendered the fusilier the best-armed soldier. By the close of the War of the Spanish Succession, therefore, foot soldiers were mostly armed with flintlock and bayonet, regardless of the traditional names their regiments might bear.

No longer was cavalry the most important branch of the military forces. Infantry, particularly when armed with gun and bayonet, had made the armoured knight an anachronism, and with him the concept of chivalry also had lost prestige. Cervantes called artillery a 'devilish invention' that enabled a 'base cowardly hand to take the life of the bravest gentleman'. As early as the fifteenth century the Swiss learned to keep mounted men at a distance by forming dense masses defended by their long pikes. In the wars of the French and Spanish at the beginning of the next century, infantry was the decisive force in battle, especially if protected by arquebusiers, and Spain's 'Great Captain' Gonzalo Fernández de Cordoba (1453–1515) reorganized his army so as to make the infantry more manoeuvrable; lighter armed, with short swords or lances and bucklers, they were able to outmanœuvre the Swiss mercenary pikemen in his enemies' ranks. As firearms improved and more and more men were armed with them, they relegated suits of armour to the status of ornamental apparel for state occasions.

Feudal castles likewise became ornamental rather than defensive as mobile cannon made unfortified strongholds less tenable. Skilful use of artillery empowered the French to drive the English out of their country in the 1450s and later to win victories against the Spanish in Italy; it aided Gustavus Adolphus, as an offensive weapon, to break up Imperialist squares in the 1630s; and it enabled Marshal de Saxe, as a defensive weapon, to disrupt enemy charges in the 1740s.

New theories of fortification were called for, and, we have seen, Vauban took a prominent part in answering the call. Multiple fortresses replaced castles. A fortress was protected not so much by moats, thick walls, and bastions (though these, too, were in evidence) as by outer gun emplacements. As artillery became a more and more decisive factor of victory in battle, so did the engineer who knew how to build roads for the transport of cannon and breastworks for defence of a fortified garrison or as a vantage for attack upon it. Marksmanship, though sharpshooting remained rare indeed, became more accurate as Leonardo da Vinci (who, however, did not publish his findings), Tartaglia, and later scientists (see Chapter XIV) entered the military field with studies of ballistics, culminating for our period in Benjamin Robin's *New Principles of Gunnery* (1742; German translation by Euler, 1745). Frederick the Great's introduction of horse-drawn cannon was the last major artillery innovation before General Jean Baptiste de Gribeauval (1715–89) issued the *réglement* (1776) that laid the foundation for the exceptional mobility of Napoleon Bonaparte's gunners.

Naval warfare also was changed by the new technology. Warships had previously been floating platforms carrying men trained for hand-to-hand combat after grappling hooks had attached an enemy vessel to their own. Greek fire had been used for centuries to destroy shipping, but its efficacy depended upon relatively close contact. As the sailing vessel replaced the galley, however, a fleet came to be considered a group of floating platforms from which to destroy hostile shipping by gun fire at a fair distance. Portholes were provided for guns, and turrets for gunners; the effectiveness of a ship's broadside became the measure of her prowess. The greater range of Portuguese guns assured their victory over the Egyptians at Diu, in 1509, and made Portugal the master of the Indian Ocean, and the greater mobility and consequent fire superiority of the English fleet partly accounted for its defeat of the Spanish Armada in 1588. Fire superiority was thenceforth the major objective of naval strategy.

Changes in Military Systems

As armies and navies grew in size and as soldiers and sailors remained for long terms in service, the military science of logistics (feeding, equipping, transporting, and housing) was put in the charge of specialized officers. Fortresses and naval stations constituted not only homes for local soldiers and sailors but also supply depots for the regional forces. Gradually, and particularly in France, which replaced Spain as the leading military power in the late seventeenth century, military strategy and tactics became systematized. Siege warfare and blockades were the mode of the day, commanders seeking pitched battle only under favourable circumstances, otherwise attempting to outlast rather than outfight the enemy. Feudal levies tended to disappear and proprietary regiments to diminish in number as standing armies grew; in times of national crisis, rulers might call out the militia, too. Troops were arrayed in uniform as against the casual dress of earlier days, and military drill was intensified in order to train them to carry out parade and battle manœuvres in elegant geometrical movements.

Better drill and fire techniques were developed by Maurice of Nassau in the Eighty Years' War, by Gustavus Adolphus in the Thirty Years' War, and by Cromwell in the English Civil War. On these models, and profiting from their own experience in the wars of Louis XIV, Prince Leopold of

Anhalt-Dessau and King Frederick William I taught the Prussian fusiliers to load and reload their pieces so rapidly as to maintain fire superiority while advancing under fire in unswerving lines to a point from which they might launch a bayonet charge. In turn, the Prussian drill methods became the standard for other armies of Europe, especially when perfected by the outflanking tactics ('oblique order') of Frederick the Great. By that time a respectable army had military bands, elaborate uniforms, colourful flags, and specialized contingents of professional and sometimes mercenary infantry, cavalry, and artillery, organized into divisions, brigades, regiments, battalions, companies, etc. It was usually a standing army, directly responsible to the crown, with a political significance that we shall consider later. The improved fusil, or rifle, of 1777 was the common weapon of the French army during the Revolution and the Empire, but it hit its target with only a small percentage of its shots. Though casualties mounted consistently in the warfare of the eighteenth century, they were bound to be light by comparison with the deadly efficiency of the technological warfare of later centuries.

THE METHODS OF AGRICULTURE

Rural Practices in the Fourteenth and Fifteenth Centuries

Although the more progressive monastic communities of the Middle Ages had improved the cultivation of grain crops, vines, and fruit trees and the breeds of domestic animals, comparatively little experimentation had been tried with new crops or breeds. The Cistercian monasteries of the twelfth and thirteenth centuries, like the pioneers on the American frontier, had accepted as their major aim turning forest and swamp into arable fields. They performed what must have seemed in that day miracles of deforestation and drainage, especially in the new lands of east Germany. Their pioneering activity demonstrates that in general until about 1300 Western agricultural methods were determined by the availability of new land rather than the need for more intensive cultivation of the old.

Thereafter, the trend toward new lands was checked, if not reversed. The poorer arable lands went back to pasture; less was produced for market and export; and conservation became more strategic than expansion. The amount of arable land was further limited by the steady increase of sheep-farming and the accompanying 'enclosure movement'. With the mounting demand for wool by the expanding textile industries, the village commons were gradually acquired by the great landlords as sheep pasture and subsequently, along with other hitherto open land, closed off from the fields. In sheep-raising areas such as England, Spain, and northern Italy, the sharp curtailment of farmland and the persistent spread of enclosures became heated political issues. Some scholars have held that, especially in its early stages before the end of the fifteenth century, the enclosure of previously common or open land was generally due not to increased demands for wool but for fresh, unexhausted soil. The fact is that enclosure often, especially in the stages after 1500, was accompanied by voluntary consolidation of the peasants' strips into compact holdings, usually individually owned in western Europe and communally in central and eastern Europe. For this process was recognized by peasants as well as landlords as a way to enlarge the amount not only of arable land for more efficient farming but also of grazing land for larger herds. Nevertheless, soil exhaustion may well have been the determining factor for certain places at certain times.

Even before 1300 progressive farmers and agriculturists had advocated new methods of restoring the soil. The ancient practice continued of 'green' fertilizing—that is, digging straw, stubble, and waste leguminous plants into the ground—as well as fertilizing with manure. Sometimes 'green' materials were strewn on the ground for the cattle to trample. By the thirteenth century, the use of marl as fertilizer was well known. At the beginning of the next century Pietro Crescenzi completed a work entitled *Opus Ruralium Commodorum*, summarizing the agricultural methods known to western Christendom at that time but overlooking the highly advanced Muslim methods prevalent in Spain. This lacuna was filled by two Iberian rulers, Denis of Portugal (1279–1325) and his contemporary Pedro of Aragon. Denis was outstanding in promoting the agricultural as well as other resources of his country. One of his many conservation projects was the planting of pine trees on the dunes of Leiria, later to become a source of timber for the ships of daring Portuguese mariners. He and Pedro encouraged the translation of Muslim works on agriculture, thus perpetuating for Christian Spain the advanced practices of the Muslims.

For the most part, however, European farming methods remained traditional from the eighth to the fourteenth century. In that interval the two-field (or field-grass) system practised by the Romans and the Germanic tribes in the Roman Empire gave way in some regions to the three-field system (two fields under cultivation and one fallow). Either system permitted a different portion of the tillable land to lie fallow each year in order to avoid too rapid exhaustion of the soil's fertility. Manure was scarce, and liming or marling was an expensive, long-range process, hardly worth while for serfs, small farmers, *métayers* (share-croppers), and tenants, who could not be certain that they would survive long enough to reap a reward from the labour and expense involved. The acreage under actual cultivation or fertilization, therefore, was relatively small in comparison to the soil available.

Because it permitted fuller use of the soil, the three-field system came to prevail throughout western and central Europe. On a manor employing this system one field would lie fallow for a given year, another would be planted in the spring, and the third in the fall. The triennial rotation of fields resulted in a primitive sort of crop rotation—improved probably about 1300 in the Netherlands by alternating legumes and grain crops. Each field was divided into strips allotted severally to the peasants of the manorial community.

Generally the manor, with its manor house or chateau, its communal village, its strip fields, and its common pasture, marsh, and waste land, was geared to self-sufficiency rather than to production for profit. It produced grain for bread; wine, ale, and beer for drink; flax and hemp for linen; sheep for woollen clothing; pigs and fowl for meat; and almost all the other necessities.

About 1300—earlier in certain urban regions of Italy and Spain—the manorial system underwent serious modifications. As prices rose (see Chapter I), the employment of wage labourers became more profitable than that of serfs or tenants on estates producing grain, wine, and other produce for proliferating town markets. Serfdom began to give way to tenancy, a trend that was accelerated in the late fourteenth century as the Black Death reduced the labour supply. In England, for example, even before 1300, landlords had begun to find it to their advantage to convert their labour hands from servile or semi-servile status to that of free wage-earners and to bid for a free labourer's services. During the period of the Black Death they were more concerned whether a labourer's wages were not too high than whether he was free or servile. The trend away from serfdom was welcomed by many landlords as a means of obtaining land and money in place of personal service from their peasantry and thus of adjusting their cash incomes to the rising standards of living. They endeavoured to take over common lands and even peasant holdings in order to grow more of the crops demanded in neighbouring or foreign markets. As landlords thus reorganized land and labour to obtain maximum profit by growing special crops, manorial self-subsistence became outmoded.

In western Europe the shift from a servile to a free-labour market apparently was accompanied by a decline in production. At any rate, much less agricultural produce was sold from western manors in the fourteenth century than previously. Food shortages sometimes forced industrial towns to draw on distant regions to feed their expanding populations. Some countries, like the Netherlands, which were able to import food by sea from the Baltic coastal lands, were more fortunate than regions such as northern Italy, which could not so readily find even distant foodstuffs to import. Food shortage and the Black Plague together brought an overall decline in population after the middle of the fourteenth century. Occasional bumper crops of grain sometimes led to a drop in prices, as, for example, during the second quarter of the fourteenth century, when grain prices declined in England as much as twenty percent, and again in the last quarter of the century, when prices of grain and bread reached unusually low levels. In the long run, however, prices tended upward.

In the fifteenth and sixteenth centuries the inclination of landlords to expand their holdings at the expense of peasants and to go in for money crops was particularly noticeable. In France land values rose so rapidly during fifty years of rapid recovery after the Hundred Years' War that about 1500 they were back to their pre-war levels. The same was happening in England, where, especially in the sixteenth century, expansion took the form of an intensified enclosure movement. In central and eastern Europe an agricultural expansion eastward across the Elbe had already reached a climax by the end of the fourteenth century, and during the fifteenth century, as peasants continued to migrate into Slavic lands, abandoned farmlands and deserted villages marred the landscape in Brandenburg, Pomerania, Mecklenburg, and Prussia. In east Germany and Poland landlords now all the more ruthlessly exploited the servile peasants who remained behind, bound to their great estates. In Poland, as well as Hungary, agriculture, nevertheless, expanded. In the sixteenth century a new agricultural boom came to the Baltic coastal regions; it encouraged new German immigration, and Baltic landlords readjusted to a system of large estates worked by landless but free peasants.

Nowhere in Europe was the peasant necessarily better off economically because he was legally free. The rising standard of living made the upper classes feel hard-pressed for money. Many landlords, hoping to profit from the increasing prices of farm products, not only appropriated more and more of the common lands but also increased their demands upon the peasantry, whether tenants or serfs, wherever they could. The peasants resented the lord's appropriation of the common lands, which they had customarily used for pasture, hay, wood, hunting, and fishing. The landlord's land hunger meant for them decreasing land resources and increasing rentals or servile obligations. Peasant discontent mounted and rebellions became more frequent. Along with the peasantry, many of the lesser, land-starved nobles, especially in Germany and France, were in desperate straits. Caught in changes that made their services almost obsolete in warfare, and unable to adjust their small estates to the new economy, they sank into poverty and humiliation. In Germany, the rise of Protestantism seemed to give a Biblical justification to social discontent. The Knights' War preceded the Peasants' War—both destined to be repressed without diminishing the dissidents' grievances (see Chapter IV).

The Increase of Articles of Commerce

The discoveries and explorations of the fifteenth and subsequent centuries introduced European man to new or relatively new commodities. Cane sugar had long been known in Europe, though only as an expensive rarity, and it now became cheaper and commoner. Originating in the Far East, the sugar cane was transported on Columbus's second voyage to the tropical New World, eventually becoming a staple crop there. In the sixteenth century the Spanish, the Portuguese, the French, and the English attempted large scale cultivation of tobacco in their respective mother countries, but with varying degrees of failure. The introduction of the potato from the New World was more successful, providing the poor man with a mainstay of his diet, and the increased use of various 'artificial grasses' (legumes) augmented the number of Europe's rotation crops. Textile cotton from the East furnished a new material for clothing, adding to the personal comfort and cleanliness of a population that had previously worn woollen garments winter and summer, and new dyestuffs made cloth more colourful. A variety of other commodities from Asia, the South Seas, and Africa—for example, citrus fruits, spices of many kinds, tea, cocoa, silk, coffee—though known in Europe before the discovery of the all-water way to India, now became more plentiful. A long list of frustrations showed that few of these exotic commodities save oranges and silk could be grown economically anywhere in Europe.

After 1500, Europe's commerce with the rest of the world expanded. Superior silks and brocades, cotton and cotton goods, rugs, chinaware, indigo, spices, perfumes, brassware, coffee, tea, and rare woods continued to be principal articles of trade with India, China, and other countries of Asia. From Africa came ivory (on a relatively negligible scale), the guinea-fowl, salt, oil, and spices as well as slaves, only a few of whom remained in Europe. With the settlement of America, certain products, formerly derived from the East, were cultivated on a grand scale on New World plantations—for example, cotton, rice, coffee, and cane sugar (with its by-products, molasses and rum). In addition, the watermelon and the grapefruit were extensively cultivated in the warmer temperate zones of America and elsewhere, the first introduced from south Africa and the second from southeast Asia. Toward the end of our period cloves and other spices were grown in some of the tropical colonies of the New World. The Americas provided, besides, rich shipments of precious metals (primarily from Mexico, Peru, and Brazil), tobacco, cotton, sugar, salt, cereals, dyewoods, furs, timber, naval stores, whale oil, turkeys, and a rich harvest of fish (particularly from the Newfoundland Banks). Wine and beer retained their prominence in Europe's economy and diet, but during the second half of our period they suffered from the growing competition of imported beverages like coffee and tea.

Certain commodities native to the Americas were adopted elsewhere after the discovery of America. The pineapple, in addition to tobacco and the potato, was an outstanding adoption in Europe. The sweet potato and the breadroot, native to America, eventually became more familiar in the Far East than in Europe. Maize (the corn of Americans) was the Amerindians' staple food. Their women cooked it into tortillas, which in the tropical areas might be washed down with pulque, the fermented sap of the maguey cactus. Maize, though widely eaten in several different forms in America still, became common in only a few areas of Europe, where it was generally grown for animal rather than human consumption. Nor did it ever replace rice as the staple of southern China, where it was introduced by the Dominicans from the Philippines, to which it had come from Mexico. It was a versatile plant, however, providing sugar, starch, bowls for smoking pipes, and fuel. The Amerindians also knew several kinds of beans that were transplanted to Europe, but they were grown there at first as fodder rather than as food for humans. The tomato was also transplanted to Europe from America but was used chiefly as an ornament (the love apple) before the nineteenth century. Peanuts, introduced, like maize, by the Dominicans into southern China, never—at least, until recent decades, if then—became so important there or in Europe, either as a food or as a producer of oil, as in America. Pumpkins and squash likewise never developed into so regular a part of the diet of Europeans as of Americans, whether Indian or white, nor was chili ever so frequently used as a spice in Europe. Cocoa and chocolate became fairly common in England and elsewhere in the seventeenth century but were too expensive to compete effectively as beverages with tea and coffee, although here and there a 'cocoa house' did acquire a reputation that compared with that of a growing number of cafes and coffeehouses.

The cacao tree was only one of the strange and useful trees found in the New World. Rubber from the caoutchouc tree of the Amazon valley was a curiosity used almost exclusively for bouncing balls until Priestley around 1770 discovered that it could rub out pencil and ink marks (hence its English name). The California sequoias were too big to be handled usefully as yet, but the sugar maple of the north not only gave sugar and syrup but also made an excellent veneer for furniture, as did the mahogany of the south. The Peruvian cinchona bark gave quinine (to mention only one of several new drugs of which the Indians knew). The brazilwood gave a red dye, and another Brazil tree gave the Brazil nut. The Mexican cactus worm gave the dyestuff cochineal. The New World also had in abundance many of the timber trees that were familiar but were becoming scarce in Europe.

The more civilized Amerindian nations like the Incas and the Aztecs knew how to make cloth from cotton, wool, and maguey (see Chapter XII), but most northern Amerindians clothed themselves in hides and skins. America bred several kinds of furred animals that were not native to the Old World—the buffalo, the ocelot, the coyote, and the bobcat, for example; and their skins entered the competitive European fur market along with the preferred skins of beaver, bear, seal, otter, and other animals found in the Eastern and the Western Hemisphere alike.

The Portuguese, as colonizers in the East, Africa, and America, were able to move tropical plants more or less freely from one set of colonies to the other. In this way they introduced into West Africa from America and the East a number of plants thitherto unknown there, among them casava nuts, peanuts, sweet potatoes, maize, squash, coconuts, citrus fruits, and cocoa, and into America from Africa and the East mangoes, jacks, cinnamon, breadfruit, and coconuts, and into India, the cashew nut.[15] The American Indians did not know the plow, steel, firearms, glassware, and other manufactured products already known in Europe by the time of the discoveries. The horse and the cow were likewise unknown to them. If the Mexicans knew the wheel and the Peruvians the sail and the rudder, it was only in a rudimentary way. On the other hand, they could travel by snowshoe and birch canoe in the north (not to mention the llama of South America)— means of transportation about which the white man learned from them. The Indians also perhaps gave pandemic syphilis to the Europeans (see above), who in return gave them decimating epidemics of measles and smallpox.

The great European powers instituted in their West Indian and American colonies the famous plantation and hacienda system (see Chapter II). These systems utilized large supplies of labour, for the most part Negro slaves from Africa or American Indians, and produced new exotic crops. Usually a plantation specialized in a particular crop, exploiting large areas of land freely rather than adopting the intensive cultivation of the small, compact farms of Europe.

The 'Agricultural Revolution'

In the seventeenth and eighteenth centuries the most advanced European agricultural practices were to be found in England and Holland. In order to extend acreage, drainage of land was undertaken in both countries. The 'polder' system increased acreage considerably in Holland; and in England, thanks to Dutch engineers and English ingenuity, the Fen country was drained. These two nations had the advantage of close commercial, political, and intellectual contact, particularly after their seventeenth-century conflicts.

In England and Holland, as elsewhere, the three-field system had long entailed the obvious disadvantage of keeping one-third of the land idle, but growing demands for higher production brought a new method of crop rotation. In the seventeenth century some Netherlands farms adopted a method which, introduced during the next century into England, became known as 'the Norfolk System'. The farmer had discovered that certain crops, especially legumes, 'revived' the soil rather than used it up. By rotating certain food crops like peas and beans or, as began to happen late in the seventeenth century, certain fodder crops like clover with wheat, oats, barley, and other cereals, he was able to maintain the productivity of the available soil without the interruption of fallow periods. We now know that the reason for this soil-reviving quality of certain plants is that they are able to fix atmospheric nitrogen. Root crops like beets and turnips, requiring deep soil and cool weather, also fitted well into a rotation system for grains. No arable land need lie fallow under this arrangement; instead a four-course rotation of crops (clover, wheat, turnips, and barley in that order) was substituted. The turnip and clover as new fodder crops changed the whole process of cattle raising, and root crops, in particular the turnip, improved the land.

Even before the Norfolk system was widely adopted in the Netherlands, it was well received in England. The English were in a better position than the Continental countries to benefit from this innovation. Since the fourteenth

ɪɪ*

century the yeoman had been gradually leaving the farm because of the enclosure movement, and the large farm under one man's control had become more common. By eliminating the small holder and the open-field system, enclosure increased the potential for efficiency in land exploitation. Nor was absentee landlordism common in England, where the country gentleman or noble proprietor took a direct and active interest in his estate.

In France, distinct agricultural improvement took place, but it was not equally marked. A long list of writers on agricultural problems had brought less practical change than the gentlemen farmers in England. Outstanding among the earlier agronomists was Olivier de Serres (1539–1619). Published with the approval of Henry IV's minister Sully and dedicated to the king, Serres' *Théâtre d'agriculture et ménage des champs* (1600) anticipated the Physiocratic doctrine that agriculture was the basis of wealth; it went through nineteen editions by 1675. Among the agricultural innovations that he championed in theory, and put into practice with considerable success on his own model farm and elsewhere, was the earnest pursuit of sericulture. The indifference and absenteeism of many, though by no means all, of the landowners and the generally conservative attitude of the French peasant nevertheless proved difficult barriers to general agrarian reform. By the eighteenth century political feudalism had diminished, to be sure, but its economic and social survivals were still jealously guarded or acquired, and, as in other parts of the Continent, the *franc-alleu* (freehold) was relatively rare. Crops were in constant jeopardy because of the hunting rights of the landowner. And a movement that has been misnamed 'feudal reaction' (i.e. a pronounced effort of landlords to get greater rentals, whether in money, land, or services) had resulted from the long-run rise in food prices. Nevertheless, numerous agricultural societies, as well as the Physiocrats, were studying and advocating reform, and some landed estates were adopting them. Perhaps the most influential French writer on the role of science in agriculture was Henri Louis Duhamel du Monceau, who in 1762 published a two-volume *Eléments d'agriculture* (English translation, 1764). On the whole, the farm and the farmer at all levels were better off in France than elsewhere on the Continent, if still behind the English, especially on the larger estates. (Pl. 108c.)

Some eighteenth-century English landlords proved exceptionally ready to adopt new mechanical devices for agriculture. The development of agricultural machinery tends to corroborate the general rule that technological improvements come through the slow accumulation of experience and knowledge rather than by startling innovation. The roots of modern agricultural mechanization lie deep in the soil of the Middle Ages and earlier. A heavy plow seems to have supplanted the light Mediterranean plow, at least on large estates, by the end of the thirteenth century. The light plow (*aratrum*) of late Roman times continued in use on small individual holdings whose proprietors could not afford heavy equipment. Obviously not well adapted to deep sub-soil plowing or the breaking up of new land, it was supplemented by the hoe or spade. The heavy plow probably had originated among the Germanic peoples of the upper Danube region. Designed for new, hard land, it eventually became the distinctive plow of the North. It was called *carruca*, from the fact that it had wheels, so that it could be moved easily from place to place. It required at least one yoke of oxen for the lightest plowing and as many as six or eight for breaking new land or turning tough sod. (Pl. 108a.) Thus it became the characteristic plow for the collective farming of the manor or of the later enlarged estates. The heavy plow was equipped with a colter and moldboard for turning sod upside down. The improvement of metal for plowshares augmented its effectiveness, but it remained generally the same from at least the fourteenth century on. In some instances subsequent changes made it less bulky and more efficient both in digging a better furrow and in turning over greater amounts of soil, but in many areas plows of old design remained in use. As often in the history of technology, the complex, newer device was used side by side with the simpler primitive one which it was destined ultimately to replace.

The use of horses instead of oxen became more common with the improvement of the horse collar. Pictures of the hard horse collar applied to the traction of agricultural machines can be found in manuscript miniatures as early as the thirteenth century, and it probably was used much earlier. Several illustrations of it appear in the beautiful portrayals of the activities of the respective months in the Duc de Berri's fifteenth-century book of hours, where a harrow as well as a plow is shown being pulled by a collared horse over a freshly seeded field. (Pl. 108b.) The horse-drawn harrow seems highly mechanized when compared with the bundles of thorns dragged over the soil by the farmers of ancient Rome and medieval Europe to cover seeds and pull weeds. In the sixteenth century in the Netherlands a plow was developed that could readily be pulled by two horses, and this change was rapidly introduced into England.

Other agricultural implements have outlasted the Middle Ages—in a few instances, with some improvement. To break up clods, which were a constant vexation to those who farmed the heavy northern soils, nothing more efficient than a mallet was known until the sixteenth century, when a roller appeared. Scythes, rakes, sheep shears, axes, mattocks, flails, and even scarecrows—in one case made to look like an archer with drawn bow—appear in contemporary paintings. From the late fifteenth century on, the scythe, known to the Romans but having acquired its projecting bar-handle only around the twelfth century, was commonly preferred to the sickle for harvesting grain.

In the eighteenth century Jethro Tull made some simple but effective agricultural innovations. For one thing, he emphasized the importance of pulverizing the earth and planting the seeds in rows so that weeds could be removed while the crop was growing. This process brought a twofold improvement since, when seeds were sown broadcast, the birds ate a large share of them, and Tull's method saved them from the birds as well as the weeds. Before Tull many had used the back-breaking method of sowing known as 'dibbling'—that is, placing the seeds in small holes in the ground made at regular intervals with a pointed implement. All this was done with handtools. Tull devised a seed-box which provided a regular distribution of seed. He then designed a complete wheat drill in which the seed-box was incorporated, and a similar machine for sowing turnips. With these and his 'Ho-Plow' [sic] for inter-row weeding, he took the first important steps in the mechanization of agriculture. His book *The Horse-Hoing* [sic] *Husbandry* (1733) described these machines, maintaining that they were more economical than the customary method of dressing fields with manure. His basically scientific approach by means of controlled experiments added to the strength of his convictions.

Over the centuries crops had been harvested by arduous manual labour. Reaping cereals, for example, meant bringing together numerous workers to cut the crop with sickles or scythes and to gather the stalks into sheaves. The search for labour-saving devices of all kinds became particularly keen in rural England in the late eighteenth century, when the accelerating migration to the cities, rapidly becoming industrialized, intensified the shortage of agricultural labour. The clamour for change in the preparation of cereal crops for market grew, but it went unsatisfied until after our period. Many attempts were made before 1775 to invent a reaper that would relieve harvesters of part of their burden, but little was accomplished; the first practical reaper came only in the nineteenth century. Threshing with the time-honoured hand-flail was both laborious and time-consuming, and as early as 1636 John Christopher van Berg patented a threshing machine. But it was not practical; a more practical one came only in 1788 with the Scot Andrew Meikle's patent.

Horticulture and Gardens

Before the seventeenth century the chief concern of horticulturists had been with herbs and a restricted number of vegetables, fruits, and flowers. The Muslims were especially advanced in horticulture, and their influence, derived not only from Spain directly but also from the observations of Westerners who travelled in the Near East, was particularly discernible in the ornamental gardens that became relatively common during the fourteenth, fifteenth, and sixteenth centuries, especially on the estates of Italian despots and of national monarchs farther north. Universities, such as that of Padua, preferred a more academic type of horticulture, the botanical garden (Chapter XIV).

The opening of the New World and closer contact with Asia brought, as noted in other contexts, an influx of new fruits and flowers to Europe. This expanding acquaintance with nature's beauty was one of the factors that inspired the contemporary interest in nature itself and in naturalism in literature and the arts (see Chapters XI and XII). The beauty of vineyards, orchards, and gardens, though long a familiar part of the European landscape, now received, in keeping with the current *sensibilité*, greater conscious attention. Gentlemen's lives and homes became more closely associated with gardens. The Dutch middle-class merchant and his English counterpart especially began to take pride in gardening, and supervision of garden work became part of their daily activity. The vogue of the tulip in its homeland, the Ottoman Empire, was duplicated in seventeenth-century Holland, and many a still life of the day reveals that, along with other species of flowers, it often graced the Hollander's home.

The garden became part of the architectural lay-out of the well planned residence. The formal garden of the eighteenth century, where even the trees were trimmed into rectangles and spheres (see Chapter XII), was an expression of the *esprit géométrique*. Le Nôtre's park at Versailles with straight avenues, rectangular pools, and Classical statuary was a spectacular example. (Pl. 51b.) Glass greenhouses and hot-houses became available as a result of the successful casting of plate glass in seventeenth-century France. The first of them were erected in the Jardin des Plantes in Paris. Northern Europeans raised in their hot-houses decorative as well as useful plants, such as oranges, lemons, and limes, better known in Spain and other southern countries. The orange won particular favour, supplying fruit for exotic dishes and lending its blossoms and fruit to the ornamentation of wealthy homes and special occasions. Planted in tubs, citrus trees graced the garden in the summer and were removed for the winter to the orangery (a special and sometimes architecturally substantial greenhouse).

> . . . . The golden boast
> Of Portugal and western India there,
> The ruddier orange and the paler lime,
> Peep through their polished foliage at the storm.[16]

The concept of the garden began to change in the latter half of the eighteenth century as the cult of nature and the influence of the Chinese garden contributed to a new vogue. Now the garden was made to conform to untrimmed nature. Trees and shrubs were allowed to thrive in untrained forms. Bridges, ponds, and garden houses were studiously placed so as to take on an air of carelessness, which was thought characteristic of Chinese gardens and which the English especially sought to cultivate. Garden houses began to look more like Chinese pagodas than Greek temples, and ponds and groves were no longer fitted into precise rectangles and circles.

Improvements in Animal Husbandry

One of the serious problems of the medieval farmer had been keeping his domestic animals alive during the winter cold. Hay had long been known as a fodder through the pastureless season, but the hay crop was rarely abundant enough anywhere for all the summer's livestock. Many of the cattle and swine were more or less mercifully butchered and sold or salted down for meat in order to keep them from starvation. By the fifteenth century additional fodders had been added—oats, vetches, and even peas and beans, but more costly foods like these were rarely fed to stock other than horses. With the improving standard of living, the demand for wool, hides, and meats increased and with improving agricultural implements the demand for horses, but increased demand could now be met with increased supply. The concurrently expanding knowledge of plants helped to introduce new fodders that enabled the husbandman to keep more of his animals alive throughout the winter. Clover, turnips, maize, and potatoes not only made available more work animals, at the same time strengthening their draft power, but also could be sold to the butcher when converted into added poundage of meat rather than to the grocer when marketed as bushels of vegetables, and so as fodder such crops were probably more profitable than as vegetables.

Progress in animal husbandry came not alone from the introduction of better and more plentiful fodder but also from a more systematic application of genetic principles. Sheep were in the eighteenth century being successfully selected and crossbred so as to produce a better quality and a more abundant yield of wool. Specialization led to the raising of better riding horses, race-horses, carriage-horses, and draft-horses and better sheep dogs, hunting dogs, watch-dogs, and pet dogs. Breeders in certain regions developed cattle better fitted for dairy needs and in others better fitted for butchering; or, if a breeder raised both kinds at the same time, he kept the two separate. Poultry breeders did likewise for egg-laying and fowl, though poultry did not become a general market product until the nineteenth century. Selection in the raising of pigs likewise improved both their quantity and quality. Thus new sources of meat were substituted for the decreasing supply of game, which hunting laws and the costliness of hunting equipment would have made a monopoly of the landlords but for the prevalence of poaching. Dairy products, markedly superior to the products of earlier generations, came to form an important component of the average man's diet. Bee-keeping, on the other hand, which had long provided the principal article used for sweetening, experienced a general decline as American cane sugar displaced honey. With the growing proficiency of fire-arms, dogs, and horses, falconry as a method of hunting also declined. On the whole, animal husbandry was rapidly becoming the more profitable of the two major agricultural pursuits.

One of the major obstacles to progress in animal breeding had been the common pasture. As a cause of promiscuity the common pasture had already been partly eliminated by the enclosure system and the controls exercised upon the animals on the larger estates. Segregated pasturage also contributed to the improvement of timber, since indiscriminate pasturing of flocks, especially sheep, in woodlands led to the ruin of trees and the destruction of seed and saplings. Segregated and cultivated—even manured—forests eventually became more common.

Before the nineteenth century the advance in flocks and herds may have been due less to selective breeding than to better feeding. In the Netherlands, for example, the lands recovered from the sea, which produced a lush grass, were used as early as the sixteenth century for fattening lean cattle from inland regions. Likewise, it was found, cattle flourished on the grass of the English fenlands and gave more milk than those fed on leaves and stubble. The selective breeding of sheep was especially difficult, and hence probably less profitable than better feeding, for even though rams of special breeds often were imported, the large flocks and their wide pasturing range prevented effective control.

Sheep flourished in hilly or waste regions all the way from Lincolnshire to Andalusia, among them several fairly pure breeds—the big-tailed Syrian, the small-tailed Arab, the merinos of Spain, and the Cotswolds of south England. In the twelfth century merino sheep were introduced by the Moors from north Africa into Spain, where they dominated agriculture during the centuries of the reconquest and numbered almost three and a half million in 1526. The sheep drivers' guild, the Mesta—given special royal privileges from the late thirteenth century onward—had the right to move their flocks from place to place, grazing as they went. Their privileges doubtless encouraged Spanish wool production but, along with an apparent change of climate in Spain in the sixteenth century, had a destructive influence on farming and forestry. The sheepwalks were a considerable factor of Spain's agricultural backwardness in that and the succeeding century;[14] the conservatism of the Spanish peasant ('*Asi lo hicieron mis padres*') did the rest. Nevertheless, the Spanish merino produced an excellent, heavy wool and was sought for breeding purposes in other countries.

Selective Breeding of Domestic Animals

Throughout the Middle Ages the horse had been a favourite among royalty and nobility, and its breeding, feeding, training, and welfare had been a paramount interest. Blooded stallions were imported, especially Arabian strains from the Muslim areas of southern Spain, for tournaments and races. At one time in the fourteenth century a French king had two stallions, twenty-eight brood mares, and twenty-eight colts on one of his stud farms. In the fifteenth century English stables were breeding fine horses and exporting them to the Continent. Numerous compendia of the late Middle Ages, well illustrated with excellent specimens of horseflesh, earnestly and extensively discuss cautery, surgery, and medicines for ailing steeds. Almost as numerous were the works on the care of dogs and falcons. The veterinary seems to have had no less prestige than the surgeon, when indeed the same man was not both. Anthrax was the veterinary's major enemy; epidemics in 1714 and 1744 led to the establishment of the first veterinary school in France, founded at Lyons in 1762.

By the sixteenth century the nations of western Europe had begun more systematic breeding of draught horses. The need for systematic breeding became more cogent as horses changed from bearer of knights in armour to sources of power for machines and implements. Breeding was based on no science of genetics, which was to remain unformulated for another three hundred years or more, but rather on common-sense selection of good examples of the type of animal needed as sires. Increasing and improving quantities of fodder throughout the succeeding centuries enabled horses to grow in size and prosper otherwise as well.

Selective breeding of sheep and cattle was introduced much later than that of horses. Robert Bakewell, an eighteenth-century English gentleman farmer, was particularly prominent in promoting the selective breeding of sheep. As a result, they grew in size and stamina, providing (to say nothing of wool) a much greater yield of meat per animal, all the more desirable in a period when undomesticated animals such as the hare and the deer were beginning to disappear before the inroads of urbanization and mechanization and when hunting was becoming a sport reserved for aristocrats rather than a method of food production. What was learned of horses and sheep was applied also to cattle as enclosures increased in number and common pasture diminished. Wherever adequate pasturage and fodder were available, an augmented production of milk and dairy products followed. The Swiss and the Dutch were the trailblazers in this field, taking advantage of almost every piece of land available in their little countries.

MEDICAL PRACTICE, PUBLIC HEALTH, AND SANITATION

As in several other lines of knowledge, the Islamic world and Orthodox Christendom were superior to the Christian West in medical practice as well as theory until late in the Middle Ages. Although by the fourteenth century Islamic civilization had passed its zenith, and in the fifteenth and sixteenth centuries western Europe forged ahead at an accelerating pace, in medicine much of Western practice was still based on the work of versatile Muslim scholar-physicians of earlier times, who in turn had borrowed from Greco-Roman and Indian medicine.

Muslim as well as Christian physicians, with some notable exceptions, long relied heavily on astrology and alchemy. They regarded certain days as lucky and certain others as unlucky—'Egyptian'—for purging, blood-letting, and the like. Since each of the planets was regarded as having benevolent or malevolent effects on critical events varying according to its position at the moment, the twelve signs of the zodiac were considered critical in determining health and sickness, and so illustrations of zodiac-men were frequently provided in medical manuscripts. Royal (that is, the best) physicians often were enthusiastic and expert alchemists, while pharmacists made practical use of alchemy in compounding medicines. The 'philosopher's elixir', if ever found and perfected, was expected to work miracles in the balance of the humours in the human body.

Hospitals, Sanitation, and Disease

Before the seventeenth century Europe's hospitals were generally run by one or another of the religious orders that cared for the sick, and they were not commonly used for teaching purposes. By the eighteenth century they were looked upon as institutions not merely for the care but also for the cure of the sick. Physicians and surgeons were now generally trained by the clinical method (see Chapter XVI), and new hospitals were built not only by the charitable orders but also by the state or by private philanthropy. The advantage, however, of improved training of physicians in the hospitals, old or new, was offset by the tremendous lack of knowledge of pathogenic bacteria. All beds were generally in one large dormitory separated only by curtains. Eighteenth-century hospitals were not always dirty, though doubtless some were, and eighteenth-century physicians or nurses were not necessarily callous. Yet those sick with contagious diseases were not carefully isolated, and in crowded hospitals several persons sometimes had to share the same bed. Nevertheless, quarantine was practised as a means of preventing the spread of such diseases as seemed to infect the healthy upon bodily contact with the diseased. Without understanding the role of the germ in disease, hospitals of that day isolated in pest-houses the unfortunate persons who had plague, leprosy, and other mutilating or killing diseases known or thought to be contagious or infectious.

The hospital too often meant a place for the sick poor to go to die, for hospital mortality rates were alarming. Yet hospitals that were better than the average medieval Hôtel-Dieu were founded in the fifteenth and sixteenth centuries. We have already encountered that of Catherine of Genoa (Chapter IV), and Italy could boast others at Florence, Milan, and elsewhere. Those at Beaune and Würzburg were also deservedly famous. In the seventeenth and eighteenth centuries hospitals were more and more regularly being adapted in architecture to medical needs as understood at the time. (Pl. 94a, b.)

The establishment and improvement of hospitals fitted well into the humanitarian trend of the eighteenth century. The crowding of cities compelled greater attention to public health, to which not only church and state but also private philanthropy now responded. Philanthropists built great hospitals, that of the Necker family in Paris being one of the finest. Lyons and Vienna erected, largely from government funds, big hospitals that became models of the latest methods. Several maternity hospitals went up in England, and clinics arranged to take care of the poor who were sick but not sick enough to go to a hospital. Lunatic asylums became more numerous. The notorious Bedlam of England goes back to 1400, and Valencia,

Zaragosa, and other Spanish cities had madhouses in the fifteenth century, but since insanity was not understood, the psychiatric treatment they afforded was little more effective than before. Enlightened rulers also encouraged sewage systems, water systems, and street-lighting. Progress in public health measures remained slow, however, until the nineteenth century.

Inoculation against smallpox (i.e. the superficial insertion of the virus in the hope of producing a mild attack and so securing future immunity) was timidly practised by some. The Turks, probably having borrowed it directly or indirectly from China, used it with a certain degree of success, and Dr Zabdiel Boylston of Massachusetts, having learned of the Turkish process, tried it on his patients in 1721–22. An English physician, Edward Jenner, began in 1775 the observations that led him in 1796 to test his theory of vaccination (inoculation with the cowpox 'vaccine'). The medical radicalism of those who advocated inoculation stood out against the contemporary background of medical conservatism. The prevalent theory of disease (see Chapter XIII) still was that it was caused by imbalance of the four bodily humours. Blood-letting persisted, though generally for specific local purposes rather than for the cure of general ailments, and cauterization was an approved method of treating wounds.

The sixteenth-century pandemic of syphilis added another costly plague to the Black Death of the fourteenth century, and both diseases were to claim their toll in later centuries. Yet, though Europe's epidemics have remained an intermittent horror, constantly improving methods of sanitation since the seventeenth century have confined their virulence. As early as the reign of Phillippe Augustus in the thirteenth century the streets of Paris had been paved, and attempts had since been made to keep them clean. No adequate means, however, of removing rubbish and garbage was provided. Paris, for all its dirt, was one of the cleanest cities of Europe. John Graunt in his *Observations* (1662) complained that 'the Fumes, Steams, and Stenches of London do so medicate and impregnate the Air about it, that it becomes capable of little more [effect upon the death rate]'. As late as the eighteenth century a passer-by on a city street constantly had to look out for refuse and slops thrown from windows as well as for robbers and cut-throats at unlighted corners.

The physician's inability to distinguish accurately between diseases made them all the more awful and mysterious. From the sixteenth century on, however, differentiation among diseases gradually became more precise and aided the study of epidemics. Guillaume de Baillou (1538–1616) described whooping cough, used the word *rheumatism* in the modern sense, and appears to have been the first since Hippocrates to distinguish between rheumatism and gout. In England Thomas Sydenham (1624–89), having studied the natural history of disease, published his classic *Methodus Curandi Febres* (1666) and made such significant contributions to the understanding of epidemics and specifics (especially laudanum and quinine) as well as to clinical medicine in general that he has been called the 'English Hippocrates'. Rickets, which by 1700 had an appalling incidence, was also recognized, but during the eighteenth century its ravages seemed to decrease, though probably not through any medical knowledge so much as through the improvement in diet. The eighteenth-century consumer knew nothing about vitamins, but empirical knowledge of the cure for disease caused by vitamin deficiency went back to the early years of the Dutch East Indies Company, which from about 1600 provided vegetable gardens at several ports of call. The increased consumption of dairy products, meat, fruits, vegetables, and, toward the end of the eighteenth century, cod liver oil, reduced the incidence of scurvy, rickets, and allied diseases.[18] On Cook's second voyage (1772–75) he lost from disease only one out of 118 men (as compared to 30 out of 85 on his first voyage, mostly from disease), primarily because he took certain anti-scorbutic precautions. Perhaps the most feared disease of all, smallpox, thanks to the introduction of inoculation and vaccination, was also brought under better control. From Jenner's discovery eventually developed the modern method of immunization against disease.

Some dubious theories of disease developed in the seventeenth or eighteenth century. One of them was that of the iatrophysicians described in Chapter XIV. A most striking theory arose in connection with the new and promising treatment of the ague (malaria and related fevers). Cinchona bark was introduced from the New World by the Jesuits in the seventeenth century and quickly justified its virtue as a 'specific' (see Chapter XIII). The quinine contained in this bark not only gave great relief to many sufferers in Europe but also brought great wealth to the Jesuits, who had a virtual monopoly of it. After its introduction, unfortunately all fevers were sometimes divided into those that would and those that would not respond to it, leading to some misuses of the drug and possibly also to some missteps in medical research.

Surgery, Anatomy, and Dentistry

Surgery developed slowly in the West but more rapidly around 1300 than before. In the early fourteenth century Mundino and other dissectors flourished in and about Bologna (see Chapter XIII). Although Mundino was a capable surgeon (he is thought to have done most of his own dissecting), his interest was in anatomy rather than surgery. His treatise on anatomy was a veritable manual of dissection. Surgery as a substantive art owed more to his contemporaries Lanfranc of Milan (d. 1315) and Henri de Mondeville (c. 1275–1325). Lanfranc, while teaching and practising in France, introduced better methods of ligature and suture. Mondeville, a French royal army surgeon, was still more advanced in his surgical methods but contemporaneously less known and influential.

Mondeville's *Cyrurgia*—also published in French translation—was the first treatise devoted to surgery by a Frenchman. It was a noteworthy compilation, derived in part from personal experience, though relying heavily on the traditional works of Classical authors such as Galen, of Muslims such as Avicenna, and, to a lesser extent, of Western predecessors such as Lanfranc. The author's genuis lay in his confidence in the possibility of surgical progress through empirical tests. He stressed a new method of treating trauma—dressing a wound with warm wine, closing it to the air (to prevent infection and suppuration if possible), and healing the closed wound by fomentations. In cases of amputation he bound the arteries—a practice known from ancient times and used long before Ambroise Paré (*c.* 1510–90), to whom it has often been attributed. With a surprisingly modern concern over infection, Mondeville urged that instruments be kept clean.

Mondeville's influence was eclipsed by less progressive but better known surgeons of the next generation. His works lay unused while those of Lanfranc, Guy de Chauliac (*c.* 1290–1368), and the Englishman John of Arderne (1307–77) circulated widely, often in lavishly illustrated manuscripts. The last was an army doctor who ventured to operate on anal fistulas and who anticipated Ambroise Paré in his practical use of medication for wounds. Another able surgeon whose influence was contemporaneously eclipsed was Jan Yperman (*c.* 1275–1330), little known outside his own vicinity of Ypres. As a surgeon he stressed, among other things, the use of anaesthetics—e.g. the soporific sponge (an inhalant of mandrake, henbane, hemlock, and poppy), rarely used in the West although it seems to have been known to the Muslims early and was mentioned in an Italian antidotary of about 1100. We have already noted the two-century lag in anatomy before the sixteenth century (Chapter XIII). The neglect of surgical innovations like Yperman's on the part of later royal, papal, and military surgeons made the applications of similar methods by sixteenth-century surgeons appear so new as to be regarded an epoch-making discoveries, but in fact the late fourteenth century and most of the fifteenth century were relatively un-productive in surgery compared with the thirteenth and early fourteenth centuries.

In the sixteenth century, another upsurge of achievement similar to that of the thirteenth century followed the intervening plateau. Paracelsus, Vesalius, Fallopius, and other Italian-trained surgeons and anatomists contributed greatly to the advance of surgical technique by their detailed knowledge of anatomy, and Ambroise Paré, a Frenchman, made perhaps the greatest contributions. Trained as an apprentice to a barber-surgeon in Paris, he became a surgeon with the armies of Francis I in Italy. He learned to sub-stitute soothing salves for searing oil in treating gunshot wounds and published a book (in French, not Latin) on the subject. He then studied anatomy at Paris and eventually published a book on that subject, too. He practised some comparatively modern methods of obstetrics (see below). And—his most eminent service—he made familiar the use of ligatures instead of cautery for controlling arterial bleeding in amputations. Yet, for all his prestige, his innovations (sometimes merely the renewal of old practices) were nearly always received with suspicion and sometimes rejected outright by conservative physicians and surgeons, and the sixteenth century ended without revolutionary betterment of general surgical practice.

The advance of surgery, along with that of dissection, is partly dependent on the quality of surgical instruments. The equipment at leading medical centres was far from primitive around 1300. The surgeon-physicians of Bologna and vicinity such as William of Saliceto, Lanfranc, and Mundino, the group at Montpellier such as Mondeville and Guy de Chauliac, and John of Arderne in England had at their disposal imposing assortments of surgical instruments. Much of their apparatus was modelled upon the amazingly varied types used by the Muslims during the Middle Ages. The surgical works of the fourteenth and fifteenth centuries contain hundreds of illustrations of the paraphernalia available for various types of operations. Special instruments were used for eye surgery and for the fistula operation described and pictured in John of Arderne's treatises. *Specula* for gynaecological observations and traction machines were also known. After the era of Mundino, Mondeville, and Arderne, little advance was made until the late sixteenth century, when an impressive number of precision instruments were put to use. Most of them were better adapted to the basic sciences of medicine—anatomy and physiology—than to surgery, and their use in those sciences help to explain how during the sixteenth and seventeenth centuries detailed anatomical sketches could be drawn. (Pl. 93a, b, c.)

The paucity of surgical triumphs in the seventeenth century is all the more glaring if contrasted with the glorious achievements of contemporary anatomy (see Chapter XIV). Individual surgeons, however, showed great ability—Jacques de Beaulieu in lateral incisions for stone (1697), Nicolas de Blegny in the use of the elastic truss for hernia (*c.* 1676), Hendrik van Roonhuyze in caesarean sections (*c.* 1663), and several surgeons of the Hôtel Dieu, the ancient hospital of Paris, in various methods of checking haemorrhage. Conspicuous efforts were made to formulate the surgery of the day into a systematic body of knowledge. Wilhelm Fabry (1560–1624) produced a lengthy and perhaps the best of the early collections of case records; Richard Wiseman (1622–76) in *Several Chirurgicall Treatises* (1672) described some of his own skilful operations; and Gabriel Le Clerc compiled *La chirurgie complète* (1692), a sort of textbook of surgery that went into eighteen editions.

French surgery set the standard during most of this period, but in the eighteenth century the work of an Englishman, John Hunter (1728–93), stands out. Together with his brother William (see below), he founded one of the famous institutions that eventually transformed the training of medical men—the museums of anatomy and pathology. Some of the chief surgical achievements of our period occurred in the field of dentistry, and not least among Hunter's several contributions to the study of bone and blood was that he helped to provide the basis of a scientific dentistry. The wandering tooth-extracter, made eternally notorious by contemporary artists, was still familiar in Hunter's day, although Pierre Fauchard early in the century had sought a professional standing for dentists. In 1728 Fauchard presented, among other dental subjects, the first systematic treatise on orthodontia in *Le chirurgien dentiste;* he himself used porcelain and gold for artificial teeth. Philipp Pfaff wrote a textbook of dentistry in 1756—*Abhandlung von den Zähnen.* Perhaps the most important single work, however, in the history of dentistry was Hunter's *Natural History of the Human Teeth* (in two parts, 1771 and 1778). It was one of his several written masterpieces which, along with his practical surgery and physiological observations, helped to transform surgery from a skilled craft to a branch of scientific medicine.

Innovations in Pharmacy

By 1300 the West had borrowed from Antiquity and the East an ample pharmacopoeia, and during the next three centuries gamboge gum from Cambodia (as a purgative) and guaiacum from America (as a treatment for syphilis) were the only significant additions to it. Alchemy contributed little basic improvement in the technique of compounding. Most of the metallic compounds of Paracelsus and his iatrochemist followers made no great contribution to pharmaceutics, and they may have killed more patients than they cured. Medieval medicines were largely herbal and generally less harmful than the mercurial concoctions of the sixteenth century.

After 1600 the *materia medica* of Europe expanded and improved. Experiments with mercury eventually led the iatrochemical school to the best way to treat syphilis available before the nineteenth century. In the seventeenth century the introduction of quinine promoted the confidence in specifics, and other medicaments from overseas supplemented the pharmacological list. Glauber's discovery of the salt that bears his name and Grew's of Epsom salt provided innocuous aperients. In the next century, Anton Störck (1731–1803) of Vienna studied the effect of hemlock, meadow-saffron, aconite, stramonium (Jimson weed), and henbane on himself and his patients. The full developments of pharmacology, however, had to wait until chemistry was more fully established as a science.

Advances in Obstetrics

Until the eighteenth century the attendance of a male physician at childbirth was considered indecent by most women, and physicians for their part frowned as much on obstetrics as they did on surgery, considering both beneath their dignity. Obstetrics therefore long remained the monopoly of the midwife, who was sometimes a skilled empiric but more often a clumsy, ignorant woman. Such practices as placing vulture feathers under an expectant mother's body or holding a sprig of herb to the vaginal orifice in order to hasten delivery, described in Classical treatises, still found mention in manuscripts of the fourteenth and fifteenth centuries. In the sixteenth century Paré, humble surgeon that he was, engaged in obstetrics and, among other useful services, made the suggestion that, in certain cases of abnormal delivery, the child should be turned in the mother's womb before delivery. Subsequently, serious works on obstetrics were published by physicians, although chiefly for the use of women attendants; Hendrik van Deventer's *Novum Lumen* (1701) was perhaps the best of them for a long time. In the late seventeenth century in France some innovations were ventured, the chief being the introduction of forceps for delivery, but forceps remained the secret of a family of male obstetricians for generations. The skill of the Dutch surgeon Van Roonhuyze with caesarean sections has already been mentioned.

Only in the late eighteenth century did objection to 'male midwives' begin to die down. Several French *accoucheurs* won approval in high places, and when William Hunter, the elder brother of John Hunter and also an esteemed anatomist and surgeon, became the leading obstetrician of London, another stronghold of social and professional prejudice collapsed. Even so until in the nineteenth century the importance of clinical sterilization was recognized, mere lack of cleanliness in large part continued to account for the high death rate of puerperal fever.

Quackery despite Genuine Advances

The advance of knowledge in physiology and pharmacology had less effect upon the medical profession as a craft than might be surmised. The physician looked askance at the pretensions of the apothecary and others to prescribe to the sick or to teach new methods. Much of his suspicion was justifiable, for charlatans abounded, and ignorance of the origin of disease made the credulous sick an easy prey.

Though alchemists and astrologers had by the eighteenth century faded out in the field of medicine, quackery retained a firm hold. With the plethora of nostrums it might even have grown worse, particularly in England where 'patent' or 'proprietary' medicines were protected by law. The credulous and the desperate have in all ages fallen dupes to downright charlatans or to half-learned if well-meaning zealots. A poster proclaimed to eighteenth-century London: 'Doctor Frederick . . . undertakes to Cure the Gout, and Rheumatism, without any return. . . . Likewise, Cures the yellow Jaundice, Stitching in the Side. He likewise Cures any Body who is bit by a Mad Dog. . . . No cure No Pay.'[19] Doctor Frederick was not so well known in the annals of magic as his contemporaries Frederick Anton Mesmer (1733–1815) and 'Count Allessandro Cagliostro' (1743–95), whose real name was Giuseppi Balsamo. But zealots like Mesmer must not be confused with quacks like Cagliostro. Mesmer, who published his theory of 'animal magnetism' in 1775, was an over-enthusiastic pioneer in the study of hypnotism, which he did not fully understand. Cagliostro was a charlatan taking advantage of the prevailing enthusiasm for freemasonry and other occult forces to make money out of misery, ignorance, and credulity. Quacks as well as some honest men also worked with electricity as a cure of disease, but with no significant results. Perhaps the most notorious of the more serious workers in this field was Dr Jean-Paul Marat (1743–93), the future 'Friend of the People'.

Revolution would perhaps be more a misnomer if used to describe the advances in medicine during the period between 1300 and 1775 than if used, as it more frequently is, to describe those in abstract science, industry, commerce, and agriculture. Much more revolutionary ideas were yet to come in the treatment of disease. Nevertheless, the advances in the field during these centuries were crucial. Not only did physiology move somewhat toward the discovery of the germ theory but also the apothecary, the obstetrician, and the surgeon began to occupy a respected professional status (see Chapter XVI). Physicians came to be less exercised about the teachings of rival Classical schools and more about the findings of recent research in anatomy, physiology, and pharmacology. Until the nineteenth century, however, medicine remained essentially empirical.

TECHNOLOGY AND THE STATE

The political implications of economic and social changes during our period have already been indicated in the first chapter, where some of those changes were attributed in part at least to scientific and technological factors. Here we shall be concerned more exclusively with the role played by technology in strengthening the modern state.

Science, Technology, and the Secular Society and State

The growth of science fairly closely coincided with the growth of the nation-state in the West. These developments combined with several others that we have examined to help weaken the hold of the organized churches on men's minds so that the Christian ethic no longer guided men's thoughts at the end of our period so prescriptively as it once had. By the eighteenth century, a secular ideology, drawn chiefly from the every day empirical world and holding man accountable to rules derived from Nature rather than from God, had come to share dominion with the Christian tradition. For those who held the secular view, Nature was still dependent upon God, to be sure, but less as First and Final Cause than as daily provider and regulator. For many (but certainly not most) educated persons God was the Great Clock-maker, who having made and wound up His clock, let it run its own course, subject to its own limitations.

In proportion as such a view of God took root, the church lost prestige. That view challenged the church's hold as a link (whether necessary, as in the Roman creed, or merely desirable, as in Protestantism) with the Father who gave man his daily bread and forgave his trespasses or sins. Rather, men tended now to turn toward the state for welfare and regulation of conduct, and—slowly at first, more rapidly later—the state took over many of the church's non-religious obligations. Charity and virtue became civic as well as religious duties, though not yet so conspicuously in our period as after the revolutions of the eighteenth century. And so to the forces that were considered worthy of royal or administrative patronage (because they might enhance state power, help to attain civic welfare, or promote good civic conduct) was added a secular kind of spiritual welfare. The same authority that undermined feudal power, that gave merchants charters for trading companies, that protected inventive men by laws of patent, that built canals, policed roads, and granted towns special privileges also tried to make church hierarchies into departments of state. The new merchant and industrial classes at times aligned themselves with the rulers against the older and higher orders of society to promote these secular purposes.

Coincident with these political changes, a new intellectual tone matured out of the scientific discoveries of the seventeenth century and after. The medieval Schoolman had assumed that man's knowledge and ability was finite, reaching toward but never grasping the plenitude of God's knowledge and providence. The Scholastic was interested in comprehending the universe in a context related particularly to God's conduct toward man and in adjusting reason to faith. If he could accomplish those ends (though he never dared to hope that he could every wholly do so) he thought he would understand all that it was necessary for him to understand. Seventeenth-century science was also interested in the comprehension of the divine purpose, and among the new scientists many, probably most, were content to look upon the Book of Nature as a material manifestation of the Will of God. But the new science rarely assumed that the acquisition of knowledge had finite limits, and it was interested in knowledge not only for the better understanding of the ways of God but for prediction and control of the ways of Nature and Man as well.

Control, some dared to hope, would become available through a proper alliance between technology and science. Leonardo da Vinci made some grandiose (if private) speculations, and Francis Bacon not only proclaimed the aim of bringing knowledge from Heaven to earth, from the speculative to the experimental, but also described the inductive method by which that transfer might be effected. Yet the transfer could not come by proclamation alone. Contemporary artisans and craftsmen could provide only a limited amount of the labour and mechanical skill needed to implement Leonardo's designs and Bacon's words. The manufacture of complex mechanical devices needed to be rationalized into standardized and costly techniques. Such a rationalization, however, required, in addition to greater theoretical knowledge, the investment of large capital sums and the employment of many hands, and so in most instances it had to wait until a later era for the necessary capital and labour pools.

In other instances, however, contemporaneous developments in politics and economics helped to answer these needs The rulers' quest for absolutism led them to provide the economic wherewithal as well as other means needed to achieve their ends. The nobility, no longer occupied with feudal warfare and knightly chivalry, looked for new interests, new sources of power, and new objects of patronage and frequently found them in economic enterprise. The rise of a merchant class and the declining prestige of the clergy induced society to respect the concept of free trade and profit rather than church scruples about money transactions. The growth of absolutism through the alliance of kings with the middle class against the nobility, the more pronounced control of church and feudality by national governments, and the growth of the capitalistic spirit through the spreading desire (not to mention the spreading approval of the desire) to invest money in order to make more money—all these may be interrelated somehow with the growth of science, although the exact relationship among them remains subject to controversy. Entrepreneurs, merchants, and industrialists certainly encouraged the sciences and technology, and the quantitative spirit of mathematics and science seems in its turn to have been at least favourable, if not conducive, to the capitalistic spirit.[20]

For their part the rulers encouraged science largely because of their hope for dynastic advantage from it The monarch's power in the time of the so-called absolute monarchy was in fact weak in comparison with that of the authoritarian dictator of subsequent times, not merely because the former was likely to feel more fully bound by history and family tradition but partly also because the technological means of implementing his authority were relatively limited. Huge areas of public activity were still inadequately supervised or wholly untouched by centralized administration, generally because of technical inadequacies; police forces, public health facilities, vital statistics, public utilities, disaster relief, social insurance, universal education, and several other responsibilities of the modern state, if not totally unknown to the central governments of the eighteenth century, were exceptional, unofficial, or local, and in any case inadequate. The problems of communication and transportation alone (and there were others) made co-ordination of such activities in the royal capital difficult. Hence no ruler could afford to be indifferent to proposals for speeding up transportation (of troops as well as goods) and production (of revenue as well as commodities), since a better method of determining longitude at sea, the drawing of more accurate charts and maps, the improvement of vehicular techniques and roads, the development of new metallurgical methods, or the invention of industrial and agricultural machines might enhance the centralization and autarky of the state and the power of the ruler. For all their patronage of science, however, rulers entertained the hope of finding new basic truths usually only as a secondary matter. The work of Newton, not immediately utilitarian, was not directly supported by the royal government during his lifetime, for what good was it? If he was buried in Westminster Abbey, it was because his name was publicly adulated. Scientific societies, to be sure, were encouraged by various rulers, but primarily to burnish the royal patrons' glory and lift the prestige and self-sufficiency of their states. In France when Louvois succeeded Colbert as protector of the Academy of Sciences he deliberately pushed French scientists toward practical work. (Pl.88a.) Perhaps it was no coincidence that during Louvois's protectorship (1683–99) French contributions to theoretical science were practically negligible.

Nevertheless, whatever their ulterior motives, governments, whether absolute or limited, generally aided nascent science and technology both directly and indirectly. They established royal porcelain and tapestry works. They patronized scientists and scientific academies. They prompted, financed, and rewarded inventors of practical instruments. In paternalistic states like Prussia and France state support was more evident than in parliamentary England. Although the English king granted patents and Parliament offered bounties to many (the collection of which, however, was sometimes not easy), the failure of the Stuart kings to establish an absolutism and the consequent growth of the power of Parliament led to restrictions upon royal expenditures and upon the granting of monopolies. In compensation, private persons in England assumed a greater share of the burden of promoting science and the arts.

Contemporary scientists were well aware of the importance of substantial support for their work and the government's mercantilist motives in providing it. Advocating the proposal to establish a scientific society in Vienna, Leibniz once wrote to Prince Eugene of Savoy:

'To perfect the arts, industries, agriculture, . . . architecture, the chorographic description of countries, the work of mines, as well as to keep the needy employed [and] to encourage inventors and entrepreneurs—in short, for whatever may affect the economy and machinery of the civil and military order, it is necessary to have observatories, laboratories, herbal gardens, menageries, collections of natural and artificial rarities, [and] a yearly physico-medical account of the reports and observations that every paid doctor will be obliged to provide.'[21]

The value of science and technology as tools of government was fully appreciated by Louis XIV, Peter the Great, Frederick the Great, and other 'enlightened despots'. Under the systematic mercantilism of Louis XIV's Colbert, the state exhibited exceptional vigour in building canals, dredging rivers, improving harbours, draining swamps, stimulating agriculture, granting bounties for the production of war material, and patronizing the arts, crafts, and sciences—primarily in order to improve communication and transport, increase production, raise revenue, assure national self-sufficiency, and add to the luster of the French crown at home and abroad. (Pl. 58b.)

The State as a Source of Social Services

The impact of technology upon government came not only from its direct application to civil and military problems but also from the more subtle effects of its application to the public warfare. The advance of technology combined with other contemporaneous developments to convert the typical European from a Christian who was incidentally a subject of his sovereign into a subject who was incidentally a Christian. For a few this conversion must have been a conscious process; for most it probably went on unperceived; and for many it may not have happened at all. *In toto*, however, it was a major change that helped to distinguish the modern mode of thought from one that had previously been common to all the world. The change is explained largely by a point already made: Europeans were likely now to look less to Providence for direct intervention in their affairs and more to political and social agencies. Although the church remained important as such an agency, by the close of our period the government had already superseded it for some social services and was assuming a larger role in all. This displacement of a force based largely upon other-worldly faith by one based largely on this worldly power was both a major sign and a cause of the secularization of European thought and manners. The number still was legion of those whose conduct was guided by the church or, at least, the servants of the church, which threatened punishment or promised reward in the hereafter, but it was diminishing proportionally to the number of those whose conduct was guided by the government or, at least, the servants of the government, which commanded bayonets and, in addition, held out the hope of health and happiness in the here-and-now. And more and more frequently men of science, either directly or indirectly, entered the service of governments.

Governmental services to individuals or communities depend in large part on the stability and strength of the central authorities, for the degree of co-operation to be expected from local, church, and voluntary agencies in the separate communities may be expected to vary with the political situation. Medieval communities, often governed indirectly by a remote, decentralized authority, were, we have observed, woefully lacking in all except the most basic governmental services. Roads and streets were often bad, dirty, poorly lighted, and poorly policed. A rare manor house might be blessed with running water, and a fortunate city might be supplied by an old Roman aqueduct, but communities had normally to depend on local wells, neighbouring streams, and water carriers. Hospitals, almshouses, and schools were generally run by the clergy, and though they were served as a rule by conscientious religious who usually were no more inefficient than the approved methods of the day obliged them to be, their guiding principle was charity rather than social service, and their ultimate goal was care rather than cure or indoctrination rather than education. Medieval governments frequently lacked not only the information requisite to adequate economic planning but even the means to acquire or interpret it.

In contrast, eighteenth-century governments generally were stronger, and a major part of their strength was a product of technological improvements. Engineering and invention had helped to provide more complete records as well as better waterways, bridges, and roads. They contributed to more rapid communication and transportation, more systematic bookkeeping and revenue collection, more effectual police and military movements, a more coordinated officialdom, and other means of efficient centralization. During our period governments advanced far on the way toward modern administrative methods.

Yet an eighteenth-century absolute government was in all probability still considerably less centralized than a twentieth-century bureaucracy. In pre-Revolutionary France, Europe's centralized monarchy *par excellence*, problems of communication and transport were so unmanageable that local government was largely guided by custom rather than royal decree. Until the Revolution the Bourbon monarchs collected some of their revenue through tax-farming and some through a revenue system that, while radiating from Paris, was discriminatory, respecting old provincial boundaries, local privileges, and class exemptions. The government of England, less complicated because of a longer common and insular political experience, still put the chief responsibility for day-to-day law and order in the hands of justices of the peace and other local authorities. The government of the Holy Roman Empire was distributed among hundreds of local units, some of them undistinguishable from *opéra bouffe* principalities.

During our period, however, European governments to a limited extent adopted the social and political pattern that has become familiar today. The point need not be belaboured again, but a few additional examples of governmental services may underline it. As the advance in medical knowledge indicated to authorities the advantage or proper precautions against plague, quarantine was enforced by municipal or other authorities. London, Toledo, Augsburg, Paris, and several other European cities made great strides in the establishment of waterworks for their growing populations, though without being able to guarantee the purity of the water. Richelieu, Sully, and Colbert had laid down so good a pattern for France that it had the best system of roads, coaches, and couriers in Europe, with the anticipated improvement in the efficiency of government functions. England was not far behind. East of the Rhine and Danube Rivers, however, road systems were bad indeed, travel was more hazardous and uncommon, and government officials (though not for that reason alone) generally less effective.

Warfare as 'Military Science'

During our period national governments were more interested in conducting war than they were to be again (except for the Revolutionary and Napoleonic era) until the twentieth century. Europe in the 1600s had only seven calendar years of general international peace; the preceding and the next century had little better records. With the introduction and step-by-step improvement of firearms, the techniques and strategy of warfare changed markedly. The feudal lord who carried on war on his own income for private purposes had become an anachronism. For that and other reasons which have been sketched elsewhere, at the same time that the Christian became more of a temporal subject, the vassal's loyalty to his liege lord gave way to the soldier's loyalty to his sovereign. Not only was the pay of soldiers now the obligation of the state: supply of weapons, and, by the eighteenth century, full support of the soldier also became the responsibility of the central government. Uniformity and regimentation became a desired military end and was reflected in the clothing of troops in garb that could easily be identified; hence the modern uniform. At the same time tactics became more specialized—not only foot and horse were needed but also artillery, grenadiers, engineers, and other specialist corps. Warfare had become an expensive and complicated branch of learning—'military science'.

By the eighteenth century the size of armies was unprecedented. Yet, in contrast to the reckless wastage of the Thirty Years' War, manpower was jealously conserved by generals and kings and saved from battle as much as possible. Thus, paradoxically, as military force waxed, the ferocity of war waned. After the Thirty Years' War, as fortresses became vital to defence and artillery to offense (see above) land strategy centred upon the siege of fortified works by means of trenches and cannon. The proper deployment of troops was learned by systematized precision drill. Eighteenth-century Continental field tactics required long, well-spaced infantry lines and presumed immediate response to orders; in drill at least it had a Baroque regularity and symmetry reminiscent of the minuet. Well-trained contingents were not readily expendable and were sparingly risked. The small principalities of the Empire and the cantons of Switzerland, without adequate finances to equip and maintain their armies, often hired them out as mercenary units. As the private forces of the condottieri or a Wallenstein disappeared, such mercenary armies took their place, and few rulers at war scrupled to hire contingents of mercenaries from other rulers. Mercenaries were not interested in annihilating one another, and commanders had to take their lack of zeal into consideration.

Despite the brilliance of Marlborough, Charles XII, Saxe, Eugene, Frederick, and other generals, and despite the large numbers engaged and killed or wounded in some of the battles of the War of the Spanish Succession and the Seven Years' War, eighteenth-century warfare in Europe essentially was *guerre en dentelle*. Professional soldiers (of the lower classes as a rule) fought under 'officers and gentlemen' according to conventional rules of strategy and tactics, rarely involving non-combatants in their professional activities. The rules sometimes did not work well, however, particularly in wilder terrain. The British General Edward Braddock lost his life and most of his army on the American frontier during the French and Indian War when he attempted to employ European tactics against American Indians in a wilderness. And sometimes officers, failing to observe the rules like gentlemen, employed ruse or broke their word of honour. Emphasis on professional discipline, gentlemanly conduct, and conventional tactics nevertheless was to continue until the rise of 'the nation in arms' during the wars of the French Revolution, when behaviour and strategy more suitable to a volunteer citizens' army fighting for a cause evolved.

Governments meanwhile came more and more to recognize the need of inventive minds and technological innovation for military purposes. Yet, if science and technology aided warfare, they were in turn stimulated by the new techniques of war. Ballistics helped to overthrow Aristotelian physics, and new metallurgical knowledge came out of the search for better alloys for making cannon. The determination of longitude at sea, the manœuvrability of ships, the quality of horses and roads, fire superiority, and a number of other largely scientific and technological matters were now factors in building up esprit de corps, shaping the strategy of commanders, and determining the outcome of battles. In the eighteenth century a ruler needed to be a good administrator rather than a military hero. Frederick the Great was a military man, to be sure, but no king of England since George II has appeared on a field of battle, nor was actual command in battle any longer normally expected of the heads of states anywhere. Warfare was now too specialized to leave to kings; kings needed trained and tested generals, and generals needed technological experts.

THE IMPACT OF SCIENCE AND TECHNOLOGY ON LIFE AND THOUGHT

Changes in Diet, Clothing, and Housing

As the scientific and geographical horizons of European man expanded, inevitable changes entered his everyday life. If the intellectual impact of invention, discovery, and exploration, and the increased opportunities for professional enterprise and economic investment affected only a limited number, the material impact reached the great majority. All classes benefited to a greater or less extent from the introduction of new items and the improvement of old ones among the staples. In Ireland and on the Continent the potato rapidly became a part of the daily diet of the poor and gradually also of the rich. The incidence of rickets, scurvy, and some other diseases diminished as greater supplies of fresh meat, fish, fruits, and vegetables made up in part for the vitamin deficiency of earlier diets (see above). Cane sugar was cheaper than honey; it added carbohydrates to, and helped to remove monotony from, the diet of rich and poor alike, and it also supplied the basis of some great fortunes derived from the operation of plantations and the slave trade. The sugar colonies of France and England became the most highly prized jewels in their crowns of empire. The introduction of snuff and other forms of tobacco from Virgina caused both controversy and pleasure upon their debut in Europe. New beverages such as coffee and tea, both introduced to Europe in the seventeenth century, brought the pleasant institution of the coffeehouse and a new repast, the 'afternoon tea' of the English-speaking world, probably borrowed from the tea ceremony initiated in Japan in the fifteenth century. The greater accessibility of the East made more available the preservative qualities as well as the gustatory delight of exotic spices. The English Grocers' Company, when incorporated in 1428, consisted chiefly of importers of spices, and to this day the French word for grocer is *épicier* (*spicer*), and the full German is *Kolonialwarenhandler* (*dealer in colonial goods*).

By the eighteenth century, in England, France, and the Low Countries the general standard of living began to rise, stimulated by mounting foreign trade, new products, and an improving technology. These conditions generally provided more urban employment as well as higher wages for the purchase of more commodities, though they also created the hardships of displacement and slums. In western Europe the poorer peasants continued, however, to live on vegetables (rarely available in winter), bread, cheese, and an occasional slice of meat, and the diet of the poor became worse the further east one went in Europe. In eighteenth-century England, on the other hand, the demand for white bread grew; dark bread (though later known to be dietetically preferable) was looked upon as a mark of poverty. Wheat became available in increasing amounts because of the increase in wheat acreage brought about by the increasing tempo of the enclosure movement.

As the rural population migrated and the cities grew, urban marketing facilities became strained, and food markets in London and elsewhere were sometimes described as revolting. Though said to be common practice in China, refrigeration of perishable items by natural ice (stored in earth houses during the summer) was introduced in Europe only at the close of the eighteenth century; before that, fish and fruit were rarely fresh after long hauls from seaports and orchards. Drunkenness was common, and the quantity of gin consumed became a national menace; Hogarth's pictorial preaching on the danger of gin probably did not overdraw the evil. Governmental intervention by means of heavy excises and licencing regulations raised the price of drink, but if it reduced consumption at all, it did not eliminate the ill. Life for the poor in factory areas may have been no more miserable—indeed, must have been better enough to induce migration to the cities—but, in spite of the probably greater comfort of city workers' dwellings as compared to country workers' cottages, personal awareness of misery seemed to increase in the early stages of 'the Industrial Revolution'.

Heavy concentration of population in slums, the tyranny of the clock and the machine, the humdrumness of specialized operations in a factory, the competition for jobs all seemed more damnable than the curse of poverty on the land. Humanitarians and landed gentry were less likely to become exercised over the country worker under the putting-out system, who converted his entire family into economic assets by turning his cottage into a spinning or weaving establishment, than over the factory hand (especially a woman or a child) who exhibited poverty, disease, and drunkenness on city streets. In righteous indignation they challenged weak and all too often reluctant municipal governments to find some solution to the problems of inadequate urban housing and public health.[22]

If cotton produced the evils of the textile factory system, it also brought some blessings. For one thing, it filled the growing demand for a cheap textile. Silk was difficult to wash, wool was rarely subjected to soap and water, but cotton cloth was easy to launder. Cotton not only made possible a higher standard of cleanliness but was also more comfortable in the summertime. Moreover, the cotton industry, not hampered by the guild regulations controlling silk and wool, was able to take advantage of technological change much more rapidly. In the seventeenth and eighteenth centuries calico became the favourite textile.

The Spread of the New Knowledge and Its Limitations

While cheap textiles were revolutionizing clothing, while timepieces were transforming social and working habits, and while mathematics was converting some of a population that had been used to thinking about the will of God into counters and calculators of quantities, the improvements in the printing press were helping to make possible a slight increase of literacy and the easier dissemination of ideas throughout society. The accumulation of knowledge in the natural sciences in the seventeenth and eighteenth centuries might well have come—though perhaps less rapidly—without the printing press, for much of the research was the work of able individuals. Young scholars travelled great distances to study with esteemed masters; older men of science visited one another and exchanged lengthy letters. Galileo, Kepler, Descartes, Mersenne, Ricci, and others kept up with distant colleagues a correspondence that imparted news of great discoveries, their own and others' (and still form some of the best sources for much of the history of science before the development of the scientific journals).

Yet in so far as these men were dependent on others' findings, they also learned and taught by easily circulated printed works, and presumably more readily than if they had been limited to scarce manuscripts and personal communication. While the great scientific academies might have owned impressive libraries if there had been no printing, for they probably could have afforded manuscript collections, many of the numerous local academies and private botanical societies would doubtless have found the cost of manuscripts prohibitive. Thus some at least of the *sociétés de pensées* given to serious discussion of political as well as scientific questions might never have come into being, and their impact on the intellectual ferment of the eighteenth century, for better or for worse, might have been lost. As it was, that impact was all the greater because the new technology had helped to promote the concept of the literate worker. Since the mid-seventeenth century, more and more jobs had become available that demanded some basic knowledge of reading and of simple sums, and education for business and the trades as well as for ecclesiastical, governmental, and professional purposes had begun to appear imperative (see Chapter XVI).

Despite the vogue of the new science, superstition retained its place in the life of the credulous or ill-informed. Waves of witchcraft persecutions continued until the late seventeenth century. They seem to have been due to political unrest as well as to superstition. Those areas of Roman Catholic and Protestant Germany most blighted by the disaster of the Thirty Years' War carried on the most extreme persecution of 'witches', and one of the most dramatic took place in New England in two waves that interrelated chrono-logically and perhaps causally with the uncertainties of the two seventeenth-century revolutions in England. Belief in witches diminished, however, as the rational spirit grew, and the last executions for witchcraft in Europe took place, scattered and singly, in the eighteenth century.

The impact of the new science on religion was ambivalent. As early as the seventeenth century Bacon spoke of the dichotomy of science and religion, undoubtedly attempting to protect science against irrelevant criticism. By the end of the century this sort of precaution was no longer necessary. Most scientists of the seventeenth and eighteenth centuries were devout; only few took occasion to attack Christianity. On the contrary, the scientist was more apt to introduce religious ideas into science, hesitating to harbour a concept of a world so mechanical as to leave no room for God or Providence. But how could one believe in the miracles and prophecies of Revelation, on the one hand, and scientific laws, on the other? How could one explain the statements in the Bible that seemed contrary to newly discovered fact? Why should the myriad souls of ethical heathen cultures be damned merely by their lack of Revelation? In spite of their awareness of such enigmas, genuine atheism was hard to find among scientists. Greater danger to orthodox Christian doctrine came from philosophic writers like Spinoza and the Deists. Spinoza's pantheism identified the Perfect Self-Existent with the Universe, discarding the concept of a transcendent personal God. The Deists retained a trans-cendent God in their cosmological scheme but robbed Him of the role of governing His universe. Yet, no matter how rife in intellectual circles, skepticism was not widespread in eighteenth-century Europe. Spinoza's pantheism was not influential, and for every Deist (who might be intensely religious in his own way) there were many Jesuits, Jansenists, Pietists,

Baptists, Hasids, ṣūfīs, or other kinds of devout and professing Catholics, Protestants, Jews, and Muslims.

Perfectibility, Humanitarianism and Rationalism

The transition from medieval to modern scientific thought in Europe came in part from, and in turn helped to bring about, a change in the concept of what kind of knowledge was important. To a medieval Scholastic, all knowledge that mattered was in a sense knowable: plenitude of knowledge existed in God's mind, and true human understanding was best directed toward coming ever closer to a knowledge of God's ways. With the 'scientific revolution', knowledge, though still valued for the sake of understanding God and His Book of Nature, assumed a new dimension; it had come to mean also a never-ending increase in human power—that is, in man's comprehension of, and control over, nature, including human nature.

An obvious problem arose from this new, or at least more fully appreciated, relationship of science and humanity: Science could be used either for good or for evil. The challenge of Francis Bacon to make science the means for the betterment of society was taken up by the *philosophes* of the eighteenth century. The medieval concept of Christian brotherhood, conceived in relationship to an all-knowing, all-powerful, and ever-loving Father, was translated into the humanitarianism of the eighteenth century. The ringing proclamation of the 'unalienable rights' of 'all men' was based on the certitude that Man could change his social structures by reasoning applied to rational principles and self-evident truths, derived not from God alone (if from God at all) but also from ascertainable unchanging laws of Nature.

Learned men of the era considered the knowledge of mathematics essential to the understanding of Nature, of a world subject to measurement. But how much in the world was in fact subject to measurement? The mathematics of probabilities suggested that the area between improbability and certainty could constantly be reduced as more data became available; differential and integral calculus suggested that much that was baffling in Nature wavered somewhere between calculable maximum and minimum limits. Were the rules of Nature as binding in human affairs, some wondered, as in the physical universe? If so, were they, too, subject to mathematical analysis? These were questions that the mathematicians as well as the *philosophes* of the eighteenth century raised (see Chapter IX), but they counted upon geometrical reasoning rather than statistical analysis or some other techniques of modern social science to furnish the correct answers.

The answers the *philosophes* derived satisfied them that society, too, was subject to ascertainable laws. Doubts regarding scientific concepts that had been considered true for centuries and regarding religious precepts that had hitherto seemed unquestionable accompanied—in fact, in some instances, incited—similar doubts regarding the structure of contemporary society.

Moreover, critics could see the abuses of society all about them. Could society, then, be better organized upon the tenets of reason? Was there a 'natural' society? What institutions best conformed to 'the laws of Nature'? This adaptation of naturalism to human institutions became the touchstone of the Enlightenment. It led to a new concept of 'perfection', to the idea of 'perfectibility' (see Chapter VII).

The new science joined with other forces to induce many intellectuals to discard the sense of inferiority to the Ancients inculcated by Renaissance man, who had adored Antiquity. Modern man had learned some things unknown to the Greeks and Romans. Might he not be equal or perhaps superior to his forbears? Sculptors might well argue subjectively over the comparative merits of Myron and Bernini, but advance in science was in some ways objectively measurable. By the eighteenth century, an intelligent schoolboy obviously had much more scientific information about some phenomena than Aristotle could have had. Together with the growing distrust of the Christian concepts of sin and the plan of God, science thus led to the eighteenth-century idea of human perfectibility. It not only seemed to point toward a steady accumulation of knowledge but it also had vaguely glimpsed the concept of an indefinite, unguided, and continuous evolution of life (see Chapter IX).

Hence, far from believing that man by nature was evil and incapable of perfection save by divine intervention, the *philosophe* was likely to hold that society made man what he was and, as society improved, man would improve. Rousseau contended that man had a *faculté de se perfectionner*. Condorcet saw reason to believe that man had embarked on a course of intellectual, moral, and biological perfectibility that was irreversible. The late-eighteenth-century concept of *perfectibility* was different from earlier notions of *perfection*, whether Jesuit or Leibnizian (see Chapter VII). *Perfection* was a Christian ideal, attainment of the Heavenly City by the grace of God for the faithful; *perfectibility* was an unending historical process of limitless improvement for all men. Change for the *philosophes* was not only in keeping with natural law, it was not even limited by Christian ideals of perfection. Both the fixed, hierarchical order of society and the intellectual tradition of church and aristocracy were thus jeopardized by the questioning brought on by natural philosophy.

This intellectual atmosphere favoured the enlightened despot and the humanitarian, each seeking in his own way to achieve the reforms that Nature, as he saw it, dictated. In the eighteenth century the number of hospitals increased throughout Europe; anti-slavery societies sprang up; prison and tax reform movements became popular; legal reform, toleration, and philanthropy (*bienfaisance*) made great strides because they were efforts by enlightened rulers or private benefactors to correct what was "unnatural'; *civilization* became a word of current usage. The benevolent state or individual seemed to stand for a more rational world against church and aristocracy, the champions of tradition; Nature and science seemed allied with Reason on the side of change and perfectibility.

So did the new knowledge of the geographical world. As every region of the world grew more aware of other regions, the growing awareness helped to shape many aspects of life in each of them. We have already examined some of the effects of extra-European art, architecture, technology, products, and customs upon Europe, and of corresponding European influences upon non-European areas. Until the end of the eighteenth century European technology, despite having outstripped all others since 1500, eagerly borrowed from the Middle East, India, and China, while they were unwilling to borrow in return. Only in the Americas had a European veneer been imposed upon the native substructure.

One of Europe's imports was a subtle influence refined, so to speak, from the raw materials of America and the South Seas—the concept of the 'noble savage'. Beginning with More's *Utopia* and La Hontan's *Nouveaux voyages . . . dans l'Amérique septentrionale* and coming down to Diderot's *Supplément au voyage de Bougainville* and Raynal's *Histoire philosophique et politique . . . des Européens dans les deux Indes*, an idealized picture of the nobility of man in primitive societies had grown up to fortify the belief of some that only civilized man is vile. This at first amorphous idea was formulated into a persuasive creed in Rousseau's writings, though probably by a misreading of his real intent. Aided by the scientists' emphasis on natural phenomena, the 'return to nature' developed into a veritable cult. Semi-learned societies turned botanical. Queens and noblemen played at being close to the soil. Urban families went out to the country or the mountains to admire the beauty of nature. Writers, with Rousseau and young Goethe showing the way, began to feel that Reason unaided by the nobler instincts might lead only to materialistic bleakness and error while inner feelings and emotions might lead to intuitive truth mingled with joy. The vogue of Rationalism declined, giving way to a nascent Romanticism.

The Savants' Contribution to the Rise of Cosmopolitanism

By the end of the eighteenth century, science had also lent support to the dream of a world community, whether based upon religious precepts regarding the brotherhood of man or utopian preachments of pacifism. In an era in which patriotic loyalties still rested most often on dynastic ties, the idea of peaceful co-operation of nations was posited on co-operation among princes rather than peoples. Crucé's *New Cyneas* had been largely ignored in its own day, but St Pierre's scheme for a perpetual peace led to Rousseau's discussion of the same problem later in the century, and Rousseau's in turn to Kant's before the century ended (see Chapter IX). An increase of intercourse among scientists and of co-operation among scientific societies kept pace with the growth of embassies, the development of the idea of international congresses to preserve or restore peace, and the publication of treatises on international law. The ideal of a world united by the collaboration of scientists, engineers, and physicians as well as princes to combat war, catastrophe, poverty, disease, and hunger was one of the favourite themes of *philosophes* and humanitarians.

As a matter of fact, the community of scientists and writers in the seventeenth and eighteenth centuries enjoyed a considerable degree of freedom of communication. National jealousies and government restrictions rarely impeded their interchanges with passport requirements, immigration regulations, and postal censorship. By the end of the seventeenth century correspondence among the learned had become commonplace, thanks to the fuller development of postal services and the rise of scientific societies and journals. If personal rivalries like the unfortunate dispute of Leibniz and Newton developed among scientists, official pressure for secrecy was nevertheless exceptional; patents and trade secrets were a greater deterrent to the general use of new devices. The co-operation of several governments in the scientific expeditions of the eighteenth century and the award of prizes and honours to foreigners by royal patrons and academies testify that the scientist was usually considered a free agent and a servant of mankind. The society of Europe's scientists was cosmopolitan, imbued with the ideal of comprehension and control of the forces of nature and with the hope that their discoveries would alleviate human misery and replace human labour with machines. No matter how ready governments might be to use technological aids for domestic advantage, seldom before the end of the eighteenth century did national interests tend to make scientific discovery into a tool of state power.

That did not mean that Europe's achievement was a universal good, for Europe's scientific and technological advance was not an unmixed blessing for less machine-minded peoples. The use of ships, firearms, and other technological devices gave to a small number of men an effective control over sprawling nations like the Aztecs and the Incas—a control that probably would have been impossible to achieve otherwise. The relatively tiny area of western Europe thus laid the foundation of political dominance and cultural influence throughout the world, and in the nineteenth century its political power at least would make itself indubitably felt. Europe's rapid advance in science and technology, functioning in an ever more receptive society, helps to explain how, by the end of the eighteenth century, western Europe was vaguely beginning to abandon the theocratic, monarchic, and agricultural pattern of life that prevailed almost everywhere and to follow a predominantly technological, middle-class, and urban pattern, which it was destined to impose upon large sections of the rest of the world in the 1800's.

NOTES TO CHAPTER XV

1. Dr B. Gille points out that the study of technology still presents to the historian a peculiar problem since methodology and basic documentation are still the subject of dispute and research among specialists. He writes:
   'The problem of the history of techniques presents several different aspects which we feel should not be neglected. The first is what may be called the internal history of individual techniques. The history of individual processes, the history—or rather the genesis—of individual machines is, in many cases, not yet written, because such work would entail methodical organization on an international plan not difficult to envisage. The second aspect is that of technical systems, that is to say the study of a balanced group of techniques, together with the essential liaisons between their different practical applications. Finally come the relationships between such technical systems and the level of scientific knowledge and social structures. It is in the light of the latter that it becomes possible to discern the main lines of the evolution of technical systems, of the imbalances involved, the delays in given sectors and the resultant brakes.'

2. Michael Confino, 'La Comptabilité des domaines privés en Russie dans la seconde moitié du XVIIIe siècle (d'après les "Travaux de la Société libre d'économie de Saint-Petersbourg")', *Revue d'histoire moderne et contemporaine*, VIII (1961), pp. 5–34.

3. A. R. Hall, *Ballistics in the Seventeenth Century* (Cambridge, 1952), p. 73.

4. Dr B. Gille says that generally speaking, mathematics rendered no fundamental services until a relatively late date. The authors rightly note this in the case of statistics and of insurance. Theoretical problems in ship building, which were to influence naval engineering, had to await the work of Bouguer and Euler in the middle of the eighteenth century. The same is true of ballistic tables and the work of Bélidor.

5. Quoted in Wolf, *16th and 17th Centuries*, p. 527.

6. Robert S. Woodbury, *History of the Lathe to 1850* (Cleveland, 1961).

7. Wolf, *Eighteenth Century*, p. 612.

8. See Charles Singer *et al.* (eds.), *A History of Technology*, Vol. III, *From the Renaissance to the Industrial Revolution, c. 1500–c. 1750* (Oxford, 1957), pp. 367–8.

9. Wolf, *16th and 17th Centuries*, p. 547.

10. Charles Singer *et al.* (eds.), *A History of Technology*, Vol. II, *The Mediterranean Civilizations and the Middle Ages, c. 700 B.C. to A.D. 1500* (Oxford, 1956), pp. 203–5.

11. Quoted in E. Poche, 'Le verre de Bohême', *Journal of World History*, V (1959), p. 438.

12. Wolf, *16th and 17th Centuries*, pp. 488–9.

13. Dr B. Gille notes that invention does not mean immediate application. Innovation, as the economists put it, takes place only when technical mutation has become indispensable. Coke smelting, born about 1709, was industrially perfected only towards 1735–40 (a time-lag often intervening between invention proper and the feasibility of its industrial application), and was finally adopted only after the development of puddling by Cort and with the widespread utilization of iron for bridge building, ship building, and in the extended use of machinery.

14. See Franz M. Feldhaus, *Die Teknik der Antike und des Mettelalters* (Potsdam, 1931), illustration (facing p. 384) of a fifteenth-century tread wheel crane.

15. See Gilbert Freyre, 'Impact of the Portuguese on the American Tropics', *Journal of World History*, IV (1958), pp. 582–602.

16. William Cowper, 'The Task' (1785).

17. Ignacio Olagüe, 'Les changements de climat dans l'histoire', *Journal of World History*, VII (1963), pp. 667–8.

18. See J. C. Drummond and Anne Wilbraham, *The Englishman's Food; a History of Five Centuries of English Diet* (London, 1939), esp. pp. 309–27.

19. Quoted in A. S. Turberville (ed.), *Johnson's England* (Oxford, 1952), II, p. 275.

20. See John U. Nef, 'The Genesis of Industrialism and of Modern Science (1560–1640)' in *Essays in Honor of Conyers Read* (Chicago, 1952), pp. 260–9.

21. Quoted in Hall, *Scientific Revolution*, p. 202.

22. See T. S. Ashton, 'The Treatment of Capitalism by Historians', in F. A. Hayek (ed.), *Capitalism and the Historians* (Chicago, 1954), pp. 33–63.

CHAPTER XVI

EDUCATION (1300–1775)

T HE rise and spread of libraries, the press, learned societies, and some of the more indirect channels for the communication of knowledge and traditions have been described above (see particularly Chapters X, XI, XIV and XV). We have also referred in several passages to guilds as intentionally providing a means of vocational training. Here we shall consider primarily the more formal systems of schools and schooling, a variety of educational theories, the popularization of science, and the modifications of professional training from the fourteenth to the eighteenth century.

EUROPEAN EDUCATIONAL INSTITUTIONS

Elementary and Secondary Schooling

In Europe during our period formal schooling became less the concern of the clergy than it had been and more the concern of secular authorities. So long as education was dominated by the church, almost all schools were church schools, and almost the only teachers by vocation were clerics.[1] Teaching, however, was not, strictly speaking, a separate profession but rather a side function of the clergy. Every clergyman, from the parish priest to the pope, was expected, at least incidentally, to give instruction in the faith to any Christian.

Outside the clerically dominated schools and universities, the educational process went on in informal ways. Sermons, lawsuits, cafés, salons, and other occasions or places permitted, even encouraged, men to air their views. In the fourteenth and fifteenth centuries this informal kind of education advanced to a high level by an unusually significant channel. Humanism, encountering resistance at first in the strongholds of Scholasticism in the universities, flourished in urban centres and at the courts of princes.[2] To cite a single example, Cosimo de' Medici's patronage made the palaces and villas of his family a centre of the new higher learning. They housed the institution known as the Platonic Academy (see Chapter VI), which helped to spread the knowledge of Greek language, literature, and philosophy far and wide. Greek diplomats and scholarly clerics met and exchanged views with Italian literati at the Academy's meetings. Ficino and others were

KK*

subsidized by this Medici 'foundation' to translate Aristotle and Plato and to write formidable philosophical commentaries, and its symposia served to enlighten courtiers, clergymen, and scholars in the intricacies of philosophy new and old. It became a model for the academies, the learned societies, and the *sociétés de pensée* that were a general feature of intellectual activity throughout Europe in ensuing centuries (see below). Such education as most of the common people received, however, was of a still more informal nature. Church windows, station pictures, altar decorations and other forms of art, much of the music and literature, and sometimes sermons and daily conversation were set in a context that was largely unintelligible except to those who knew the Christian tradition. These visual and aural media were ubiquitous, and the learning they imparted was gratuitous.

In communities where priests were readily accessible, children were likely to be more formally instructed. Catechism, chanting, and perhaps some religious reading constituted the common curriculum of the medieval parish schools. Choir boys would be taught singing and a little more in a 'song school'. In some of the larger towns there were chantry schools, endowed by wealthy citizens. Sometimes at the higher grades they were 'grammar' schools, giving fairly intensive training in reading and writing. Some guilds established schools, taught by their priests, for the children of their members. At a time when books were few and cumbersome and in Latin, book-learning was difficult to acquire, and at the lower levels most learning was by rote.

A more advanced type of education was also available for maturer students. It was restricted to unusually intelligent children (usually boys) who showed promise of a learned (and therefore clerical) career. Such education was carried on in monastic or cathedral schools, but no sharp break separated primary from secondary classes; pupils from five or six to the teen ages often went to the same schools. The *trivium* (grammar, rhetoric, and logic) and at a higher level the *quadrivium* (arithmetic, geometry, astronomy, and music) were the basic categories of knowledge. They were commonly taught without serious concern with the concrete or the practical and with a religious and moralistic emphasis.

In most cultures, until comparatively recent times, the education of girls was generally (but not necessarily) carried on in the home, and Europe was no exception to this rule. Well into modern times, European girls were trained to be housewives, whether the house was a peasant hut or a servant-filled palace. Their teachers were their mothers or (in wealthy, aristocratic homes) trusted governesses or servants. Girls were not often exposed to book-learning, and when they were, it was likely to be religious in character. Sometimes girls were taught in parochial schools by their parish priests, but if their parents could afford to send them away from home, they went to convent schools run by nuns. Most of the wives or daughters of princely families, especially in Italy, received their elementary training from tutors at home or in palace schools. The linguistic ability and breadth of learning of some of these women was impressive. Whether in a private home or at a school, the teachers emphasized the religious tradition—an emphasis (as well as the pupils' reaction against it) that is reflected in the stories of princesses who concealed their secular reading matter in prayerbook covers. The impact of this rigid training may perhaps be measured by the influence of an imposing number of women mystics upon both secular and ecclesiastical leaders.3 For all that, book-learned girls were the exception; schools were restricted mostly to boys.

Boys, like girls, began their training at home—so to speak, at their fathers' knees. For the lower social classes it included practical instruction in farm activities or industrial crafts. A boy learned by doing. For young noblemen, training in horsemanship, hunting, and the handling of weapons was paramount. A number of still surviving handbooks indicate that princes and exceptional young men of the upper classes received instruction also in political, social, and cultural matters. Such instruction was carried on chiefly by tutors in the home.

During the late Middle Ages a few secular schools arose, especially in Italian towns, and they departed from the ecclesiastical pattern in a number of ways. In this new kind of school the pupils, generally children of the middle classes, were given an education that fitted them for middle-class vocations. They might be taught to read and write the vernacular as well as Latin; they studied commercial arithmetic and other fundamentals of business life. They might be divided into elementary and secondary groups. Villani's *History of Florence* indicated that there were three types of schools in that city about 1300; nine hundred boys and girls attended elementary parish schools, about eleven hundred attended business schools, and about six hundred attended secondary schools of liberal arts. Some of these schools were coeducational. All of them were essentially vocational, providing the early steps in the training of young men for clerical, business, or professional careers.

In fact, during the fourteenth and fifteenth centuries, continuing an earlier trend, educational institutions, whether primary, secondary, or higher, were generally tending toward vocationalism. Bourgeois fathers who were ambitious for their sons to rise in the practical world were apt to start them in early youth toward a professional education, usually in law, perhaps in medicine or business rhetoric (*ars dictaminis*). Petrarch, Boccaccio, Luther, Calvin, and a number of less famous men broke away from the paternal preference for a practical, professional education to follow their own literary or religious inclinations.

The trend toward vocational education seems to have been less marked in circles not directly associated with a university. Three of the most remarkable examples of broadly enlightened education were provided in non-university towns—one in the Netherlands, one in England, and one in northern Italy. The religious mystic Groote (see Chapter III) inspired the

Brethren of the Common Life during the late fourteenth and early fifteenth centuries to establish schools in towns spread throughout the Netherlands. The school at Deventer was the most famous of them: under Master Alexander Hegius (*c.* 1433–98) it had over two thousand pupils. As befitted the atmosphere of the Renaissance, he added to its strictly religious curriculum serious instruction in the Classics. Students were trained to read and write Ciceronian Latin and to appreciate the virtues of Classical civilization, though without prejudice to the ideals and practices of Christianity. The effectiveness of the Brethren at Deventer and elsewhere in both instruction and school administration made them a weighty educational force in the North.[4] They trained boys and young men for the professions, to be sure, but also for a pious, intellectual life. Nicolas of Cusa, Pope Adrian VI, Erasmus, and Luther were merely a few of the outstanding men who were moulded at least in part in the Brethrens' schools.

At Deventer there prevailed the distinctively pious spirit of northern scholarship which was to become so evident in the Protestant Reformation. Colet's school of St Paul's in London provided another example of this spirit. It was a run-down establishment when he took charge, but he restored it with his own inherited fortune. Although it was connected with St Paul's Cathedral in London, he placed it under lay control—an innovation that reflected his critical attitude toward the clergy. Here, as at Oxford, he expounded and encouraged the pious humanism characteristic of the group known as the 'Oxford Reformers'. Milton eventually was to receive his early education at St Paul's.

Mantua was a third centre of education without direct association with a university. Here the initial impulse was provided by a princely patron of Classical learning. In 1425 Marchese Giovan Francesco II invited Vittorino da Feltre, a humanist layman, to create a palace school in which young nobles might receive a good education. Several enlightened rulers had established such institutions in earlier centuries, and about twenty years before Vittorino, Gasparino de Barzizza had founded a humanistic school in Padua, which Vittorino himself had attended. What made Vittorino a pioneer was his broadening of the Classical curriculum.

The educated man of the late Middle Ages was likely to be interested in harmonizing what he knew of mathematics, physics, and cosmology with the teachings of the church,[5] but Vittorino envisaged a program that would surmount the current emphasis upon religious content and vocational training. Since his objectives were at the same time moral, intellectual, and physical, he introduced a broad plan of instruction. His pupils studied not only Latin and Greek but also the vernacular so that they might be grounded in recent as well as church and Classical literature. In addition, they received schooling in mathematics, music, and art. Particularly exceptional for educational institutions of Vittorino's day was his emphasis on physical training; riding, swimming, marching, and fencing were obligatory. Perhaps the most noteworthy of his educational principles was equality of opportunity for learning. Though employed by a prince to educate princelings and young noblemen, he admitted to his school the children of the lower classes and—a radical departure in his day—at least one girl. His institution was thus both co-educational (to a limited degree) and democratic (in comparison with the common standards of the day). All pupils, regardless of social status, observed the same rules of dress, food, and good manners. He also provided attractive buildings and grounds, calling his school Casa Giocosa (Happy House). At several other Renaissance courts, boys and girls of princely and aristocratic families were given somewhat the same broad training for intelligent and cultured leadership in the affairs of state.

Unlike Deventer or St Paul's, Casa Giocosa reflected the secular trends of Renaissance civilization at its best, but, like Deventer and St Paul's, it exerted a tremendous influence through the many famous scholars it sent forth. In Vittorino's school can be seen the lay influence of rulers on education; in the school at Deventer (and despite lay management, even at London) can be seen the persistence of clerical influences. The Bible, the medieval church fathers, and other religious sources were, of course, studied at Mantua, but whereas at Deventer the curriculum was primarily religious, supplemented with the Classics, Vittorino's curriculum was primarily the Classics, supplemented with religious instruction.[6]

Hegius', Colet's, and Vittorino's ideal of breadth of schooling was not regularly entertained in educational circles. Most clerical educators were not humanist, and humanist educators, even when relatively free from religious dogmatism, occasionally went to other extremes, such as narrow emphasis on Classical syntax and style to the sacrifice of subject matter. In England this tendency was especially conspicuous in the schools that were endowed by laymen for the education of young gentlemen—among them, Winchester College (founded in 1382) and Eton College (1441). These colleges were among those which eventually became the 'great public schools' that played a proverbial role in the British scheme of secondary education. They prepared their pupils for the most part for careers in the law or the church. A large share of their school day, which, according to the season, began at six or seven in the morning and ran until five or six at night, went to instruction in Latin, but a little time was given also to Greek and, at the higher levels, some Hebrew. The cult of the Classics in the school curriculum, which was to reach its high point in the early seventeenth century, was probably even more marked in Italy than in England.

Higher Learning and the Universities

The institutions of higher learning in the West had grown out of the medieval monastic and cathedral schools. During the twelfth and thirteenth centuries some cathedral schools expanded so rapidly in curricula and population that they evolved a new form, commonly referred to as the *studium generale* (*school for all*).⁷ This expanded school was eventually to become the university. Although Muslim cities such as Cairo, Tunis, and Fez already had attached to their mosques centres of learning that had grown famous as universities, western cities lagged far behind. The universities of Salerno, Pavia, and Bologna have a certain claim to be counted among the first in the West, on the grounds of having been the earliest to give advanced instruction, particularly in medicine or law. For the creation of the modern university, however, something more than the vocational training given in these Italian schools was needed—advanced instruction in the liberal arts or, at least, a sufficient combination of the liberal arts with theology, medicine, or law to provide a higher education on a broad scale. France's faculties provided such a combination.

Shortly after 1200 the faculty guild of the overgrown school of the Cathedral of Notre Dame in Paris gained recognition as an independent corporation (*universitas*). Soon it became the model faculty for advanced instruction in the liberal arts, theology-philosophy, medicine, and law. For several centuries it was Europe's most respected educational centre. Meanwhile a twelfth century 'hospice' near Notre Dame in Paris had become the College of Eighteen,⁸ and a college for sixteen theological students had been endowed by Robert de Sorbon (1257). The 'Sorbonne' increased in numbers and expanded its functions, having in the fourteenth century become the theological school of the University. By the fifteenth century resident fellows or masters were giving courses in these and a number of other colleges. In similar fashion at other French universities, the faculties took over almost all higher educational functions, and universities became corporations of professors and students.⁹

In England, and especially at Oxford and Cambridge, the evolution of universities followed a slightly different course. Along with a *universitas* of four faculties (arts, theology, law, and medicine) colleges also developed out of endowed rooming houses for students. The tutors at these 'halls' became so important in the *studium generale* that the activity of the *universitas* for a long time was restricted to little more than administration of the federated colleges, until in 1570–71 the universities were reorganized. The cloistered halls of the separate colleges have survived in all of their late-medieval beauty at Cambridge and Oxford, and although the college-hall system existed elsewhere, it has been especially characteristic of English universities.

Still another type of federation was the one whereby several newer faculties joined with an ancient one, which remained dominant. Thus the faculties of Montpellier, long a centre of medical education in southern France, clustered around its medical school.¹⁰ At Bologna, famous since about 1100 for its professors of Roman law, the professorial guild was dominated by the legalists, and by the end of the thirteenth century was subordinated also to a powerful student organization. This *universitas* (or guild) of students, also led by those in the law school, was not only self-governing, it regulated such things as professors' salaries and the speed of their lectures, required prompt dismissal of classes, and punished professors' absences and similar infractions with appropriate fines. With its student administration and its curriculum of Roman law, Bologna exercised a secular, vocational influence comparable to the influence of Paris in religious and more broadly intellectual education.

The endowment of a university by a private philanthropist was rare in this era, but several distinguished institutions derived their funds from some ruler's purse. In the 'golden age of the university', the thirteenth century, a number of universities had been established in that manner—Naples (1224), Toulouse (1229), and Salamanca (1230), for example. The University of Rome was founded by the pope in 1303, though it did not become famous until the fifteenth century. The first universities of central Europe were initiated under Emperor Charles IV—Prague in 1348, Cracow in 1364, and Vienna in 1364; one founded at Pécs (Hungary) in 1367 did not long survive. The German princes were somewhat late in organizing universities, but, not to mention all, Heidelberg was founded in 1385, Leipzig in 1409, and Tübingen in 1477. The German clerical orders had meanwhile created new universities at Erfurt (1379) and Cologne (1388), and the archbishop of Sweden that of Uppsala (1447). In Armenia Gladzor University was founded at the close of the thirteenth century and Tathev University in the fourteenth; during their brief periods of glory they were the centres of Armenian culture and strongholds of the Armenian Church in the conflicts with Mongol invaders and Dominican missionaries. (See map overleaf.)

After the glorious era of origin and growth came an era of crystallization of curricula. During the fourteenth and fifteenth centuries, the universities that survived grew more and more inflexible, tradition-bound, and impervious to new needs. Scholasticism lost much of its earlier vitality and constructive rationalism and deteriorated into 'logic chopping'. Theology stuck to academic traditionalism and approved authorities, for the most part oblivious to rising trends like humanism and experimental science. While humanism was welcomed with enthusiasm in court circles and secondary schools like Deventer and Mantua, universities such as Oxford, Paris, and Bologna at first passively disregarded or actively opposed it, and professors showed less interest in the beauty of Classical learning and literature than in Scholastic rationale. On the other hand, the burgeoning universities had begun in the thirteenth and fourteenth centuries to expand the traditional mathematical subjects (astronomy, geometry, arithmetic, and music) of the quadrivium by the inclusion of Euclid, Ptolemy, Aristotle, and other scientific writers; individual scholars (e.g. Nicholas of Cusa) occasionally carried on experiments; and sometimes groups of scholars became famous as a school (e.g. the Merton and Vienna mathematicians and the Paris Ockhamists). For all that, the professorial guilds of the *studia generalia* as a whole did less than the craft guilds to encourage empirical science. Although the universities clearly recognized contemporary needs in educating for the professions,

Uppsala 1477

Copenhagen 1479

Greifswald 1456

Rostock 1419

Leipzig 1409

Jena 1558

Würzburg 1582

Prague 1348

Heidelberg 1386

Tübingen 1477

Vienna 1365

Graz 1585

Munich 1472

Padua 1222

Ferrara 1391

Bologna 1088

Florence 1321

Macerata 1290

Rome 1303

Perugia 1200

Catania 1434

Naples 1224

Messina 1548

Cologne 1388

Marburg 1527

Mainz 1476

Leiden 1575

Lille 1562

Paris

Sorbonne 1253

Nancy 1572

Strasbourg 1538

Freiburg Br. 1457

Besançon 1422

Basle 1460

Turin 1405

Pavia 1361

Parma 1065

Modena 1180

Pisa 1343

Siena 1247

Sassari 1562

Caen 1431

Rennes 1461

Poitiers 1432

Bordeaux 1441

Grenoble 1339

Montpellier 1180

Toulouse 1229

Barcelona 1377

Cambridge 13 Cent.

Oxford 1163

Dublin 1591

Santiago 1501

Oviedo 1574

Salamanca 1243

Madrid 1508

Coimbra 1190

Granada 1533

Cairo 970

THE FOUNDATION OF UNIVERSITIES FROM 10 TH TO 16 TH CENTURY

especially law, medicine, and the *ars dictaminis*, in these fields too they tended to preserve the learned tradition rather than to promote intellectual pioneering. In general, until the sixteenth century independent thought and free inquiry were not regarded as the major aims of higher learning. The University of Padua, however, provided a shining exception to this general rule (see Chapter XII).

Thus, despite the marked inclination toward secularism and specialization, the universities remained largely dominated by ecclesiastics and by traditional programmes of study. Henry IV's statute of 1600 aimed to put the University of Paris more fully under state control than theretofore, but clerical control persisted, at first under Jesuits, who had gradually displaced the Dominicans, and later, for a time, under Jansenists. Jesuit colleges or universities at Douai, Antwerp, Louvain, Köln, Ingolstadt, Vienna, and elsewhere remained strongholds of Jesuit influence, while Oxford and Cambridge continued to be dominated by Anglican divines. The new universities of Europe usually had influential theological faculties, those established in Anglo-America were essentially theological schools, and those in Spanish America (Mexico City, Caracas, Santiago, and elsewhere) were distinctly under one form or another of clerical influence.

But for the intervention of the states the ecclesiastical viewpoint might have triumphed in pedagogy. Especially (but not exclusively) in non-Catholic countries, the higher schools were fast passing under the influence of the state. Most of the European universities that were founded after the Reformation were from the outset state-controlled and state-supported, with curricula and professors that were intended to train for the civil service or for other lay professions rather than for the clergy. In western Europe the universities of Leiden and Halle were excellent examples. In Russia, where leading men of letters like Tatishchev and Lomonosov lent their weight to a plea for a less traditional approach to education, several educational institutions were created by imperial initiative. Peter the Great founded a School of Mathematics and Navigational Science in Moscow (1701) and, associated with the Academy of Sciences, the University of St Petersburg (1725); Tsarina Elizabeth founded the University of Moscow (1755); and Catherine the Great founded the Smolny Institute for the secondary education of girls of the upper classes and other secondary schools in some of the larger cities. This secularizing tendency helps to explain why, though the Russian lower schools continued largely in the hands of a rarely well-prepared clergy, the higher schools were hotbeds of the eighteenth-century Enlightenment.

At Oxford and Cambridge the same secular trend emerged, though less vigorously. Several regius professorships of traditional subjects were endowed by Henry VIII in the sixteenth century, but they were supplemented by regius chairs in modern history and modern language set up by George I in 1724, intended largely to train recruits for the diplomatic service. The new chairs, however, did little to modify clerical predominance. Indeed, in

English America the secular tendency for a time was reversed. Several new universities sprang up as a result of the revival movement known as the Great Awakening (see Chapter IV). Princeton University was founded (as the College of New Jersey) by the Presbyterians in 1746, Columbia (as King's College) by the Anglicans in 1754, Brown by the Baptists in 1764, Rutgers by the Dutch Reformed in 1766, and Dartmouth by the Congregationalists in 1770, each intended at first to provide ministers for its respective sect. In 1749, however, Franklin was instrumental in planning the Academy (later University) of Pennsylvania with a curriculum that included technical training, agriculture, modern languages, and other utilitarian subjects still uncommon in the older universities.

Religion and the Growth of Learning

In the sixteenth century the wars of religion brought out the potentiality of the educational system, especially of schools for children and adolescents, as an arsenal of religious propaganda. As Protestant princes appropriated the church, they nationalized the church schools, and Protestant children were indoctrinated with Protestant dogma, just as Roman Catholic children with Catholic dogma. Nearly all education for a long time thereafter was chained to religious parochialism. Rarely did educators teach even the non-theological subjects dispassionately.

The importance to Protestants of Bible reading and of a learned ministry led to a demand for widespread educational facilities in Protestant countries. Luther gave the matter serious attention, and with Melanchthon's blessing a number of old schools and universities were reorganized and new ones founded in Germany (e.g. Marburg in 1527, Königsburg in 1544, and Jena in 1558). Saxony and Württemberg showed the way, providing not only elementary schools but also Latin schools for many communities. Melanchthon's plan of education was both Biblicist and humanist. It gave a prominent place to Greek (as the language of the New Testament) as well as to Ciceronian Latin. Johannes Sturm (1507–89) founded a school at Strasbourg which, along with Latin and Greek, taught not only the catechism in German but also some science; it became the model for the German *gymnasium*. In England the colleges at Oxford and Cambridge were incorporated as universities when the Elizabethan struggle over Anglican independence seemed definitely settled, and Rugby (1567) and Harrow (1572) joined the ranks of the secondary institutions destined to become the 'great public schools'. In Scotland the Church Assembly of 1560, under the prodding of John Knox, required every considerable town to have a Latin school, every country parish a teacher, and each of the larger towns a college to give instruction in logic, rhetoric, and languages. Other Protestant countries provided opportunities to acquire at least enough literacy to read the Bible.

The Catholic Church, seeking to bring back to the fold as many heretics as possible, emphasized the training of teachers and advisers. Not only the

Society of Jesus but several other new orders gave major attention to teaching and conversion.[11] The Somaschi and Ursulines have already been mentioned (Chapter IV): the first undertook to school destitute children; the second, under the patronage of Cardinal Carlo Borromeo (1538–84), archbishop of Milan, dedicated themselves to the schooling of girls. The Oratorians were founded by Filippo de Neri in Rome (1575) and by Bérulle in Paris (1611), the Piarists by José de Calasanza in Rome (1617), and the Brethren of the Christian Schools by Jean Baptiste de la Salle in Rheims (1681). The Piarists and the Brethren were concerned with the training of poor boys. Other orders, old and new, also maintained schools at varying levels.

Perhaps the most noteworthy examples of the propagandist-teacher were to be found among the Jesuits.[12] They courted and won success in both elementary and higher education, serving as tutors to royal and other powerful families and as schoolmasters in humble church schools. Even though, with the rise of secular schools, the number of lay teachers increased, at no time during our period was the profession formalized. The Jesuits, however, closely approximated a professionally trained staff of teachers, for, carefully selected and highly trained themselves, they studiously specialized in the techniques of effective teaching and, though clergymen, taught secular as well as religious subjects.

The early Jesuits understood the importance of indoctrination as a key to men's minds. During a vacation in Flanders Loyola had been the guest of Erasmus's friend Juan Luis Vives (1492–1540), who was one of the renowned professors of his day (at Louvain and Oxford). Vives was a devout Christian, but he was also an opponent of the Scholasticism of his day.[13] In *De Disciplinis* (1532) and several other works on pedagogy, he had advocated a system of education wherein kindly teachers would hold forth in well-constructed buildings, giving special attention to superior pupils. A century before Francis Bacon he advocated learning by experiment and the inductive method. The Jesuits adopted some of the pedagogical ideas of humanists like Vives and Erasmus (see below) but discarded the humanists' emphasis upon freedom of inquiry and the play element in schooling in favour of strict discipline and militant Catholicism.

Loyola had a gift of keen observation and self-analysis that enabled him to understand the processes of his own mind. In the months of meditation and visions that had preceded his conversion to the religious life and in the long years devoted to ascetic practices, he had painstakingly recorded the details of his spiritual experiences and practices. From his notes, later probably supplemented by knowledge gleaned from the *Ejercitatorio de la vida espiritual* of Garcia Cisneros, abbot of Montserrato, he evolved the *Spiritual Exercises* (first published in 1548).

The Jesuit ideal of absolute obedience within the Church Militant and the Jesuit program of educational missions demanded a strict and highly selective training for the would-be Jesuit. Loyola's *Spiritual Exercises* provided a methodical textbook intended to guide the would-be Jesuit, or 'exercitant', along the path travelled by Loyola himself. During four weeks devoted to this purpose, the exercitant, usually under the guidance of a spiritual director, advanced from the contemplation of man's sinfulness through the mysteries of Jesus' passion and resurrection toward a voluntary dedication to God. The exercitant was instructed to evoke certain religious visions in all their historical, geographical, and individual aspects and to employ his five physical senses to make his spiritual experiences graphically realistic.[14] The *Exercises* thus led to a controlled mysticism, becoming an instrument by which the exercitant merged his identity with his religious community.

After an exercitant had become a novice, two years of probation followed, and he was finally directed into either the temporal or the spiritual branch of the society. The temporal service consisted of 'lay coadjutors', who were charged with the administrative and household duties of the order. If selected for spiritual service, novices took the simple vows of poverty, chastity, and obedience and became 'scholastics'. They now had to pass through long years of additional probation in which they received a thorough training in the sciences, letters, theology, and teaching. They then were ordained as priests and as 'spiritual coadjutors' became missionaries and teachers or performed other tasks of the Society. Those who showed special aptitude became the 'professed of the four vows', highest rank of the order, who in addition to taking solemn vows of poverty, chastity, and obedience also vowed to serve wherever the pope through their general might send them. The 'Rules for Thinking with the Church', appended to the *Exercises*, prescribed thorough submission of individual will and opinion in ecclesiastical matters. Rule 1 reads: 'Laying aside all private judgment, we ought to hold our minds prepared and prompt . . . to obey in all things . . . the hierarchical Church'; and Rule 13: 'To arrive at the truth in all things, we ought always to be ready to believe that what seems to us white is black, if the hierarchical Church so defines it'.[15, 16]

The Jesuits were thus educated to play a leading part in the propagation of the revitalized Catholic Church. Lainez, the second general of the Society, urged it to pay serious attention to higher learning, and before he died (1565), he helped to establish a hundred and thirty colleges. These colleges became centres of training in orthodox Catholicism, at the same time providing a general education that for many years remained the best available. Jesuit emphasis upon education through schooling and the printed word was largely attributable also to Peter Canisius (Pieter de Hondt), a Dutch-born Jesuit. Renowned for his humanistic learning and strict morality, he became first provincial of the Jesuits in Germany and a close adviser of Emperor Ferdinand I, who called upon him to carry the fight against Protestantism into the very land of its birth. Active successively at the universities of Cologne, Ingolstadt, and Vienna, Canisius was an effective agent of the

Counter-Reformation in various parts of Germany, Austria, and Switzerland. At the instigation of Ferdinand he published his *Summa Doctrinae Christianae* (1555) and followed it a year later with his *Catechism* for children and adults, which was patterned upon Luther's very successful *Shorter Catechism* of 1529 (see below). Both of Canisius's works became standard texts for religious instruction in Catholic Germany.[17]

In the hands of the Jesuits the school became a methodical and disciplined tool of reform and Counter-Reformation. They permitted no deviation from what they considered orthodox doctrine (though sometimes they were themselves suspected of heresy). Jesuits soon acquired envied reputations for their new methods of instruction, their new schools (where education was provided free of charge), and their new textbooks. Within a century of its inauguration the Society had created over five hundred schools, particularly in the Catholic countries most threatened by Protestantism, such as Poland, Hungary, and Austria. Their work as teachers (not to mention their power through deliberately cultivated influence in high places and their readiness to countenance forceful measures) was so respected that even Protestants sometimes voluntarily sent their children to Jesuit schools. Their fifth general, Claudius Aquaviva, reduced a half-century of educational experience to a *Ratio Studiorum*, completed in 1599, which prescribed the curriculum by which Descartes, Calderón, Corneille, Bossuet, Voltaire, and other future charges of the Jesuits were educated. It emphasized discipline, Latin, and the Catholic tradition (see below).

The Jesuits gave spiritual instruction also by preaching and the confessional. Their churches, modelled upon the Gesù at Rome, were designed, and their pulpits elaborated, with an eye to more effective preaching. Breaking with the tradition that sermons should be delivered only on specific holidays and other special occasions, they preached throughout the year. The emphasis upon the psychological value of frequent confession originated with Loyola himself; his 'Rules for Thinking with the Church' recommended 'confession to a priest, and the reception of the Most Holy Sacrament once a year, and much better every month', and 'much better still' every week.[18] From his own experience Loyola had learned that despair of salvation impeded joyous and active Christianity. He therefore wanted confession to be a solace to the penitent and urged leniency in the confessional so that even a sinner to whom absolution might be denied would return hopefully to his church and his confessor.

Departures like these from accepted practice and doctrine roused hostility among other orders and orthodox theologians. The Jesuits' emphasis upon education made them open rivals of the Dominicans, who previously had held a near monopoly on theological education. Some Dominicans, prominent as teachers in leading Catholic universities, worked to bring about reform in the training of priests. Perhaps the most zealous educational reformer among them was Melchior Cano (1509–60), one of the great Salamanca theologians of his day. He was an outspoken opponent of the Jesuits, for he was a jealous guardian of his theological reputation, an inflexible collaborator of the Spanish Inquisition as a national instrument, and a willing supporter of Spanish absolutism against the papacy. As a humanist, he was sincerely interested in freeing Scholasticism from the stultifying wrangles that had come to be so characteristic of its adherents. His posthumously published work, *De Locis Theologicis*, stands out as an inspired plea that a clear and scientific theology be applied to a genuine revitalization of Catholicism. His scholarly efforts helped to promote the reform of theology and of clerical training. In France, where the Sorbonne, dominated by Dominican influence, held sway as interpreter of orthodox Catholic doctrine, the Jesuits likewise encountered great difficulties in establishing themselves and their colleges, but ultimately they won out. Independently, Cardinal Borromeo placed clerical training high among his numerous ecclesiastical reforms, establishing several seminaries and other schools for aspirants to the priesthood.[20]

The Rise of Secular Institutions

Despite continuing religious tensions, between 1500 and 1775 the universities' role in secular learning grew more impressive. Outstanding men of science in the sixteenth, seventeenth, and eighteenth centuries (e.g. Copernicus, Galileo, Newton, Boerhaave, Linnaeus) were associated with universities as students, teachers, or both, and the universities boasted significant figures in other fields besides (e.g. the Cambridge Platonists, the German cameralists, Pufendorf, Blackstone, Adam Smith, Kant). Moreover, there were continually appearing (see below), new kinds of professional training within the universities themselves as well as independent technical and professional schools, some of which were eventually to become parts of nearby universities. Even in the older universities famous men who were not theologians, sometimes not even clerics, were employed as teachers in the professional faculties more often. Such men might well give instruction in their professions without special attention to religious implications.

Gradually, in the schools no less than in the scientific academies, non-clerical specialists gained predominance in the new sciences and technology. King Francis I, prompted by Budé and other humanists, inaugurated a series of royal lectures (1530) more or less frankly intending to offset the theological concentration at the Sorbonne; eventually these lecturers became the Collège de France, giving instruction in mathematics and science as well as the usual humanist subjects. As new universities arose in Protestant countries—among them, Leiden (1575), Giessen (1607), Utrecht (1634), Lund (1666), Halle (1694), and Göttingen (1736)—they tended to react against the Aristotelianism of the Jesuits and to make the new sciences as well as the old cultural tradition a part of their curricula. While some of the new institutions were conservative, they too helped to lay a foundation for the later prestige of their countries in the sciences. A persuasive precedent was set with the endowment of special chairs in mathematics and science by Thomas Gresham at Gresham College in London (1596), Henry Savile at Oxford (1619), and Henry Lucas at Cambridge (1663). As indicated in Chapter XIV, the University of Leiden acquired a botanical garden and an anatomical theatre—and it also took steps toward offering an engineering curriculum (see below)—shortly after its founding, and by the end of the seventeenth century courses in the natural sciences there and in other Dutch universities were firmly ensconced. Under Newton's influence, Cambridge became a centre of scientific learning. In the eighteenth century, we shall soon see, engineering schools were established in several European cities, and we have already encountered a veterinary school that was founded in Lyons.

Continuing Clerical Domination of Schooling

The early universities had commonly been dominated by religious orders or by *magistri* who were at least nominally members of the church hierarchy. Even after the Reformation similar domination was the rule, even in Protestant countries. For instance, Oxford and Cambridge restricted teaching to Anglican clergy or bachelor members of the Church of England. In the course of time, however, the number grew of persons who thought of themselves as teachers, even when they were clergymen, rather than as clergymen. Some of these teachers were devoted humanitarians as well.

The Pietist university at Halle provided some good examples of this type. Under the guidance of Thomasius, instruction there was modernized, history and science were given a prominent place in the curriculum, and university courses were for the first time given in German rather than Latin. As a humanitarian Thomasius raised doubts about the justice of current court practices in connection with witchcraft and torture. Since Pietist doctrine stressed the importance of good works as a sign of regeneration, Christian charity became an important aspect of life at Halle.[21] While a professor there, Francke, most important of the Pietist ministers after Spener, founded a number of schools including a Paedagogium for better-off pupils and an Orphan Asylum, where instruction was given not only in religion but also in traditional learning and vocational skills. Francke's institutions became a model for other schools in Germany, and his own series of schools at Halle, organized as the *Franke'sche Stiftungen*, enjoyed an enduring career.

Other sects displayed a similar mixture of humanitarian and missionary purposes in their pedagogy. In England the Society for Promoting Christian Knowledge opened in 1698, and within a matter of decades thousands of 'charity schools' for children who at a tender age would have to go to work were dispensing a modicum of reading, writing, and arithmetic along with shop and religious training. In the Catholic school systems the number of teaching orders steadily increased until in the eighteenth century some thirty of them existed. One of the most important remained the Brothers of the Christian Schools, who, though they took monastic vows, became not priests but teachers of the poor.[22] A fine example of the rare lay humanitarian-teacher was Giacobbo Rodriguez Pereire (1715–80), who, having had to devise a sign language in order to communicate with his deaf wife, began a movement for the education of deaf mutes.

Thus literacy was step by step ceasing to be regarded as a monopoly for a privileged few and was becoming instead, though slowly and often painfully, a possible possession for even the underprivileged. Education was not yet considered, however, an obligation of society to give and of the individual to get. The number of schools at the end of our period was greater than before, but the increase meant only rarely gratuitous and hardly ever compulsory education. Nor was the curriculum a broad one. In Catholic and Protestant countries alike, schooling was still largely dominated by clerics, whose major aim was to mould their pupils into good Christians.

EDUCATIONAL METHODS AND THEORY IN EUROPE

The Decline of the Schoolmen

Throughout the early centuries of Western educational history intensive study in specialized subjects was absent from monastic and cathedral schools. Specialization was found rather in the practical training of guild apprentices and in certain professions. In the thirteenth century, specialized training began to appear in university faculties of theology, law, and medicine. Each faculty was autonomous, even when one of the faculties was dominant. Theology was the recognized speciality at Paris, medicine at Salerno and Montpellier, law at Bologna. In most schools a baccalaureate degree, and in some a master's, in the liberal arts was prerequisite to specialization, which might then require five additional years of study.

In both the liberal arts and the specialized courses, the lecture method was common. Until the development of printing, textbooks were rare and expensive, and the owner of a textbook was a potential lecturer. He might read portions, say, of the text of Galen, the Justinian Code, or the papal decretals, and comment thereon. A student who took careful notes and transcribed them onto parchment had the basic equipment for lectures of his own if he became a professor. Lectures were supplemented either by discussions, especially in courses in the liberal arts and theology, or, in courses of medicine, by assisting a physician or observing an autopsy.

The growth of urban communities and the increase of wealth in the towns augmented the number of young people desirous of, and financially prepared for, advanced instruction concerning the things of this world as well as the next. Cathedral schools, in the larger urban centres, tended to acquire larger student bodies and wider intellectual horizons. Business schools, especially in Italian towns, made for still wider breaches in the citadel of religiously dominated education. By 1300, several universities were centres of vigorous discussion of many aspects of life on earth as well as in Heaven.

Nevertheless, religion still was the major subject of education, and theology the queen of the sciences. In the thirteenth century Thomas Aquinas and contemporary Scholastics had made Aristotle safe for Christianity. The Thomist identification of faith with reason was a beautifully balanced thought structure, sometimes compared with the Gothic cathedral. It was upset, in its turn, by the Scholastics of the succeeding period, for they made Aristotelian logic more an end than a means. A sort of hyper-intellectualism was prominently displayed in the professorial disputations which were characteristic of the late-medieval educational process. In keeping with his realistic approach Vives complained: 'Disputations have blinded judgment. . . . A base desire for distinction took possession of the minds of the disputants and, just as in battle, victory came to be the chief consideration rather than the elucidation of the truth'.[23] Revulsion at Scholastic 'logic chopping' combined with the growing professionalism of the medical, legal, and business schools of the day to work toward the secularization of education.

Educational Theory before the Enlightenment

In the period between the rise of the universities and the Protestant upheaval, educational techniques were largely traditional, objectives were largely fixed, and little was written on educational theory. One of the few social changes to raise questions of educational theory was the decline of chivalry, and several serious works took up the question of knightly education and conduct. Ramon Lull's *Order of Chivalry* appeared in early-fourteenth-century Spain, William Caxton's treatise with a similar title in late-fifteenth-century England, and Castiglione's *Book of Courtier* in early-sixteenth-century Italy. All three works give evidence of the changing concept of the nobleman's role in society. Lull's pre-Renaissance rules stand in marked contrast to Castiglione's for the cultured Renaissance gentleman and gentlewoman (see below). Caxton (between the two in time) bewailed the decadence of his own day and the passage of true knighthood. A cruder variation on both themes is found in a book of instructions written by the nobleman Geoffrey de la Tour Landry for his daughters. To impress upon them that even a noblewoman's place was the home and she should subject herself to her lord and master, he told of a burgher housewife who suffered a broken nose for using haughty language to her husband.

Until the Protestant upheaval Renaissance writers tended to add the humanistic to the chivalric concept of education. Aeneas Sylvius (later Pope Pius II) wrote for King Ladislas of Bohemia a work entitled *De Librorum Educatione* (1450), in which he recommended that the education of gentlemen should include, along with the study of certain parts of the Bible, attention to Latin historians and, in order to converse with the common people, the vernacular languages.[24] In More's non-Christian Utopia (1516), to be sure, girls as well as boys received their formal training at the feet of the country's chosen men, who imparted virtue along with knowledge to all comers, for all the deserving were equal and knowledge was inseparable from virtue. But that was in Utopia. Humanist educators generally made more of an effort to reconcile humanism with the aristocratic tradition.

Erasmus was the outstanding proponent of this compromise. His *Enchiridion Militis Christiani* (1503), though it preached the Christian ideal, looked for worldly welfare not through a pious clergy but rather through the welding of scholarly and humanist interests with aristocratic virtues in the Christian nobleman. In his *Encomium Moriae* (*Praise of Folly*, (1509) the heroine, Lady Folly, embodied the finest of Classical and Christian principles as compatible ideals. His *Institutio Principis Christiani* (1516) revealed a sanguine trust in princely readiness to learn to respect human aspirations. In Erasmus' theory of education youth was to be trained to approach the problems of life with an armament of high-minded principles and an ability to think independently. His works on the education of boys, such as *De Pueris* and *De Ratione Studii*, tried to teach good maxims along with good Latin style.

For adults, the humanist leaning toward a broad education for a flesh-and-blood world came closer to realization in Italian court life. Machiavelli's 'Prince', forerunner of the *Realpolitik* of a later age (see Chapter VIII), presented a marked contrast to Erasmus' 'Christian Prince'; Machiavelli was cynical where Erasmus was sanguine; in Machiavelli's politics *virtu* was essentially patriotism, to which all other scruples must yield. Castiglione's *Courtier* was more nearly the Italian counterpart of Erasmus' moralistic work, but it too illustrated the dominantly secular character of educational ideals in the humanist circles of Italy. All over Europe, at least partly under Castiglione's inspiration, arose 'academies' for the sons of noblemen and gentry, where arms and gymnastics as well as Latin, modern languages, mathematics, and 'natural philosophy' were taught.[25] In Germany these schools were frankly designated *Ritterakademien*.

The Protestant Revolt and the Catholic Reformation turned schooling more explicitly toward religious objectives. Its initial effect was to discourage educational innovations. Erasmus expressed the opinion that science decayed where Lutheranism accumulated. Luther's emphasis on faith rather than good works and on Scripture rather than Scholasticism, and his arguments with Catholic theologians led him and his more evangelical followers to denounce clerically dominated universities and schools as enemies of true religion. The Synod of Dort, while calling upon the Dutch authorities to reform old schools, establish new ones, and provide gratuitous instruction for the poor, also demanded strict school regulation in the interests of Calvinist orthodoxy. The *collèges* (secondary schools) and *académies* (higher schools and seminaries) established in the Huguenot cities of France were primarily run by pastors to train pastors. Later in the seventeenth century, the Puritan-controlled Barebones Parliament of England contemplated the abolition of universities because they were centres for the propagation of worthless 'carnal knowledge' (i.e. Aristotelian Scholastic education not based on Scripture or God's Book of Nature).

In general, the quarrel of governments with the Roman hierarchy had the effect of placing schools along with churches more closely under monolithic state control. When Protestant princes secularized ecclesiastical property, they felt obliged to assume responsibility for the continuation of the church's functions, education prominent among them, and they created new royal schools. The things that were Caesar's and the things that were God's thus seemed closer to becoming the same things. Certain Protestant leaders recognized the importance of educating young men for the more effective spread of their territorial faith. Moreover, the Protestant reformers, subscribing to the principle of direct acquaintance with God through the study of the Bible, were logically impelled to favour national programmes of popular education. To be sure, the principal Lutheran educator, Melanchthon, had been a student at humanist Heidelberg, had taught the Classics at Tübingen and Wittenberg, and had acquired little fear of humanism. Yet Lutheran-controlled schools usually fell short of the Erasmian ideal of the Christian humanist gentleman. As in most other countries of the sixteenth century, education in Germany, in both theory and method, was rather an instrument for the indoctrination and defence of the sovereign's faith; schools and universities were instruments of government, controlled and carried on by the established clergy. A corollary of *cuius regio, eius religio* was *cuius religio, eius educatio.*[26]

Since the teaching profession had been practically a clerical monopoly, the frequent closing of monasteries and the recurrent attacks upon the priesthood in the Protestant areas of Germany reduced the number of available teachers. At the same time the radical wing of the reform movement preached a mysticism that emphasized divine inspiration, and though some of its leaders were well educated men, they deprecated formal education. As a result, at Wittenberg, Erfurt, and elsewhere the number of students steadily decreased. Luther early opposed this trend away from formal schooling. He prepared (1529) a *Shorter Catechism* and a *Larger Catechism* in German for the training of children, and he urged governments to assume responsibility for public instruction. In an *Open Letter to the Christian Nobility of the German People* he indicated certain educational reforms to be instituted by the princes. He would centre education around the teaching of the Gospel and remove from the curriculum all those authors and compilations that had constituted the core of Scholastic education—Aristotle, canon law, the decretals. Of Aristotle only the works on logic, the *Rhetoric*, and the *Poetics* were to be retained, because of their practical value; the law of the land would replace canon law, which was no longer needed.

In an appeal *To the Councilmen of All Cities in Germany That They Establish and Maintain Christian Schools* (1524) and again in *A Sermon on the Duty of Keeping Children at School* (1530) Luther elaborated his educational theory. He decried the traditional method of teaching by often brutal discipline and deadening memorization. He gave detailed instructions regarding the subjects to be taught: Hebrew along with Latin and Greek for a better understanding of Scripture; the best commentaries and books by Classic authors; law, medicine, arts, and sciences according to the best available texts; history for a better understanding of the past; and music as a means of inspiration and relaxation. He reserved higher education for the gifted but proposed training in a practical trade along with elementary education for all children, girls included. Education, he insisted, was important for a stable and efficient civil government and, therefore, a concern of the entire citizenry. Since 'wealthy greedbugs' were the 'monks of Mammon', and since 'born princes and lords are incapable of doing it by themselves', for 'they know nothing at all about the Spiritual realm', the direction of both the temporal and the spiritual on earth 'must remain in the hands of the middle class and common people and their children.'[27] Therefore municipal authorities should provide schools and teachers.

Despite Luther's emphasis upon religion and his war against Rome, his writings contributed to the secularization of education in Germany by upholding the school as an institution maintained by the civic authority and serving the public interest. The humanistic touches of his programme are unmistakable: rejection of Scholastic methods and disciplines, emphasis upon a thorough knowledge of ancient languages, advocacy of liberal educational methods, and respect for the importance of historical studies. In form and curriculum his proposals in several ways anticipated the later German *Gymnasium*.

Calvin also gave considerable attention to the problem of schooling. As early as the *Ordonnances* of 1541 he made educational reform a vital part of his program for Geneva. In 1559 the foundations were laid for the College and Academy of Geneva, which was eventually to become the University of Geneva. It was patterned after the school founded by Sturm in Strasbourg.[28] Its curriculum too was clearly humanistic; though religious instruction and observances were stressed, it emphasized Classical literature, Greek, and Hebrew as languages, and except in matters of theology, full freedom of discussion was granted. Unlike Luther's proposed schools, however, the curriculum at Geneva neglected history and science.

The most effective Catholic educational order was that of the Jesuits. We have described above the exacting method by which Jesuit teachers were selected and prepared. The Society adapted the broad intellectualism of the humanists to the intense devotionalism of their order. They taught the Classics, especially those in Latin, and at the same time strove to revitalize Scholasticism. As masters in their colleges and as tutors in royal courts, they were expected to inculcate in Catholic youth respect for both intellectual attainment along traditional lines and strictness of discipline. They emphasized class-room instruction by means of lectures, repetition, discussion, and examinations, but made individual tutoring also easily available. Competition was encouraged by prizes and class rivalry. Discipline was strictly enforced through a system of student 'decurions' (monitors) and non-Jesuit 'correctors', who might dismiss maladapted or unqualified pupils. In the Catholic universities, where they sometimes monopolized the professorships, Jesuit theologians defended and propagated the orthodox faith with a logical skill reminiscent of the days of Aquinas. They studiously cultivated and often won the respect of popes and princes as well as parents and pupils.[19]

The Secular Trend in Educational Theory

Despite the persistence of religious controversy, by the close of the seventeenth century schools no longer aimed so largely as before to train clerics. By that time the law had become increasingly a special avenue to political and clerical preferment, medicine was recognized not only as a specialized but also as a possibly lucrative profession, science had grown into an arcane field that required special training, and specialized engineering education was more and more in demand for both civil and military purposes. The number of special schools rose (see below) and by the end of the eighteenth century had produced many graduates who had received specialized training and as men of professional standing exerted a palpable influence in their communities.

In general, specialized training in the schools tended to reinforce the secular bent. An increasing tendency to depart from public lectures and to restrict them to matriculated students alone encouraged secularism by giving greater privacy to pedagogical opinions. Moreover, for centuries students and faculty alike had fought for the freedom of the gown from the town, and occasionally the political authorities, particularly in new state-supported universities like Halle and Göttingen, voluntarily accepted, at least in principle, the idea of academic freedom from clerical or political domination, thus also aiding the trend toward secularism and pedagogical privilege inside the schools. The growth of libraries independent of ecclesiastical supervision (see Chapter XI) further promoted secularism outside as well as inside the schools.

Educational theory reflected and perhaps influenced the general secular tendency in schools and among scholars. As early as the fifteenth century Matteo Palmieri (1406–75) in his *Della vita civile* (published posthumously in 1529) held up civic virtue as the objective of education, as did his friend Alberti (see Chapter X). They shared Machiavelli's idea of *virtu* without equalling his ruthless *raison d'état*. Erasmus, we have seen, looked for worldly welfare through the Christian ruler who would weld humanist interests with aristocratic virtues, while Castiglione portrayed a courtier who would be a Christian but was more interested in acquiring the humanist accomplishments. Thomas Elyot in *The Booke Named the Governour* (1531) pleaded that prospective officials undergo a serious humanistic training rather than a course of elegant or pious study, and that incumbent officials be guided by an intuitive, gentlemanly sense of justice and responsibility. In Thomas More's *Utopia* (1516), service to the state was the objective of all education whether formal for children or informal for adults, and control was placed in the hands of an 'order of the learned'. For him learning included prominently 'a knowledge of human affairs . . . so useful even to a theologian'; he approved of those 'who make the knowledge of things natural a road to heavenly contemplation, and so pass from philosophy and the liberal arts . . . to theology'.[30,31]

Some Theorists of the Sixteenth and the Seventeenth Century

In the sixteenth century humane letters were the mark of the gentleman and aristocrat. The new Collège de France, the new Protestant colleges, particularly those modelled on Sturm's school at Strasbourg, and the early Jesuit colleges promoted the teaching of 'the liberal arts', those studies regarded as befitting a free gentleman, as opposed to servile, vocational, or mechanical pursuits. They presumed, however, a different kind of servility. Lessons were often, like the faults of Shakespeare's Cassius, 'set in a note book, learn'd and conn'd by rote'.

As a general rule sixteenth-century writers extolled the Classics as the core of a good education, but Rabelais and Montaigne were exceptions. Rabelais' character Ponocrates took a special interest, as the tutor of Gargantua, in teaching the natural sciences. Rabelais, himself a physician, put considerable stress on physical matters such as exercise, wholesome food, loose garments, and fresh air. Montaigne, who had learned to speak Latin before French, emphasized the *sana mens in corpore sano*, insisting upon physical and moral health, even, if necessary, at the expense of Latin books. He decried corporal punishment as a means of inculcating knowledge or morality and suggested indirect methods such as plays and games in its stead. Both Rabelais and Montaigne believed that pupils should be urged to learn by excitement of their curiosity rather than by coercion.

Among the outstanding pedagogical theorists of the seventeenth century were a number of Protestant teachers, advocates of popular and willing Bible-study in the vernacular. The German pedagogue Wolfgang Rathke (1571–1635) maintained that knowledge was better imparted by the mother tongue than by Latin and by direct observation than by rote, and he tried to guide children by their natural curiosity rather than by the rod. Subscribing to similar principles, the leader of the Moravian Brethren, Comenius, made explicit his conviction that learning proceeds best from the known to the unknown. His fundamental educational programme was the study of God's nature by the inductive method, the elucidation of the human conscience by reason, and the understanding of Revelation through Holy Writ. One of the first to set forth clearly the gradation of education into infant, elementary, secondary, and advanced levels, he insisted that the study of Latin should be postponed until about the age of twelve. He favoured educating girls as well as boys. Like Rabelais, Montaigne, and Rathke he urged rousing the spirit to voluntary effort rather than beating the reluctant flesh, a practice all too common in their day, as the best way of exciting a zeal for learning, and, as Vittorino and Vives had done before him, he advocated school playgrounds and large, airy schoolrooms. Believing that school books should be adapted to the pupil's ability to comprehend, he wrote a series of six textbooks, graded in both vocabulary and content from elementary to more advanced levels, and provided parallel translations and basic vocabularies for some of them. His beginner's book, *Orbis Sensualium Pictus* (Nuremberg, 1657), taught Latin vocabulary by means of pictures, giving Latin phrases and their vernacular translation side by side.

When driven from his own country in 1628 by the ravages of the Thirty Years' War, Comenius settled at first in Poland, where he taught school, wrote books, and tried, as their bishop, to keep the Brethren from despair. He went to England in 1641 on the invitation of the Long Parliament, which hoped, until frustrated by contemporary political tensions and civil wars, to reform the English school system and to provide an example of state education. Though mentioned for the presidency of the freshwater Harvard University, he took a post instead in Sweden (1642). In nearly eighty years of life he taught school in several different cities and in at least three vernaculars, and personally introduced his pedagogical ideas into Poland, England, Sweden, Germany, Hungary, and Holland. His writings, translated into about fifteen languages, including Arabic, Persian, and Turkish, aimed at a set of ideals which he apparently considered practicable—a united Protestant church, a world organization for peace, and an encyclopedic ordering of knowledge ('pansophy'). While living in Amsterdam, he collected a number of them in his *Opera Didactica Omnia* (4 volumes, 1657). Didactics (i.e. education) was for Comenius 'the whole art of teaching all things to all Men'.[32] Such an objective, he was convinced, if communicated by uniform textbooks in a universal language in common schools, would bring an organic unity to at least the evangelical groups, perhaps to the whole Christian world, and ultimately even to all the other religions.

Though Comenius did not stay long in England, his influence remained strong among those who hoped that political revolution might bring educational reform. His Prussian-born English publisher, Samuel Hartlib, planned to create a school along Comenian principles, and, probably at Hartlib's instigation, Milton published his *Tractate of Education* (1644), written much earlier, and shortly afterward Petty published his *Advice . . . for the Advancement of Some Particular Parts of Learning* (1648). Milton's *Of Education* favoured a mixture of religious and humanistic schooling for gentlemen's sons, 'a complete and generous education which fits a man to perform justly, skilfully and magnaminously all the offices, both private and public, of peace and war'. While Milton said little about experimental science and technology, Petty propounded a more revolutionary system that would provide rich and poor children alike with technical as well as language training.

Locke's educational theory was less mystical than Comenius's and less radical than Petty's. His *Some Thoughts concerning Education* (1693) was perhaps the most influential pedagogical essay of its day. He seems to have been impressed by Rabelais and Montaigne, and he certainly made an impression upon Rousseau. Like his French predecessors, he stressed the importance of health, wholesome physical surroundings, and play in educating the young. Virtue and wisdom, he felt, rather than religion should be taught, and taught early, and not by corporal punishments so much as by appealing to the child's honour, reason, and sense of shame. Departing from the contemporary emphasis on the Classics, Locke advocated a practical education that should prepare for citizenship and a trade or profession rather than for a genteel love of letters. He objected to learning by rote. The child, if of the upper classes, should, he thought, first learn to speak his own language correctly, then another living language, and then Latin (but not Greek). Useful studies like geography, arithmetic, astronomy, geometry, history, law, and 'natural philosophy' (science) should fill in the young gentleman's curriculum until finally he acquired a manual trade and accounting. For the children of the poor between the ages of three and fourteen, Locke's *Proposals for the Bringing Up of the Children of Paupers* (1697) advocated a system of 'working schools' providing, along with food and shelter, a compulsory training in some kind of work.

French Education and Its Enlightenment Critics

The extent of innovation advocated by Comenius, Locke, and their followers can be well appreciated if contrasted with educational theory and practice in contemporary France. Bishop Fénelon was one of the leading French educational theorists of the day. He set forth his ideas on teaching in a work which, though entitled *De l'éducation des filles* (1687), dealt in part with the general problems of pedagogy. He believed in beginning the child's education in the cradle, making the learning process attractive by stories, play, gentle prompting, and other indirect methods. He wished to counteract the neglect of girls' schooling and the current prejudice against educated women (mirrored in several of Molière's plays). Nevertheless, the good abbé held that women's education should continue to be inferior to men's, because women not only needed to know less but were less competent to learn some subjects, such as the intricacies of the law; all they needed was reading, writing, arithmetic, and a few other things that might make them good wives, mothers, and housekeepers. Prominent among these things was the Catholic religion, with enough about other Christian religions to enable them to recognize and avoid heresy. Fénelon was the tutor of one of Louis XIV's grandsons, for whose guidance he wrote *Télémaque*, *Dialogues des morts*, and a collection of *Fables*, seeking by means of fiction to inculcate responsibility and morality.33

Fénelon's programme was followed in a general way by the two outstanding French schools for girls—Port Royal and Saint-Cyr. For all Port Royal's significance in letters and in boys' education (see below), its convent school for girls was a dreary place, whose routine made Fénelon feel sad when he mentioned it. The programme at Saint-Cyr, a school founded in 1686 by Madame de Maintenon, was at first intended to counteract the dreariness characteristic of the convent school. As Louis XIV's wife, she was allowed to teach at Saint-Cyr, as well as to direct it by written instructions and daily visits, thus becoming one of the earliest lay school-mistresses of France. But after five or six years of a liberal spirit, Saint-Cyr lapsed into something like other convent schools.

In contrast, some of the schools for boys were venturesome and exhilarating. The short-lived Little Schools of Port Royal for boys, founded by the Abbé de Saint Cyran, had excellent teachers and used new and challenging methods of instruction. Here small groups under the constant guidance of kindly tutors underwent a serious training that, though aiming to cultivate Jansenist judgment and austerity rather than knowledge and science, was by a conscientious effort fitted to their capacities.34 Elementary education in France began to be based upon a series of common principles after La Salle founded at Rheims (1685) a seminary for the Brethren of the Christian Schools—in fact, one of the first 'normal schools' of Europe (though the term itself did not become current until the end of the century). The teachers in the Brethren schools now received some training in pedagogy and a set of instructions on how to conduct themselves; they were forbidden, for instance, to give more than five blows with ferule or rod without special permission.

Still, at the beginning of the eighteenth century, teaching practice in France was, by modern standards, lamentable (and France's educational institutions were perhaps more advanced than those of other countries). As Charles Rollin's *Traité des études* (1726-28) showed, the schools permitted corporal punishment, ordinarily afforded girls only a rudimentary education, considered Latin the proper medium of learned communication, left no time for the study of modern history, provided little for the study of science beyond an elementary and theoretical level, and at every step gave much attention to religious instruction. With the mixture of truth and hyperbole that makes for caricature, Diderot described the secondary curriculum similarly:

'There are still taught today, under the name of belles-lettres, two dead languages which are . . . studied for six or seven years without being learned; under the name of rhetoric, the art of speaking is taught before the art of thinking, and that of speaking elegantly before having ideas; under the name of logic, the head is filled with the subtleties of Aristotle . . .; under the name of ethics, I do not know what is said . . .; under the name of metaphysics, there are discussed . . . the first elements of scepticism and bigotry . . .; under the name of physics, there is endless dispute about the elements of matter and the system of the world; but not a word on natural history, not a word on real chemistry, very little on the movement and fall of bodies; very few experiments, less still of anatomy, and nothing of geography.'[35]

For this state of affairs Diderot and his fellow *philosophes* blamed not only the Jesuits but also other teaching orders, such as the Christian Brethren, now known by their enemies as *ignorantins*.

Between 1762 and 1764, the Jesuits of France were dispersed by a series of decisions of several parlements (see Chapter IV). With either the intention that the control of the schools should or the expectation that it would now pass to other hands, several writers directed their minds to the problem of education. Since the parlements had played a leading role in the prosecution of the Jesuits, members of those courts were prominent among those who examined the problem. The Breton parlementarian Louis René de La Chalotais wrote an *Essai d'éducation national* (1763), in which he pleaded for an essentially secular education to be provided by the state for citizens rather than by the church for Christians. Learning, he contended, ought to be based on observation, history, geography, living languages, mathematics, and natural history, with training in the Classical languages only in the maturer years and in ethics only toward the close of schooling. Schoolhouses should be spread widely over the country and easily accessible. The useful crafts should be taught along with the sciences, so that pupils of both high and low society might benefit from them.

The staff of the University of Paris in 1763–64 also turned its attention to the problem of education and prepared some memoirs on the subject. The Paris parlementarian Barthélemi-Gabriel Rolland (1734–94) in 1768 submitted a *Report* to his colleagues, largely derived from the university's memoirs. He advocated a scheme of state schooling that would attempt to give each pupil the education best suited for his needs, and for the better training of more teachers he suggested the creation of normal schools. In order that the pedagogical system might be well integrated and kept to high standards he proposed that a centralized national bureau be set up and vested with the obligation and authority to conduct annual school inspections.

Rousseau's *Emile* came in part from the educational crisis created by the dissolution of the Jesuit order. This work was less directly, however, a response to the need to replace the Jesuits than were La Chalotais' or Rolland's and was rather an essay in its author's philosophical system, premised upon the potential penchant for good in natural man. In two earlier discourses on the arts and sciences, Rousseau had argued that man is perpetually engaged in a conflict between his self-concern (*amour de soi-même*) and his altruism (*pitié*), and that civilization tends to turn his justifiable self-concern into selfishness (*amour-propre*), discouraging his nascent inclination toward altruism. Rousseau now faced the question how to educate the young so as to retain the advantages of civilization without incurring its corrupting effects. In *Emile* he proposed a system of private tutoring that until the age of twelve would remove the child from almost all contact with civilization (save such as his omniscient tutor saw fit to allow) and after that would permit only a limited contact until the age of twenty.

Emile was a fictitious biography of such a child. Although Rousseau insisted that an infant be nursed by his mother, he deliberately made Emile an orphan. Since 'the poor man has no need of an education' because he 'may make a man of himself' (Book I), Rousseau made Emile also a rich aristocrat. Until Emile was about fifteen, he learned mostly through the senses. He read no books but *Robinson Crusoe* and, living in the country, saw almost no one but his tutor. Until he was twelve, he played outdoors a great deal and was encouraged to study such concrete things as geometry, drawing, and music by indirect guidance and by enticement of his curiosity, by doing and seeing. From thirteen to fifteen, he developed his reason and judgment, being occupied chiefly in learning the natural sciences. He also acquired a trade, since only thus could he be economically independent and fully competent; besides, since the times were precarious, his tutor wanted him to be prepared for possible revolution. Emile would probably have learned to read (though not from books) before he reached fifteen, but at that age he was deliberately stimulated to read. From fifteen to twenty, he was taught moral and social values and how to live in society; he learned about human relations from history and literature mostly in his own language; and he learned Latin in order to know French better. At twenty he acquired a knowledge of religion by conversation with a kindly vicar (who was essentially a Deist, however). By that time Emile was prepared to marry the heroine of Rousseau's *Sophie*, whose education had been distinctly inferior to his, largely mere preparation for marriage to him.

Rousseau's *Emile* demonstrated how far some writers of the eighteenth century were willing to go in the direction of permissive education. The author favoured a system that would teach the pupil through personal supervision how to solve his own problems rather than one that would discipline him along the lines that his elders considered good for him to know. Rousseau made the guidance of a child's growing ability to absorb rather than the adequacy of the curriculum the criterion and aim of an educational programme. Obviously such guidance would be costly and hence was no scheme of public education.

In his *Considérations sur le gouvernement de Pologne* Rousseau advocated an intensely patriotic form of national education that was considerably more practical, but it seems to have made no appreciable impact upon the Polish school system. The reforming efforts of the Piarist father Stanislaw Konarski (1700–73) were more efficacious. He founded a college for young gentlemen in 1740, emphasizing Polish and other modern languages rather than the Classical languages and giving considerable attention to the natural sciences. The Piarist monk was a Polish patriot. He wrote an attack, *An Effective Method of Government* (1761–64), on the *liberum veto*, attributing to it the instability of the Polish government. He gradually won some of the other teaching orders, including some Jesuits, to his pedagogical theories. When the Jesuit order was abolished in Poland (1772), a state Commission of Education was set up and, taking over the Jesuit schools, ran them as a secular school system with leadership provided by Konarski's disciples and former Jesuits.

Emile was contemporaneously perhaps Rousseau's most influential work, although the French Revolution was to make his *Contrat social* appear more so. Some parents tried to apply Rousseau's pedagogical method to the education of their children, and it provided a pattern for the eccentric Johann Bernhard Basedow to follow. Basedow adhered to the theory of active pupil participation in the classroom, and it was exemplified in his elementary school, the Philanthropinum, founded at Dessau in 1774. The Philanthropinum, though short-lived, was, in turn, a source of inspiration for Friedrich Eberhard von Rochow's schools and writings (e.g. *Kinderfreund*, 1775) and for other German elementary schools, as well as for Johann Heinrich Pestalozzi's work with poor children, begun in 1774, and later with war orphans.

Rousseau's educational theories have been warmly attacked by some and warmly defended by others. There is less debate about the inadequacies of contemporary school methods. *Emile* exposed some of the current educational shortcomings—the frustration of education by pedagogical cruelty, the meaninglessness of noble phrases if learned by rote, the wastefulness of teaching foreign languages to those ignorant of their own, the high price placed upon parroting and affectation where mere wordiness is esteemed, and the futility of appeals to the reason of the immature and inexperienced. But the practical reformers did not need Rousseau's diatribes to recognize these evils; upon the withdrawal of the Jesuits they found an obligation and an opportunity. Several formerly Jesuit schools revised their curricula. The Collège Louis-le-Grand, where Voltaire had received an apparently good education early in the century, after 1763 gave its classes in French instead of in Latin and introduced new disciplines such as the sciences and history.

Rousseau incurred deep hostility in both Catholic and Protestant quarters, and from both *philosophes* and anti-*philosophes*, because of his views (among others) on religion and religious education, which were neither orthodox enough for some nor unorthodox enough for others. The problem of religious and moral training was a difficult one for the *philosophes*. Some of them, believing that the mind was the product of the senses alone, looked upon religious education as exclusively a matter of inculcating a sense of duty and obedience to law. Whether because the souls of the authors were troubled or because they themselves or their friends feared the censorship authorities, several manuscripts on this subject were left unpublished during their lifetimes. Hume's *Dialogues concerning Natural Religion* (1779) and Diderot's *Neveu de Rameau* (published in 1804 in German by Goethe) illustrate the concern of the religious skeptic with the moral problem. In a philosophy that preached the derivation of sensitive mind from sensible matter, the hope for immortality and salvation was likely to be regarded as mere superstition, though it might be converted to good use in the police system.

A thoroughgoing materialism was the basis of the educational system proposed by Helvétius. The full title of his major work reveals its nature: *De l'homme, de ses facultés intellectuelles et de son education* (1773). For Helvétius, *cogito, ergo sum* had been displaced by *sentio, ergo sum*; hence, differences in intellect among men were largely attributable to differences in their environment. The business of the state was to eliminate those differences by raising all its subjects to the highest possible intellectual level through a system of state education. Religious instruction should be given by the state for its own secular purposes and not for the purposes of salvation.

This stark materialism proved too much even for Diderot, Helvétius' friend and (in earlier works) collaborator. In a *Réfutation de l'ouvrage d'Helvétius intitulé 'L'homme'* (not published until 1875) he cast doubt on the assumption that man's intellect was as much a product of the natural environment as was the lower animal's, for, if it were, he could not explain the subordination of man's senses to man's reason and the constant improvement of that reason. Diderot was forced to conclude, more reluctantly than (but much in the manner of) Kant afterward, that there might possibly be more things even on earth than were dreamt of in Helvétius' (and hence his own earlier) philosophy:

'In the development of the egg and several other operations of nature, I clearly see organized but apparently inert matter pass from the state of inertia to the state of sensitivity and of life by purely physical agents, but the necessary link of the transition escapes me. . . . The organization and the co-ordination of inert parts does not at all lead to sensitivity, and the general sensitivity of the molecules of matter is no more than a supposition which derives all its strength from the difficulties' it does away with—which in good philosophy is not sufficient.'[36]

When, therefore, Diderot was called upon to propose a system of state education, his scheme differed from that of Helvétius. In a *Plan d'une université*, written around 1776 at the request of Catherine the Great, he advocated a school system 'whose door is open without discrimination to all the children of a nation and in which the teachers, paid by the state, impart to them an elementary knowledge of all the sciences'.[37] In other words, he advocated universal elementary education, centralized in a department of state and emphasizing the sciences. In his scheme not only would schools be gratuitous but poor pupils would be fed free. So far Diderot did not depart radically from Helvétius. But in assigning to spiritual studies like religion, ethics, and history a prominent place in his curriculum, he did. In his educational scheme at the secondary and advanced school levels (ages twelve to twenty), stress was to be laid upon the sciences, to be taught in an order which he thought intrinsic to the student's understanding, but he made room in the last three years for language studies, and he permitted Moses and the Prophets to appear alongside Homer, Virgil, and other Classics. He also gave considerable attention to arts like drawing and music. In short, Diderot's school system provided not merely a utilitarian programme but also spiritual training. It attested as well that some educational theorists of pre-Revolutionary France were prepared to march a long way toward a secular, gratuitous, universal, state-controlled system of education.[38]

Educational Reform outside France

Outside of France a similar reaction to traditional educational methods set in. The German Gymnasium, which under the inspiration of Melanchthon and Sturm had instituted a new curriculum in reaction to the tradition of the Middle Ages, in the eighteenth century seemed to some critics too old-fashioned for practical training. The reaction was most effectively reflected in the Ökonomisch-Mathematische-Realschule opened in Berlin in 1747 by the Pietist Johann Julius Hecker (1707–68). That school was planned to prepare boys for the realities of middle-class life and so offered less Latin and Greek and more economics, mathematics, history, geography, mechanics, drawing, and other 'real' subjects, without becoming a mere trade school. Always acting the role of the 'enlightened despot', Frederick II undertook to make the schools an instrument of the Prussian state. With Hecker's aid he formulated a General-Landschul Reglement (1763) for Prussia, and after Prussia acquired Silesia from Austria, the Silesian educator Abbot Johann Ignaz von Felbiger (1774–88) helped him to extend it (1765) to the Roman Catholics of that province. On paper it required the parents of his realm, under penalty of fine for disobedience, to send their children aged five to thirteen to school, provided stipends for the poor, licensed teachers, and outlined a curriculum, but this school code proved during his lifetime to be little more than an aspiration.

British dissenters, with much the same practical purpose in mind as the German Pietists, created 'academies' for secondary schooling, of which Warrington (founded 1665) was probably the most famous. Priestley taught the Classics there, but its curriculum included also science, modern languages, law, history, geography, and other mundane subjects as well as religion and the Classics, The Philadelphia Academy, opened in 1751 under Franklin's sponsorship, evolved rapidly into a school where trade and the mechanical professions were taught along with Latin, English, mathematics, science, and other subjects.

No school reform, however, was more thorough than that carried out under Abbot von Felbiger's direction because of the dissolution of the Jesuit school system in Austria. Upon the invitation of Maria Theresa, Felbiger wrote an Allgemeine Schulordnung (1774) that proposed, at the elementary level, subsidized, compulsory *Trivialschulen* and *Volkschulen* with a kindly attitude toward children and, at the secondary level, *Hauptschulen* for technical training as well as *Gymnasien* for Classical education. Emperor Joseph II also reformed the University of Vienna so as to make it primarily an institution for the preparation of civil servants. The result was a highly centralized, strictly regimented state system of education chiefly concerned with lay rather than ecclesiastical matters, and for all its shortcomings, it won Vienna widespread admiration as an educational centre.

The Prevalence of Illiteracy

Thus, well before the French Revolution the educational systems of Europe were undergoing a series of critical changes. Where once they had been church-controlled, they were now well on the way to being controlled by the state. Where once the curriculum had been theologically oriented and controlled, it was fast becoming humanistic, scientific, and professional. Where once the objective had been the training of Christians, it was now changing to the training of subjects. Where once corporal punishment had been a major incentive to rote learning, satisfaction of native curiosity was slowly taking its place. And where once school faculties had emphasized the preservation of the cultural tradition, they were now finding more room for the specialized professions and for the probing of new frontiers. Moreover, more persons were becoming literate.

In the early Middle Ages literacy had been limited almost entirely to the clergy, and not all clergymen were literate. With the expansion of town life, schools, and universities during the twelfth and thirteenth centuries, a higher proportion of nearly all classes of the population became literate. Young nobles often went to liberal-arts schools and ambitious middle-class scions attended both liberal-arts and business schools, though educated peasants and girls were still rare. If Villani was correct in estimating that about the year 1300 over 10,000 pupils (including some girls) attended the Florentine schools, and if the population of Florence reached 90,000 (a probably generous estimate), Florence would seem to have had a highly literate citizenry. While Florence may have been an unusually progressive town, and while lay education was more advanced in Italy than elsewhere, all indications lead to the conclusion that at the opening of the fourteenth century clerical education in general was improving and that more laymen were getting a better education than before.

The gains in literacy seem to have slackened in the two succeeding centuries. In England in 1530 only 2,600 boys (out of a probable population of 5,000,000) are estimated to have attended elementary schools. Even when due allowance is made for differences in culture, economic structure, and statistical base, these figures of school population for fourteenth-century Florence and sixteenth-century England would suggest that no notable advances in literacy occurred between 1300 and 1530 despite the fact that the intervening era was that of the Renaissance in Italy and its beginnings in the north. The probability of the suggestion is enhanced by the consideration that for about two centuries after 1350, when (approximately) a 'commercial revolution' braked to a halt, most regions of western Europe suffered a decline in population and a prolonged economic depression. To be sure, during those centuries imaginative educational enterprise was exhibited in certain types of schools, such as those of Vittorino da Feltre and the Brethren of the Common Life, but it had little influence on the population as a whole or upon institutions of higher learning.

The sixteenth and succeeding centuries were marked by new vigour in education as Reformation and Counter-Reformation encouraged rival school systems. The reputation of individual artists, writers, and scientists and their works induced colleagues, admirers, and *curiosi* to travel great distances to visit them, so that eventually the Grand Tour (generally to France, Italy, Switzerland, and Germany) came to be regarded, particularly in eighteenth-century England, as a necessary part of a gentleman's education.[39] Autocratic dynastic states, competing with the churches in shaping education, siphoned the products of the educational institutions into their administrative and military machinery. In England, France, and Holland especially, schools were opened in the late seventeenth century to teach the children of the less fortunate, who might thereby become equipped to raise their status in society. The ancient complaint that learning would make the lower classes discontent to perform the simple tasks that God had allotted to them was frequently voiced, yet before the revolutions of the eighteenth century the possibility of universal literacy seemed too remote to constitute a genuine concern, except to a few *philosophes* who favoured it.

THE POPULARIZATION OF SCIENCE IN EUROPE

If university authorities remained for the most part conservative regarding the dissemination of the new science, other institutions, and in particular the scientific societies, assiduously furthered it. The scientific societies of the seventeenth century were both a symptom and a cause of a conscious striving to bring about co-operation among scientists, craftsmen, entrepreneurs, and governments. Scientific periodicals—for example, the *Journal des sçavans* of the Académie Royale des Sciences, the *Philosophical Transactions* of the Royal Society of London, the *Giornale de letterati* of Rome, and the *Acta Eruditorum* of Leipzig—became mines of information throughout the Western world. Scores of them had come into existence, though some only ephemerally, by the end of our period. Private individuals published encyclopedic volumes of information of a technological type; Jacob Leupold's *Theatrum machinarum* (Leipzig, 1724-27, in seven volumes, supplemented by two posthumous ones) and the *Encyclopédie* edited by Diderot and d'Alembert (thirty-five volumes in the complete edition, 1751-80) were the outstanding but by no means the only endeavours of this kind. The scientific societies set up laboratories, simple in scale and style in comparison with modern ones but of unprecedented excellence for their own day; other laboratories were instituted by private researchers, like Lavoisier's, or instituted by governmental agencies, as those of the royal industries in several countries. With some exceptions the introduction of the scientific laboratory into regular systems of higher learning had to wait until the end of the eighteenth century or the beginning of the nineteenth.[40]

Each of the great national academies was created by some group of interested persons or some powerful monarch or minister. By the eighteenth century nearly every principality had its scientific and literary academy, and nearly every major city had or was planning to have one. In addition, since the science of the day required relatively simple laboratory operations and since a little expenditure might suffice to acquire the necessary equipment and the reflected glory, any man of means might aspire to become a scientist or a patron of science. Thus the rich layman, royal or commoner, supplied much of the money needed to advance the new knowledge. Along with state subsidies private philanthropy began to appear as a main source of funds for scientific research and education.

As the interest in science and technology quickened, a number of writers undertook to make the new knowledge popular. In a long lifetime Bernard de Fontenelle (1657-1757), secretary of the French Academy of Sciences, was a rare combination of philosopher and scientist; he wrote several eloquent works relating to cosmology, progress, and contemporary science that won a wide reception. A number of highly respected scientists—Fahrenheit, Hawksbee, and Desaguliers among them—gave popular lectures on physics with dramatic demonstrations. Voltaire deliberately undertook to popularize Newtonian physics for the French-reading public, and by the middle of the eighteenth century (though only in small part because of his efforts) Newtonianism had definitely triumphed over Cartesianism in French scientific circles (see Chapter VII). Count Francesco Algarotti published an Italian popularization entitled *Il Newtonianismo per le donne* (1737), which went through several editions in several languages, and Benjamin Martin's *A Plain and Familiar Introduction to the Newtonian Philosophy in Six Lectures* (1751) met with similar success. Nor were these the only popular books on the subject.[41]

The churches did not regard the new perspectives in physics, biology, and
LL*

other natural sciences as dangerous in and of themselves. In fact, Newton's theistic empiricism was a welcome ally against the deistic implications of Descartes or the pantheistic declarations of Spinoza. Priests and parsons were fearful, however, of some of the possibly heretical inferences of natural philosophy, especially when it dealt with metaphysical problems like monism and infinity, and they counted upon the states to subject dangerous views to censorship. In the British empire, after the passage of the law of libel in the late seventeenth century, official censorship slackened while private suits mounted in number. In France, though censorship was a regular function of the ministry of the royal household, the problem of control of opinion nevertheless remained largely a religious matter. Diderot's *Encyclopédie* used subterfuge more often with questions of a religious than of a political context; and Voltaire lived in exile or at Ferney, near the frontier, as much out of fear of Jesuits as of royal disapproval. Books were burned in France by the parlements, to be sure, and not by the clergy, but no less often for their religious than for their political unorthodoxy. In other Continental countries the censorship by royal household or Inquisition was usually more severe. Nevertheless, the day had passed when ideas could be effectively controlled by the old methods of censorship, for literacy had become common, though far from general, and the means of communication had outgrown the manuscript book and the town crier. Expanding literacy and communication, of course, sometimes promoted respect for the ancient traditions as well as the desire for *novae res* (and, paradoxical though it may seem, these were often allied sentiments). In any case, the prevailing order was obviously changing and yielding place to a new.

EDUCATION OUTSIDE EUROPE

In 1300 the aims, the methods, and even the content of education in other advanced cultures were not strikingly different from those in the West, but by 1775 the gulf between the two areas in those regards had become enormous. This widening separation was attributable, in the first place, to the growing emphasis on natural science and the scientific method in the West, while the basic aim of education in other regions continued to be to preserve and transmit the fundamental cultural pattern. At least two major consequences followed from this difference. In the first place, whereas by 1775 in the West it had become an aim of some prominent educators to develop independence of thought, rote memorization and humble dependence on a teacher remained an essentially undisturbed characteristic of education elsewhere. Furthermore, while at the beginning of our period the core of education had everywhere been religious and moral teachings, by 1775 in the West subjects divorced from religion and ethics had likewise become essential elements of the curriculum.

Despite the contrast, certain similarities were also conspicuous even in

1775. In both Europe and elsewhere, the home remained an essential centre of education. Arts, crafts, and business methods were still largely taught by mother to daughter, by father to son, or by master to apprentice. Advanced education was limited to relatively few, most of whom came from the families most favoured economically or socially, while the vast majority remained essentially illiterate. Still, if general education at public expense such as is now common existed nowhere except perhaps on paper, it was not everywhere entirely limited to the wealthy and high-born. More than other countries east or west, China through its system of public civil-service examinations provided incentive and opportunity for members of the lower social groups to acquire an education, and in Islamic lands qualified peasant lads were afforded a chance to get to the *madrasas*. Although teachers often maintained themselves at least partly by charging fees, teachers, schools, and sometimes elaborate educational centres were not uncommonly supported by either private or public endowments and contributions, and many schools were open, tuition free, to those who could otherwise qualify for entrance. In India, however, higher learning was largely for Brahmans and Kshatriyas, in Buddhist countries for nobles and monks (but nearly every man could be a monk for a while), and in Japan for samurai and monks. Considerable care went into the education of princes and sons of the higher classes everywhere, as was evidenced by the literary skill of many a ruler and courtier.

In Asian countries more than in Europe, for almost all forms of advanced education the disciple system was the rule; a student attached himself to a teacher in a sort of apprentice-master relationship. At the lower levels of education the methods were more varied. The elite might educate their own children, employ tutors at home, or arrange for instruction by a scholar or learned man with whom the family had traditional ties, and they did not eglect the education of women, especially not in India. Poorer families among the elite had to depend more on the village, temple, mosque, monastic, or endowed school, and occasionally a bright boy even from the submerged classes got an opportunity in schools of this sort.

Islamic Education

In an all-embracing social and mystical sense, religion dominated Islamic intellectual life in the fourteenth and fifteenth centuries more than in some periods before the Mongol invasions. Education had come to be shared between two institutions representing the two aspects of religion, *sharī'a* (the law) and Ṣūfism (the life of mystical devotion). The *'ulamā'*, guardians of the *sharī'a*, were formed in the *madrasas*, which taught a fairly wide range of 'religious' and allied disciplines. In preparation for entrance into a *madrasa*, a child learned to recite the Koran from memory—in Arabic, whatever his own tongue—and was sometimes also given linguistic training through the study of poetry and religious tradition, together with the essential precepts of Islam. The only significant critic of this system in the earlier centuries of our period was Ibn Khaldūn, who frowned upon too early and too exclusive preoccupation with Koranic recitation.

The *madrasa* taught chiefly through memorization and lively discussion between students and teachers, It inculcated the approved circle of studies in the all-embracing *shari'a*, together with auxiliaries like grammar and such elementary mathematics as was needed for determining times of prayer and dividing inheritances. More enterprising students could take, in addition, such subjects as natural philosophy, music, astronomy, or magic. The period 1300–1500 was especially notable for the production of textbooks—often rhymed for easier memorization—that continued to be used long after; a fourteenth-century Syrian, Ibn-al Shiḥna, wrote a series of versified textbooks (though not the most important ones) on various subjects. Having thus been trained in the tradition, the graduate of a *madrasa* became one of the *'ulamā'*, pledged in turn to maintain the hold of the prescribed circle of orthodox views on the general public and on the next generation.

The chief alternative form of intellectual education was that in the *khānaqāhs* (convents of the *ṭarîqas*), where the youth learned the way of Ṣūfism. This way consisted of partly personal discipline and partly mystical speculation, which often meant considerable freedom for adults but not for the young student. He was expected to accept unquestioningly, as if at divine behest, the least command of his master. Ṣūfism was eventually taught also in the regular *madrasas*.

The civil service was recruited to a large degree from the *'ulamā'*. Training for civil service, however, was in part independent of the *madrasas*, being designed to develop a polished linguistic skill as well as an essential administrative competence. In the time of the great empires, this administrative education increased in importance. In the Ottoman Empire a special educational system developed to prepare for government office the cream of the conscripted (and converted) Christian children, of whom the less gifted were trained for military purposes. This system, heavily emphasizing the Persian humanities though offering little natural science, produced highly cultivated gentlemen.

Otherwise both lower and higher education among Muslims was dominated by theology through the eighteenth century. This system of instruction, comparable to the Scholastic instruction that the West was outgrowing, continued in all the Islamic world under the leadership of a state-supported religious class. As in Christendom, the theologically dominated educators tended to drift into subtleties of interpretation, and controversies arose that were not always fruitful.

The schools, especially before 1500, were largely free of government interference. Ample estates devoted by endowment (*waqf*) to education provided for professors and book-copyists and made available scholarships for even the most impecunious students, enabling them to spend years in intensive study, often travelling from one teacher to another. The universality of

Arabic and Persian eliminated serious barriers for peripatetic students and professors who had mastered those languages. The number of students from the middle and lower classes was large, though their lack of cultural background frequently delayed their progress, especially in their younger years. In the higher branches of learning, individual teachers rather than formal curricula were of primary importance. Ibn-Baṭṭūṭa's wanderings led him to fourteen masters, two of them women. Medicine and astrology were especially dependent on individual instruction.

Education followed essentially the same pattern in all Islamic countries. Elementary training in the teachings of Islam was considered a religious obligation for all. Children of the nobles or the wealthy were generally instructed beyond that level by tutors, learning the Koran chapter by chapter along with the subjects considered auxiliary to it. Poorer boys were sent to the *maktab*, or mosque school, conducted by a *mullah* (a man learned in the lore of Islam and attached to the mosque), where they were instructed in reading (Arabic and Persian), writing, and arithmetic. They memorized the words of the Koran and some *hadīth* (sacred reports about the Prophet). Penmanship was also cultivated. After completing their preliminary education, children of the poorer classes were often apprenticed to an *ustād* (or master), while children of the elite might go on to the *madrasa*.

We have already named the famous universities in Cairo, Tunis, and Fez. Timbuktu also had a flourishing university, famed particularly as the seat of the historian Aḥmed Baba (died 1607). In Muslim India the *madrasas*, or colleges, at Delhi, Agra, and Bidar were among the most famous institutions of higher learning. Theology, metaphysics, mathematics, physics, and Persian literature were the major subjects taught in these colleges, and many Hindus were trained there along with Muslims in the Persian literary tradition. Such different personalities as Akbar and Aurangzīb complained that the method of education was not very practical and urged more attention to subjects like geography, history, politics, medicine, and the newer sciences. Islamic rulers supported some of the colleges and gave stipends to some of the scholars but did not establish a public system of education. Although Akbar founded a girl's school at Fathpūr Sikri, the *purdah* (the custom of seclusion) generally kept women from the schools. Governesses were employed, however, to educate the daughters of noblemen at home, and Islamic India had reason to be proud of a good number of women of learning and literary skill.

As Islam spread in Indonesia and Malaya, the older Buddhist educational order declined and was replaced by mosque schools and *pesantren*. A *pesantren* was a community of teachers and students. Such communities were located in the vicinity of most mosques but also in villages and towns without mosques. The larger ones contained several residence and prayer halls and afforded rather elaborate courses of study. Some specialized in particular aspects of Islamic learning and religion, but in general they taught Islamic law and doctrine, some form of Islamic mysticism, and auxiliary subjects. Most of the pupils did not go on to complete the course of instruction but were content to learn only certain elementary things, including parts of the Koran, prayers, and the ritual of ablutions. Those who obtained only this limited training often rose to preside over the village prayer halls, where they also gave rudimentary instruction to village boys in reading and daily devotions. Those who completed the training could expect to be employed in the mosques or other *pesantren*.

Hindu and Buddhist Education

The traditional system of education of Hindu and Buddhist India suffered, though unevenly, under an Islamic policy of repression. In the north, where Islamic rule was stronger, many schools were destroyed, and several famous university centres came to an end, while princely patronage of Hindu and Buddhist institutions declined. In south India, on the other hand, local patronage continued, and throughout India new sectarian centres of learning associated with the various *bhakti* groups arose. Generally speaking, Hindu educational centres were able to carry on the traditional pattern, but the Buddhist centres gave way rapidly. Instruction was given more and more in the vernaculars, while at an equal pace Sanskrit became a monopoly of the Brahmans.

Supported by endowments, Brahmans largely monopolized teaching. They educated their own children or arranged for their education under a guru from another Brahman family. Many Brahmans also took disciples into their homes and assumed complete responsibility for their training; the disciple, in turn, became a sort of assistant to the teacher and remained closely attached to him for life. The wealthier members of the other two higher classes—the Kshatriyas and the Vaishyas—employed Brahmans as tutors. Brahmans were responsible in particular for the education of princes, who were instructed in the Vedas as well as in the military sciences, philosophy, grammar, logic, *dharma*, belles-lettres, fine arts, and the art of government (*arthashāstra*), which included economics and politics.

For the mass of Hindus the only formal education came through the village school, presided over by a Brahman supported by village funds or some endowment. Schools were provided for girls as well as boys. A pupil might acquire the basic elements of reading, writing, and arithmetic in a class that met in the shade of a tree or on a temple veranda. Memorization was the usual method of study. Writing was often taught by means of lines drawn in white sand strewn on the ground. More advanced education required a guru, or attendance at lectures and expositions by endowed teachers, or study at some *matha* (*college*). The traditional subjects of study were the four Vedas, their six auxiliaries (phonetics, prosody, grammar, etymology, astronomy, and ritual), philosophy, the *purānas*, logic, exegesis, law, medicine, archery, music, politics, and economics.

Hindu educational institutions of the period took several forms. One was the *bhāttavritti*, an endowment for a single learned man requiring him to perform some public teaching such as reciting and expounding the Vedas, epics, or *purānas* or offering instruction in mathematics, astronomy, or grammar. In some places several such teachers were organized into corporate colleges known as *brahmapurīs* or *ghatikās*. Another set of educational institutions were the *vidyāpīthas*, endowed quasi-monastic organizations founded by Shankara and his followers; here scholarly and holy men, presided over by learned abbotts, engaged in the study and spread of Hinduism and Sanskrit learning. Especially famous institutions of this sort located at Kūnchi, Shrīrangam, and Jagannāth became, along with their branches, centres for the advanced training of scholars. The *mathas* established by the various Vishnuite and Shivaite sects were very similar to the *vidyāpīthas* but emphasized the views of their respective sects. Still another form of educational institution consisted of temple endowments, which sometimes provided free instruction in various subjects. Pilgrimages to holy places or to learned men also served an educational purpose, as did wandering minstrels. Among the more celebrated educational centres of India were Benares, Madura, Chidambaram, Tirupati, Tirunāvāi, and Tirichur. A medical school was located at Tiruvāduturai, and a school of Panini grammar at Tiruvorriyūr; the Yādavas of Devagiri in the Deccan emphasized law and astronomy.

In the Buddhist countries of southeast Asia from Ceylon to Cambodia education centred in the monasteries or monastic schools. Teachers and religious leaders were supported in the monasteries by gifts and endowments from rulers and the wealthy classes. Almost every village had some kind of monastery where the monks gave elementary instruction in reading, writing, arithmetic, and the basic elements of Buddhism. Almost every boy, rich or poor, attended these schools for a while and then spent a brief period as a novice in the monastery, where he learned a little Pali, the sacred language, and memorized various Pali creeds, chants, and incantations. In larger centres more advanced monastic schools taught the Pali scriptures and more arithmetic, in addition to geometry, astrology, and a fanciful history and geography. The most learned men were the monks of certain monasteries and those few Brahmans whom the rulers and nobility continued to employ as teachers and advisers. This function of the Brahmans in a Buddhist country was a vestige from the time before the spread of Pali Buddhism, their Hindu lore and knowledge being still considered an essential part of government.

Sometimes boys were pledged to monkhood by their parents and so underwent a special training. The ceremony of initiation involved ten primary vows; they pledged to refrain from taking life, lying, stealing, being unchaste, trading in liquor, boasting, speaking evil, being avaricious, feeling hatred, or blaspheming. Violation of these vows might incure expulsion from the order and ruin every hope of attaining Buddhahood. A second initiation followed upon further training. This ceremony meant commitment to the two hundred and fifty vows or commandments of the ancient *Prātimoksha*, which were in the main an elaboration and refinement of the ten primary vows. In Hīnayāna countries the initiate then became a full-fledged monk (*bhikkhu*), thereby embarking fully on the path of the *arhat*. In Mahāyāna lands a third ceremony, an early Indian ascetic practice apparently unknown to Hīnayāna and Tantric Buddhism and surviving only in the Far East, was required: the initiate pledge himself to the fifty-eight vows of the 'Net of Brahmā', thereby embarking upon the career of a bodhisattva, and his head was burned in from three to eighteen places (according to his zeal).

Education in China

In China the monasteries, especially some of the Ch'an sect, were centres of Buddhist scholarship and learning, and monks received in them some degree of education. Otherwise Chinese education was dominated by the requirements of the civil service examination and the ideals of a Confucian society (see Chapter VI). The civil service examinations were the chief route to appointed office, and hence the acquisition of the type of learning required to pass them became a dominant social incentive. The examination system was stereotyped and unimaginative, tending to discourage originality and unfamiliar ideas. Sometimes, and especially in the seventeenth and eighteenth centuries, eminent Confucian teachers and thinkers who were out of sympathy with the official versions of Confucianism either failed the highest examinations or avoided official life entirely (see Chapters VII and IX). By the same token the system promoted cultural uniformity and stability. Governed by scholar-officials, the state was a liberal patron of the official scholarship and learning, and—at least in principle—maintained a system of public education designed to perpetuate Confucian society and train its leaders.

Although not particularly favourable to education, the Mongols in general kept the traditional system of public schools; the Ming rulers strengthened it; and it was continued under the Manchus. In theory, it provided village, district (*hsien*), departmental (*chou*), and prefectural (*fu*) schools, provincial colleges (*shu-yüan*), and the National University (Kuo-tzu-chien) in the capital. In fact, the village schools were not maintained by the central government, and although government funds were used to subsidize scholars in the higher schools, it is not clear that any formal course of study was available at the district, departmental, prefectural, and provincial levels. Perhaps during the best years of the Ming era these schools actually offered systematic instruction, but in the later Ch'ing (Manchu) period they were little more than groups of subsidized scholars, who gave occasional lectures, and students both subsidized and unsubsidized, who, having attained a certain standard of learning (passage of the matriculation examination), were required to present themselves periodically for examinations.

The objective of students was to move up 'the ladder of success' by civil service examinations. Upon passing the matriculation examination in the districts and prefectures, they enrolled in the district or prefectural schools, and the more promising were given scholarships to help finance their further study. Passing the district examination led to the *hsiu-ts'ai* degree, the first of the three main degrees in the civil service system, and assured further scholarships. Passing the provincial examination led to the *chü-jen* degree and assured further help and an opportunity to try for the third (*chin-shih*) degree in examinations given every three years in the capital. The *chin-shih* degree was highly prized, for it not only potentially qualified the holder for any office but was also the hallmark of the full-fledged literatus. One of the academic honours most coveted in China, appointment to the Han-lin Academy, went automatically to those receiving the highest marks in the metropolitan civil-service examination.

In actual practice education for the most part was a private affair. It began either at home with parents or tutors or in a family, clan, private, temple, or village school. Families that could afford to do so used private tutors or family or clan schools, and poorer boys went to the village school. The village schools were maintained by the villages or subsidized by private donations. Many village youths received a limited training in reading and writing, but only a few of the brighter ones ever reached a stage where they could try the matriculation examination that might open the doors of government subsidy to them. The lower schools were staffed for the most part by relatively unsuccessful scholars who had failed to attain the higher degrees and public office. Advanced education was usually obtained through tutors or self-directed study. As a rule, the formal schooling of women was neglected. Although some families employed private tutors to train their daughters in reading and writing, girls were, as a matter of course, carefully instructed only in such things as the management of a household, courtesy, ceremonials, needlework, and their duties toward husband and parents-in-law.

Inevitably attempts were made to counteract the shortcomings of this system. During the later Ming dynasty many academies of scholars were endowed where discussions took place and students might thereby receive better instruction. More advanced students sought master-pupil associations with some famous scholars, and the disciple system was highly developed. Probably the most famous teacher and educational theorist of our period was the Ming philosopher and official Wang Yang-ming (see Chapters VII and IX), who held that knowing should be associated with doing (practice), but his theory, though it impressed later thinkers, had little influence on contemporary educational methods.

The ultimate aim in education at all levels was, by building character and inculcating Confucian ethical and social principles, to produce the *chün-tzu* (the ideal man). By 1300 the civil service examinations were largely based on the Five Classics and the Four Books as interpreted by Chu Hsi (see Chapter II). Through the official Board of Rites and the state Cult of the Scholars the government schools were expressly organized to teach this formidable list of classics, and because Confucian learning was the most important road to office, private schools, academies, and the schools maintained by the villages also were conducted by Confucian scholars along similar lines, at the expense of Taoism and other persuasions.

Instruction in the elementary schools began with memorization of certain standard works and training in writing (calligraphy). Later came elucidation of the texts. Hours were long, discipline was rigid, and the scholar, despite Wang Yang-ming's injunction, was kept from physical activity. Instruction began with the *San tzu ching* (*Three Character Classic*), written by Wang Ying-lin during the Mongol period. It was a short compendium of Confucian knowledge in rhymed lines of three characters each, setting forth the essentials of Confucian philosophy, history, and literature. Next came instruction in other books, including the *Thousand Character Essay* (in which no character appeared twice) and the *Hsiao ching* (*Classic of Filial Piety*). The student then went on to the Four Books and the Five Classics, which were memorized. Those preparing for the official examinations pored over the official compendium of the classics embodying the interpretations of Chu Hsi and his *Comprehensive Mirror of History*. More advanced students conned the poets and essayists, the dynastic histories, and the compendia on government and history. At all levels, the curriculum centred on philosophy, ethics, literature, history, and government; mathematics and science were hardly touched except in the most general and elementary terms.

Outside the traditional system of public schools, the government maintained a number of extra institutions. Both the Ming and the Manchu dynasty provided military academies, which, along with composition, taught archery, horsemanship, and other military arts. The two dynasties also made schools available at the capital for the children of nobles and other favoured persons. The Mongols and the Manchus established special schools, in addition, for their own people. The Mongols showed considerable interest in the study of medicine, divination, astronomy, and mathematics, and the later dynasties supported bureaux of astronomy and medicine and an observatory to serve the court and central government. Since, however, the few who were trained in these bureaux generally remained in their service, such specialized knowledge was rarely disseminated.

The educational system culminated in the National University, the Kuo-tzu-chien. In Ming times this university was open to the sons of officials, to students who had passed certain provincial examinations or were recommended by the provincial colleges, and to foreigners. It was divided into six departments, and students were required to pass from one to another in a ten-year course of study. Successful completion of the course led to a degree equivalent to that acquired by passing the provincial civil-service examinations. During the Manchu period the National University offered two courses of study. One emphasized the classics, with specialization in one or more of them; the other emphasized government administration, with specialization in one or more of the following fields: public rites, taxation, law, frontier defence, waterways, and mathematics. During the early Ming period graduates readily found government posts, but as the civil-service-examination system expanded, the advantages of the university degree diminished.

Education in Japan

In Korea and Annam the system of education was modelled on that of China, and in Japan the subject matter of education had long been a combination of Confucian with Buddhist learning. Japanese learning was at a low ebb during the period of Ashikaga feudalism. Members of the military class received a limited literary training as part of the family instruction in the military arts. Some court nobles and military families employed private tutors for their sons.

The formal education of women was generally neglected. Although some attended temple schools, as a rule they were taught little more than the arts of home-making in their own homes. Kaibara Ekken, one of the more broad-minded educators of the period, and his wife, Token, were concerned about the neglect of women's education (see Chapter VII), but even they went no further than to recommend that the virtues of chastity and obedience and the arts of sewing and conversation be taught.

For the most part, formal literary education was confined to temple or monastic schools (terakoya), a few family or clan schools, the Ashikaga College, and the Kanazawa Library. The temple schools were normally open to all social classes. Their curricula included the Chinese language and Confucian learning, but they naturally emphasized Buddhist learning and training for monkhood. The number of non-ecclesiastics who attended these schools was not great, and the knowledge acquired, even by monks, was most elementary; the Zen schools were the best of them and the most numerous (see Chapter II). The Ashikaga College under the direction of Zen scholars developed into the leading centre of Chinese learning in Japan. By 1550 it had acquired a considerable library and was reported to have as many as three thousand students. It now emphasized philosophical studies. Francis Xavier spoke of it and the monastic centres of Mt Koya (near Osaka) and Mt Hiyei (near Kyoto) as the chief institutions of learning in Japan. The Kanazawa Library, connected with the Shomyoji Temple in Kurakigun (Musashi province), was built up under the patronage of the Hōjō family. It functioned also, and became important, as a school.

Under the Tokugawa regime, political stability and the policies of the shoguns greatly stimulated scholarship, printing, and education. The founder of the Tokugawa shogunate, Ieyasu, encouraged Confucian scholarship within the samurai class, promoted temple and clan schools, transferred the Kanazawa Library to Edo, and established a school in Kyoto. By patronizing the Neo-Confucian scholar Hayashi Dōshun (1583–1637), he in reality laid the foundations for the Tokugawa College at Edo, though only in 1630 did the third shogun grant land to Dōshun for its establishment. In 1690 it was made an official government school. It was placed under the direction of Hayashi Razan, and the headship remained hereditary in the Hayashi family. Known as the Shōhei School (after the Japanese rendition of Confucius' birthplace), it became the chief centre for expounding the Chu Hsi version of Neo-Confucianism, which had been adopted by the shogunate. Its curriculum emphasized Chinese language, history, the classics, and the military arts. Its students lived in dormitories under the supervision of monitors, were examined annually, and were forbidden to discuss heretical philosophical views. Before 1797, it seems to have been open to all samurai.

Usually the great feudal lords established secular schools for the sons of their samurai. These clan schools became centres of Chinese learning throughout Japan, most of them emphasizing the orthodox Chu Hsi philosophy and the classics, but they also taught archery, horsemanship, and military science. Their professors commonly gave public lectures. One of the most famous of the clan schools was the Kodokwan of Mito, established by Tokugawa Mitsukuni, head of one of the collateral branches of the Tokugawas. It placed great emphasis on the study of Japanese history and literature and was responsible for compiling the *History of Great Japan*, which contributed to the ultimate downfall of the shogunate (see Chapter IX). The Zoshikwan, established at Kagoshima by Shimadzu, head of the Satsuma clan, also enjoyed enormous prestige. It was open to the sons of all Satsuma samurai, but the sons of tradesmen were permitted to occupy the lowest seats in the lecture halls. Clan schools whose course of study did not depart markedly from the orthodox philosophy generally received subsidies from the shogun. In most of these samurai schools children from six to nine years of age learned to read and write about a thousand characters, were trained in manners, ethic, and etiquette, and studied the *Classic of Filial Piety* and other literature, including the T'ang poets. They then embarked on a study of the classics and various Chinese history books.

Temple schools provided both elementary education for pupils, sometimes girls, below the samurai class and more advanced training for priests. They gave less emphasis to Confucian and more to Buddhist ideas than the clan schools; some of them were Shinto schools. Temple schools were normally run by priests in buildings attached to the temples, but sometimes the teachers were *ronin*, or samurai who were no longer attached to a feudal lord.

A somewhat more advanced school known as the *shijuki* was of a private nature. It was usually open to all, regardless of class, who were able to pay the required fees. Though such schools stressed Confucian learning, some of them taught unorthodox Confucian philosophies. They were generally taught by *ronin* who had turned to teaching as a means of livelihood. An especially prominent private school, established by Itō Jinsai in Kyoto about

1680, emphasized the study of the Han interpretation of the classics, Japanese literature, and Japan's national heritage.

The curriculum and methods of the several kinds of Japanese schools varied. Some of the temple and private schools paid more attention to arithmetic and other subjects useful to merchants than did the samurai schools. In all schools the disciple system was emphasized, but it was especially strong in the more advanced temple and private schools. All samurai instruction aimed at character building above all else.

The Feebleness of Western Influences

Western schools and theories of education had little influence in the East during our period. Such influence as they had was limited to the Philippine Islands, where the Catholic orders dominated education after 1570. A few Western schools were established in India by the Portuguese and in the East Indies by the Dutch, but their importance during our period was as yet fairly negligible.

PROFESSIONAL TRAINING IN THE WEST

Training in Medicine and Law

Between the fourteenth and the eighteenth century some striking changes took place in the training of Europeans for the old professions, and some entirely new professions came into being. Along with theology and law, medicine was the oldest of the learned professions. Until late in the Middle Ages physician, surgeon, pharmacist, and veterinarian were not sharply distinguished one from the other. In the early centuries, medical study had been chiefly concerned with medicines, urine analysis, pulse taking, blood letting, and purging, and a physician aided by his assistant performed these services. The theoretical aspects of medicine were taught in the liberal arts courses of the *trivium* and *quadrivium*, and at a professional level by the medical faculties of the universities. Actual practice was begun with a sort of apprenticeship, either in guilds—for the lower types of healer—or as an assistant to a practising physician. In the later Middle Ages some governments demanded a certain amount of practical experience of this sort before granting a licence.

Only rarely did a physician undertake surgery, and the practice of the independent profession of surgeon remained relatively uncommon until the later centuries of the Middle Ages, when dissections became more frequent. Physicians were prone to view with suspicion the upstart surgeons' guilds and their efforts to attain formal education and professional status— including the physician's long robe. Similarly, professional surgeons looked askance at the barber-surgeons, pharmacists, and midwives, who likewise sought to raise the standards of their professions. And all these groups disdained as charlatans the great majority of sub-professional practitioners of healing, who actually handled most of the sick and ailing. In the fourteenth and fifteenth centuries governmental agencies generally supported the organized professionals, and official action against unlicensed practitioners was frequent. Government restrictions thus reinforced university requirements for a degree and placed almost impassable gulfs between the groups, thereby upholding "professional standards" though medical care for the needy lagged. In the fifteenth century the universities finally began to recognize separate guilds of surgeons and pharmacists and to make available to them certain educational facilities generally limited to physicians.

Slowly the clinical method of teaching medicine developed. Students, who once had merely heard lectures by experienced professors, now also attended the sick in hospitals or homes under the eye of a responsible physician. At Salerno and Montpellier, as early as the thirteenth century, though no regularized system of teaching hospitals existed, a sort of internship-apprenticeship had been required for the license degree.[42,43] At Padua a similar teaching method was employed in the sixteenth century. At Leiden, which Sylvius and Boerhaave made famous the next century as a centre of medical instruction, the clinical method was convincingly established as the best way to train physicians and surgeons (see Chapter XIV), and thereafter schools in England, Austria, and elsewhere adopted it.

The distrust of the *a priori*, speculative approach to medicine and the demand for more empirical methods of training physicians were reflected in the satires of Molière. By his time, nevertheless, the training of physicians had already become comparatively empirical. With the steady growth of hospitals (see Chapter XV), doctors and prospective doctors acquired greater clinical facilities, and medical students, particularly in Britain, more regularly completed their training by the clinical method in metropolitan hospitals. Museums of anatomy and pathology began in the eighteenth century but did not become a widely effective teaching medium until the nineteenth.

Training for the law underwent changes that, though less pronounced than those in medical training, were similarly directed toward lifting both professional standards and status. Nearly always law schools, like medical schools, remained parts of the old universities, but they received greater emphasis, as time went on, within the corporate plan. The Inns of Court and Chancery at London were a special case, for legal training at the universities of Oxford and Cambridge, as in Continental universities, was limited essentially to civil and canon law, and English common law had to be learned by some sort of apprenticeship (often fictional) to a master in the lodgings of the masters—'the Inns'. Lawyers thus trained could aspire to the enviable title of 'barrister', the right to plead in the High Court, and, if fortunate or able enough, an appointment to a judgeship. Lesser lawyers, also after a period of apprenticeship in their respective guilds, became attorneys or solicitors, and still lesser ones notaries or scriveners. Only the barristers (or 'counsellors') were in their own eyes true members of the profession, but in the Anglo-American colonies frontier conditions obliterated such distinctions.

The thirteenth-century beginning of the Inns is obscure, but by the fifteenth century they were a flourishing quasi-university. English common law was taught at no regular university until Blackstone gave his lectures in common law at Oxford in 1753. The changing stress in the teaching of Roman law on the Continent—from the *mos italicus* to the *mos gallicus* has been described in Chapter IX.

Training in Architecture and Engineering

Among the crafts which gained the status of professions after 1300 were architecture, engineering, music, and art. The role of the designer-architect as we know it today began to develop in the fourteenth-century Italian Renaissance. Prophetic of this change was the appointment in 1334 of the painter Giotto to the position of chief architect of the cathedral and city of Florence. Among the reasons for his appointment was the authorities' belief that the master mason should be a famous citizen as well as an artist, and although (as far as we know) he had no training in the mason's craft, what artist was more famous than he?

From the fifteenth century on, the designer-architect became a familiar figure. Often trained as a painter or, in the case of Brunelleschi, as a goldsmith, the new architect was concerned primarily with the reasoning and delineation of the proper proportions of the plan and the component parts of a building. His theory of proportions, learned in part from his study of ancient monuments and in part from his discourse with mathematicians, served as a substitute for the science later called 'statics', which is concerned with the action of forces in producing an equilibrium or relative rest. Surely, he reasoned, the mathematical proportions on the basis of which God ordered the universe and the ancient Romans had constructed their buildings would assure stability in his own constructions. The knowledge of mathematics and even philosophy which he brought to bear on his carefully proportioned designs raised architecture from the status of a mechanical to that of a liberal art or profession. While the young architect may have learned the basic principles of design in the academies of painting and sculpture which began to appear in the latter half of the sixteenth century (see below, p. 1038), he still gained most of his knowledge of building and engineering through practice under the direction of an established architect or mason-builder. Not until Colbert established the Royal Academy of Architecture in Paris in 1670 (a comparable institution being founded in Rome the next year) was the architect's training entrusted to academicians.

The rise of engineering schools has been mentioned in Chapter XV. Early in the seventeenth century Stevin was entrusted with the organization of a school of engineering to be associated with the University of Leiden; Peter the Great created the Moscow School of Mathematical and Navigational

Science in 1701; and an academy for military engineers was begun at Wool-wich in 1721 (re-established in 1741); but probably the most famous of the early schools of engineering was that of the French 'Corps des Ingénieurs des Ponts et Chaussées'. The Corps itself was inaugurated in 1716 by the French government, and it soon contained some of the best road and bridge engineers in the world. After 1744 France's ablest engineers were generally trained in the École des Ponts et Chaussées in Paris, which was formally established as a royal school in 1747.[44] The Collegium Carolinum was founded in Brunswick in 1745. Other schools followed in Germany—among them those at Freiberg (1765) and Clausthal (1775).

Training in Music

Music, sometimes taught in separate 'song schools', had played a leading part in the elementary education and in the *quadrivium* of the more advanced schools during the Middle Ages. The cantor, the teacher in charge of music, was usually an important member of a school's staff, especially when he was also the chanter or precentor (*Kapellmeister, maître de chapelle*) of a nearby church. The St. Thomas School at Leipsig can boast a long succession of cantors since the sixteenth century, of whom Bach was the most distinguished. The several *conservatorios* of Naples, founded in the sixteenth century, and of Venice and other Italian cities were in the beginning orphan asylums that emphasized singing in the schooling of their wards. Some of them became famous as music schools because of outstanding teachers—Scarlatti, for example. Some private music schools were established in Rome, and Palestrina taught at one of them. Singing and instrument-playing were commonly regarded as part of a lady's or gentleman's education, with good results that we have already had occasion to mention (see Chapter XII). Musical education had not, however, been formalized by 1775, and the great composers and virtuosi of the period usually learned directly from a master. Among Bach's masters were his father and brother, and he in turn taught his sons. Mozart learned from his father.

Training in Painting and Sculpture

Before 1300 in many parts of the world artists had been esteemed only as skilled craftsmen who produced objects for use or ornament. In some areas, however, such as Africa and Oceania, those who made cult objects were sometimes priests or sorcerers with important political posts; and in China and Japan painters frequently were scholars, monks, courtiers, or other elite. In most other cases, artists were not regarded as intellectual leaders comparable to theologians, philosophers, or poets.

During at least the early part of our period painters were preservers of an esthetic consciousness whether or not they were creators, and their reverence for the art of the past frequently tended to preclude a creative role. Such reverence was true also of Chinese and Japanese painters for most of the period, but with a difference; they often sought for originality and individual expression, and their tradition was more ancient, continuous, and accomplished than perhaps any other. If artisans in many other areas during the fourteenth century shared this respect for past forms, their models were generally recent and local works, and even when they knew the art of the distant past or of other cultural areas, they rarely departed from the forms of their immediate predecessors.

Before 1300 the work of European artisans usually was anonymous and often lacked individuality. Judgments of their art were less likely to be concerned with originality or creative imagination than with excellence of materials, skill of workmanship, and faithfulness to traditional forms. Most craftsmen were trained within some continuing organization, such as a family of craftsmen or a guild of approved masters. When an apprentice met the technical standards of the group to which the continuity of the craft was entrusted, he was allowed to practice in the area under its jurisdiction.

Much the same was true in several other societies before 1300, but somewhere around 1400 the attitude changed in several of the more advanced cultures. In Islamic countries for example, the artist began to win greater esteem as an individual of talent. Favourite painters on occasion attained prominent positions in Mogul and Rajput India and in Iran. Artistic innovation was often prized, especially after the striking changes following the Mongol times, and the works of individual masters were eagerly sought by collectors. Styles of painting and of rug-weaving changed with considerable rapidity. Frequently architects of the mosques in Turkey were, like Christian cathedral builders, highly respected men of learning. About the same time the 'artisan' of medieval Europe began to become an 'artist'. The departure took place most significantly in the field of painting but was shared by sculpture and architecture as well.

The metamorphosis in the status and activity of the artist in Europe and its cultural extension in the Americas was in some regards unparalleled. It began in central Italy of the *trecento*. Artists not only acquired learning in history, poetry, and philosophy but also came to realize that in Antiquity painting, sculpture, and architecture had been considered intellectual rather than mechanical arts. Writers like Dante, Boccaccio, and Petrarch lamented the failure to recognize the intellectual as well as the simply manual aspects of the visual arts, and learned artists like Ghiberti, Brunelleschi, and Alberti furthered the artists' intellectual claims. The impressive knowledge acquired by artists who successfully imitated nature rather than medieval symbols and forms and who were proficient in 'natural philosophy', particularly the problems of ocular perception, elevated their field of knowledge in the eyes of contemporaries from the manual to the liberal arts. Their calling was considered capable of embodying truths equal to those imparted by poetry, philosophy, geometry, and even theology. This Italian idea of the visual arts and the artist as something loftier than the crafts and the artisan gradually spread over Europe.

In keeping with this development artists of the late fifteenth century in Tuscany attempted to liberate themselves from the artisans' guilds and to institute a freer and more dignified relationship between pupil and teacher than existed between apprentice and master. They sought instead to create something like the Classical 'academies', where noble young men, in free association, had pursued philosophical and scientific studies. A school for the training of artists was established in 1490 by Lorenzo the Magnificent in the Medici Gardens. It was attended by Michelangelo and other selected youths and flourished under the leadership of the sculptor Bertoldo di Giovanni. A group gathered around Leonardo da Vinci in Milan appears also to have called itself an academy, and several mid-sixteenth-century engravings show students at work in a studio labelled 'Academy of Baccio Bandinelli'. All these groups. however, were too loosely organized and too short-lived to be accurately classified as academies.

Vasiri's Accademia del Disegno, founded in Florence in 1563 under the protection of the Grand Duke Cosimo I, was Europe's first artists' academy in the modern sense. It was composed of the 'thirty-six best artists of Italy', and Cosimo I and Michelangelo were named honorary *capi*, or leaders—a gesture suggesting the comparable status of Florence's political head and the leading artist in this organization. When a talented student of art had advanced sufficiently in the workshop of his master, he might be recommended to this academy, where he might be accepted for further instruction by the three masters elected to teach each year. Vasari's academy became famous all over Europe, and other cities followed the example of Florence. The Accademia di San Luca was formed at Rome in 1593 from a nucleus called the Virtuosi al Pantheon, which had met since 1543. Similar organizations were founded by the early seventeenth century in Genoa, Naples, Milan, and Turin.

The Accademia del Disegno managed to free Florence's painters and sculptors from the guilds in 1571 and to take over some of the guild's administrative duties, but it was less successful in its important teaching programme. The Roman academy had the same aims as those of Florence, and the revision of its rules in 1627 suggested that it too accomplished little of its ambitious teaching programme. Perhaps the studio of the Carracci in Bologna more completely realized the teaching aims of an academy than did the more elaborate and official institutions of Florence and Rome. Still, academies were more concerned with studying the esthetic and philosophical aspects of art than with teaching techniques or maintaining standards of craftsmanship. Though they created a greater solidarity among practitioners of the visual arts and though their constitutions outlined the kind of institution artists wanted in place of the guilds, the system of apprenticeship remained the main means of acquiring the training and recognition necessary to practise the arts.

In France, the rules established for the guild of *peintres et tailleurs* in 1260 continued to govern art activities until the seventeenth century. During the sixteenth century, however, various Italian artists working in France were exempt from guild rules, while many French artists who went to Italy experienced a still greater freedom. The French, perhaps more readily than any other people of Europe outside Italy, accepted the Italian Renaissance assumptions that art was an objective imitation of nature, that such imitation could be taught, and that exact artistic judgments could be made. Arguments essentially like those offered by the Italians in the sixteenth century in favour of an art academy were successfully set forth by LeBrun in 1648, when the Academy of Painting and Sculpture was created. And Simon Vouet, representing the painters' guild, established an opposing academy with more professors than LeBrun's.

Colbert caused these two factions to merge and granted the combined academy some rooms in the Louvre and some funds from the royal coffers. The academy thus became a royal enterprise. Colbert soon realized that if it were strongly centralized, it would be a more effective instrument for the glorification of the king, and in 1661 he demanded that all artists join the academy, establishing grades of membership within it. Although a few, such as Pierre Mignard, continued to paint outside the academy, most artists conformed. Opposition was effectively suppressed by an order forbidding courses in life drawing outside the Royal Academy. By 1676, academies had been founded in other cities of France, but they were all dependent on that of Paris, and, in this way, the academicians in Paris came to control the art activities of the country.[45]

The Academy's study programme was prescribed. It included copying works of other artists, drawing from scupture and plaster casts, and finally drawing from the nude figure. This sequence was followed because, during the seventeenth century, it was considered inadvisable for an untutored eye to approach nature directly. Although Rubens observed that drawing from casts resulted in a tendency toward hard contours and surfaces, harsh lighting effects, and stiffness in the figures, and although Chardin in the 1760's lamented the loss of freshness after years of slavish copying, drawing from plaster casts continued into the twentieth century as a basic part of academic training. From this practice, together with the criticisms and corrections actually drawn upon his work by his teachers, the student gained the ability to draw and, with it, the basis for not only painting but also sculpture, architecture, and the decorative arts. Lectures on geometry, perspective, and anatomy rounded out a programme aimed at the effective depiction of the human body and human emotions. A large reference library supplemented the approaches to art provided by the Academy's professors. Outstanding students won an opportunity to study for extended periods at the Académie de France established in 1666 in Rome. The academies gave French art a clarity of direction and an unfaltering continuity (though also at times an 'academic' conventionality) unparalleled in contemporary Europe and probably account for the eventual emergence of Paris as the world's leading centre of art.

Arts in other parts of Europe also were inclined to abandon the guild system. In 1665 Dutch artists transformed their guild into an academy of the French type. Similar academies were established during the late seventeenth and the early eighteenth century in Nuremberg, Augsburg, Dresden, Berlin, Vienna, and London, but the original enthusiasm with which they were founded was seldom sustained. Only later, with the spread of Neoclassicism during the third quarter of the eighteenth century, did art academies vigorously multiply and flourish, finally realizing the teaching purposes that Vasari had envisioned.

Training in these academies was different from that of an apprentice in the fourteenth-century workshop. To gain admission to an academy and recognition as a master the aspiring artist still had to submit a work for approval, but a system which made all members of the academy his judges allowed much greater latitude than one which induced him as an apprentice to duplicate the manner of a single master. In addition, the academies provided a wide range of works (or copies of them) for the young artist to examine, encouraging him to study the art produced since 1500 as well as that of the Ancients. They also fostered the inclination to travel in other lands, particularly to Rome and Paris, and acquaintance with art abroad increased the artist's experience beyond his immediate and local tradition. Another source of instruction not available in 1300 was provided by the many treatises on art written since the fifteenth century and frequently available in various translations (see Chapter XII). The European artist by this time was no longer merely a guardian of a tradition; he was prepared to be a critic of his masters and to develop an independent style.

NOTES TO CHAPTER XVI

1. Professor A. Dupront emphasizes the following: first, that the evidence is clear that in the predominantly monastic Western mediaeval world, education normally proceeded from the clerks; second, that, the clerk being the one who knows—principally how to write—the layman is *illiteratus*.

2. In this connection, Professor A. Dupront draws attention to the role of the cities, concerned, like the church, with securing the necessary administrative personnel, whose main function was to commit to writing and to draft. From the thirteenth century onwards, urban life, administration, and the slowly differentiated education of the clerical schools went hand in hand. The influence of the Brothers of Common Life in the northern Rhineland area is largely attributable to their urban locations.

3. For women as well as for men of a certain social level, according to Professor A. Dupront, consideration must be given to the importance of the Book of Hours, which, first in manuscript form—and therefore expensive—and later printed, often became the sole reading matter of an entire social category in the West.

4. In Professor A. Dupront's view, this was notably true for a time at Deventer itself, where a school was conducted by a humanist in association with a house of the Brothers, serving as boarding house. Above all were their powerful and highly ramified dissemination, their wide recruitment—open to poor children, and the primordial importance which they placed on books, reading, and libraries. They were quick to use printing for the vulgarization of both mystic and Classical writings. Their concern for moral training was also admirably suited to fill the need for urban education in citizenship.

5. See George Boas, 'A Fourteenth-Century Cosmology', *Proceedings of the American Philosophical Society*, XCVIII (1954), pp. 50–9.

6. A characteristic common to all three schools, in other respects so different (Deventer, St Paul's in London, and Mantua), was the introduction of a so-called humanist instruction, the aim of which was threefold. The first objective was towards 'philological' knowledge, important mainly for the interpretation of the sacred books; the second was towards an ethical training, by means of the progressive discovery of certain confirmatory correspondences between lay Christian morality and the traditions of the great classical philosophies of the Mediterranean world; the third was social, consisting in development of the capacity for expression, that is to say the advent of rhetoric. In his *Inventio Dialectica*, Rudolph Agricola, an Italianized Frisian, was to try to reconcile dialectic and rhetoric, an effort symbolic of the demand of a whole sector of society then in process of throwing off the bonds of the established exercises of the universities. (Alphonse Dupront.)

7. The appellation *studium generale* is to be understood, ambiguously, as referring both to subjects taught and to recruitment, particularly geographical recruitment. (Alphonse Dupront.)

8. Professor A. Dupront points out that founded in 1180, this was a foundation for poor clerks attached to the Hôtel-Dieu. This establishment which has been called 'the first educational college in the world' is still in the church's tradition of auto-recruitment.

9. Professor A. Dupront adds that it should be mentioned that many of these colleges were boarding establishments; only in a few of them was teaching conducted. From this time onward, the problem of the evolution of university structure becomes that of the interrelationship between *universitas* and colleges. On the one hand—the Anglo-Saxon solution—the colleges constitute the *universitas*. On the other—the French solution—the *universitas* is the powerful centralizer of the colleges, concentrating in its faculties the greatest possible amount of teaching.

10. Professor A. Dupront emphasizes that as far as Montpellier is concerned, not only the medical school but also the arts school were already prosperous by the middle of the twelfth century. The beginning of the next century saw the establishment of the school of medicine, a purely ecclesiastical corporation. The *studium generale* was established by papal bull in 1289. In connection with the medical school stress should be laid on the importance of the small Jewish community of the Languedoc region of the Midi, which may well have served to transmit the teachings of Arab medicine. Together with church teaching, the Judeo-Arab contribution remains a constant element of education in mediaeval (and hence also in modern) western Europe. (See *History of Mankind: Cultural and Scientific Development*, Vol. III, Part 4.)

11. Professor A. Dupront underlines that neither the Oratorians nor even the Jesuits were created for the education of children. The Jesuits were the first in the field, starting with their own colleges, set up primarily for the purposes of their own recruitment. The Oratorians, at least in Italy, came to it much later. This is a clear indication of social pressure towards education, at least in certain milieux.

12. Does this necessarily infer, as will be stated in the case of the Jesuits, that it is a case of 'propaganda'? What is clear is that the need for instruction sprang from a lay impulse.

As far afield as Italy, in Rome and Milan, for example, were to be found simple men, rapidly gaining popularity, who set themselves up as teachers for the street children. This example, while restricted in scope, is significant in itself.

It is also evident that teaching was restricted to what people needed to learn. For the children of the people this meant the elements of Christian doctrine, more prayers than catechism, and, obviously as the result of a secular demand, 'leggere, scrivere ed abacco', as proposed by the first Scolopes in Rome, that is to say reading, writing, and counting.

Further evidence of the demand for schools with a teaching content to all intents and purposes similar to that defined by the monks of San Pantaleo in Rome is provided by the questionnaire on the occasion of canonical visits. In France in particular a comparison of canonical visits at different periods throughout the seventeenth century shows that a question as to the existence or non-existence of a school makes a regular appearance in the episcopal enquiry from the middle of the century on. During the eighties and nineties this question often appears side by side with one on the existence or non-existence of Protestants in the parish. The way in which the inquiry was put, confirmed by the replies, reveals that the question was considered important, even in small communities, sometimes counting several masters, who, in the old French tradition, were known as 'regents'. The wide spread, along with the carefulness of the questions, shows that, as a social phenomenon, instruction extended far beyond both the framework and the authority of a church society. (Alphonse Dupront.)

Author's rejoinder: 'The point of view of this remark, while correct, does not explain away what the text means by propaganda—*the indoctrination of pupils in revealed Truth rather than the impartial and disinterested quest for knowledge and wisdom. We do not mean to imply that the Jesuits in particular or Catholics in general were alone concerned with such indoctrination.'*

13. Professor A. Dupront wants it not to be forgotten that, as certain recent research has confirmed, Juan Luis Vives was of Jewish extraction. Moreover, Prof. Bataillon has clearly elucidated the role of the Marranos in Erasmian circles, in Flanders and even as far afield as England. Hence the Talmudic Schools represent another source of the formation of modern methods of instruction, also dating back to the remote Middle Ages.

14. W. H. Longridge (ed. & trans.), *The Spiritual Exercises of St. Ignatius of Loyola* (3rd ed., London, 1930), p. 67.

15. *Ibid.*, pp. 197 and 199.

16. To Professor A. Dupront these pages devoted to the *Spiritual Exercises* of Ignatius Loyola seem to make an attempt to extract the essence of a work capital to the beginnings of the modern Western world. Two problems are, however, raised by the very premise on which the chapter is based. One is to know to what extent the Company of Jesus remained faithful to the practice of these exercises in the training of its educational cadres. The other, far more important, is to assess the possible influence of the actual technique of the exercises on Jesuit 'pedagogy'.

In point of fact, it appears that the exemplary treatise of mental therapy constituted by these *Spiritual Exercises* was not exploited by the Company itself for its real content. Western teaching based on the Jesuit humanities was to be a substantive teaching rather than a method of mental training, remaining so, indeed, even down to the present day. Hence a serious lack of psychic training, individual as well as collective, particularly in the face of Oriental teaching, for which the West is now showing itself an avid customer.

Ignatius Loyola, moreover, imposed on his sons another rule, destined rapidly to go equally unheeded, that of studying the humanities only after attaining a certain well settled age, between 25 and 35, providing not only for priority to be given to philosophical and religious training but also for a certain harmonious measure of correspondence between the study of great texts and the capacity to understand them other than as exercises of pure rhetoric. The prescription laid down for the masters in their teaching methods was, in fact, reversed by the Jesuits, the humanities becoming the often irreligious sustenance of adolescents studying for worldly careers—an evident sign of the Company's dependence on secular 'ambitions' and, even at this early date, on a secular 'ideal'.

Author's rejoinder: 'The Jesuits here (in this section, which is entitled "European Educational Institutions") are being described as the institution their founder intended them to be. Their actual methods at subsequent times are discussed (on pp. 1008–9, in the section entitled "Educational Methods and Theory in Europe") as combining humanism with devotion.'

17. To present the Jesuit college as an institution practically connatural with the Company would be somewhat to distort historical perspective. The Epistolario of Father Nadal, the great founder of colleges during the first decades of the Company's existence, amply illustrates the considerable hesitation felt in passing from auto-recruiting establishments to houses of education for laymen. The latter were to force their way into the Jesuit colleges, thereby leading them to discover in the exploitation of their establishments much of their social, temporal, and cultural success.

The catechism was a basic element of education essential to Christian religious life, whether Protestant or Catholic, during the sixteenth century. It should, however, be emphasized that the *Catechism* of Canisius corresponds to an attempt at religious uniformization on the part of the emperor and that the Tridentine or Roman Catechism was intended primarily for priests. The generalization of the practice of catechismic teaching, slow as it was, had considerable effects on the 'secularization' of the religious conscience of the masses in various Western countries. (Alphonse Dupront.)

18. *The Spiritual Exercises of St. Ignatius of Loyola*, p. 197.

19. Professor A. Dupront wonders whether so much stress should be laid on Dominican-Jesuit rivalry? The Dominicans neither dominated the Sorbonne nor reigned supreme over the most famous Catholic universities. The situation was, of course, more complex. While the famous school at Salamanca was Dominican, in Germany, Würzburg and, above all, Ingolstadt were Jesuit, as was Vienna. The conflict was on another plane—not between the sons of St Dominic and the sons of St Ignatius but between strongly established universities and young Jesuit colleges rapidly rising to prosperity. Paris and Louvain provide vivid examples, but even more significant is that of Rome, where the Company's Collegio Romano, founded by St Ignatius in the middle of the century (1553), becoming Gregoriana, i.e. a university, in 1592, grew into a strong rival to the Sapienza, the University of Rome, which had difficulty in surviving, let alone in maintaining itself in the lead, despite the protection of Paul II and succeeding popes during the second half of the sixteenth century.

The authors believe that the Dominican influence was predominant in the University of Paris before the Jesuits could establish themselves there. See Bataillon, Erasme et l'Espagne, pp. 10–11, 542–4, 755–6, 759 and 768.

20. To Professor A. Dupront Carlo Borromeo was in fact no more than the resolute executor of the provisions of a famous chapter of the Council of Trent (Sess. XXIII, Cap. XVIII, 15. VII. 1563). His work in his own diocese of Milan, the example he gave, his personal authority, his saintly figure and unflagging will made of this timid but dauntless man an example that contemporary religious historiographers find more and more influential in Italy, France, and the Netherlands as well as in central and eastern Europe. But here too, it is a question only of a return to traditional clerical education and auto-recruitment. The 'invention' of the seminary formula is often attributed to the English cardinal, Reginald Pole.

For France, the Abbé A. Degert's, *Histoire des séminaires français jusqu'à la Révolution* (2 vols., Paris, 1912) still holds good.

On the influences of the 'Borromean' model, see P. Proutin, *La Réforme pastorale en France au XVIIe siècle* (Paris, 1956), 2 vols.

21. As Professor A. Dupront reminds us, the originality of Halle is also illustrated by the fact that it was there that Thomasius, jurist and philosopher of law of the Pufendorf school, first established the teaching of political science (*studio politico*).

22. To restrict the Brothers of the Christian Schools to their vocation of popular teaching their founder took the wise precaution of forbidding them to teach in Latin, which constituted the social watershed. (Alphonse Dupront.)

23. Translated in Arthur O. Norton, *Readings in the History of Education: Mediaeval Universities* (Cambridge, Mass., 1909), pp. 121–4.

24. See Chapter VII, p. 492 and n. 16.

25. Professor A. Dupront's opinion is here more reserved. The interpretation of *virtu* in Machiavelli remains highly restrictive. The opposition *fortuna/virtu* implies something quite different, a philosophy of power and existence (see F. Gilbert, *Politics and History in Renaissance Florence: Machiavelli and Guicciardini* [Princeton U.P., 1964]).

In the perspective of a history of education taken in its broadest possible sense, *Il Principe* and *Il Cortegiano* cannot be placed on the same plane. One is a treatise on the art of government, accompanied by a few traits sketching the portrait of the prince; the other a treatise on the art of social behaviour. In *Il Cortegiano*, the whole milieu of the court of Urbino in the early decades of the sixteenth century is held up as an example. As for 'academies', apart from 'academic schools', what do they owe to Castiglione?

Authors' note: 'The text has dealt with Machiavelli and Guicciardini as historians and political thinkers in other contexts. This passage is only to remind the reader that "essentially" (not fully, not exhaustively) Machiavelli's concept of patriotism was the quality which he believed Italy most needed of its leaders. As the authors imply, the 'academics' owed little to Castiglione.'

26. The formula is a happy one, conveying perfectly the deliberate secularization of ecclesiasticism. Is there any reason to be surprised? Certainly not in the perspective of contemporary history, and indeed, apart from the change in the concept of 'religio', have things changed so very much since the sixteenth century? (Alphonse Dupront.)

27. *A Sermon on the Duty of Keeping Children at School*, quoted in MacKinnon, IV, pp. 99–100.

28. Sturm was indeed the inventor of the 'model', but the original features of his model were, on the one hand, the new form of Gymnasium and, on the other, municipal (i.e. secular) control of teaching. The Strasbourg Gymnasium was transformed into an Academy only in 1566.

Many studies exist on Jean Sturm and his educational work; a good survey is contained in three articles appearing in *L'Humanisme en Alsace* (Paris, 1939). (Alphonse Dupront.)

29. While the main trends of the Jesuit pedagogic synthesis are here outlined, two points deserve greater emphasis in Professor A. Dupront's opinion. The first was their rôle as educators of the upper classes, from the point of view of their predilection for form and demand for rhetoric and style. Their reconciliation of Antiquity and religion led in fact to a juxtaposition in which social content was sacrificed to formal performance. Hence the tremendous output of Latin poetry, of more or less religious drama, in which the cultivated élite of Europe was to delight for at least a century. To say nothing of the style of social behaviour, the 'ballets' of the Jesuit schools had cultural value. The second was the slow but deliberate decision of the Company to educate the ruling classes and, even more deliberately, the future wielders of authority in all its forms.

Material for a history of Jesuit pedagogy is contained in the *Monumenta Paedagogica Societatis Jesu* (Nova editio; Roma, Monumenta Hist. SS., 1965). A useful presentation of their work in France is given in F. de Dainville, S.S., *Les Jésuites et l'éducation de la société française* (Paris, 1940). For a quasi-exhaustive study of a famous French example see Dupont–Ferrier, *La vie quotidienne d'un collège parisien pendant plus de 350 ans. Du collège de Clermont au Lycée Louis-le-Grand (1563–1920)* (Paris, 1921–25), 3 vols.

30. Quoted in Fritz Caspari, *Humanism and the Social Order in Tudor England* (Chicago, 1954), pp. 70 and 75.

31. More entrusts the education of the youth of Utopia to the priests. It is true that the priests are few, even though a few women are admitted to the priesthood. Potential 'secularization' of education in the Utopian world is inherent in the fact that each individual is free to spend his leisure moments in study, but the gate remains narrow. And the study of letters is a 'profession'. (Alphonse Dupront.)

32. Quoted from the title-page of *The Great Didactic*, given in facsimile in Luella Cole, *A History of Education, Socrates to Montessori* (New York, 1950), p. 334. See Matthew

Spinka, *John Amos Comenius, That Incomparable Moravian* (Chicago, 1943), pp. 65–71 and 153–5; and Josef Polisensky, 'Comenius and His Time', *Journal of World History*, VI (1960), p. 65.

33. Fénelon's reflections must be considered in a definite context: that of his task as royal tutor. What Fénelon did for his pupil, the Duc de Bourgogne, Bossuet and Huet had done before him for the Grand Dauphin. Where the education of princes was concerned, models were sought and tools provided: hence the celebrated collection of classics *ad usum* made by the tutors of the Grand Dauphin. It must also be stressed that the definition of a man given by the 'Swan of Cambrai' is Christian, sometimes expressed in highly traditional and aristocratic form but with an exquisite sense of style rarely attained before him. But viewed in a pre-revolutionary perspective, Fénelon was no innovator. See among recent studies Jeanne-Lydie Goré, *L'Itinéraire de Fénelon* (Paris, 1957) and Françoise Gallouedec-Genuys, *Le prince selon Fénelon* (Paris, 1963). (Alphonse Dupront.)

34. Professor A. Dupront remarks that as regards the education given in the 'little schools' of Port-Royal it should be stressed that to religious training and, above all, the inculcation of moral austerity including psychological analysis, and the exercise of lucidity and scruple must be added reflection on language, grammar, and systems of thought— in other words, secular reflection, in a religious milieu, in the vernacular, then in process of becoming the sole language.

It would be impossible to 'place' Port-Royal without *Logique de Port-Royal ou art de penser*, by Arnauld and Nicole (complete critical edition by P. Clair and Fr. Girbal, Paris, 1965).

The Oratorians did not lag behind the Jansenists. In *L'Art de parler* (1675) primarily a treatise on rhetoric, one of their number, François Lamy, reaches the point of expounding the problem of 'the relationship of language to operations of the mind'. Used as a textbook in the Oratorian colleges, it reveals a growing awareness of language as a tool, and thence as an element in the formation of the personality, even if only through commerce with other men.

35. *Oeuvres*, III, p. 459, quoted in Gabriel Compayre, *The History of Pedagogy*, trans. W. H. Payne (Boston, 1892), pp. 321–2.

36. Translation borrowed (with slight changes) from Lester G. Crocker, *The Embattled Philosopher, a Biography of Denis Diderot* (London, 1955), pp. 409–10.

37. Quoted in Henri Seé, *Les idées politiques en France au XVIIIe siècle* (Paris, 1920), p. 142.

38. To Professor A. Dupront, Diderot's Plan of a University—a largely posthumous publication (1813–14)—will be easier to place if given its full title: *Plan d'une université pour le gouvernement de Russie ou d'une éducation publique dans toutes les sciences*. The plan was to have been applied in Russia, still a Utopian land, especially when the tsar was called Catherine.

Much more significant is Diderot's life-work, the *Encyclopédie*, an enterprise which, independently of any forerunners or imitators, is itself sufficient evidence of a firm intention to raise the mechanical arts to the level of the liberal arts solely by the power of the printed word. Viewed as a revolutionary—or at least an exceedingly bold—act of education, this work could with advantage have been accorded more importance than that given to a 'philosophical' work of more interest to specialists than historically important.

Much more closely geared to life and therefore historically valuable are Condorcet's five memoirs *Sur l'instruction publique* between 1791–92, completed by the *Rapport et project de décret sur l'organisation générale de l'instruction publique*, presented to the Legislative Assembly in the name of the Comité d'Instruction Publique on April 20 and 21, 1792 (*Oeuvres de Condorcet*, ed. A. Condorcet, O'Connor, and F. Arago, Vol. VII).

Authors' note: *The* Encyclopédie *is considered in other contexts above and below.* Condorcet's *memoirs doubtless will receive attention in Vol. V.*

39. The 'Grand Tour' had been preceded by the sixteenth century 'Italian journey'— another collective acculturation exercise conferring a social seal. To judge by Robert

Adam, the Grand Tour also served to accumulate academic degrees on the continent. (Alphonse Dupront.)

40. Professor A. Dupront underscores the whole 'cultural' phenomenon of the vulgarization of the sciences in modern Europe as the result of the rising tide of 'curiosity', so far little studied, swollen both by the taste for collection and by the desire for direct experience, with all the passions, pure and impure, liable to accompany them. Note the importance of the home physical laboratories with which rich bourgeois and even some French farmers-general in the eighteenth century were to become enamoured.

41. Carl Becker, *The Declaration of Independence* (New York, 1922), pp. 42–7. See C. H. C. Lippold and C. P. Funke (eds.), *Neues Natur- und Kunstlexicon . . . zum bequemen Gebrauch insonderheit auch für Ungelehrte und für gebildete Frauenzimmer* (Weimar, 1801).

42. L. C. MacKinney, 'Medical Education in the Middle Ages', *Journal of World History*, II (1955), pp. 851–3, esp. notes 69 and 76; Vern Bullough, 'The Development of the Medical University at Montpellier to the End of the Fourteenth Century', *Bulletin of the History of Medicine*, XXX (1956), p. 513.

43. The good name and historical repute of the faculty of medicine at Montpellier ultimately depended on two complementary stipulations already appearing in the statutes of 1239. One fixed an obligatory period of six-months' probation as indispensable to the practice of medicine; the other, highly consequential on account of the precedent involved, set the obligation to appear for examination before two masters of the faculty. For surgeons, on the contrary, no examination was required. (Alphonse Dupront.)

44. E. J. Dijksterhuis (ed.), *The Principle Works of Simon Stevin*, Vol. I: *General Introduction, Mechanics* (Amsterdam, 1955), p. 10; Richard A. Preston, Sydney F. Wise, and Herman O. Werner, *Men in Arms, a History of Warfare and its Interrelationships with Western Society* (New York, 1956), p. 135; Frederick B. Artz, *L'Éducation technique en France au dix-huitième siècle (1700–89)* (Paris, 1939), p. 26.

45. The role of Paris was rendered even clearer by the accommodation of the academicians in the Louvre itself—thus affirming both their dependence and their 'promotion'—as well as by the social phenomenon of the 'salons'. Reserved exclusively to the Academy and taking place in the royal palace itself, these 'salons' played a doubly important role in eighteenth-century France by extending the clientèle of the royal artists and setting up the seal of 'criticism', timidly established at this time and achieving real recognition only in the first half of the nineteenth century. (Diderot's *Salons* were not published until this period, although they appeared as a sort of Paris letter in Grimm's *Correspondance littéraire* between 1739 and 1781.) (Alphonse Dupront.)

CHAPTER XVII

SUMMARY AND CONCLUSION

THE GROWTH OF WORLD CONSCIOUSNESS

EVERY period of recorded history may, of course, properly be regarded as an age of transition, but the period of this volume (*c.* 1300–*c.* 1775) is perhaps especially notable as such. In Europe it covers the years that intervened between the Middle Ages and the revolutions of the late eighteenth century. It includes the eras known as the Renaissance, the Reformation, the Age of Discovery, the Scientific Revolution, the Absolute Monarchies, the Enlightenment, and the initial stages of the Industrial Revolution. Outside Europe it witnessed such developments as the last flowering and the decline of the Amerindian civilizations, the rise of new Islamic empires, the spread of Islam in the old civilizations of Africa, India, and Indonesia, the end of the great Mongol conquests, the reorientation of life in China under the Ming and Manchu dynasties, the growth of the isolated culture of Japan under the Ashikaga and Tokugawa shogunates, and the highest development of several African empires and kingdoms.

Our period closes with a series of events centring about 1775 that can be readily recognized as marking, in one way or another, either the end of an old era or the beginning of a new one. That series includes several events of crucial importance in political affairs—the first effort of the British to require direct government supervision of the affairs of the East India Company (the Regulating Act of 1773); the concessions to French Canadians that were eventually to help make of Canada the first dominion within the British empire (the Quebec Act of 1774); the beginning of 'the Polish Question' with the First Partition of Poland in 1772 and of 'the Near Eastern Question' with the Treaty of Kutchuk Kainarja in 1774; the collapse of the first formidable revolutionary effort in Russia (the Pugashev Revolt of 1772–75); the outbreak in 1775 of the first successful anti-colonial revolt in modern times (the American War of Independence); and the ultimately victorious alliance in 1778 of an absolute monarchy, France, with a republican confederation, the United States of America, which had proclaimed that governments are instituted to secure the rights of man and derive their just powers from the consent of the governed.

In addition to the American Declaration of Independence (1776) some decisive events of the period in the history of thought may likewise be designated as forming part of the series—the publication of Adam Smith's classical exposition of laissez-faire economics (*Wealth of Nations,* 1776); a turning point in the Enlightenment with the conjucture of the Franco-American alliance with the death of Voltaire and Rousseau (1778); and the completion of the *Encyclopédie* (1772), of its supplementary volumes (1777), and its Index (1780).

Also the period covered a set of significant developments in the history of science and technology—the first patentings of Watt's steam engine (1769 and 1775); the explorations (1767–79) by Captain Cook of Australia and the Pacific Islands; the observations by Herschel (1774–81) that led to the discovery of the planet Venus; the findings in the 1770's by Scheele, Priestley, and Lavoisier which laid the basis of modern chemistry; the initial experiments of Jenner (1775) that led ultimately to the control of smallpox by vaccination and to the modern science of immunology.

Somewhere about the year 1775 can be placed, too, some dramatic episodes in the history of the arts, literature, and education. That date marks the mid-points in the long career of Haydn and the short career of Mozart. Neo-classicism began a triumphant course in the arts with a young painter (David), a promising sculptor (Houdon), well-known architects (Soufflot and Gabriel), and respected critics (the recently deceased [1768] Winckel-mann and the still vigorous Lessing). About the same time literary Roman-ticism was struggling to be born in the works of Rousseau, young Goethe, and their confreres. And a major crisis came in 1773 in ecclesiastical affairs with the temporary suppression (until 1814) of the Jesuits with its jolting impact upon Catholic educational and missionary efforts. Thus almost every aspect of modern culture experienced some kind of climax around 1775.

Furthermore, during the age that we have been considering in this volume all the cultural areas of the world were for the first time brought into regular physical contact with one another. Navigators, conquerors, adventurers, explorers, scientists, traders, pirates, slavers, colonists, and missionaries established a world-wide intercommunication. Men and women, plants and animals, raw materials and finished products, food and clothing, skills and inventions, customs and traditions were transplanted bodily from region to region, and art, thought, and religious beliefs within a single civilization were often modified through contact with other civilizations. While in some areas the peoples of an old culture, particularly those of the Far East, tried (still with considerable success, during this period) to protect their ways of life against foreign influences, in others, particularly those of Spanish America, they showed either less hesitancy to mingle their cultural heritage with that of the intruders or less ability to keep it pure.

In either case, however, cultural particularism and intolerance remained strong, for men everywhere are likely to assume the superiority of their own religion, their own local beliefs and customs, their own peculiar traditions of art and science, their own familiar institutions, and their own system of values. Where foreign technology in patently superior, they may readily borrow artifacts, commodities, and methods, but even in such instances they yield to resulting change in their mores only reluctantly, and in their values more reluctantly still, if at all. Conscious striving for acculturation either was likely to be a reflection of the intruder's desire for the triumph abroad of his own persuasion or was missing altogether. Spanish conquerors, for example, went out in all directions to convert people to their own brand of 'catholicism' (universalism). Puritans, on the other hand, were unwilling to have their areas of refuge in America contaminated by Quakers or Anglicans. The Muslim might grant his Hindu, Christian, or Jewish subjects toleration, yet never failed to consider them infidels and outsiders. The shoguns closed their country to 'corrupting' influences from across the seas. The Chinese emperors were convinced that their superior society had no need of Western contributions. European explorers and conquerors frequently believed that they were the carriers of genuine civilization to childishly innocent races; at times, indeed, they did not seem to be aware that they were dealing with fellow human beings of a venerable history rather than with negotiable goods.

Underneath this superciliousness, however, cultural influences were being more or less subtly interchanged. The European conqueror might vanquish the American Indian, and yet his own life was extensively affected by such borrowings from the conquered as tobacco, caoutchouc, potatoes, quinine, and the gold and silver of American mines. The Chinese government might forbid Christian practices but yet employed the artistic, astronomical, and mathematical skill of the Jesuit fathers and permitted commerce with Europeans in porcelain, silks, and other Chinese fineries. The American planter might try to preserve his way of life from contamination by his Negro slave and yet was unable to forestall crossbreeding or his great grandchildren's liking for sounds, accents, and rhythms derived from Africa. Dissimilar and hostile peoples thus might often influence each other, sometimes despite or beyond intention.

In other instances, a common tradition, usually based upon a religious preference, intentionally served as a bond among widespread but similar peoples. Inside Europe, although numerous dynastic, national, and sectarian conflicts persisted, culture was largely derived from a shared inheritance—overwhelmingly Caucasoid in race, Indo-European in language, and Christian in religion. Within the Islamic world a common religious law and two widely known languages as well as a common cult spread from the Straits of Gibraltar to the outmost reaches of the East Indies. Hinduism or its offspring Buddhism stretched from India eastward. Confucianism had moved from China to Japan, Korea, and Vietnam. A few million Jews were scattered throughout the world.

Moreover, during this period certain ideas were unfolding that were someday to have a unifying effect upon mankind as a whole. One of the most powerful of these was the increased reliance on human reason and universally applicable knowledge in the search for an understanding of man's biological and physical circumstances. For a scientist like Newton the general laws of mathematics, gravity, magnetism, or optics were valid (due allowances made) at any spot on earth. For an anatomist like Vesalius the number of bones and muscles of a Chinese corpse could be presumed to be the same as of an Italian one. Animals and plants may differ from continent to continent, but an ingenious biologist like Linnaeus could hope to classify them all by applying a few general principles. In this period even relatively uneducated men came to realize that the earth was not the centre of the universe but only one of several planets in a solar system. A telescopist in the Bureau of Astronomy at Peking might perceive other stars in the heavens than his English counterpart at Greenwich, but both sets of observations nonetheless corroborated the same astronomical laws and fitted into a concept of stellar space that dwarfed the Earth with its separate nations and cultures into relative insignificance. Thus, even as the Earth and its peoples became better known one to another, its importance in the universal scheme of things shrank.

Where general laws did not seem applicable, the very comparison of differences sometimes led to speculation about humanity as a whole. Those who reflected on man's nature, activities, and beliefs increasingly dissociated their theories from the supernatural explanations of earlier, more ethnocentric ages. This development reached far in European thought, where, besides, in certain circles the axiological principles of non-Christian cultures won no less respect than those of their own. Instead of or, more often, in addition to attempting to reconcile faith with reason, European students of foreign philosophies were deeply concerned with grasping the varying concepts of human knowledge, of man's relation to the physical world, and of his moral and social obligations. Feeling unable to confine thought to Biblical axioms, some European philosophers took reason, usually but not necessarily tempered by human experience, as their main guide to truth.

This process reached a culmination in the Enlightenment. Not content with a Christian philosophy for a Christian Europe, the *philosophes* of the eighteenth century created vast rational systems meant to apply to humanity universally—systems that knew no religious, national, cultural, or colour boundaries, since reason was accessible to all members of the species *homo sapiens*. For these *philosophes* the dawn of a new golden age for all mankind awaited chiefly the elimination of arrogance, bigotry, superstition, prejudice, stupidity, inertia, and other obstacles to the free operation of the human mind.

Religious thought, too, sometimes partook of this unifying rationalist tendency. For some rationalistic theists, the Christian ideal of God as a World-God was acceptable even if the idea of Redemption and Salvation for only the faithful, the elect, the righteous, or the initiate was not. The theistic corollaries of rationalism were pantheism and Deism, which—at least, so their proponents believed—eliminated the tribal features that had tended to make religion a divisive factor among peoples.

With the spread of the notion of a common humanity, Christian ethical theories, available despite widening missionary endeavours to only a limited section of mankind, tended in the minds of the Deists to merge into supposedly universal norms like the Golden Rule or 'natural man' or natural religion. In European social and political theory, arguments were based with greater regularity on the notion that all human beings were subject to 'the Laws of Nature' (now more regularly considered synonymous with 'the laws of physics' than with 'the laws of God') and that all enjoyed certain inalienable natural rights. The concept of a common, universal human nature dominated much of social thought, leading to a readiness to believe in 'natural' ethics along with 'natural' political institutions. It entered the field of international relations, where 'reasonableness' was advocated by 'sensible' persons; and a few bold thinkers—Vitoria, Grotius, Pufendorf, St Pierre, Rousseau—advanced codes of international law or engaging schemes designed to preserve peace among all the nations. In general, and even though denominationalism, racism, and nationalism flourished simultaneously, the impression spread to many minds (though doubtless still a minority) by the eighteenth century that human beings were more alike than unlike, and this cosmopolitanism, this idea of a common humanity with common potentials and a common destiny, no matter how often defeated, would never be lost again in the Western world and was destined to go forth from there to fortify whatever similar views flourished elsewhere.

THE RISE OF SECULARISM IN EUROPE

As has been pointed out several times earlier in this book, from the fourteenth century on, thought tended to become more earth-centred than it had ever been before. In the first place, the world became better known to its inhabitants as a result of the explorations that steadily intensified from the days of Marco Polo and Ibn-Baṭṭūṭa to those of Captain Cook. In the second place, although the Earth lost the central position in the universe that in earlier times it had been thought to hold, its relation to the other planets became better understood as a result of astronomical observations stretching from the Alphonsine Tables to Herschel (and beyond). In the third place, more men than ever before came to think, with the humanists and Alexander Pope, that the proper study of Mankind is Man, Humanity rather than Divinity.

For all that, during the centuries from 1300 to 1775 religious sects multiplied, each gaining devout adherents and re-emphasizing other-worldly principles. Yet often the sects lost power as they split one from the other. The decentralization of Catholic church authority, for example, was part cause and part effect of a gradual but steady growth of secularism in Europe.

Ironically, some of this secular trend was due to the acerbity of the religious conflict of the era. Christendom, which had previously been divided only between an eastern Orthodox Church and a western Roman Catholic Church, was after 1300 plagued by numerous schisms and sectarian movements. Efforts to reconcile the eastern and western churches failed and soon proved harder than ever to achieve. For while, with the Turkish invasion of Europe, the eastern churches passed step by step under the temporal suzerainty of Turkish or Muscovite rulers, in the west the papacy, becoming involved in serious and debilitating conflicts with rising separatistic forces, ceased to speak for the whole of Western Christendom.

About the same time, where the Christian religion had once ruled supreme, other than Christian principles and teachings were beginning to claim attention and loyalty. That phase of the Renaissance which is sometimes called the Revival of Classical Learning brought not only a more precise understanding of Greek philosophy, Roman law, and Classical science, art, and literature but also a rediscovery of many lost Classical masterpieces and an increased respect for pagan thought. The employment of the Ciceronian phrase *studia humanitatis* to designate the major pursuit of the humanists implied an interest in a learning that not only was more global, more cosmopolitan, than that commonly available but also was distinguishable from the cultivation of theological learning, from the study of divinity. With it came a greater appreciation of secular activities (as embodied, for example, in the Italian *virtuoso*) and of secular learning (as in Italian humanism) and a desire for innovation (as in vernacular literature and scientific investigation).

Changing religious loyalties interplayed with changing political loyalties. During the Middle Ages Christians had generally felt bound first to their religion and church and only afterward to a neighbouring lord or a distant overlord. In the centuries after 1300 the dynastic state (sometimes loosely described as 'the national state') gradually assumed such pre-eminent importance in the lives of its subjects that it claimed their primary loyalty. As the ruler established centralized control over lay and ecclesiastical affairs and as he took over significant services previously performed by the church and the feudal nobility, the remotest subject became more and more dependent upon temporal authority—that is, upon the activities of his king or his king's agents. Justice was now dispensed more often by royal judges; economic life was increasingly regulated by royal decrees; military power (and with it the preservation of domestic peace, the conduct of foreign war, and the protection of the subject's security) was slowly gathered into the hands of officers commissioned by the king; frequently changes in the religion of the ruling prince determined changes in the religion of his people; education showed signs of eventually passing under government control; and the care of the needy and the sick began gradually to move from ecclesiastical almshouses and hospitals to secular eleemosynary institutions. The growth of the secular state at the expense of the church meant in some instances that the individual Christian merely exchanged loyalties or, if he had previously been torn between two, now gave prior allegiance to a single one. Most Christians, however, continued to find allegiance to one master compatible with allegiance to the other, especially as the state-dominated church usually received only intermittent attention. In certain respects (notably in the freer choice among creeds) Europeans as a whole, where they could move from state to state, gained greater personal freedom; in other respects the decline of the church's power left the individual within the separate states subject to an arbiter, who, to be sure, might be more undisputed than in the days when rulers and church had divided authority between them and had supported each other's opponents, but whose purposes were now more likely to be frankly concerned with *raison d'état* than with religious tradition and precepts.

In economic enterprise the decline of church influence and the rise of secular authority conjoined to exert a concurrent impact. During the Middle Ages the church had attempted to a good extent to pass upon commercial affairs. Although the clergy had material concerns of its own and although religious precepts rarely contended successfully against man's striving for possessions, power, and comfort, clerical authority had often tempered the drive toward self-advantage with certain spiritual and at times even ascetic demands and ideals. Some of the clergy's own self-seeking and the church's loss of prestige for that and other reasons enfeebled the efforts of the more saintly churchmen to stem the growth of materialism, which both helped to further a more secular-minded world and was furthered by the development of the secular mind.

The beginnings of a class of society in western Europe primarily concerned with economic endeavour had anticipated the splitting of the unified church. The rise of towns, the gradual crumbling of self-sufficient manorialism, the increase of commerce and trade, the initiation of industrialized processes on a large scale, and the maturing of monetary and fiscal practices such as stock companies and banking brought power and prestige to a class of people for whom commerce and industry were the *raison d'être*. Wealth in forms other than landed possessions began to accumulate and became not only a mark of social distinction but also of political influence. Rulers who had to call upon city dwellers in their struggles with their feudal vassals or with foreign enemies grew more and more dependent on income derived from bourgeois activities and consequently were prone to protect and promote bourgeois interests. When the church's power to enforce its precepts against usury or to impose its ideals of poverty and asceticism diminished, church weakness conspired with royal favour to widen the road to worldliness as men became less and less concerned with preparing themselves for the hereafter by leading holy lives at the cost of earthly enjoyment. Piety, ritual, prayer, faith, and good works, without ever completely losing their hold, more often won only lip service while increasing numbers paid genuine

MM*

allegiance to the ideals of wealth, power, leisure, comfort, a higher standard of living, competitive display, personal status, and other secular longings.

The shift in political and religious loyalties combined with economic conditions to bring about a change in the dominant ideologies, and vice versa. Labour, thrift, and substance became more commendable in many minds both as tokens of a well-spent life and, if not as desirable ends in themselves, at least as a means toward desirable ends, at the very time that commerce, finance, and industry were expanding. The resulting increase in the number of men of substance provided yet another reason why the state, whether Protestant or Catholic, should be more attentive to the needs and demands of a now highly respected middle class, and political theory was more frequently formulated by members of that class. The religious concept of the paternalistic divine-right monarch and the empirical concept of the king as a partner in a social contract to create a 'natural' government converged with practical politics in tempering absolutism. By the end of the period under consideration in this volume 'the enlightened despot' who regarded it as his function to strive, more in deference to 'the laws of nature' than to 'the voice of God', to establish a state that should guarantee the material welfare of his subjects—and hence his own—had become the rule rather than the exception in Europe.

The secular interests of mercantilist ruler and merchant prince grew with the amazing geographic discoveries of the age. The augmenting knowledge in each part of the world of all the other parts stimulated the growth of trade, and mounting trade brought vast commercial companies, expanded stock holding, fresh business speculation, improved or entirely new banking and insurance practices, and the ills as well as the benefits that come with cut-throat competition. The Atlantic nations were in the best position to profit by the newer trade routes, and their burgher classes accumulated wealth and comfort to a degree that had never before been equaled. Exotic products like sugar, spice, perfume, tobacco, and chocolate gave life an added savour. The increasing importation into Europe of gems, precious metals, fine leather goods, porcelains, and *de luxe* textiles helped to raise the level of the competitive ostentation of those who could afford luxuries; and cotton, tobacco, drugs, dyestuffs, potatoes, tea, and coffee to some extent improved the well-being of even the lower classes. Besides, for those who dared, virgin lands and a chance for a better economic life lay across the seas. For those who preferred to stay at home new crops like American maize or new uses for old crops like the European turnip directly or indirectly provided a richer yield, a better diet, and so a firmer insurance against hunger and disease. With the rising standard of living after 1500, the populations of western Europe multiplied so rapidly that some observers even before Malthus expressed anxiety about the balance between population and food supply. A fuller knowledge of the world's geography and a wider distribution of the world's goods seemed to fortify terrestrial rather than celestial aspirations.

The age of geographic discovery roughly coincided with the age of scientific discovery. Scientists from Buridan and Oresme through Copernicus and Galileo to Newton and Lavoisier studied both stellar and earthly phenomena with methods that likewise encouraged the trend toward secularization. These men usually were respectful of, but not necessarily concerned with, 'the other world' in their scientific work. As scientific theorists from Roger Bacon and Francis Bacon through Descartes and Boyle to d'Alembert, Franklin, and Lomonosov extolled the role of inductive reasoning and experiment in the promotion of human knowledge, revelation and saintly miracles were relegated in many learned minds to a compartment unrelated to the natural sciences. At least one school, the *philosophes* of the Enlightenment, included in the study of nature the study of human institutions as well. Their universe had ceased to be not only geocentric but also theocentric and had become anthropocentric. 'Natural philosophy' became for them and their disciples not so much, if at all, the study of God's Book of Nature as a better guide to the understanding of human affairs. It provided norms, 'laws of nature', uninfluenced by either an infallible pope or an infallible council, and judgments according to such norms might now differ, if not with impunity, at least with less fear than formerly of excommunication, interdict, or social ostracism.

The new knowledge not merely made possible many technological contributions to man's material welfare (such as better housing, cheaper fuel and metals, improved agricultural methods, more labour-saving machinery, and a wider range of sanitation) but also occasioned some re-orientation of man's spiritual outlook. The preoccupation of scientists with material and measurable phenomena, the quantitative emphasis in the new biological, medical, and chemical findings, seemed to lend the weight of their prestige to those who called for greater attention to the physical and material than to the ideal and qualitative concerns of human life. The validity of man's transcendental and metaphysical thought came under increased questioning by some of the most critical minds of Europe. Daring thinkers of the later decades of our period frankly advanced purely mechanistic and materialistic philosophies that earlier would probably have encountered effective suppression not only by church and state but also by public scorn. Perhaps nothing else exemplified so palpably as the reception of some eighteenth-century materialist writings how far Europe's educated public (a small but influential group) had exchanged a religion-centred mode of life for a secular one.

FROM MIDDLE AGES TO MODERN TIMES

Some date near 1500 has usually been accepted for pedagogical purposes as a convenient marker for the transition from the medieval to the modern way of life. Such a transition has conventionally been considered valid only for

Europe, and it is true that several of the events that have traditionally been regarded as crucial in that transition had essentially intra-European effects. Yet, let us take some of them in chronological order and examine their significance to a world that as a whole was gradually becoming more inter-dependent. The year 1453 marked the fall of Constantinople, which thereupon ceased to be the capital of the Byzantine Empire, the Roman Empire of the east, and became the capital of the Ottoman Empire, which within decades stretched from Asia and Europe into Africa and came into friendly contact or open conflict with the new Ṣafavid empire in Persia, the new Mogul empire in India, and other Muslim states while continuing its conquests in Europe. The year 1454, decisive in the improvement of the printing press, marked the culmination of a phase of cultural borrowing by Europe from the East and the beginning of the wholesale communication of learning and thought that was to begin in Europe but gradually to move to all other parts of the world. The year 1492, when Columbus discovered America, marked the beginning of a world of two hemispheres and was a key step toward the circumnavigation of the globe. The year 1498, when Vasco da Gama suc-ceeded in finding a sea route from Europe to India, marked the beginning of European imperialism in Asia. The year 1517, when Luther nailed his Ninety-Five Theses to a church door in Wittenberg, marked the precipitation of a German religious conflict that was to spread and eventually to play a part in impelling emigrants and missionaries to go from all parts of Europe to various parts of the world and to proselytize whole continents across the Atlantic. The year 1543 marked the publication of Copernicus' *De Revolu-tionibus Orbium Coelestium* and thereby the beginning of the end of the geo-static concept of the universe, a milestone on the road toward a new scientific attitude that, based largely on borrowed mathematics, astronomy, and alchemy, was to attain high levels in Europe and thence reach out to leave its impress upon the whole world. Of the more important dates that are widely held to point the passage from medieval to modern times in Europe there is one that seems at first glance to have had no direct and explicit interrelation with the non-European world—1496, the year that the army of King Charles VIII of France returned from Italy, accelerating the growth of Italian Renaissance influences in France and other parts of Europe—but even that event can be considered exclusively intra-European only if we overlook non-European roots and influences in Italy's culture and France's subsequent role in extra-European affairs.

In short, to speak diagrammatically, somewhere through the fifteenth and sixteenth centuries seems to run a curve that highlights the transitional nature of this era—chiefly perhaps but not exclusively for Europe. For that reason most of the developments that we have considered above have been discussed under two chronological headings, breaking somewhere around 1500. During the nearly five centuries under examination in this volume extraordinary things happened that sooner or later shook life everywhere out of old ways and forced it into new. The Earth was proved to be not only a sphere but also a mere speck in the universe. Its various civilizations moved from the relative ignorance of each other even in the Eurasian-African complex into direct and accelerating contact with each other across all the oceans. Europeans, sparse peoples from a small corner of the immense Eurasian continent, began to roam the surface of the earth, to people new continents, to ship the earth's treasures to all corners of the globe, and to establish themselves as masters or exploiters in some ancient coherent empires as well as in some loosely knit tribal areas—in America permanently and elsewhere at least temporarily.

Europe underwent more rapid and thorough cultural changes than other civilizations. The loss of ecclesiastical unity brought on a more manifest cultural diversity. Secular and science-oriented philosophies began to replace Scholasticism, as scientific discoveries followed each other in rapid succession. Notwithstanding the temporary Latinist revival in the scholarly world of humanism, vernacular languages began to push out Latin and Church Slavonic, and national literature to overshadow Classical and church literature. In the realm of music and the visual arts the old skills, methods, and instruments developed to an unparalleled perfection, and new ones were elaborated. Loosely organized political units, largely feudal, gradually made way for considerably centralized and powerful national states; the last 'universal' political authority gave up even the pretence of world control with Charles V's abdication as Holy Roman emperor in 1555. The urban middle classes steadily acquired power, and with their rise a capitalist-minded economy with interests in trade, industry, and finance seriously began to compete with the age-old predominance of agriculture. The guild system in the towns and the manorial system in the country yielded eventually to individual, group, corporate, or collectivist enterprise. If some proverbial slumberer like Sleeping Beauty had closed her eyes somewhere in Europe in 1450 and opened them only in 1550, she would have waked up in a strikingly transformed environment still in a process of transformation that was to speed up during the ensuing centuries.

This European transformation proceeded according to a diversified schedule. Some changes were of an abrupt nature, while others were mere steps in a lengthy process in which old and new mingled to produce a different way of life and thought only gradually. The innovations in agricultural methods and products, the increasing urbanization, the growth of finance, commerce, and industry, the discovery of cheap new land across the seas and the emigration of Europeans there, the rising importance of bureaucracy and administrative centralization, the improvement of military and naval techniques, the change in religious outlook—all these not only immediately affected great masses of people in Europe but also had more or less rapid repercussions abroad. At the same time events took place in Europe that, though destined to have immense consequences for all of humanity, exerted their full impact only several generations later and were hardly noticed by most contemporaries. Many of the scientific wonders, philosophic systems, and artistic masterpieces that were created during our period were known and treasured by mere handfuls of connoisseurs. The resolution of the calculus by Newton and Leibniz, the elementary discoveries in magnetism and static electricity by experimenters like Gilbert and Franklin, the findings of microscopists like Leeuwenhoek and Grew or of telescopists like Galileo and Herschel, the exposition of the circulatory system by Harvey and Malpighi, the teaching methods of Comenius and Boerhaave, and the initial gropings toward a theory of evolution by Tremblay and Buffon came to full fruition only long after these men were gone. The subtleties of Spinoza's philosophical theories and the implications of the historical concepts advanced by Vico were to be generally appreciated only in the nineteenth century. The music of Johann Sebastian Bach had to wait for rediscovery by Felix Mendelssohn. The effects that some of these slowly appreciated contributions were destined to have on both Western and non-Western civilization therefore really belong to the story told in the volumes of this *History* that follow.

THE COMMON PATTERN OF HUMAN BEHAVIOUR[1]

The era before the one dealt with in this volume was characterized by a number of features of culture and human behaviour roughly similar in all parts of the world. During our era, however, the rapid changes that took place in Europe brought about several significant deviations from the common pattern. In a loose fashion and with proper regard to notable exceptions (especially the independent minds of the great civilizations), this common human pattern can be outlined.

In general, before 1300 the common man's attitude toward nature nearly everywhere was governed by mystery and superstition. He conformed to nature or, more rarely, rebelled against it, without trying to understand it; except in an immediate, practical fashion he did not try to predict or control it. No matter how tragic to him as an individual personal disaster and death might be, they were seldom a challenge to him as a member of society or of mankind, since he was inclined to regard life on earth as a mere transitory phase, an ephemeral passage toward another existence whether as ancestral spirit, reincarnation, or eternal soul. Even recurrent catastrophes like earthquakes, plague, famine, or flood called for religious or governmental action, usually after the event, rather than for individual provision. The thinking of the common man was likely to concern life-after-death rather than the here-and-now, and only uncommon men took thought about bettering their own lot by planning their future.

The common man's thinking in general was about day-to-day problems. It was most often in images, in terms of concrete experience, or along traditional lines. Hence, unless it was theological, it was unlikely to be in the form of original abstract generalizations or of speculative plans. Holy days, the difference between seasons or between day and night, and the appointed moments for prayer were concrete measures of time, but otherwise time was but 'a succession of todays'—not something mathematical, abstract, and general, precisely measurable and divisible by hours, minutes, and seconds and not something valuable in terms of money. The concept *mankind* was also concrete. It was generally limited to 'we' and 'others', whether 'we' was the family, the community, or the nation.

The future of mankind was for God or for the gods and demons, and not for men, to determine. Wealth or poverty, power or submission (all most often a product of the amount of land controlled) were accepted as expressions of the will of God or the gods, whether by Christians in Europe rendering unto Caesar the things that are Caesar's, by Confucians, Taoists, Hindus, or Buddhists in Asia seeking the favour of ancestors or a nobler *karma*, by Muslims in Asia, Africa, and Europe trusting in Allah and His Prophet, or by animists on every continent bribing their gods with choice offerings. Magicians, seers, priests, or sages might have special knowledge of or influence with the supernatural, but their power to induce the Divine to alter Its will was limited, and even in cults that left room for some freedom of the human will, divine will remained inscrutable and paramount.

Earthly power, too, was hard to limit or to modify, although the good ruler was expected to be a patriarch. A middle class serving as a buffer between those with temporal authority and those subject to it was rare and, where it existed at all—as the bourgeoisie of Europe, the merchants of India's main ports, or the *chonin* of Japan—small in size. Status was more or less fixed by God and heredity; some were born to earn their bread by the sweat of their brows, and others to live in luxury; some to command and others to obey. While outstanding individuals often departed from and even rebelled against the common pattern, especially in the golden ages of Greece, Rome, India, China, and Islam, individualism seldom was stressed while conformity usually was.

Thus roughly similar attitudes toward nature, life, thought, time, mankind, authority, work, status, and individualism prevailed in most cultures before 1300. In several of the more advanced civilizations of the world, however, even before 1300 exceptions to this common human pattern had appeared. In China, for example, a system of civil service examinations supplemented the hereditary principle of authority with a graded 'literocracy', and the idea of a provident patriarchal ruler was particularly well elaborated. In ancient Greece an objective attitude toward nature emerged, permitting abstract, generalized, non-theological systems of thought to arise. In the Greco-Roman city-states the notion of popular sovereignty, of government as the servant of the people, was highly developed. In medieval Europe a strong church hierarchy, preaching a monotheistic Catholicism based on Judaic and Greco-Roman foundations, counterbalanced the political authority of the hereditary princes. In various parts of the world labour-saving devices like harness, wheels, cranks, windmills, rudders, and sails had reduced some of the labourer's pains, making it possible for man the *animal laborans* to become *homo faber*.

For a time before and about 1300 it looked as if these separate departures—administrative, political, philosophical, theological, and technological—might converge in and be absorbed by the Islamic countries, where an unusual degree of social mobility and a high intellectual flexibility accompanied a uniquely rapid spread of a new society. But thereafter the Islamic readiness to absorb cultural importations declined; the printing press, for example, was not introduced into the Ottoman Empire until 1727. In contrast, Christian Europe proved to be not only more receptive of divergences from the common pattern diffused from other areas but also extraordinarily fertile in devising divergences of its own.

The reasons for Europe's greater receptivity to innovation can only be surmised; they may not be unrelated to the rise of the religious idea of a better natural world to come propounded by Joachim of Floris in the twelfth century and the subsequent vogue of the idea of progress, but they doubtless also had some causal interrelation as well as concomitance with the pronounced rise of the urban middle class. At any rate, few of the divergences of Europeans from the prevailing human pattern produced a more productive concatenation of change and innovation than the urbanization of Western society. European towns, without ceasing to be, as before, fair or market hubs, trade stations, depots, or ports, political capitals, administrative headquarters, military posts, ecclesiastical seats, or educational centres now, less exceptionally than before, became something besides; they became business communities. As the locale of shops, offices, and factories, they were also the homes of the educated, professional, financial, commercial, and industrial classes that stood somewhere between the landowning, military aristocracy and the working population. Sometimes these middle classes, this new bourgeoisie, co-operated with kings against the feudal nobles, their common competitor, at the same time that they buttressed their own local power through co-operation in their guilds; in so doing, they helped build large, centralized political and economic units—dynastic or national states. Governments now seemed to be held together against centrifugal forces not alone by God-ordained leaders but also increasingly by the consent, though still silent and implicit for the most part, of the governed. As merchants, manufacturers, and bankers came to look upon wealth as not merely useful but even as pleasant in the eyes of the Lord and accumulated wealth not only in real property and precious metals but also in business paper, capital investments, factories, and labour-saving machinery, they disregarded the Biblical injunction and took thought for the morrow. They brought forth banks, insurance companies, professional training programmes, capital accumulations, public sanitation systems, improved methods of transportation and production, and a myriad of political reform proposals. The more altruistic among them planned not only for themselves as individuals and for their immediate associates but eventually also for mankind in general. In the minds of the more secularly inclined a notion of the destiny of mankind was emerging that depended less on God and more on man, that departed from the concept of religious perfection (man created in the image of the Creator and saved by divine grace) toward that of secular progress, that envisaged a common humanity and even a world political organization for the preservation of global peace and human prosperity.

The ideal of secular progress tended to modify the attitudes toward traditions and usages of those who entertained it. It left plenty of room for human action and decisions, since progress could come only from change, and change could obviously be made by human choices. For those who believed in a considerable margin of freedom of the human will the will of God, even when God was not repudiated as First Cause and Final Cause, was a less immediate and pressing object of attention than the problems of man and man's environment. Eventually inquiring minds began to question tradition, the Classics themselves included, on the basis, if they were religiously inclined, of their direct reading of Scripture and, if they were less religiously inclined, of empiricism or reason, if not of both. Tradition and conformity were not obliterated thereby, nor did they lose all of their appeal; there was never a lack of persons who fought innovation in favour of tradition. But Europe's intellectuals found different traditions to adhere to, no one ecclesiastical authority having the power to interpret tradition once and for all, and different traditions led or seemed to lead toward different ends. And innovation itself acquired a tradition, a tradition of continual and unending accumulation. For a great number of Europeans, even among those still unquestioningly loyal to their respective churches, mankind's salvation as mortals (regardless of what might happen to the immortal soul) seemed achievable by a new system of faith and good works, of which Francis Bacon was the prophet—the ceaseless and boundless expansion of knowledge and the constant and irreversible advancement of the frontiers of science. As knowledge accumulated, some of the long accepted truths were rendered suspect, and new ones were enthroned in their place. It no longer seemed self-evident that what was good for one level or group of society should *ipso facto* be respected by another as ordained, and it no longer was generally conceded that what was good for father was good also for son. In short, the idea of progress tended to promote an attitude favourable not only to secularization of thought but also to individualism and innovation.

Amid the innovations that, whether borrowed from abroad or produced at home, flooded Europe from 1300 (and before) to 1775 (and beyond), the common human pattern survived. For a large part of Europe's population nature was still an unquestioned mystery, life was a transient phase in eternity, thought was still about immediately, concrete problems, mankind was still divided between 'we' and 'they' (though now increasingly in nation-states rather than in feudal communities), authority was still sacrosanct, work was still an unmitigable hereditary curse, social status was still fixed, conformity was still the best guide of conduct, and strange ideas were suspect. But for some Westerners a new world seemed altogether possible in the future—a world where ultimately nature would be subject to human control by scientific knowledge, the human organism would be capable of ascertaining and acting upon abstract and eternal truths, or 'natural laws', mankind would all be brothers, government would be explicitly derived from the consent of the governed, labour would be reduced to the minimum necessary to a healthy, happy, peaceful, and prosperous society, and individual enterprise would achieve the best allocation of social prestige and the world's goods.

This ameliorist philosophy, this idea of never-ending and essentially irreversible perfectibility, had grown up alongside the ancient Judeo-Christian faith and by the eighteenth century was ready to be exported, together with Europe's new technology and traditional religions, to the other continents. From 1300 on, and especially after 1500, Europe had been exporting its ideas, institutions, and inventions at an accelerating pace. By 1775 this process of 'Europeanization' was decisive in the Americas but as yet had only a spotty and superficial effect in other non-European areas. Europe's borrowing, in its turn, from non-European cultures, already appreciable before 1300, also increased, particularly after the great explorations brought more immediate contact with those cultures. Thus Europe's culture, even as it was being exported, was becoming more diversified, more international, more cosmopolitan, more 'modern'.

SOME INTERRELATIONS OF RELIGION, STATE, CULTURE, AND TECHNOLOGY

Church, State, and Freedom of Thought

The line between civil allegiance on the one hand and religious allegiance on the other was generally harder to draw during our period than subsequently. A clear separation of church and state was sometimes openly advocated by Western theorists like the Anabaptists, Milton, and Roger Williams and often doubtless privately desired by heretics and non-conformists everywhere. Yet officialdom rarely was prepared to admit that a subject might be loyal without belonging to the established church. The English colonies of Rhode Island, Connecticut, and Pennsylvania were exceptional in not requiring religious tests for citizenship or office-holding.

Buddhism, in comparison with the other great religions, was relatively lacking in desire to constitute itself an organic part of a political and social system. This indifference to politics was perhaps due to its concept of the ideal man, the *sannyāsī*, the contemplative, celibate ascetic. Unlike Christian asceticism, in theory at least Buddhist asceticism was not restricted to a select few and so, if carried relentlessly to its logical conclusion, would ultimately have ended in the extinction of Buddhists, rendering political and social theories irrelevant. In actuality, Buddhism tended rather to adapt itself to one or another viable pattern within the political and social systems of the countries to which it spread.

Buddhist doctrinal indifference to politics induced indifference to, and hence toleration of, the religion of others. In Buddhist countries like Ceylon, Burma, Siam, and Cambodia, the Hindu theory of divine kingship generally prevailed and the ruler often conceived of himself as a bodhisattva; he might, therefore, use his position to promote Buddhism and to regulate the monks, but he was generally tolerant also of non-conformist groups if they were not actively hostile. In turn, in countries like China and Japan, which were not predominantly or continuously Buddhist, the Buddhists sought and normally obtained the tolerance, protection, or patronage of the rulers. Indeed, Buddhist monks, especially in Japan, were often high-level advisers to the rulers, and during the Tokugawa period Buddhism was the state religion, serving as an effective tool of the shoguns in combating Christianity and controlling the population. In Tibet, Buddhism attained the position of a theocracy, but even there the state's power was not used to wipe out opposition groups.

In Islam, the unity of church and state was theoretically complete, and to enforce Islamic religious law was the only duty of the state. Non-Muslim groups were tolerated, however, though subjected to the political control of sultans. Though forced to pay a poll tax and to suffer other disabilities, they were allowed their own systems of personal law within an Islamic context.

Hinduism was the most tolerant of the great religious systems. Any group that accepted the social and intellectual leadership of the Brahmans could hope to find a place in the caste system. The Brahmans seldom sought to exercise ruling power directly, since in their system it belonged to another class, but they expected to be among the intimate advisers of rulers. Although the state was merciless toward any group, religious or otherwise, that threatened the ruling prince, a Hindu ruler used power only rarely to enforce a particular creed or dogma. Sikhism, the offspring of a union of Hinduism and Islam, departing from ths tolerant attitude, was the only Hindu sect to work out a complete fusion of church and state.

The mixed religious systems of China, Japan, Korea, and Vietnam tended toward permissiveness. To be sure, in all these countries religious ceremonies were a part of a state system, and the machinery of government was used to conduct religious ceremonies believed to be necessary or beneficial to the state's well-being. In China, where Confucianism was the philosophy of the state and the ruler was the nominal head of all religious groups, the government promoted Confucianism. Hence, the minority creeds of Buddhism and Taoism were regulated and restricted in various ways and the number of their priests, monks, and nuns was officially limited. Nevertheless, heterodox teachings, though nominally prohibited, were in practice allowed unless they appeared to be a threat to the ruling power. In Japan Shintoism as well as Buddhism was supported by the state, and Shinto propagandists during the Tokugawa period went so far as to favour its establishment as the exclusive state cult.

The line between theology and philosophy was also during this period generally indistinct. In the West, as humanism and the new scientific spirit gained in strength, theology was first obliged to share its throne as the queen of the sciences with the *studia humanitatis*, and subsequently an even more secular 'natural philosophy' took its reginal place. On the other hand, to distinguish between religion and philosophy elsewhere—or, for that matter, for all Western thinkers—would be to a large extent factitious. Muslims, indeed, sought to distinguish *kalām* from *falsafa* but not without an area of overlapping (see Chapter VI). In Hindu thought the distinctions between theology and philosophy were even less formal, and the great religious thinkers of India were also its great philosophers. As in the West, those who were primarily theistic found the principal route to salvation in devotion to a bersonal deity, and the less theistic, although they disagreed regarding the pest way to express that devotion, thought in terms of enlightenment through knowledge and the realization of the unity of the individual with the absolute *brahman* (not wholly unlike the Western philosopher's Nature). In Buddhist thinking no greater distinction was made between theology and philosophy. The Neo-Confucian thinkers of China, however, were fundamentally interested in philosophic, political, and social problems and not in theology, and since Buddhist and Taoism produced no really outstanding thinkers during this period, the posture of Chinese thought, apart from ceremonial practices, was secular rather than religious. Japanese Buddhist thinkers were strongly influenced by Chinese philosophy, while Shinto thinkers, influenced by a native nationalism as well as by both Neo-Confucianism and Buddhism, fused religious, philosophical, and political conceptions into a theory of pure Shinto.

In contrast, in Europe the distinction between church and state, between pope and emperor, between theology and political philosophies was fairly perceptible even before 1300, and after that date the line between the divine and the secular became clearer still. The decline of the concept of a Holy Roman Empire was a further aid to the secularization of political thought. Never more than a pale reflection of the old Roman Empire, it steadily lost ground to the sanguine ideal of the nation state, and the ideal of a universal church ruled by a strong hierarchy and harbouring all believers within its flexible embrace was irrevocably impaired by the Protestant revolts. At first, despite pleas for tolerance from the Bodins and the Comeniuses, the effect of the religious wars was increased intolerance, and Calixtus fruitlessly advocated syncretism, a reunion of the churches. Bishop Bossuet in 1688 wrote an *Histoire des variations des églises protestantes* decrying the splintering tendencies of Protestantism, only to be reminded by other writers, both Protestant and Catholic, that Catholicism also had its variations. Indeed, Leibniz, syncretist though he was, contended that variety might not be undesirable as pointing toward the amelioration of religion. And it indeed proved true that increasing variety, though it tended away from syncretism, led at least toward confusion and eventually, if not toward official tolerance, at least toward official indifference—though far from complete in either case by 1775. Growing religious permissiveness and indifference interacted— sometimes as cause, sometimes as effect—with the secularization of thought, whether in science, politics, philosophy, or art, but secularization, for all its looming significance, was to remain gradual and sparse until the close of the eighteenth century.

Secularization and Diffusion of Culture

While many other areas stayed in most regards even less secularized than Europe, they tended more noticeably toward secularization in art than in philosophy. Hindu art, consisting largely of temple architecture and the sculpture of deities, continued to draw its major inspiration from religion, but Rajput painting represented secular court scenes to some extent. While Japanese architecture and sculpture still reflected interest in Buddhism, landscape painting became popular, and during the Tokugawa period the secular colour print and secular architecture came to dominate their respective fields. In China, although landscape painting always mirrored a certain Taoist mysticism and many favourite scenes in paintings and prints dealt with Buddhist and Taoist themes, secular art stood out in imperial palaces and tombs, huge stone animals, colour prints of popular subjects, and landscape paintings, and the famous Chinese porcelains of the period were for secular use.

The secular trend in art was far from universal, however, particularly where Buddhist influences prevailed. In Burma, Siam, and Cambodia the great pagodas, monasteries, and sculptured figures were Buddhist-inspired, and even royal buildings reflected Buddhist religious ideas. Much the same can be said for the figures, monasteries, and palaces of Tibet. In Indonesia the rise of Islam blighted the development of Hindu-Buddhist sculpture and temple architecture but gave nothing of significance to replace it.

Europe eagerly absorbed decorative processes and motifs from Islamic lands and the Far East, and this receptivity to the minor arts of other cultural areas contrasts notably with Europe's amazing independence in the development of her major arts. The contrast may have a partly theological explanation —the greater acceptability of the minor arts as purely ornamental, having no non-Christian meanings such as might have been associated with infidel and heathen painting, sculpture, and architecture. Yet, more mundane explanations may also hold partly true. Contact of European artists was easier with the more portable objects of the decorative arts, and most of the techniques adopted by Europe were those that lent themselves to factory production; the much admired but laboriously made rugs of the Islamic lands and China never inspired a leading imitative effort in the decorative arts of Europe. Europeans readily adopted the ideals of refinement and luxury embodied in the decorative arts of Islam, China, Japan, and India. Previously accustomed to relatively drab and uncomfortable lives, they had become conscious of the magnificence of the East during the Crusades, and by the eighteenth century, in admiration for and use of beautifully made and elaborately ornamental articles, Europeans equalled the most luxury-loving peoples.

The history of the arts and letters during our period illustrates two paradoxes that have frequently been noted in the development of art. Art is both indigenous and international; art is both primitive and polished. The paradoxes are easily explained. All peoples, no matter what their stage of culture, express themselves in imaginative lore, song, dance, and picture long before and long after they learn to express themselves in written words. Art thus often is the articulation of the aspirations, joys, sorrows, triumphs, and defeats, and the record of the great moments in the history, of a primitive people. It often is also the outlet for the expression of frustration by the suppressed in places where the written word of protest would be punished. Folklore, picture, song, and dance are therefore to be found whenever aspirations or emotions of joy or sorrow are expressed. Since such aspirations and emotions nearly always give vent to hope, these expressions easily lend themselves to religious faith. Art thus everywhere becomes a handmaiden of the priest as well as an expression of popular affects and a means of popular entertainment. It passes from church to palace to commoner's home, and from country to country, meanwhile undergoing adaptations and accretions that fit it to the tastes not only of different peoples but also of different eras and of different layers of society. The spontaneous, simple, indigenous, local, primitive art rarely dies, but alongside it flourishes a teeming progeny which is cultivated, composite, and learned or even sophisticated, and which, while retaining its indigenous roots, borrows heavily from other parts of the world. In its more refined forms, art speaks to the cultivated few no more eloquently than in its more popular forms it speaks to the many.

The history of art, whether religious or secular (including music, though not musical forms or notation), constitutes perhaps the best example our period affords of mankind's trend (often unconscious; often resisted, if conscious) toward cultural unity in diversity, toward a cosmopolitan culture. The oneness of science did not equally provide room for diversity, and the idioms of language, the pride of races and nations, and the divisiveness of theological and philosophical persuasions did not equally permit unity of literary creativity and standards. Yet literature, too, forwarded the trends toward unity in diversity: literary themes were often common property, philosophy and theology dealt with universal problems and aspirations, folklore was readily interchanged, and literature, if sometimes inadequately, was capable of translation. Art and music, more than other products of the human mind, spoke a universal language without forgetting their native patois; literature spoke in many tongues but often about the same things.

Technology, too, easily migrates from place to place. In our period Europe borrowed in technological processes connected with such things as compass, gunpowder, printing, porcelains, textiles, and decorative arts more than it loaned. In fact, before the nineteenth century Western technology for the most part stayed at home in Europe and America, and modern science, too, remained limited largely to Europe, both waiting for a later day to play a role upon the world stage. But eventually, technology and science were, like art and music, to speak a language equally intelligible all over the world, and, like literature, to deal with problems common to men everywhere.

Probably as late as 1775 Europe was still taking more from the non-Western civilizations in cultural influences, commodities, and human labour than it gave to them. If the shift in the balance had begun, the day was still distant when non-Western civilizations would have to choose between their traditional ways and 'Westernization', so much of which had been borrowed from outside the West. But the choice would never be limited to two sheer alternatives—tradition or Westernization—for each non-Western people would be able to mix the two according to its own prescription for 'modernization', eventually borrowing scientific knowledge, technical products, and technologies with greater alacrity than mores or values, whether artistic, literary, or behavioral. If in a subsequent age there would be room to wonder whether what the several cultures had borrowed from each other was for better or for worse, in a less sceptical epoch, when nearly all men had faith in either God's design or the perfectibility of man or in both, few could doubt that it must be for the better.

NOTES TO CHAPTER XVII

1. This discussion borrows from J. M. Romein, 'The Common Human Pattern', *Journal of World History*, IV (1958), pp. 449–63, but has taken into account the variant points of view expressed by Oscar Halecki in 'The Place of Christendom in the History of Mankind', *Journal of World History*, I (1954), pp. 927–50, and by Pieter Geyl in 'The Vitality of Western Civilization', *Delta, a Review of Arts, Life and Thought in the Netherlands* (Spring, 1959), pp. 5–19.

SELECTED BIBLIOGRAPHY

Note: The titles that follow are selected almost exclusively from works that have appeared from 1957 to 1966. With a few exceptions, it was superfluous to include works that appeared before 1957, for such works probably are listed in George Frederick Howe *et al.*, eds., *Guide to Historical Literature* (New York: Macmillan Company, 1961; for the American Historical Association). (Titles will be given only once, but some may well belong under more than one heading.)

CHAPTER I: INTRODUCTION
THE POLITICAL, ECONOMIC, AND SOCIAL BACKGROUND

National Developments, 1300–1775

FERNANDO BENITEZ, *The Century after Cortes* (Chicago, 1965).

E. W. BOVILL, *The Golden Trade of the Moors* (London, 1958).

CHRISTOPHER BROOKE and D. M. SMITH, eds., *A History of England* (Edinburgh, 1961–   ) [Vols. III (1272–1485) and V (1603–1714) are the only ones published before 1966 that are relevant to this period.]

A. BULTMANN, 'Early Hanoverian England (1714–1760), Some Recent Writings', *Journal of Modern History*, XXXV (1963), 46–61.

G. B. CARSON, JR., 'Recent works on the History of Russia in the period from the Tatars to Catherine II', *Journal of World History*, VIII (1964), 548–63.

WILLIAM F. CHURCH, 'Publications on Cardinal Richelieu since 1945, a Bibliographical Study', *Journal of Modern History*, XXXVII (1965), 421–44.

G. N. CLARK, eds., *Oxford History of England* (Oxford, 1955–62), Vols. IV–XII (1216–1815).

G. N. CLARK *et al.*, eds., *The New Cambridge Modern History* (Cambridge, 1957–   ). [For the period of this volume Vols. I (1493–1520), II (1520–1559), V (1648–1688), VII (1713–1763) and VIII (1763–1793) had appeared before 1966.]

ROBERT CORNEVIN, *Histoire de l'Afrique*, Vol. I: *Des origines au XVIe siècle* (Paris, 1962).

P. D. CURTIN, *African History* (New York, 1964).

K. K. DATTA, 'A Brief Review of Works of Indian Scholars on the Medieval and Modern Periods of Indian History', *Journal of World History*, VI (1960), 380–402.

BASIL DAVIDSON, *Old Africa Rediscovered* (London, 1959) [which is the same work as *The Lost Cities of Africa* (Boston, 1959)].

RAYMOND DAWSON, ed., *The Legacy of China* (New York, 1964).

JAN DEN TEX, *Oldenbarnevelt* (Haarlem, 1960–62).

MICHEL FRANCOIS and NICOLAS TOLU, eds., *International Bibliography of Historical Sciences*, Vol. XXVII–XXXI, 1958–1962 (Paris, 1960–   ; for the International Congress of Historical Sciences).

J. H. ELLIOTT, *Imperial Spain, 1469–1716* (Cambridge, 1963).

——, *The Revolt of the Catalans: A Study in the Decline of Spain (1598–1640)* (New York, 1963).

PIETER GEYL, *The Netherlands in the Seventeenth Century*: Part 2: *1648–1715* (London, 1964).

LINO GOMEZ CANEDO, *Los archivos de la historia de América, periodo colonial español* (Mexico, D.F., 1961), 2 vols.

STANKO GULDESCU, *A History of Medieval Croatia* (The Hague, 1964).

OTTO HAINTZ, *König Karl XII von Schweden* (Berlin, 1958), 3 vols.

C. O. HUCKER, *China: A Critical Bibliography* (Tucson, Ariz., 1962).

R. JACOBS, *The American Colonies Come of Age, 1689–1763* (Chicago, 1965).

FRITZ KERN et al., *Historia Mundi*, Vols, VI–IX [late Middle Ages to Enlightenment] (Bern, 1957–1960).

GUSTAVE LANCTOT, *Histoire du Canada: Des origines au régime royal* (Montreal, 1959).

HENRYK LOWMIANSKI et al., 'Etat des recherches', in JULIUSZ BARDACH et al., eds., *La Pologne au XIIe Congrès international des Sciences Historiques à Vienne* (Warsaw, 1965), pp. 163–399 [Bibliography of Polish historiography, 1945–1965].

JOHN LYNCH, *Spain under the Habsburgs*, Vol. I: *Empire and Absolutism* (New York, 1964).

RAYMOND MAUNY et al., eds. 'Le problème des sources de l'Afrique Noire jusqu'à la colonisation européenne', XIIe Congrès International des Sciences Historiques *Rapports* (Horn/Vienna, 1965), II, 177–232.

FREDERIC MAURO, *Le Portugal et l'Atlantique au XVIIe siècle (1570–1670): Etude économique* (Paris, 1960).

W. H. MACNEILL, *Europe's Steppe Frontier, 1500–1800* (Chicago, 1964).

KANTARO MURAKAWA et al., eds., *Japan at the XIIth International Congress of Historical Sciences in Vienna* (Tokyo, 1965). A bibliography of Japanese historical publications, 1958–1962.

ROLAND OLIVIER and J. D. FAGE, *A Short History of Africa* (Harmondsworth, 1962).

DENISE PAULME, 'L'Afrique noire jusqu'au XIVe siècle, deuxième partie', *Journal of World History*, III (1957), 561–82.

CONYERS READ, *Bibliography of British History, Tudor Period, 1485–1603* (2nd ed., New York, 1959).

HELLMUT ROSSLER and GUNTHER PRINZ, *Sachwörterbuch zur deutschen Geschichte* (Munich, 1956–1958), 2 vols.

JOHN C. RULE, 'The Old Regime in America: A Review of Recent Interpretations of France in America', *William and Mary Quarterly*, 3d. ser., XIX (1962), 575–600.

STEVEN RUNCIMAN, *The Fall of Constantinople, 1453* (Cambridge, 1965).

A. M. SAKHAROV, 'Les Mongols et la civilisation russe', *Journal of World History*, special no., *Contributions to Russian History* (1958), 77–97.

B. S. SILBERMAN, *Japan and Korea: A Critical Bibliography* (Tucson, 1962).

ROBERT WALCOTT, *The Tudor-Stuart Period of English History (1485–1714): A Review of Changing Interpretations* (New York, 1964).

J. B. WOLF, 'The Reign of Louis XIV: A Selected Bibliography of Writings since the War of 1914–1918', *Journal of Modern History*, XXXVI (1964), 127–44.

PEREZ ZAGORIN, 'English History, 1558–1640, A Bibliographical Survey', *American Historical Review*, LXVIII (1963), 364–84.

The Centralization of Political Power

C. B. ANDERSON, 'Ministerial Responsibility in the 1620's', *Journal of Modern History*, XXXIV (1962), 381–89.

MICHEL ANTOINE, 'Les Conseils des finances sous le règne de Louis XV', *Revue d'histoire moderne et contemporaine*, V (1958), 161–200.

G. E. AYLMER, *The King's Servants: The Service of Charles I, 1625–1642* (London, 1961).

SIMONE BLANC, 'La pratique de l'administration russe dans la première moitié du XVIIIè siècle,' *Revue d'histoire moderne et contemporaine*, X (1963), 45–64.

CH'Ü T'UNG-TSU, *Local Administration in China under the Ch'ing* (Cambridge Mass., 1962).

BERNARD S. COHN, 'Political Systems in Eighteenth Century India: The Banaras Region', *Journal of the American Oriental Society*, LXXXII (1962), 312–20.

JEAN DELUMEAU, 'Les progrès de la centralisation dans l'état pontifical au XVIe siècle', *Revue historique*, CCXXVI (1961), 399–410.

J. W. FESLER, 'French Field Administration, The Beginnings', *Comparative Studies in Society and History*, V (1962), 76–111.

R. E. GIESEY, 'The juristic Basis of Dynastic Right to the French Throne', *Transactions of the American Philosophical Society*, LI, part 5 (1961).

ALBERT GOODWIN, 'The Social Structure and Economic and Political Attitudes. The French Nobility in the Eighteenth Century', XIIe Congrès international des Sciences Historiques, *Rapports*, (Vienna, 1965), I, 356–68.

C. O. HUCKER, *The Traditional Chinese State in Ming Times (1368–1644)*, (Tucson, Arizona, 1961).

J. R. MAJOR, *Representative Institutions in Renaissance France, 1421–1559* (Madison, Wisc., 1960).

——, 'The Crown and the Aristocracy in Renaissance France', *American Historical Review*, LXIX (1964), 631–45.

N. MAJUMDAR, *Justice and Police in Bengal, 1765–1793: A Study of the Mizamat in Decline* (Calcutta, 1960).

C. R. MAYES, 'The Sale of Peerages in Early Stuart England', *Journal of Modern History*, XXIX (1957), 21–37.

A. L. MOOTE, 'The French Crown versus Its Judicial and Financial Officials, 1615–83', *Journal of Modern History*, XXXIV (1962), 146–60.

O. A. RANUM, *Richelieu and the Councillors of Louis XIII: A Study of the Secretaries of State and Superintendents of Finance in the Ministry of Richelieu, 1635–1642,* (New York, 1963).

J. RICOMMARD, 'Du recrutement et du nombre des subdélégués en titre d'office dans l'intendance de Bretagne (1704–1715)', *Revue d'histoire moderne et contemporaine,* VIII (1961), 121–52.

HANS ROSENBERG, *Bureaucracy, Aristocracy, and Autocracy: The Prussian Experience, 1660–1815* (Cambridge, Mass., 1958).

The Quest for Liberty and Social Justice

YEHOSHUA ARIELI, *Individualism and Naturalism in American Ideology* (Cambridge, Mass., 1964).

BERNARD BAILYN (ed.), *Pamphlets of the American Revolution, 1750–1776,* Vol. I: *1750–1765* (Cambridge, Mass., 1965).

M. R. BECKER, 'Florentine Popular Government (1343–1348)', *Proceedings of the American Philosophical Society,* CVI (1962), 360–82.

F. L. CARSTEN, *Princes and Parliaments in Germany from the Fifteenth to the Eighteenth Century* (New York, 1959).

L. G. CROCKER, *Rousseau et la voie du totalitarisme,* Institut International de Philosophie Politique, *Annales de Philosophie Politique,* No. 5 (1965), 99–136.

DENISE EECKAUTE, 'Les brigands en Russie du XVIIe au XIXe siècle: 'mythe et réalité', *Revue d'Histoire moderne et contemporaine,* XII (1965), 161–202.

F. L. FORD, *Strasbourg in Transition, 1648–1789* (Cambridge, Mass., 1958).

J. P. GREENE, *The Quest for Power: The Lower Houses of Assembly in the Southern Royal Colonies, 1689–1776* (Chapel Hill, North Carolina, 1963).

PAULINE GREGG, *Free-born John: a Biography of John Lilburne* (London, 1961).

P. H. HARDACRE, 'Writings on Oliver Cromwell since 1929', *Journal of Modern History,* XXXIII (1961), 1–14.

JACK H. HEXTER, *Reappraisals in History* (Evanston, Ill., 1961).

F. G. HEYMANN, 'City Rebellions in Fifteenth Century Bohemia and Their Ideological and Sociological Background', *Slavonic and East European Review,* XL (1962), 324–40.

JEAN JACQUART, 'La fronde des princes dans la région parisienne et ses conséquences matérielles', *Revue d'histoire moderne et contemporaine,* VII (1960), 257–90.

J. R. MAJOR, *The Deputies to the Estates General of Renaissance France* (Madison, Wisc., 1960).

K. B. MCFARLANE, 'The English Nobility in the later Middle Ages', XIIe Congrès International des Sciences Historiques, *Rapports,* (Vienna, 1965) I, 337–45.

ROLAND MOUSNIER, 'Recherches sur les soulèvements populaires en France avant la Fronde', *Revue d'histoire moderne et contemporaine,* V (1958), 81–113.

J. E. NEALE, *Elizabeth I and her Parliaments, 1584–1601* (New York, 1957).

S. PASCU et al., 'Mouvements paysans dans le centre et le sud-est de l'Europe du XVe au XXe siècle', XIIe Congrès International des Sciences Historiques, *Rapports* (Vienna, 1965), IV, 211–35.

BORIS PORCHNEV, *Les soulèvements populaires en France de 1623 à 1648* (Paris, 1963) (tr. from the Russian).

E. S. TEALL, 'The Seigneur of Renaissance in France: Advocate or Oppressor?' *Journal of Modern History*, XXXVII (1965), 131–50.

C. L. VER STEEG. *The Formative Years, 1607–1763* (New York, 1964) ('The Making of America').

C. V. WEDGEWOOD, *The Great Rebellion* (London, 1955, 1958), 2 vols.

PEREZ ZAGORIN, 'The English Revolution, 1640–1660', *Journal of World History*, II (1955), 668–81 and 895–914.

Economic Changes and their Political Import

W. O. AULT, *Open-field Husbandry and the Village Community: A Study of Agrarian By-laws in Medieval England* in *Transactions of the American Philosophical Society*, LV (1965).

BERNARD and LOTTE BAILYN. *Massachusetts Shipping, 1697–1714: A Statistical Study* (Cambridge, Mass., 1959).

R. BARÓN CASTRO, 'El desarrollo de la poblacion hispanoamericana (1492–1950),' *Journal of World History*, V (1959), 325–43.

JEAN-FRANCOIS BERGIER, *Genève et l'économic européenne de la Renaissance* (Paris, 1963).

FRANÇOIS BILLACOIS, 'La Batellerie de la Loire au XVIIe siècle', *Revue d'histoire moderne et contemporaine* XI (1964), 163–90.

M. R. BLOCH, 'The Social Influence of Salt', *Scientific American*, CCIX (July, 1963), 88–98.

MICHAEL CONFINO, *Domaines et seigneurs en Russie vers la fin du XVIIIe siècle. Etude de structures agraires et de mentalités économiques.* Préface de Roger Portal (Paris, 1963).

EMILE CORNAERT, *Les français et le commerce international à Anvers, fin du XVe–XVIe siècle* (Paris, 1961), 2 vols.

PHILIPPE DOLLINGER, *La Hanse (XIIe–XVIIe siècles)* (Paris, 1964).

W. K. FERGUSON, *Europe in Transition: 1300 to 1520* (Boston, Mass., 1963).

PING-TI HO, *Studies on the Population of China, 1368–1953* (Cambridge, Mass., 1959).

HENRI LAPEYRE, 'Anvers au XVIe siècle d'après des travaux récents', *Revue d'histoire moderne et contemporaine*, XI (1964), 191–202.

G. T. MATTHEWS, *The Royal General Farms in Eighteenth-Century France* (New York, 1958).

JOHN NEF, *The Conquest of the Material World: Essays on the Coming of Industrialism* (Chicago, 1964).

R. M. MORSE, 'Some Characteristics of Latin American Urban History', *American Historical Review*, LXVII (1962), 317–38.

PAUL CHRISLER PHILLIPS, *The Fur Trade*, Vol. I [to 1783] (Norman, Oklahoma, 1961).

MARCEL REINHARD and ANDRE ARMENGAUD, *Histoire générale de la population mondiale* (Paris, 1961).

LADISLAS REITZER, 'Some Observations on Castilian Commerce and Finance in the Sixteenth Century', *Journal of Modern History*, XXXII (1960), 213–23.

H. VAN DER WEE, *The Growth of the Antwerp Market and the European Economy (fourteenth–sixteenth centuries)* (The Hague, 1963), 3 vols.

J. VICENS VIVES, *Historia económica de España* (Barcelona, 1959).

PHILIPPE WOLFF, *Histoire de Toulouse* (Toulouse, 1958).

Social Changes and Their Political Import

PAUL WALDEN BAMFORD, 'The Procurement of Oarsmen for French Galleys, 1660–1748', *American Historical Review*, LXI (1959), 31–48.

BERNARDO BLANCO-GONZALES, *Del cortesano al descreto: examen de una decadencia*, Vol. I (Madrid, 1962).

JEROME BLUM, *The European Peasantry from the Fifteenth to the Nineteenth Century* (Washington, 1960).

——, *Lord and Peasant in Russia from the Ninth to the Nineteenth Century* (New Haven, Conn., 1961).

ALFRED COBBAN, *The Social Interpretation of the French Revolution* (Cambridge, England, 1964).

ADELINE DAUMARD, 'Une préférence pour l'étude des sociétés urbaines en France aux XVIIIe et XIXe siècles, projet de code socio-professionel', *Revue d'histoire moderne et contemporaine*, X (1963), 185–210.

LAJOS FEKETE, 'La vie à Budapest sous la domination turque, 1541–1686', *Journal of World History*, VIII (1964), 525–47.

ROBERT FORSTER, *The Nobility of Toulouse in the Eighteenth Century: A Social and Economic Study* (Baltimore, 1960).

——, 'The Provincial Noble: a Reappraisal', *American Historical Review*, LXVIII (1963), 681–91.

HEINZ FRIESE, *Das Dienstleistungs-System der Ming-Zeit (1368–1644)* (Wiesbaden, 1959).

JACQUES HEERS, *L'occident aux XIVe et XVe siècles: aspects économiques et sociaux* ('Nouvelle Cléo') (Paris, 1963).

CHRISTOPHER HILL, *Society and Puritanism in Pre-Revolutionary England* (New York, 1964).

PING-TI HO, *The Ladder of Success in Imperial China: Aspects of Social Mobility, 1368–1911* (New York, 1962).

J. JACQUART, 'Propriété et exploitation rurales au sud de Paris, dans la seconde moitié du XVIe siècle', *Bulletin de la Société d'histoire moderne*, 12s., nos. 15–16 (October–December, 1960), 10–16.

MICHEL LAUNAY, 'La société française d'après la correspondance de J. J.–Rousseau (textes inédits),' *Annales historiques de la Révolution française*, XXXIII (1962), 397–420.

GEORGES LEFEBVRE, *Etudes Orléanaises*, I, *Contribution à l'étude des structures sociales à la fin du XVIIIe siècle* (Commission d'histoire économique et sociale de la Révolution, Paris, 1962).

ERIK MOLNAR, 'Les fondements économiques et sociaux de l'absolutisme', in Erik Molnar *et al.*, *Nouvelles études historiques* (Budapest, 1965), I, 285–99, and also in XIIe Congres International des Sciences Historiques, *Rapports* (Vienna, 1965), IV, 155–69.

JOHN U. NEF, *Cultural Foundations of Industrial Civilization* (Cambridge, England, 1958).

Z. P. PACK, *Die ungarische Agrarentwicklung im 16–17. Jahrhundert:* Abliegung vom westeuropäischen Entwicklungsgang (Budapest, 1964).

LIONEL ROTHKRUG, *Opposition to Louis XIV, the Political and Social Origin of the French Enlightenment* (Princeton, N.J., 1965).

J. C. RUSSELL, *Late Ancient and Medieval Population* (*Transactions of the American Philosophical Society*, XLVIII, part 3, 1958).

ALAN SIMPSON, *The Wealth of the Gentry, 1540–1660: East Anglican Studies* (Chicago, 1961).

GY. SZEKELY, 'Les rapports des citadins et des paysans dans la Confédération helvétique à l'époque de la Réforme', in E. Molnar *etal.* (eds.), *Nouvelles études historiques* (Budapest, 1965), pp. 181–96.

The Growing Interdependence of People

ROBERTO ALMAGIÀ, 'The Contribution of Italian Navigators to the Politico-Commercial Expansion of the XVIth Century', *Journal of World History*, VII (1963), 285–89.

RODOLFO BARÓN CASTRO, 'The Discovery of America and the Geographical and Historical Integration of the World', *Journal of World History*, VI (1961, special Spanish issue), 809–32.

WOODROW BORAH and S. F. COOK, *The Aboriginal Population of Central Mexico on the Eve of the Spanish Conquest* (Berkeley, 1962).

C. R. BOXER, *The Golden Age of Brazil, 1695–1750: Growing Pains of a Colonial Society* (Berkeley, 1962).

HUGUETTE ET PIERRE CHAUNU, *Seville et l'Atlantique* (1504–1650) (Paris, 1956–1959), 8 vols.

B. S. COHN, *The Development and Impact of British Administration in India, a Bibliographic Essay* (New Delhi, 1961).

GILBERTO FREYRE, 'Impact of the Portuguese on the American Tropics', *Journal of World History*, IV (1958), 582–602.

LEWIS HANKE, 'The Dawn of Conscience in America: Spanish Experiments and Experiences with Indians in the New World', *Proceedings of the American Philosophical Society*, CVII (1963), 83–92.

M. G. S. HODGSON, 'The Interrelations of Societies in History', *Comparative Studies in Society and History*, V (1963), 227–50.

D. F. LACH, *Asia in the Making of Europe*, Vols. I, Books I and II: *The Century of Discovery* (Chicago, 1965).

GUSTAVE LANCTOT, *A History of Canada*, Vol. I: *From Its Origins to the Royal Regime, 1663*, tr. by Josephine Hambleton (Cambridge, Mass., 1963).

FREDERIC MAURO, *L'expansion européenne (1600–1870)* ('Nouvelle Clio', No. 27; Paris, 1964).

A. METRAUX, 'Les précurseurs de l'ethnologie en France du XVIe au XVIIIe siècle', *Journal of World History*, VII (1963), 721–38.

J. L. PHELAN. *The Hispanization of the Philippines, Spanish Aims and Filipino Responses, 1500–1700* (Madison, Wisc., 1959).

MARIANO PICÓN-SALAS, *A Cultural History of Spanish America: From the Conquest to Independence*, tr. by Irving A. Leonard (Berkeley, 1962).

ROGER PORTAL, 'Les Russe en Sibérie au XVIIe siècle', *Revue d'histoire moderne et contemporaine*, V (1958), 5–38.

A. J. PRICE, *The Western Invasion of the Pacific and Its Continents: A Study of Moving Frontiers and Changing Landscapes, 1513–1958* (New York, 1963).

D. B. QUINN, 'Exploration and the Expansion of Europe', XIIe Congrés International des Sciences Historiques, *Rapports* (Vienna, 1965), I, 45–59.

A. L. SALLS, *The Paradise of Travellers: The Italian Influence on Englishmen in the Seventeenth Century* (Bloomington, Ind., 1964).

J. VINCENS VIVES (ed.) *Historia social y economica de Espana y América* (Barcelona, 1957) (3 vols. to the 18th century)

SILVIO ZAVALA, *The Colonial Period in the History of the New World*, abridged in English by Max Savelle (Mexico, D.F., 1962).

CHAPTER II

THE MAJOR RELIGIONS (*c.* 1300)

Animism

HAROLD E. DRIVER, *The Indians of North America* (Chicago, 1961).

CHARLES GOLLENKAMP, *Maya: The Riddle and Rediscovery of a Lost Civilization* (New York, 1959).

PAUL KIRCHHOFF et al., 'Origins and Continuity of the Mesoamerican Civilizations', XIIe Congrès International des Sciences Historiques, *Rapports* (Vienna, 1965), II, 233–62.

G. P. MURDOCK, *Africa, Its People and Their Culture History* (New York, 1959).

ANTONIO TOVAR LLORENTE, 'L'incorporation du nouveau monde à la culture occidentale', *Journal of World History*, VI (1961, special Spanish number), 833–56.

Hinduism and Jainism

CHARLES ELIOT, *Hinduism and Buddhism: An Historical Sketch* (New York, 1957), 3 vols.

CLIFFORD GEERTZ, *The Religion of Java* (Glencoe, Ill., 1960).

K. W. MORGAN, *Asian Religions: An Introduction to the Study of Hinduism, Buddhism, Islam, Confucianism, and Taoism* (New York, 1964).

K. A. NILAKANTA SASTRI, *A History of South India from Prehistoric Times to the Fall of Vijayanagar* (London, 1959, 2nd ed.).

V. A. SMITH, *The Oxford History of India* (Oxford, 1958, 3rd ed.).

PERCIVAL SPEAR, *India: a Modern History* ('University of Michigan History of the Modern World') (Ann Arbor, Michigan, 1961).

T. K. VENKATARAMAN, 'South India and Indian Culture', *Journal of World History*, VI (1960), 348–69.

Buddhism

M. GHOSH, *The History of Cambodia* (Saigon, 1960).

B. P. GROSLIER, *Angkor et le Cambodge* (Paris, 1958).

M. F. HERZ, *A Short History of Cambodia: from the Days of Angkor to the Present* (New York, 1958).

TIEH-TSENG LI, *Tibet; Today and Yesterday* (New York, 1960).

G. P. MALALASEKERA (ed.) *Encyclopedia of Buddhism*, fascicles *A-Aoki* (Ceylon, 1961–66).

P. N. NAZARETH, *An Outline of Malayan History* (London, 1958).

TRAN van TUNG, *Vietnam* (New York, 1959).

K. E. WELLS, *Thai Buddhism, Its Rites and Activities* (Bangkok, 1960).

PAUL WHEATLEY, *The Golden Khersonese: Studies in the Historical Geography of the Malay Peninsula before A.D. 1500* (Kuala Lumpur, 1961).

ARTHUR F. WRIGHT, *Buddhism in Chinese History* (Stanford, Calif., 1959).

Confucianism, Taoism, and Shintoism

W. T. DE BARY et al. (eds.) *Sources of the Chinese Tradition* ('Introduction to Oriental Civilizations' (New York, 1960).

J. W. HALL, *Japanese History, New Dimensions of Approach and Understanding* (Washington, 1961).

PING-TI HO, *Studies on the Population of China, 1368–1953* (Cambridge, 1960).

HOMER HULBERT, *Hulbert's History of Korea*, ed. by Clarence Norwood Weems (New York, 1962), 2 vols.

LIN YU-T'ANG, *Imperial Peking: Seven Centuries of China* (New York, 1961).

GEORGE SANSOM, *A History of Japan* (Stanford, Calif., 1958–1963), 3 vols. to date [to 1867].

WEINER SPEISER, *China, Spirit and Society* (New York, 1960).

NN

A. F. WRIGHT, 'The Study of Chinese Civilization', *Journal of the History of Ideas*, XXI (1960), 233–55.

A. F. WRIGHT (ed.), *The Confucian Persuasion* (Stanford, Calif., 1960).

A. F. WRIGHT and DENIS TWITCHETT (eds.), *Confucian Personalities* (Stanford, Conn., 1962).

Islam

H. A. R. GIBB, *Mohammedanism: An Historical Survey* (New York, 1962, rev. ed).

H. A. R. GIBB *et al.*, *The Encyclopedia of Islam* (Leiden, 1954 to date, new ed.) [To the letter H with fascicle 42 in Vol. III in 1965].

S. M. IKRAM, *Muslim Civilization in India*, ed. T. Embree (New York, 1964).

Judaism

S. W. BARON, *A Social and Religious History of the Jews* (New York, 1952–1960, rev. ed.), 8 vols.

SIMON DUBNOW, *Jewish History*, ed. by Koppel Pinson (Philadelphia, 1958).

TONI OELSNER, 'Wilhelm Roscher's Theory of the Economic and Social Position of the Jews in the Middle Ages, a Critical Examination', *Yivo Annual of Jewish Social Science*, XII (1958–9), 178–195.

Christianity

MARC BLOCH, *Feudal Society*, tr. by L. A. Manyon (Chicago, 1961).

LUIS DIEZ del CORRAL, 'Expérience historique nationale et supranationale de l'Espagne', *Journal of World History*, VI (1961; special Spanish no.), 919–47.

FRANCIS DVORNIK, *The Slavs in European History and Civilization* (New Brunswick, N.J., 1962).

KURT GALLING *et al.*, (eds.), *Religion in Geschichte und Gegenwart; Handwörterbuch für Theologie und Religionswissenschaft* (Tübingen, 1951–62, 3rd ed., 7 vols.).

GEORGE VERNADSKY, *A History of Russia*, Vol. IV: *Russia at the Dawn of the Modern Age* (New Haven, Conn., 1959).

CHAPTER III
MAJOR RELIGIOUS EVENTS (1300–1500)

Hinduism and Buddhism

S. N. HAY and M. H. CASE (eds.), *Southeast Asian History, a Bibliographical Guide* (New York, 1962).

HELMUT HOFFMAN, *The Religions of Tibet*, tr. by Edward Fitzgerald (New York, 1960).

Confucianism, Taoism, and Shintoism

E. O. REISCHAUER and J. K. FAIRBANK, *A History of East Asian Civilization*, Vol. I: *East Asia: the Great Tradition* (Boston, 1960).

Islam

AZIZ AHMAD, 'Dār al-Islām and the Muslim Kingdoms of Deccan and Gujarat', *Journal of World History*, VII (1963), 787–93.

Judaism

S. W. BARON, 'Some Recent Literature on the History of the Jews in the Pre-emancipation Era (1300–1800)', *Journal of World History*, VII (1962), 137–71.

JACOB KATZ, *Tradition and Crisis: Jewish Society and the End of the Middle Ages* (Glencoe, Illinois, 1961).

TONI OELSNER, 'The Place of the Jews in Economic History as viewed by German Scholars, a Critical-Comparative Analysis', in *Year Book VII of the Leo Baeck Institute of Jews from Germany* (London, 1962).

Greek Orthodox Christianity

MICHAEL CHERNIAVSKY, '"Holy Russia": a Study in the History of an Idea', *American Historical Review*, LXIII (1958), 617–637.

——, *Tsar and People: Studies in Russian Myths* (New Haven, Conn., 1961).

NICHOLAS V. RIASANOVSKY, *A History of Russia* (New York, 1963).

IHOR SEVCENKO, 'The Decline of Byzantium Seen through the Eyes of Its Intellectuals', *Dumbarton Oaks Papers*, XV (1961), 169–86.

Roman Catholicism

OSCAR HALECKI, *From Florence to Brest (1439–1596)* (Rome, 1958).

——, 'Diplomatic pontificale et activité missionaire en Asie aux XIIIe–XVe siècles', XIIe Congrès International des Sciences Historiques, *Rapports* (Vienna, 1965), II, 5–32.

F. G. HEYMANN, 'The Hussite-Utraquist Church in the Fifteenth and Sixteenth Centuries', reprinted from the *Archiv für Reformationsgeschichte*, LII (1961).

——, *George of Bohemia: King of Heretics* (Princeton, Conn., 1965).

HOWARD KAMINSKY, 'Chiliasm and the Hussite Revolution', reprinted from *Church History*, XXVI (1957).

FRANTISEK KAVKA, 'The Hussite Movement and the Czech Reformation', *Journal of World History*, V (1960), 830–56.

OTAKAR ODLOZILIK, *The Hussite King: Bohemia in European Affairs, 1440–1471* (Brunswick, N. J., 1965).

CHAPTER IV

CATHOLICS AND PROTESTANTS IN EUROPE (1500–1775)

Demands within the Catholic Church for Reform

RAMÓN CEÑAL, 'La philosophie et les sciences humaines à l'époque moderne', *Journal of World History*, VI (1961, special Spanish number), 857–77.

ALAIN DUFOUR and R. M. DOUGLAS, 'Humanisme et Reformation'. XIIe Congrès International des Sciences Historiques, *Rapports* (Vienna, 1965), III, 57–86.

SEARS JAYNE, *John Colet and Marsilio Ficino* (New York, 1963).

HUBERT JEDIN, *Ecumenical Councils of the Catholic Church: an Historical Outline* (New York, 1096, 2nd ed.).

A. LATREILLE *et al.*, *Histoire du Catholicisme*, Vol. II: *Sous les rois très chrétiens* (Paris, [1960]).

BERND MOELLER, 'Das religiöse Leben in deutschen Sprachgebiet am Ende des 15. und am Ende des 16. Jahrhunderts', XIIe Congrès International des Sciences Historiques, *Rapports* (Vienna, 1965), III, 129–51.

ROBERTO RIDOLFI, *The Life of Girolamo Savonarola*, tr. from the Italian by Cecil Grayson (New York, 1959).

Luther and Lutheranism in Germany (to 1529)

R. H. BAINTON, 'Interpretation of the Reformation', *American Historical Review*, LXVI (1960), 74–84.

CARL COHEN, 'Martin Luther and His Jewish Contemporaries', *Jewish Social Studies*, XXV (1963), 195–204.

JEAN DELUMEAU, *Naissance et affirmation de la Réforme* (Paris, 1965).

J. R. ELTON, *Reformation Europe, 1517–1559* (London, 1963).

E. H. ERIKSON, *Young Man Luther: A Study in Psychoanalysis and History* (New York, 1958).

R. H. FIFE, *The Revolt of Martin Luther* (New York, 1957).

H. J. GRIMM, 'Luther Research since 1920', *Journal of Modern History*, XXXII (1960), 105–118.

——, 'Social Forces in the German Reformation', *Church History*, XXXI (1962), 3–13.

——, *The Reformation in Recent Historical Thought* (New York, 1964).

HAJO HOLBORN, *A History of Modern Germany*, Vol. I: *The Reformation*, Vol. II: *1648* (New York, 1959–63.)

ERWIN ISERLOH, *Luthers Thesenanschlag: Tatsache oder Legende?* (Wiesbaden, 1962).

Zwingli and Calvin

JOHN CALVIN, *Institutes of the Christian Religion* (Philadelphia, 1961).

R. W. GREEN (ed.), *Protestantism and Capitalism: The Weber Thesis and Its Critics* (Boston, 1959).

R. M. KINGDON, 'Calvinism and Democracy: Some Political Implications of Debates on French Reformed Church Government, 1562–1572', *American Historical Review*, LXIX (1964), 393–401.

The Tudors and Anglicanism

A. J. DICKENS, *The English Reformation* (London, 1964).

——, 'The English Reformation and Religious Toleration', XVIIe Congrès International des Sciences Historiques, *Rapports* (Vienna, 1965), I, 177–89.

C. H. GEORGE and KATHERINE GEORGE, *The Protestant Mind of the English Reformation: 1570–1640* (Princeton, Conn., 1961).

DAVID KNOWLES, *The Religious Orders in England*, Vol. III: *The Tudor Age* (Cambridge, 1959).

CONYERS READ, *Lord Burghley and Queen Elizabeth* (New York, 1960).

R. TRIMBLE, *The Catholics in Elizabethan England 1588–1603* (Cambridge, 1964).

The Anabaptists

RUTH WEISS, 'Herkunft und Sozialanschauungen der Täufergemeinden im westlichen Hessen', *Archiv für Reformationsgeschichte*, LII, No. 2 (1961), 162–88.

G. H. WILLIAMS, *The Radical Reformation* (Philadelphia, 1962).

GEORGE WILLIAMS and A. M. MERGAL (eds.), *Spiritual and Anabaptist Writers: Documents Illustrative of the Radical Reformation* (Philadelphia, 1957).

Some Other Protestant Creeds

STANISLAS KOT, *Socinianism in Poland: The Social and Political Ideas of the Polish Antitrinitarians in the Sixteenth and Seventeenth Centuries*, tr. from the Polish by Earl Morse Wilbur (Boston, 1957).

Protestant Expansion and Catholic Resistance (1521–1598)

W. T. BOUWSMA, *Concordia Mundi: the Career and Thought of Guillaume Postel (1510–1581)* (Cambridge, Mass., 1957).

L. CHRISTIANI, 'Tolerance et intolérance religieuses au XVIe siècle,' *Journal of World History*, IV (1960), 857–78.

LUCIEN FEBVRE, *Au coeur religieux du XVIe siècle* (Paris, 1957).

GORDON GRIFFITHS, 'The Revolutionary Character of the Revolt of the Netherlands', *Comparative Studies in Society and History*, II (1960), 452–72.

AMBROISE JOBERT, 'La Pologne dans la crise de la Chrétienté (XVIe–XVIIe siècles), *Bulletin de la Société d'Historie moderne*, 12 s., No. 3 (May–July, 1957), 2–8.

The Council of Trent

HUBERT JEDIN, *A History of the Council of Trent*, 2 vols., tr. by Ernest Graf (Edinburgh, 1957–61).

MARIO SCADUTO, *Storia della Compagnia de Jesu in Italia*, Vol. III: *L'epoca di Giacomo Lainez: il governo, 1556–1565* (Rome, 1964).

Religious Conflict and Non-conformity (1598–1775)

D. W. BAHLMANN, *The Great Moral Revolution of 1688* (New Haven, Conn., 1957)

D. D. BIEN, *The Calas Affair: Persecution, Toleration, and Heresy in Eighteenth-Century Toulouse* (Princeton, 1960).

HERBERT LÜTHY, *La Banque protestante en France: de la Révocation de l'Edit de Nantes à la Révolution* (Paris, 1959–61), 2 vols.

T. K. RABB, 'The Effects of the Thirty Years War on the German Economy', *Journal of Modern History*, XXIV (1962), 40–51.

E. REVESZ, 'Entre l'orthodoxie et les lumières. Tolérance et intolérance dans le protestantisme calviniste des XVIe—XVIIe siècles en Hongrie', E. Molnar *et al.*, (eds.), *Nouvelles études historiques* (Budapest, 1965), 415–36.

W. C. SCOVILLE, *The Persecution of Huguenots and French Economic Development, 1680–1720* (Berkeley, 1960).

JANUSZ TAZBIR, 'La tolérance religieuse en Pologne aux XVIe et XVIIe siècles', in Juliuz Bardach *et al.*, (eds.), *La Pologne au XIIe Congrès International des Sciences Historiques à Vienna* (Warsaw, 1965), 31–48.

CHAPTER V

OTHER RELIGIOUS EVENTS (1500–1775)

Christianity outside Europe

GEORGES BALANDIER, 'Le Royaume de Kongo et l'acculturation râtée', XIIe Congrès International des Sciences Historiques, *Rapports* (Vienna, 1965), I, 95–102.

C. R. BOXER, *The Dutch Seaborne Empire: 1600–1800* (New York, 1965).

——, *Portuguese Society in the Tropics: The Municipal Councils of Goa, Macao, Bahia, and Luanda, 1500–1800* (Madison, Misc., 1965).

CARL BRIDENBAUGH, *Mitre and Sceptre: Transatlantic Faiths, Ideas, Personalities, and Politics, 1689–1775* (New York, 1962).

J. S. CUMMINS, 'Palafox, China and the Chinese Rites Controversy', *Revista de Historia de America*, No. 52 (December, 1961) 395–427.

——, (ed.), *The Travels and Controversies of Friar Domingo de Navarrete, 1618–1686* (New York, 1962), 2 vols.

H. de la COSTA, *The Jesuits in the Philippines, 1581–1768* (Cambridge, Mass., 1961).

P. M. D'ELIA, 'La reprise des missions catholiques en Chine à la fin des Mings (1579–1644)', *Journal of World History*, V (1960), 679–99.

G. H. DUNNE, *Generation of Giants: The Story of the Jesuits in China in the Last Decades of the Ming Dynasty* (South Bend, Ind., 1962).

ARIMICHI EBISAIVA, 'The Jesuits and Their Cultural Activities in the Far East', *Journal of World History*, V (1959), 344–74.

CHARLES GIBSON, *The Aztecs under Spanish Rule: A History of the Indians of the Valley of Mexico, 1519–1810* (Stanford, Calif., 1964).

LOUIS JADIN, 'L'Afrique et Rome depuis l'époque des découvertes jusqu'au XVIIe siècles', XIIe Congrès International des Sciences Historiques, *Rapports* (Vienna, 1965), II, 33–69.

MARIANO PICÓN-SALAS, *A Cultural History of Spanish America: From Conquest to Independence*, tr. by J. A. Leonard (Berkeley, 1962).

F. B. TOLLES, 'Nonviolent Contact: The Quakers and the Indians', *Proceedings of the American Philosophical Society*, CVII (1963), 93–106.

A. DE ZORITA, *Life and Labor in Ancient Mexico: The Brief and Summary Relation of the Lords of New Spain*, tr. by Benjamin Keen (New Brunswick, N.J., 1963).

The Orthodox Christians

P. SHEPPARD, *The Greek East and the Latin West: A Study in the Christian Tradition* (New York, 1959).

L. S. STAVRIANOS, *The Balkans since 1453* (New York, 1958).

T. STOIANOVICH, 'The Conquering Balkan Orthodox Merchant', *Journal of Economic History* (June, 1960), 234–313.

Islam

P. N. CHOPRA, 'Rencontre de l'Inde et de l'Islam', *Journal of World History*, VI (1960), 370–79.

R. H. DAVISON, *The Near and Middle East: An Introduction to History and Bibliography* (Washington, 1959).

M. G. S. HODGSON, 'The Unity of Later Islamic History', *Journal of World History*, IV (1960), 879–914.

BERNARD LEWIS, *Istanbul and the Civilization of the Ottoman Empire* (Norman, Okla., 1963).

Hinduism and Buddhism

W. T. de BARY et al. (eds.), *Sources of Indian Tradition* ('Introduction to Oriental Civilizations') (New York, 1960).

MARCELLE LALON, *Les religions du Tibet* (Paris, 1957).

KHUSHWANT SINGH, *A History of the Sikhs*, Vol. I: *1469–1839* (Princeton, Mass., 1966).

Confucianism, Taoism, Shintoism

R. A. BELLAH, *Tokugawa Religion: The Values of Pre-Industrial Japan* (Glencoe, Ill., 1957).

W. T. de BARY et al. (eds.), *Sources of Japanese Tradition* ('Introduction to Oriental Civilizations') (New York, 1960).

Judaism

I. S. EMMANUEL, 'Seventeenth Century Brazilian Jewry: a Critical Review', *American Jewish Archives*, XIV (1962), 32–68.

T. W. PERRY, *Public Opinion, Propaganda, and Politics in Eighteenth-Century England: A Study of the Jew Bill of 1753* (Cambridge, Mass., 1962).

SELMA STERN, *Der preussische Staat und die Juden*. Part I: *Die Zeit des grossen Kurfürsten und Friedrichs I* (Tübingen, 1962), 2 vols.

ARNOLD WIZNITZER, *Jews in Colonial Brazil* (New York, 1960).

CHAPTER VI

THEOLOGY AND METAPHYSICS (1300–1500)

Hindu Developments

S. M. S. CHARI, *Advaita and Viśiṣṭádvaita* (New York, 1961).

K. S. MURTY, *Revelation and Reason in Advaita Vedanta* (New York, 1959).

Islamic Developments

K. M. MUNSHI, R. C. MAJUMDAR et al. (eds.), *The Delhi Sultanate* ('The History and Culture of the Indian People') (Bombay, 1960).

W. M. WATT, *Islamic Philosophy and Theology* (Edinburgh, 1962).

Judaic Developments

JACOB KATZ, *Exclusiveness and Tolerance; Studies in Jewish-Gentile Relations in Medieval and Modern Times* (New York, 1961).

Developments in the West

EMILE BREHIER, *The History of Philosophy: The Middle Ages and the Renaissance*, tr. by Wade Baskin (Chicago, 1965).

MGR. CHRISTIANI, 'La tolérance et l'intolérance de l'église en matière doctrinale, depuis les premiers siècles jusqu'à nos jours', *Journal of World History*, V (1959), 71–93.

E. DELARUELLE, 'La spiritualité aux XIVe et XVe siècles', *Journal of World History*, V (1959), 59–70.

ALOIS GERLO and EMILE LAUF, *Bibliographie de l'humanisme belge, précédée d'une bibliographie générale concernant l'humanisme européen* (Brussels, 1965).

DENYS HAY, *The Italian Renaissance in Its Historical Background* (Cambridge, 1961).

F. G. HEYMANN, *John Rokycana—Church Reformer between Hus and Luther*, reprinted from *Church History*, XXVIII (1959).

DAVID KNOWLES, *The English Mystical Tradition* (New York, 1961).

ERICH MEUTHEN, *Die letzte Jahre des Nikolaus von Kues; biographische Untersuchungen nach neuen Quellen* (Cologne and Opladen, 1958).

ALBERT RIVAUD, *Histoire de la philosophie* (Paris, 1950–63), 4 volumes to date [to 1830].

RAYMOND DE ROOVER, 'The Concept of the Just Price: Theory and Economic Policy', *Journal of Economic History*, XVIII (1958), 418–34.

CHAPTER VII

THEOLOGY AND METAPHYSICS (1500–1775)

Metaphysical Speculation within Hinduism and Jainism

K. M. MUNSHI, R. C. MAJUMDAR, et al. (eds.), *The Struggle for Empire* ('The History and Culture of the Indian People' (Bombay, 1957).

Theological and Epistemological Speculation in the West

F. H. ANDERSON, *Francis Bacon: His Career and His Thought* (Los Angeles, 1962).

F. L. BAUMER, *Religion and the Rise of Scepticism* (New York, 1960).

ROSALIE L. COLIE, 'Spinoza in England, 1665–1730', *Proceedings of the American Philosophical Society*, CVII (1963), 183–219.

——, *The Church and the Age of Reason (1648–1789)* (London, 1960).

G. R. CRAGG, *Reason and Authority in the Eighteenth Century* (New York, 1964).

M. J. HAVRAN, *The Catholics in Caroline England* (Stanford, Calif., 1962).

R. HOOYKAAS, *Humanisme, Science et Réforme: Pierre de la Ramée (1515–1572)* (Leiden, 1958).

P. O. KRISTELLER, *Eight Philosophers of the Italian Renaissance* (Stanford, Calif., 1964).

ELIZABETH LABROUSSE, *Pierre Bayle* (The Hague, 1963–64), 2 vols.

F. E. MANUEL, *The Eighteenth Century Confronts the Gods* (Cambridge, 1959).

S. I. MINTZ, *The Hunting of Leviathan, Seventeenth-Century Reactions to the Materialism and Moral Philosophy of Thomas Hobbes* (New York, 1962).

C. B. O'KEEFE, 'Conservative Opinion on the Spread of Deism in France, 1730–1750', *Journal of Modern History*, XXXIII (1961), 398–406.

W. J. ONG, *Ramus, Method, and the Decay of Dialogue* (Cambridge, Mass., 1958).

WALTER REX, *Essays on Pierre Bayle and Religious Controversy* (The Hague, 1965).

L. C. ROSENFELD, 'Peripatetic Adversaries of Cartesianism in 17th Century France', *The Review of Religion* (November, 1957), 14–40.

Metaphysical Speculation in China

C. O. HUCKER, 'The Tung-lin Movement of the Late Ming Period', in *Chinese Thought and Institutions*, ed. J. K. Fairbank (Chicago, 1957), 132–62.

CHAPTER VIII

SOCIAL AND POLITICAL THOUGHT (*c.* 1300–*c.* 1500)

Political Theory and Practice

PETER BROCK, *The Political and Social Doctrines of the Unity of Czech Brethren in the Fifteenth and Early Sixteenth Centuries* (The Hague, 1957).

C. B. DAY, *The Philosophers of China* (New York, 1962).

FREDERICK HERTZ, *The Development of the German Public Mind. A Social History of German Political Sentiments, Aspirations and Ideas. The Middle Ages. The Reformation* (New York, 1957).

DAVID KNOWLES, *The Evolution of Medieval Thought* (Baltimore, 1962).

GEORGES de LAGARDE, *La naissance de l'esprit laïque au déclin du Moyen-âge*, Vol. IV: *Guillaume d'Ockham: Défense de l'Empire* (Louvain, 1962).

FRANCIS OAKLEY, *The Political Thought of Pierre d'Ailly* (New Haven, Conn., 1964).

NN*

FRANCIS OAKLEY, 'Almain and Major: Conciliar Theory on the Eve of the Reformation', *American Historical Review*, LXX (1965), 673–90.

J. H. RANDALL, JR., *The Career of Philosophy: From the Middle Ages to the Enlightenment* (New York, 1962).

E. F. RICE, JR., *The Renaissance Idea of Wisdom* (Cambridge, Mass., 1958).

P. E. SIGMUND, *Nicholas of Cusa and Medieval Political Thought* (Cambridge, Mass., 1963).

LEO STRAUSS and JOSEPH CROPSEY (eds.), *History of Political Philosophy* (New York, 1963).

JEAN TOUCHARD, *Histoire des idées politiques* (Paris, 1959), 2 vols.

WALTER ULLMANN, *Principles of Government and Politics in the Middle Ages* (London, 1962).

WANG YANG-MING, *Instructions for Practical Living, and Other Neo-Confucian Writings*, tr. with notes by Wing-tsit Chan (New York, 1963).

Legal Thought and Practice

CRANE BRINTON, *A History of Western Morals* (New York, 1959).

CH'U T'UNG-TSU, *Law and Society in Traditional China* (Paris, 1961).

C. M. GRAY, *Copyhold, Equity, and the Common Law* (Cambridge, Mass., 1963).

JAN KORÁN and VACLAV VAŇEČEK, 'Czech Mining and Mining Laws', *Journal of World History*, VII (1962), 27–45.

F. J. PEGUES, *The Lawyers of the Last Capetians* (Princeton, N.J., 1962).

Economic Thought and Practice

RAYMOND de ROOVER, *The Rise and Decline of the Medici Bank, (1397–1494)* (Cambridge, Mass., 1963).

DOMENICO GIOFFRE, *Gênes et les foires de change: de Lyon à Besançon* (Paris, 1960).

HENRI LAPEYRE, 'Banque et crédit en Italie du XVIe au XVIIIe siècle', *Revue d'Histoire Moderne et Contemporaine*, VIII (1961), 211–26.

R. S. LOPEZ and H. A. MISKIMIN, 'The Economic Depression of the Renaissance', *The Economic History Review*, 2 series, XIV (1962), 408–426.

PHILIPPE WOLFF and FREDERIC MAURO, *L'âge de l'artisanat (Ve—XVIIIe siècles)* (Vol. II of 'Histoire générale du travail', ed. L. H. Parias) (Paris, 1960).

M. M. POSTAN, E. E. RICH, and EDWARD MILLER (eds.), *The Cambridge Economic History of Europe*, Vol. III: *Economic Organization and Policies in the Middle Ages* (Cambridge, 1963).

Historical Thought

W. G. BEASLEY, E. G. PULLEYBLANK *et al.*, *Historians of China and Japan* (London, 1961).

D. G. E. HALL *et al.*, *Historians of South-East Asia* (London, 1961).

F. G. HEYMANN, 'City Rebellions in 15th Century Bohemia and Their Ideological and Sociological Background', *Slavonic and East European Review*, XL (1962), 324–40.

IBN-KHALDÛN, *The Mugaddimah: An Introduction to History*, tr. by Franz Rosenthal (New York, 1958), 3 vols.

MARTIN KLEIN, 'Bibliography of Writings on Historiography and the Philosophy of History' in Louis Gottschalk (ed.), *Generalization in the Writing of History* (Chicago, 1963), pp. 213–47.

P. O. KRISTELLER, *Renaissance Thought: The Classic, Scholastic, and Humanistic Strains* (New York, 1961).

BERNARD LEWIS and P. M. HOLT (eds.), *Historians of the Middle East* (New York, 1962).

C. H. PHILIPS et al., *Historians of India, Pakistan and Ceylon* (London, 1961).

A. V. RIASANOVSKY, 'A Fifteenth Century Russian Traveller in India: Comments in Connection with a New Edition of Afnasii Nikitin's Journal', *Journal of the American Oriental Society*, LXXXI (1961), 126–30.

A. F. WRIGHT, 'On the Uses of Generalization in the Study of Chinese History' and DERK BODDE, 'Comments on the Paper of Arthur F. Wright', in Louis Gottschalk, ed., *Generalization in the Writing of History* (Chicago, 1963), pp. 36–65.

CHAPTER IX
SOCIAL AND POLITICAL THOUGHT (1500–1775)

Political Theory

HANS BARON, 'Machiavelli: The Republican Citizen and the Author of *The Prince*', *English Historical Review*, LXXVII (1961), 217–53.

I. U. BOUDOVNITZ, 'La litterature politique et sociale russe au XVIe siècle', *Journal of World History*, special no. 'Contributions to Russian History' (1958), 145–80.

H. N. BRAILSFORD, *The Levellers and the English Revolution*, ed. and prepared for publication by Christopher Hill (Stanford, Calif., 1961).

J. BRONOWSKI and BRUCE MAZLISH, *The Western Intellectual Tradition: from Leonardo to Hegel* (New York, 1960).

FEDERICO CHABOD, *Machiavelli and the Renaissance*, tr. by David Moore, with an introduction by H. P. d'Entrèves (London, 1958).

E. W. COCHRANE, 'Machiavelli: 1940–60', *Journal of Modern History*, XXXII (1961), 113–36.

BERNICE HAMILTON, *Political Thought in Sixteenth-Century Spain: A Study of the Political Ideas of Vitoria, Soto, Suàrez and Molina* (New York, 1963).

HAROLD HUME, *The Life of Sir John Eliot* (New York, 1957).

BERNHARD KNOLLENBERG, *Origins of the American Revolution: 1759–66* (New York, 1960).

LEONARD KRIEGER, *The Politics of Discretion: Pufendorf and the Acceptance of Natural Law* (Chicago, 1965).

PETER LASLETT, *John Locke: Two Treatises of Government, a Critical Edition with an Introduction and Apparatus Criticus* (Cambridge, Eng., 1959).

LIANG CH'I-CH'AO, *Intellectual Trends in the Ch'ing Period (Ch'ing-tai hsueh-shu kai-lun)*, tr. by Immanuel C. Y. Hsü (Cambridge, Mass., 1959).

J. A. MARAVALL CASESNOVES, 'The Origins of the Modern State', *Journal of World History*, VI (1961, Special Spanish number), 789–808.

JACQUES PROUST, 'La contribution de Diderot à l'Encyclopédie et les théories du droit naturel', *Annales historiques de la Révolution française*, XXXV (1963), 257–86.

ERNST REIBSTEIN, *Völkerrecht: eine Geschichte seiner Ideen in Lehre und Praxis* (Freiburg, 1958–63), (2 vols.).

ROBERTO RIDOLFI, *The Life of Niccolo Machiavelli*, tr. by Cecil Grayson (Chicago, 1963).

CAROLINE ROBBINS, *The Eighteenth-century Commonwealthman: Studies in the Transmission, Development and Circumstance of English Liberal Thought from the Restoration of Charles II until the War with the Thirteen Colonies* (Cambridge, Mass., 1959).

W. VOISÉ, 'A propos d'Andrzej Frycz Modrzewski: les critères de l'appréciation du progrès dans l'histoire des sciences sociales', *Journal of World History*, V (1959), 251–6.

Legal Thought and Practice

ERNST EKMAN, 'The Danish Royal Law of 1660', *Journal of Modern History*, XXIX (1957), 102–9.

T. D. EUSDEN, *Puritans, Lawyers, and Politics in Early Seventeenth Century England* (New Haven, Conn., 1958).

RENE FÉDON, *Les hommes de loi lyonnais à la fin du Moyen-âge: Etude sur les origines de la classe de robe* (Paris, 1964).

J. H. FRANKLIN, *Jean Bodin and the Sixteenth-Century Revolution in the Methodology of Law and History* (New York, 1963).

ROBERT ROBSON, *The Attorney in Eighteenth-Century England* (New York, 1959).

W. J. STANKIEWICZ, *Politics and Religion in Seventeenth-Century France: A Study of Political Ideas from the Monarchomachs to Boyle, as reflected in the Toleration Controversy* (Berkeley, Calif., 1960).

HERMANN WEILL, *Frederick the Great and Samuel von Cocceji: A study in the Reform of the Prussian Judicial Administration, 1740–55* (Madison, Wisc., 1961).

R. J. ZWI WERBLOWSKY, *Joseph Karo: Lawyer and Mystic* (New York, 1962).

Economic Thought and Practice

ROBERT ASHTON, *The Crown and the Money Market, 1603–40* (New York, 1961).

S. A. BURRELL, 'Calvinism, Capitalism, and the Middle Classes: Some Afterthoughts on an Old Problem', *Journal of Modern History*, XXXII (1960), 129–41.

RAYMOND DE ROOVER, 'Joseph A. Schumpeter and Scholastic Economics', *Kyklos* (fasc. 2, 1957), 115–46.

V. K. JACRENSKY, 'The Rise of Economic Historiography', *Journal of World History*, VIII (1964), 576–84.

HERMANN KELLENBENZ, 'Probleme der Merkantilismusforschung', XIIe Congrès International des Sciences Historiques, *Rapports* (Vienna, 1965), IV, 171–90.

W. K. JORDAN, *Philanthropy in England, 1480–1660: A Study of the Changing Pattern of English Social Aspirations* (New York, 1959).

LIONEL ROTHKRUG, 'Critique de la politique commerciale et projets de réforme de la fiscalité au temps de Colbert', *Revue d'histoire moderne et contemporaine*, VIII (1961), 81–102.

C. D. SHELDON, *The Rise of the Merchant Class in Tokugawa Japan, 1600–1868* (Locust Valley, N.Y., 1958).

J. WELLMAN, 'Merkantilistische Vorstellungen im 17. Jahrhundert und Ungara' in E. Molnar *et al.* (eds.) *Nouvelles études historiques* (Budapest, 1965), 315–54.

GEORGES WEULERSSE, *La Physiocratie à la fin du règne de Louis XV (1770–1774)* (Paris, 1959).

Historical Thought

J. H. BRUMFITT, *Voltaire Historian* (London, 1958).

COMITÉ JAPONAIS DES SCIENCES HISTORIQUE;, *Le Japon au XIe congrès international des sciences historiques à Stockholm: l'état actuel et les tendances des études historiques au Japon* (Tokyo, 1960).

FELIX GILBERT, *Machiavelli and Guicciardini: Politics and History in Sixteenth-Century Florence* (Princeton, Mass., 1965).

F. E. MANUEL, *Isaac Newton, Historian* (Cambridge, Mass., 1963).

ERIK MOLNAR *et al.*, 'Biographie d'œuvres choisies de la science historique hongroise 1959–63', *Nouvelles études historiques*, publiée à l'occasion du XIIe Congrès International des Sciences Historiques par la Commission Nationale des Historiens Hongrois (Budapest, 1965), II, 463–629.

FAUSTO NICOLINI, 'Jean-Baptiste Vico dans l'histoire de la pensée', *Journal of World History*, VII (1963), 299–319.

D. S. NIVISON, *The Life and Thought of Chang Hsueh-ch'eng (1938–1801)* (Stanford, Calif., 1965).

ROBERTO RIDOLFI, *Vita de Francesco Guicciardini* (Rome, 1960).

L. SALVATORELLI, 'L'historiographie italienne au XVIIIe siècle', *Journal of World History*, VII (1963), 321–40.

HENRY WYVERBERG, *Historical Pessimism in the French Enlightenment* (Cambridge, Mass., 1959).

MIRIAM YARDENI, 'La conception de l'histoire dans l'oeuvre de la Popelinière', *Revue d'histoire moderne et contemporaine*, XI (1964), 109–26.

The Enlightenment and Social Thought

BERNARD BAILYN, 'Political Experience and Enlightenment Ideas in Eighteenth-Century America', *American Historical Review*, LXVII (1962), 339–51.

PAOLO CASINI, *Diderot 'philosophe'* (Bari, 1962).

ALFRED COBBAN, *In Search of Humanity, The Role of Enlightenment in Modern History* (London, 1960).

E. W. COCHRANE, *Tradition and Enlightenment in the Tuscan Academies, 1690–1800*, (Chicago, 1961).

——, 'French Literature and the Italian Tradition in Eighteenth-Century Tuscany', *Journal of the History of Ideas,* XXIII (1962), 61–76.

FREDERICK COPLESTON, *History of Philosophy*, Vols. IV to VI [from Descartes to Kant] (Westminster, Md., 1959–60).

L. G. CROCKER, *An Age of Crisis: Man and World in Eighteenth Century French Thought* (Baltimore, 1959).

——, *Nature and Culture, Ethical Thought in the French Enlightenment* (Baltimore, 1963).

——, 'Voltaire's Struggle for Humanism' in *Studies on Voltaire and the Eighteenth Century*, IV (1957), 137–69.

——, 'Recent Interpretations of the French Enlightenment', *Journal of World History*, VIII (1964), 426–56.

DURAND ECHEVARRIA, *Mirage in the West: a History of the French Image of American Society to 1815* (Princeton, N.J., 1957).

JEAN EHRARD, *L'idée de nature en France dans la première moitié du XVIIIe siècle* (Paris, 1963).

PETER GAY, *Voltaire's Politics: The Poet as Realist* (Princeton, N.J., 1959).

L. H. GIPSON, *The British Empire before the American Revolution*, Vol. X: *The Triumphant Empire: Thunder-Clouds Gather in the West, 1763–66* (New York, 1961).

RONALD GRIMSLEY, *Jean d'Alembert (1717–83)* (Oxford, 1963).

PIERRE GROSCLAUDE, *Malesherbes témoin et interprète de son temps* (Paris, 1961).

FRITZ HARTUNG, *Enlightenment Despotism* (London, 1957).

RICHARD HERR, *The Eighteenth-Century Revolution in Spain* (Princeton, N.J., 1958).

RICHARD HERR and HAROLD PARKER (eds.), *Ideas in History* (Durham, 1965).

A. O. LOVEJOY, *Reflections on Human Nature* (Baltimore, 1961).

ROBERT MAUZI, *L'idée du bonheur dans la littérature et la pensée française au XVIIIe siècle* (Paris, 1962).

S. T. MCCLOY, *The Humanitarian Movement in Eighteenth-Century France* (Lexington, Kentucky, 1957).

R. PORTAL et al., *La Pologne de l'époque des Lumières au duché de Varsovie*, special no. of *Annales historiques de la Révolution française*, XXXVI, No. 177 (July-Sept. 1964), 257–416.

JACQUES PROUST, *Diderot et l'Encyclopédie* (Paris, 1962).

ROBERT SHACKLETON, *Montesquieu: A Critical Biography* (New York, 1961).

LOUIS TREMARD, 'Pour une histoire sociale de l'idée de bonheur au XVIIIe siècle', *Annales historiques de la Révolution française*, XXXV (1963), 309–30 and 428–52.

I. O. WADE, *The Search for a New Voltaire, Studies in Voltaire Based upon Material Deposited at the American Philosophical Society* ('Transactions of the American Philosophical Society', Vol. XLVIII, Pt. 4; Philadelphia, 1958).

A. M. WILSON, *Diderot: The Testing Years* (New York, 1957).

CHAPTER X

LITERARY COMMUNICATION AND BELLES-LETTRES (1300–1500)

Manuscripts, Books, and Printing

PAUL CHAUVET, *Les ouvriers du livre en France, des origines à la Révolution de 1789* (Paris, 1959).

D. J. GEANAKÖPLOS, *Greek Scholars in Venice: Studies in the Dissemination of Greek Learning from Byzantium to Western Europe* (Cambridge, Mass., 1962).

K. M. SETTON, 'From Medieval to Modern Library', *Proceedings of the American Philosophical Society*, CIV (1960), 371–90.

The Development of Vernacular Languages

R. E. CHANDLER and KESSEL SCHWARTZ, *A New History of Spanish Literature* (Baton Rouge, Louisiana, 1962).

CH'EN SHOU-YI, *Chinese Literature: A Historical Introduction* (New York, 1961).

GEORGE SAMPSON, *The Concise Cambridge History of English Literature* (2nd ed. New York, 1962).

Poetry, Drama, and Story in Europe

NICOLA ABBAGNANO, 'Italian Renaissance Humanism', *Journal of World History*, VII (1963), 267–83.

CARLOS CLAVERÍA, 'Les mythes et les thèmes espagnols dans la littérature universelle', *Journal of World History*, VI (1961; special Spanish no.), 969–89.

W. K. FERGUSON, 'The Interpretation of Italian Humanism: the Contribution of Hans Baron' and HANS BARON, 'Moot Problems of Renaissance Interpretations: An Answer to Wallace K. Ferguson', *Journal of the History of Ideas*, XIX (1958), 14–34.

——, *Europe in Transition* (Boston, 1962).

RAYMOND QUENEAU (ed.), *Histoire des littératures* (3 vols.) (Paris, 1955–58).

MARTIN DE RIQUER MORERA, 'La culture au bas Moyen-âge', *Journal of World History*, VI (1961; special Spanish no.), 771–86.

I. O. WADE, *Voltaire and 'Candide'* (Princeton, N.J., 1959).

E. H. WILKINS, *Life of Petrarch* (Chicago, 1961).

Belles-Lettres in the Far East

FENG YÜAN-CHUN, *A Short History of Classical Chinese Literature*, tr. by Yang Hsien-yi and Gladys Yang (Peking, 1958).

HOWARD HIBBETT, *The Floating World of Japanese Fiction* (New York, 1959).

LU HSUN, *A Brief History of Chinese Fiction*, tr. by Yang Hsien-yi and Gladys Yang (Peking, 1959).

P. G. O'NEILL, *Early Nō Drama, Its Background, Character and Development, 1300–1450* (London, 1959).

SAIKAKU'S '*The Japanese Family Storehouse*', tr. with an Introduction and Notes by G. W. Sargent (New York, 1959).

A. C. SCOTT, *The Classical Theatre of China* (London, 1957).

WU SHIH-CH'ANG, *On the Red Chamber Dream. A Critical Study of Two Annotated Manuscripts of the XVIIIth Century* (Oxford, 1961).

CHAPTER XI
LITERARY COMMUNICATION AND BELLES-LETTRES (1500–1775)

The Technical Apparatus of Literature

JOSEPH FRANK, *The Beginnings of the English Newspapers, 1620–60* (Cambridge, Mass., 1961).

FRANÇOIS FURET, 'La "Librairie" du royaume de France au XVIIIe siècle', XIIe Congrès International des Sciences Historiques, *Rapports* (Vienna, 1965) I, 423–50.

STANLEY MORISON and KENNETH DAY, *The Typographic Book, 1450–1935* (Chicago, 1964).

D. T. POTTINGER, *The French Book Trade in the Ancien Régime, 1500–1791* (Cambridge, Mass., 1958).

PH. SCHMIDT, *Die Illustration der Lutherbibel, 1522–1700* (Basel, 1963).

A. A. SIDOROV, 'Les anciens livres imprimés slaves en tant que documents de l'interaction culturelle', *Journal of World History*, special no. 'Contributions to Russian History' (1958), 126–54.

Poetry, Drama, and Fiction in Europe

DÁMASO ALONSO, 'The Spanish Contribution to the Modern European Novel', *Journal of World History*, VI (1961, special Spanish no.), 878–97.

GEOFFROY ATKINSON, *Le sentiment de la nature et le retour à la vie simple (1690–1740)* (Geneva, 1960).

DOUGLAS BUSH, *English Literature in the Earlier Seventeenth Century, 1600–60,* (2nd ed., 'Oxford History of English Literature', New York, 1962).

R. W. GIBSON et al. (eds.), *St. Thomas More: a Preliminary Bibliography of His Works and of Moreana to the Year 1750* [with a bibliography of Utopiana] (New Haven, Conn., 1961).

A. J. GUIBERT, *Bibliographie des œuvres de Molière publiées au XVIIe siècle* (2 vols.).

G. J. KOLB and C. A. ZIMANSKY, *English Literature, 1660–1800*, Vols. III and IV (Princeton, N.J., 1962). [Annotated bibliography.]

JULIAN MARÍAS, 'Contemporary Spain in World Culture', *Journal of World History*, VI (1961, special Spanish no.), 1006–22.

CHRISTOPHER MARLOWE, *Doctor Faustus*, ed. by J. D. Jump (Cambridge, Mass., 1962).

ANGEL VALBUENA PRAT, 'Le théâtre espagnol et ses rapports avec le théâtre européen', *Journal of World History*, VI (1961, special Spanish no.), 898–915.

G. W. STONE *et al.* (eds.), *The London Stage, 1660–1800* (8 vols. to date [1660–1776]; Carbondale, S. Ill., 1960–63).

FRANCO VENTURI (ed.), *Illuministi Italiani*, Vol. V: *Reformatori Napoletani* (Milan and Naples, 1962).

C. V. WEDGWOOD, *Poetry and Politics under the Stuarts* (New York, 1960).

BERNARD WEINBERG, *The Art of Jean Racine* (Chicago, 1963).

D. M. WOLFE *et al.* (eds.), *Complete Prose Works of John Milton* (4 vols. to date [to 1655] (New Haven, Conn., 1953–65).

Belles-Lettres around and in China

TS'AO HSUEH-CH'IN, *Dream of the Red Chamber*, tr. by Chi-chen Wang (New York, 1958).

ARTHUR WALEY, *Yüan Mei* (London, 1957).

Imaginative Literature in Japan

[CHIKAMATSU], *Major Plays of Chikamatsu*, by Donald Keene (New York, 1961).

KENNETH YASUDA, *The Japanese Haiku: Its Essential Nature, History, and Possibilities in English with Selected Samples* (Rutland, Vt., 1957).

CHAPTER XII

THE VISUAL ARTS AND MUSIC (1300–1775)

Note: The standard bibliography for the history of art is Mary W. Chamberlin, *Guide to Art Reference Books* (Chicago, 1959). Titles listed in that work are not given below.

Painting in Europe

SYLVIE BÉGUIN, *L'école de Fontainebleau; le maniérisme à la cour de France* (Paris, 1960).

BERNARD BERENSON, *Italian Pictures of the Renaissance. Florentine School* (London, 1963), (2 vols.).

ANDRÉ CHASTEL, 'La légende médicienne', *Revue d'histoire moderne et contemporaine*, VI (1959), 161–80.

——, *Italian Art*, trans. by Peter and Linda Murray (London, 1963).

COUNCIL OF EUROPE (sponsor), *Le triomphe du maniérisme européen de Michel-Ange au Gréco*. Catalogue of an exhibition held at Rijksmuseum, Amsterdam, July 1–October 16, 1965.

E. T. DEWALD, *Italian Painting, 1200–1600* (New York, [1961]).

ALBRECHT DOHMANN, 'Les événements contemporains dans la peinture hollandaise du XVIIe siècle', *Revue d'histoire moderne et contemporaine*, V (1958), 265–82.

MICHEL FLORISOONE, *Le dix-huitième siècle: la peinture française* (Paris, 1948).

S. J. FREEDBERG, *Painting of the High Renaissance in Rome and Florence* (Cambridge, Mass., 1961), (2 vols.).

——, *Andrea del Sarto*, (Cambridge, Mass., 1963), (2 vols.).

JAN GERRIT VAN GELDER, *Dutch Drawings and Prints* (London, 1959).

ENRIQUE LAFUENTE FERRARI, 'De Velasquez à Picasso, suggestions pour une compréhension de l'art espagnol', *Journal of World History*, VI (1961, special Spanish no.), 990–1005.

JAROMIR NEUMANN, 'L'art du baroque dans les pays tchèques', *Journal of World History*, IV (1958), 688–708.

MASSIMO PALLOTTINO *et al.* (eds.), *Encyclopedia of World Art* (New York, 1958), (10 vols. published to 1965).

ERWIN PANOFSKY, *Renaissance and Renaissances in Western Art* (Stockholm, 1960), (2 vols.).

NICOLAS POWELL, *From Baroque to Roccoo* (New York, 1959).

E. H. RAMADEN (tr. and ed.), *The Letters of Michelangelo* (Stanford, 1963), (2 vols.)

EARL ROSENTHAL, 'Changing Interpretations of the Renaissance in the History of Art', in Tinsley Nelton (ed.), *The Renaissance: A Reconsideration of the Theories and Interpretations of the Age* (Madison, Wisc., 1961), pp. 53–75.

SEYMOUR SLIVE, 'Realism and Symbolism in Seventeenth-Century Dutch Painting', *Daedalus, the Journal of the A.A.A.S.*, XCI (1962), 469–500.

GERALD VAN DER KEMP *et al.* (eds.), *Treasures of Versailles: A Loan Exhibition from the French Government Organized by the Art Institute of Chicago* (Chicago, 1962).

ELLIS K. WATERHOUSE, *Baroque Painting in Rome, the Seventeenth Century* (London, 1937).

JOHN WHITE, *The Birth and Rebirth of Pictorial Space* (London, 1957).

Sculpture in Europe

JOHN POPE-HENNESSY, *An Introduction to Italian Sculpture* (New York, 1955), (3 vols.).

WOLFGANG SCHOENE, *Über das Licht in der Malerei* (Berlin, 1934).

Architecture in Europe

PAUL FRANKL, *The Gothic, Literary Sources and Interpretations through Eight Centuries* (Princeton, N.J., 1960).

WERNER GROSS, *Die abendländische Architektur um 1300* (Stuttgart, [1948]).

WERNER HAGER, *Die Bauten des deutschen Barocks, 1690–1770* (Jena, [1942]).

HANS JANTZEN, *Die Gotik des Abendlandes* (Cologne, 1962).

GEORGE KUBLER and MARTIN SORIA, *Art and Architecture in Spain and Portugal and Their American Dominions 1500–1800* (Baltimore, 1959).

LEWIS MUMFORD, *The City in History: Its Origins, Its Transformations, and Its Prospects* (New York, 1961).

NIKOLAUS PEVSNER, *An Outline of European Architecture* (6th ed.; Baltimore, 1960).

EARL E. ROSENTHAL, *The Cathedral of Granada* (Princeton, N.J., 1961).

VICTOR-L. TAPIÉ, *Baroque et classicisme* (Paris, 1957).

RUDOLPH WITTKOWER, *Architectural Principles in the Age of Humanism* (2nd ed.; London, 1952).

The Decorative Arts in Europe

HUGH HONOUR, *Chinoiserie, the Vision of Cathay* (London, 1962).

E. POCHE, 'Le verre de Bohème', *Journal of World History*, V (1959), 434–62.

Theories of Art and the Role of the Artist

FRANCIS HASKELL, *Patrons and Painters* (New York, 1963).

RENSSELAER LEE, 'Ut Pictura Poesis: The Humanist Theory of Painting', *Art Bulletin*, XXII (1940), 197–263.

DENIS MAHON, *Studies in Seicento Art and Theory* (London, 1947).

NIKOLAUS PEVSNER, *Academies of Art Past and Present* (Cambridge, Eng. 1940).

GEORGES WILDENSTEIN, *Le goût pour la peinture dans le cercle de la bourgeoisie parisienne autour de 1700* (Paris, 1958).

——, *Le goût pour la peinture dans la bourgeoise parisienne au début du règne de Louis XIII* (Paris, 1959).

The Dance and Music in Europe

WILLI APEL, *Harvard Dictionary of Music* (Cambridge, Mass., 1958).

HOWARD MAYER BROWN, *Music in the French Secular Theatre, 1400–1550* (Cambridge, Mass., 1963).

A. GEOFFROY-DECHAUME, *Les 'secrets' de la musique ancienne. Recherches sur l'interpretation XVIe, XVIIe, XVIIIe siècles* (Paris, 1964).

DONALD GROUT, *A History of Western Music* (New York, 1960).

JOHN HAWKINS, *A General History of the Science and Practice of Music* (New York, 1963), (2 vols.).

ANSELM HUGHES and GERALD ABRAHAM (eds.), *Ars Nova and the Renaissance, c. 1300–1540* (Vol. III of the *New Oxford Dictionary of Music*, edited by J. A. Westing *et al*. (New York, 1960).

ROGER LONSDALE, *Dr. Charles Burney. A Literary Biography* (Oxford, 1965).

E. E. LOWINSKY, *Tonality and Atonality in Sixteenth-Century Music* (Berkeley, California, 1962).

ROLAND MANUEL (ed.), Histoire de la musique ('Encyclopédie de la Pleiade', Paris 1960–3), (2 vols.).

GUSTAVE REESE, *Music in the Renaissance* (rev. ed., New York, 1959).

The Arts in Islam

W. G. ARCHER, *Indian Miniatures* (Greenwich, Conn., 1960).

R. ETTINGHAUSEN, *Persian Miniatures in the Bernard Berenson Collection* (London, 1962).

Hindu and Buddhist Art

THEODORE BOWIE (ed.), *The Arts of Thailand: A Handbook of Architecture, Sculpture and Painting of Thailand* (Bloomington, Ind., 1961).

HERMAN GOETZ, *India—Five Thousand Years of Indian Art* (New York, 1959).

O. GOSWAMI, *The Story of Indian Music: Its Growth and Synthesis* (Bombay, 1957).

B. P. GROSLIER, *The Art of Indochina including Thailand, Vietnam, Laos and Cambodia* (New York, 1962)

RADHAKAMAL MUKERJEE, *The Culture and Art of India* (New York, 1959).

DIETRICH SECKEL, *Buddhist Kunst Ostasiens* (Stuttgart, 1957).

F. A. WAGNER, *Indonesia: The Art of an Island Group* (New York, 1959).

The Arts in China, Vietnam, and Korea

ANDREW BOYD, *Chinese Architecture and Town Planning, 1500 B.C.–A.D. 1911* (Chicago, 1962).

JAMES CAHILL, *Chinese Painting* (Cleveland, 1960).

R. H. VAN GULICK, *Chinese Pictorial Art as Viewed by the Connoisseur* (Rome, 1958).

G. R. LOEHR, 'The Sinicization of Missionary Artists and Their Work at the Manchu Court during the Eighteenth Century', *Journal of World History*, VII (1963), 795–815.

EVELYN MCCUNE, *The Arts of Korea, an Illustrated History* (Rutland, Vt., 1961).

OSVALD SIRÉN, *Chinese Painting: Leading Masters and Principles*, Part II: *The Later Centuries* (New York, 1960), (4 vols.).

CHIANG YEE, *Chinese Calligraphy* (Cambridge, Mass., 1958), 2nd ed.

The Arts in Japan

LAURENCE BINYON and J. J. O'BRIEN SEXTON, *Japanese Colour Prints*, ed. by Basil Gray (Rev. ed.; London, 1960).

W. P. MALM, *Japanese Music and Musical Instruments* (Tokyo, 1959).

J. A. MICHENER, *Japanese Prints, from the Early Masters to the Modern* (Rutland, Vt., 1959).

HUGO MUNSTERBERG, *The Arts of Japan: An Illustrated History* (Rutland, Vt., 1957).

The Arts outside Eurasia

ANGULO INIGUEZ, 'Caracteristicas generales de el arte hispano-americano.' *Journal of World History*, IV (1957), 59–82.

PÁL KELEMEN, *Baroque and Roccoco in Latin America in the Seventeenth and Eighteenth Centuries* (New York, 1946), (2 vols.).

DIEDRICH WESTERMANN, 'Cultural History of Negro Africa', *Journal of World History*, III (1957), 983–1004.

CHAPTER XIII
SCIENCE AND TECHNOLOGY (1300–c. 1530)

General Characteristics

MARIE BOAS [Hall], *The Scientific Renaissance, 1450–1630* (New York, 1962). (See also Hall.)

MARSHALL CLAGETT (ed.), *Critical Problems in the History of Science* (Madison, Wisc., 1959).

MAURICE DAUMAS (ed.), *Histoire de la Science* ('Encyclopédie de la Pleiade', Paris, 1957).

T. K. DERRY and TREVOR I. WILLIAMS, *A Short History of Technology: From the Earliest Times to A.D. 1900* (New York, 1961).

R. J. FORBES and E. J. DIJKSTERHUIS, *History of Science and Technology* (London, 1963), (2 vols.).

BERTRAND GILLE, 'Le developpement technologique en Europe de 1100 à 1400', *Journal of World History*, III (1956), 63–108. (English translation in Guy S. Métraux and François Crouzet [eds.], *The Evolution of Science* (New York, 1963), 168–219.

MARIE BOAS HALL, *History of Science* a bibliography, (2nd ed.; Washington, D.C. 1964). (See also Boas.)

R. HOOYKAAS, 'Science and Theology in the Middle Ages', *Free University Quarterly*, III (1957), 77–163.

FRIEDRICH KLEMM, *History of Western Technology*, tr. by D. W. Singer (London, 1959).

PEDRO LAIN ENTRALGO and JOSE M. LOPEZ PINERO, 'The Spanish Contribution to World Science', *Journal of World History*, VI (1961, special Spanish no.), 948–68.

ROBERT K. MERTON, 'Singletons and Multiples in Scientific Discovery: A Chapter in the Sociology of Science', *Proceedings of the American Philosophical Society*, CV (1961), 470–86.

J. H. RANDALL, JR., *The School of Padua and the Emergence of Modern Science* (Padua, 1961).

CHARLES SINGER, *A Short History of Scientific Ideas to 1900* (rev. ed.; New York, 1959).

CHARLES SINGER, E. J. Holmyard, *et al.* (eds.), *A History of Technology*, Vols. II–IV [from *c.* 700 A.D. to *c.* 1850] (Oxford, 1956–8).

JOSEPH R. STRAYER, 'The Promise of the Fourteenth Century', *Proceedings of the American Philosophical Society*, CV (1961), 609–11.

RENÉ TATON (ed.), *Histoire générale des sciences*, Vols. I and II [from the origins to 1800], (Paris, 1957–8).

LYNN WHITE, JR., *Medieval Technology and Social Change* (New York, 1962).

Mathematics in Europe

A. C. CROMBIE, 'Quantification in Medieval Physics', *Isis*, LII (1961), 143–60.

The Physical Sciences in Europe

MARSHALL CLAGETT, *The Science of Mechanics in the Middle Ages* (Madison, Wisc., 1959).

——, 'Nicole Oresme and Medieval Scientific Thought', *Proceedings of the American Philosophical Society*, CVIII (1964), 298–309.

EDWARD GRANT (with a commentary by Benjamin Nelson), 'Hypotheses in Late Medieval and Early Modern Sciences', *Daedalus, The Journal of the American Academy of Arts and Sciences*, XCI (1962), 599–616.

E. J. HOLMYARD, *Alchemy* (London, 1957).

ANNALIESE MAIER, *Zwischen Philosophie und Mechanik* (Rome, 1958).

The Biological Sciences in Europe

LOUIS DULIEU, 'La peste à Montpellier', *Montpellier Médical*, LI (1957), 787–810.

T. H. GRAINGER, JR., *A Guide to the History of Bacteriology* (New York, 1958).

L. S. KING, *The Growth of Medical Thought* (Chicago, 1963).

L. C. MACKINNEY, 'Medical Illustrations in Medieval Manuscripts of the Vatican Library', *Manuscripta*, III (1959), 3–8 and 76–88.

——, 'Medieval Medical Miniatures in Central and Eastern European Collections', *Manuscripta*, V (1961), 131–50.

——, 'The Beginnings of Western Scientific Anatomy: New Evidence and a Revisionary Interpretation of Mandeville's Role', *Medical History*, VI (1962), 233–39.

——, *Medical Illustrations in Medieval Manuscripts* (London, 1965).

V. L. SAULNIER, 'Médecins de Montpellier au temps de Rabelais', *Bibliothèque d'Humanisme et Renaissance*, XIX (1957), 425–79.

H. SCHIPPERGES, 'Mondino dei Luzzi: Anatomia (1316)', *Neue Zeitschrift für ärtzliche Fortbildung*, XLVIII (1959), 340–401.

Science and Technology outside Europe

JOSEPH NEEDHAM, *The Development of Iron and Steel Technology in China* (London, 1958).

JOSEPH NEEDHAM and WANG LING, *Science and Civilization in China* (Cambridge, 1954–65), 4 vols. [to be completed in seven volumes].

LYNN WHITE, JR., 'Tibet, India, and Malaya as Sources of Western Medieval Technology', *American Historical Review*, LXV (1960), 515–26.

The Beginnings of World Geography

LEO BAGROW, *History of Cartography*. Revised and enlarged by R. A. Shelton. (London, 1965).

C. R. BOXER, *Four Centuries of Portuguese Expansion, 1415–1825: a Succinct Survey* (Johannesburg, 1961).

ARMANDO CORTESÃO and AVELINO TEIXEIRA DA MOTA, *Portugaliae monumenta cartographia* (Lisbon, 1960), (6 vols.).

H. A. R. GIBBS (tr.), *The Travels of Ibn Battūta, A.D. 1325–54* (2 vols.: 'Hakluyt Society, Second Series', Numbers CX and CXVII; New York, 1958 and 1962).

F. C. LANE, 'The Economic Meaning of the Invention of the Compass', *American Historical Review*, LXVIII (1963), 605–17.

CARLOS SECO SERRANO, 'El siglo de los grandes descubrimientos geograficos', *Journal of World History*, IV (1958), 553–81. [With further comments *ibid.*, V (1959), 509–11.]

A. O. VIETOR, 'A Pre-Columbian Map of the World, circa 1489', *Yale University Library Gazette*, XXXVII (1962), 8–12.

W. E. WASHBURN, 'The Meaning of "Discovery" in the Fifteenth and Sixteenth Centuries', *American Historical Review*, LXVIII (1962), 1–21.

CHAPTER XIV
SCIENCE (*c.* 1530–*c.* 1775)

Scientific Epistemology and Methodology

HERBERT BUTTERFIELD, 'The Scientific Revolution', *Scientific American*, CCIII (Sept. 1960), 173–92.

C. C. GILLESPIE, *The Edge of Objectivity: An Essay in the History of Scientific Ideas* (Princeton, Mass., 1960).

A. R. HALL, *From Galileo to Newton* (New York, 1963).

R. HOOYKAAS, 'Pierre de la Ramée et l'empirisme scientifique au XVIe siècle', in *La science au seizième siècle*, Colloque international de Royaumont, 1–4 juillet 1957, of the Union Internationale d'Histoire et de Philosophie des Sciences (Paris, 1957).

A. KOYRE, 'Newton, Galilée et Platon', *Annales: Economics, Sociétés, Civilisations*, XVI (1960), 1041–59.

T. S. KUHN, *The Structure of Scientific Revolutions* (Chicago, 1962).

R. MORGHEN, 'The Academy of the Lincei and Galileo Galilei', *Journal of World History*, VII (1963), 365–81.

ROLAND MOUSNIER, *Progrès scientifique et technique au XVIIIe siècle* (Paris, 1958).

NETHERLANDS SOCIETY FOR THE HISTORY OF MEDICINE, MATHEMATICS AND EXACT SCIENCES, *Dutch Classics on History of Science* (The Hague, 1961–6), (15 vols. to date).

IGNACIO OLAGÜE, 'Les changements de climat dans l'histoire', *Journal of World History*, VII (1963), 637–74.

J. W. OLMSTED, 'The Voyage of Jean Richer to Acadia in 1670: A Study in the Relations of Science and Navigation under Colbert', *Proceedings of the American Philosophical Society*, CIV (1960), 612–34.

M. L. PERKINS, 'Late Seventeenth-Century Scientific Circles and the Abbé de Saint-Pierre', *Proceedings of the American Philosophical Society*, CII (1958), 404–12.

FRANÇOIS RUSSO, 'Role respectif du Catholicisme et du Protestantisme dans le développement des sciences au XVIe at XVIIe siècles', *Journal of World History*, IV (1957), 854–80.

LYNN THORNDIKE, *A History of Magic and Experimental Science*, Vol. VIII: *The Seventeenth Century* (New York, 1958).

A. A. ZVORIKINE, 'Remarques sur l'historie des inventions et de la pensée scientifique et technique russes des XVIIIe et XIXe siècles,' *Journal of World History*, special no. 'Contributions to Russian History' (1958), 183–211.

Mathematics in Europe

J. F. SCOTT, *A History of Mathematics from Antiquity to the Beginning of the Nineteenth Century* (London, 1958).

BENIAMINO SEGRE, 'The Rise of Algebra and the Creation of Algebraic Geometry', *Journal of World History*, VII (1963), 383–406.

The Physical Sciences in Europe

MARIE BOAS, *Robert Boyle and Seventeenth-Century Chemistry* (New York, 1958).

M. H. CARRÉ, 'New Heaven of Thomas Digges', *History Today*, XX (1961), 779–885.

MAX CASPAR, *Kepler*, tr. and ed. by C. D. Hellman (New York, 1959).

A. G. DEBUS, 'The Significance of the History of Early Chemistry [a review article]', *Journal of World History*, IX (1964), 39–58.

MICHELE GORTANI, 'Italian Pioneers in Geology and Mineralogy', *Journal of World History*, VII (1963), 503–19.

HENRY GUERLAC, *Lavoisier—The Crucial Year: The Background and Origin of His First Experiments on Combustion in 1772* (Ithaca, N.Y., 1961).

——, 'Quantification in Chemistry', *Isis*, LII (1961), 194–214.

BROOKE HINDLE, *David Rittenhouse* (Princeton, N.Y., 1963).

ALEXANDRE KOYRE, 'La dynamique de Nicola Tartaglia' in *La Science au seizième siècle: Colloque international de Royaumont, 1–4 juillet 1957* (Paris, 1960).

L. M. MARSAK, *Bernard de Fontenelle: The Idea of Science in the French Enlightenment* (*Transactions of the American Philosophical Society*, XLIX, Pt. 7 [1959]).

ANTONIO MARUSSI, 'Italian Pioneers in the Physics of the Universe; Third Part: Geodesy', *Journal of World History*, VII (1963), 471–83.

J. R. PARTINGTON, *A History of Chemistry*, Vols. II, III, and IV (London, 1961–4).

ANTONIO SIGNORINI, 'Contributions italiennes à la méchanique théorique de Léonard de Vinci à Levi-Civita,' *Journal of World History*, VII (1963), 419–33.

H. W. TURNBULL (ed.), *The Correspondence of Isaac Newton* (3 vols. to date [to 1964], Cambridge, Eng., 1959–61).

HARRY WOOLF, *The Transits of Venus: A Study of Eighteenth-Century Science* (Princeton, N.J., 1959).

FRANCES A. YATES, *Giordano Bruno and the Hermetic Tradition* (Chicago, 1964).

VASSILI PAVLOVITCH ZOUBOV, 'Vitruve et ses commentaires du XVIe siècle' in *La science au seizième siècle, Colloque international de Royaumont, 1–4 juillet 1957* (Paris, 1960).

World Geography

J. C. BEAGLEHOLE et al. (eds.), *The Journals of Captain James Cook on His Voyages of Discovery* (2 vols. from 1768 to 1775; New York, 1956 and 1961).

J. L. GIDDINGS, 'Seven Discoveries of Bering Strait', *Proceedings of the American Philosophical Society*, CVI (1962), 89–93.

J.–E. MARTIN-ALLANIC, *Bougainville, navigateur, et les découvertes de son temps* (Paris, 1965), (2 vols.).

ALAN MOOREHEAD, *The Blue Nile* (New York, 1962).

CHARLES E. NOWELL (ed.), *Magellan's Voyage around the World: Three Contemporary Accounts* (Evanston, 1962).

JAMES A. WILLIAMSON, *The Cabot Voyages and Bristol Discovery under Henry VII*, with a cartography of the voyages by R. A. Skelton (New York, 1962).

The Biological Sciences in Europe

A. G. DEBUS, 'Paracelsian Doctrine in English Medicine' in *Chemistry in the Service of Medicine*, edited by F. N. L. Poynter (Philadelphia, 1963).

ERNST EKMAN, 'Gothic Patriotism and Olof Rudlick', *Journal of Modern History*, XXXII (1962), 52–63.

BENTLEY GLASS et al. (eds.), *Forerunners of Darwin 1745–1859* (Baltimore, 1959).

——, 'Eighteenth-Century concepts of the Origin of Species', *Proceedings of the American Philosophical Society*, CIV (1960), 227–34.

GIUSEPPI MONTALENTI, "La pensée biologique en Italie depuis la Renaissance jusqu'à Spallanzani', *Journal of World History*, VII (1963), 523–46.

C. D. O'MALLEY, 'The Anatomical sketches of Vitus Tretonius Athasinus and Their Relationship to Vesalius' "Tabulae Anatomicae" ', *Journal of the History of Medicine and Allied Sciences*, XIII (1958), 395–407.

——, *Andreas Vesalius of Brussels, 1514–64* (Berkeley, Calif., 1964).

WALTER PAGEL, *Paracelsus: An Introduction to Philosophical Medicine in the Era of the Renaissance* (Basel, 1958).

JACQUES ROGER, *Les sciences de la vie dans la pensée française du XVIIIe siècle: la génération des animaux de Descartes à l'Encyclopédie* (Paris, 1963).

MARIA ROOSEBOOM, 'Antoni van Leeuwenhoek vu dans le milieu scientifique de son époque', *Archives internationales d'histoire des sciences*, XII (1959), 27–46.

R. F. RUSSELL, *British Anatomy, 1525–1800. A Bibliography* (Melbourne, 1965).

C. SINGER, 'Eighteen Years of Vesalian Studies', *Medical History*, V (1961), 210–20.

Science outside Europe

FURUKAWA TETSUSHI, 'The Growth of Anti-Religious Rationalism and the Development of the Scientific Method in Japan', *Journal of World History*, VII (1963), 739–55.

YABUUTI KIYOSI, 'The Pre-History of Modern Science in Japan, the Importation of Western Science during the Tokugawa Period', *Journal of World History*, IX (1965), 208–32.

C. D. O'MALLEY, 'A Latin Translation of Ibn Nafis (1547) related to the problem of the circulation of the blood', *Journal of the History of Medicine*, VII (1957), 248–53.

G. WIET, 'Ibn an-Nafis et la circulation pulmonaire', *Journal asiatique*, CCXLIV (1956), 95–100.

CHAPTER XV
TECHNOLOGY AND SOCIETY (1300–1775)
Machines, Industry, and Power

CHARLES COULSTON GILLESPIE (ed.), *A Diderot Pictorial Encyclopedia of Trades and Industry: Manufacturing and the Technical Arts in Plates Selected from 'L'Encyclopédie ou Dictionnaire raisonné des sciences, des arts et des métiers'* of Denis Diderot (New York, 1959).

L. S. PRESSNELL (ed.), *Studies in the Industrial Revolution, presented to T. S. Ashton* (London, 1960).

R. S. WOODBURY, *History of the Gear-Cutting Machine* (Cambridge, Mass., 1958).

——, *History of the Grinding Machine* (Cambridge, Mass., 1959).

——, *The Story of the Lathe to 1850: A Study in the Growth of a Technical Element of an Industrial Economy* (Cleveland, Ohio, 1961).

Heating, Mining, and Metallurgy

JUAN FRIEDE, 'La introduccion de mineros alemanes en America por la compañia Welser de Augsburgo', *Revista de Historia de America*, no. 51 (June 1961), 99–104.

O. PAULINYI, 'Die Edelmetallproduktion der Niederungarischen Bergstädte, besonders jene von Schemnitz, in der Mitte des 16. Jahrhunderts', in E. Molnar *et al.* (eds.), *Nouvelles études historiques* (Budapest, 1965), 181–96.

C. S. SMITH, *A History of Metallography, the Development of Ideas on the Structure of Metals before 1890* (Chicago, 1960).

T. A. WERTIME, *The Coming of the Age of Steel* (Chicago, 1962).

Transport and Navigation

M. N. BOYER, 'Roads and Rivers: Their Use and Disuse in Late Medieval France', *Medievalia et Humanistica*, XIII (1960), 68–80.

J. J. MALONE, *Pine Trees and Politics, the Naval Stores and Forest Policy in Colonial New England, 1691–1775* (Seattle, Washington, 1965).

FRÉDÉRIC MAURO, 'Types de navires et constructions navales dans l'Atlantique portugais aux XVIe et XVIIe siècles', *Revue d'histoire moderne et contemporaine*, VI (1959), 181–209.

D. A. STEVENSON, *The World's Lighthouses before 1820* (New York, 1959).

E. G. R. TAYLOR, *The Geometrical Seaman: A Book of Early Nautical Instruments* (New York, 1962).

The Technology of Warfare

GEORGE CLARK, *War and Society in the Seventeenth Century* (New York, 1958).

ANDRÉ CORVISIER, *L'armée française de la fin du XVIIe siècle au ministère de Choiseul* (Paris, 1964), (2 vols.).

GARRETT MATTINGLY, *The Armada* (Boston, 1959).

CAPITAINE PICHENÉ, *Tactique et stratégie des origines à la guerre mondiale* (Paris, 1957).

ROBERT S. QUIMBY, *The Background of Napoleonic Warfare: The Theory of Military Tactics in Eighteenth-Century France* (New York, 1957).

THEODORE ROPP, *War in the Modern World* (Durham, N.C., 1959).

D. W. SINGER, 'On a 16th Century Cartoon concerning the Devilish Weapon of Gunpowder: Some Medieval Reactions to Guns and Gunpowder', *Ambix*, VII (1959), 25–33.

H. J. WEBB, *Elizabethan Millitary Science, the Books and the Practice* (Madison, Wisc., 1965).

The Methods of Agriculture

MICHAEL CONFINO, 'La comptabilité des domaines privés en Russie dans la seconde moitié du XVIIIe siècle. (D'après les "Travaux de la Société libre d'économie" de Saint-Petersbourg)', *Revue d'histoire moderne et contemporaine*, VIII (1961), 5–34.

GILBERT FREYRE, 'Impact of the Portuguese on the American Tropics', *Journal of World History*, IV (1958), 582–602.

Medical Practice, Public Health, and Sanitation

H. C. CAMERON, *A History of the Worshipful Society of Apothecaries of London*, Vol. I: *1617–1815*, edited by E. A. Underwood (New York, 1963).

GEORGE CLARK, *A History of the Royal College of Physicians*, Vol. I [to 1688] (Cambridge, 1965).

ALCIDE GAROSI, *Siena nella storia della medicina (1240–1555)* (Florence, 1958).

M. D. GRMEK, 'Ancient Slavic Medicine', *Journal of the History of Medicine and Allied Sciences*, XIV (1959), 18–40.

E. A. HAMMOND, 'Physicians in Medieval English Religious Houses', *Bulletin of the History of Medicine*, XXXII (1958), 105–20.

——, 'Income of Medieval English Doctors', *Journal of the History of Medicine and Allied Sciences*, XV (1960), 154–69.

RICHARD SHRYOCK, *Medicine and Society in America, 1660–1860* (New York, 1960).

Technology and the State

ED. ESMONIN, 'L'Abbé Expilly et ses travaux de statistique', *Revue d'histoire moderne et contemporaine*, IV (1957), 241–80.

The Impact of Science and Technology on Life and Thought

T. K. RABB, 'Puritanism and the Rise of Experimental Science in England', *Journal of World History*, VII (1962), 46–67.

RICHARD S. WESTFALL, *Science and Religion in Seventeenth-Century England* (New Haven, Conn., 1958).

CHAPTER XVI
EDUCATION (1300–1775)

European Educational Institutions

J. L. CATE, *The Scholars Got Bows and Arrows* (San Marcos, Texas, 1962).

KENNETH CHARLTON, *Education in Renaissance England* (Toronto, 1965).

COMITÉ INTERNATIONAL DES SCIENCES HISTORIQUES, XIth Congress, Stockholm, 1960, Vol. I: *Méthodologie—Histoire des universités—Histoire des prix avant 1750* (Göteborg, 1960).

L. J. DALY, *The Medieval University, 1200–1400* (New York, 1961).

M. S. FOSTER, *'Out of Smalle Beginnings . . .': An Economic History of Harvard College in the Puritan Period (1636 to 1712)* (Cambridge, Mass., 1962).

L. S. KHACHIKYAN, 'Mongols in Transcaucasia', *Journal of World History*, 'Contributions to Russian History' (1958), 98–125.

PEARL KIBRE, *Scholarly Privileges in the Middle Ages: The Rights, Privileges, and Immunities of Scholars and Universities of Bologna, Padua, Paris, and Oxford* (Cambridge, Mass., 1962).

E. KOVACS, 'L'Université de Cracovie et la culture hongroise aux XVe–XVIe siècles', in E. Molnar *et al.* (eds.), *Nouvelles études historiques* (Budapest, 1965), 197–218.

JACQUES LE GOFF, 'Les universités et les pouvoirs publics au Moyen-âge et à la Renaissance', XIIe congrès international des sciences historiques, *Rapports* (Vienna, 1965), III, 189–206.

Educational Methods and Theory in Europe

V. L. BULLOUGH, 'Medieval Bologna and the Development of Medical Education', *Bulletin of the History of Medicine*, XXXII (1958), 201–15.

A. B. FERGUSON, *The Indian Summer of English Chivalry; Studies in the Decline and Transformation of Chivalric Idealism* (Durham, N.C., 1960).

JAMES MULHERN, *A History of Education, a Social Interpretation* (2nd ed.; New York, 1959).

JOSEF POLIŠENSKY, 'Comenius and His Time', *Journal of World History*, VI (1960), 45–77.

L. V. RYAN, *Roger Ascham* (Stanford, Calif., 1963).

ALBERT THIBAUDET, *Montaigne*, ed. by Floyd Gray (Paris, 1963).

Education outside Europe

E. S. MORGAN, *The Gentle Puritan: A Life of Ezra Stiles, 1727–1795* (New Haven, Conn., 1962).

CLIFFORD K. SHIPTON. *Biographical Sketches of Those who Attended Harvard College in the Classes of 1746–50, with Bibliographical and Other Notes* (Boston, 1962).

TILEMANN GRIMM, *Erziehung und Politik im Konfuzianischen China der Ming-Zeit* (Wiesbaden, 1960).

A. S. TRITTON, *Materials on Muslim Education in the Middle Ages* (London, 1957).

L. L. TUCKER, *Puritan Protagonist: President Thomas Clap of Yale College* ('Institute of Early American History and Culture'; Chapel Hill, N.C., 1962).

Professional Training

ANNE BLANCHARD, ' "Ingénieurs du roi" en Languedoc du XVIIIe siècle,' *Revue d'histoire moderne et contemporaine*, IX (1962), 161–70.

HENRI HOURS, *La lutte contre les épizooties et l'École Vétérinaire de Lyon au XVIIIe siècle* (Paris, 1957).

K. A. KOENIG, 'Die Stellung der Anatomen unter den medizinischen Lehrern in Padua im 16 Jahrhundert. (Vesal und Fabrizio d'Acquapendente),' *Centaurus* (*Kbh*), VII (1960), 1–5.

CHAPTER XVII
SUMMARY AND CONCLUSION

PETER AMANN (ed.), *The Eighteenth-Century Revolution: French or Western?* (Boston, 1963).

HANNAH ARENDT, *The Human Condition* (Chicago, 1958).

——, *On Revolution* (New York, 1963).

PIETER GEYL, 'The Vitality of Western Civilization', *Delta, a Review of Arts, Life and Thought in the Netherlands* (Spring, 1959), pp. 5–19.

JACQUES GODECHOT, *Les Révolutions (1770–99)* (Paris, 1963).

M. B. JANSEN (ed.), *Changing Japanese Attitudes toward Modernization* (Princeton, N.J., 1965).

MARSHALL HODGSON, 'Hemispheric Interregional History as an Approach to World History', *Journal of World History*, I (1954), 715–23.

HIDEO KISHIMOTO, 'Modernization versus Westernization in the East', *Journal of World History*, VII (1963), 871–74.

KARL LOWITH, *Meaning in History* (4th impression; Chicago, 1957).

W. H. MCNEILL, *The Rise of the West* (Chicago, 1963).

R. R. PALMER, *The Age of the Democratic Revolution, a Political History of Europe and America, 1760–1800*, Vol. I: *The Challenge* (Princeton, N.J., 1959).

J. M. ROMEIN, 'The Common Human Pattern (Origin and Scope of Historical Theories)', *Journal of World History*, IV (1958), 449–70.

J. J. SAUNDERS, 'The Problem of Islamic Decadence', *Journal of World History*, VII (1963), 701–20.

INDEX

Names of persons are selected from the literary and visual arts, religion, science and technology.
Names omitted, apart from popes, rulers and politicians, are those mentioned briefly on one page only. Access to these names may be had by consulting the appropriate collective entries under place names and subject headings.

PLATES

(b)

(a)

1 *Andrei Rublev*

(a) *'The Trinity of the Old Testament'. Moscow, Tretyakov Gallery.* (b) *Detail*

(a)

2 (a) *Giotto, 'The Flight into Egypt'. Padua, Scrovegni (Arena) Chapel*

(b) *Simone Martini, 'The Annunciation'. Detail. Florence, The Uffizi*

(b)

(a)

(b)

3 (a) Masaccio, 'The Holy Trinity, with the Virgin, Saint John and the Donors'. Florence, Church of Santa Maria Novella

   (b) Andrea Mantegna, 'The Martyrdom of Saint James'. Detail. Padua, Church of the Eremitani

ECCE VIRGO CONCIPIET Z PARIET FILIVM Z VOCABIT NOMEN EIVS EMANVL . YSA.VI.C

ECCE CONCIPIES IN VTERO Z PARIES FILIVM Z VOCABIS NOMEN EI IHESVM . LVCE .I. C

REGES TARSIS Z INSVLE MVNERA OFFERET REGES ARAEV Z SABEA DONA ADDVCET.PS. LXXI . C

(a)

4 (a) *Fra Angelico, 'The Annunciation'. Florence, Museum of San Marco*
     (b) *Paolo Uccello, 'The Profanation of the Host'. Detail. Urbino, National Gallery*

(b)

5 (a) *Jean Fouquet, 'Etienne Chevalier Worshipping the Madonna'. Miniature. Chantilly, Musée Condé*

(b) *H. and J. Van Eyck, 'The Adoration of the Lamb', 1432. Detail. Ghent*

(a)

(a)

6 (a) *Conrad Witz, 'The Miraculous Draught of Fishes'. Geneva, Musée d'Art et d'Histoire*

(b) *Albrecht Dürer, 'The Passion of Christ—The Ascension'. Munich, Bayerische Staatsbibliothek*

(b)

(a)

7 (a) *Hans Holbein, the Younger,*
    'Portrait of Bonifacius
    Amerbach', 1519. Basel,
    Oeffentliche Kunstsammlung

   (b) *Lucas Cranach, 'Portrait*
    of Melanchthon'. Berlin,
    Staatlichen Museen

(b)

8   *Giorgione, 'The Tempest'. Venice, Accademia*

(a)

(b)

9   (a) Titian, 'The Assumption of the Virgin'. Venice, S. Maria Gloriosa dei Frari

     (b) Titian, 'Emperor Charles V'. Madrid, Prado

(a)

(b)

10 (a) Leonardo da Vinci, 'Madonna of the Rocks'. Paris, Musée du Louvre

11   Michelangelo, 'Fall and Expulsion of Adam and Eve'. Rome, Sistine Chapel

Alinari-Giraudon

(a)

Alinari

(b)

12 (a) Tintoretto, 'The Funeral of Saint Marc'. Venice, Palazzo Reale

13   El Greco, 'The Burial of the Count of Orgaz'. Toledo, Church of Saint Thomas

(a)

14 (a) *Annibale Carracci, 'The Triumph of Bacchus'. Rome, Palazzo Farnese*

      (b) *Nicolas Poussin, 'The Reign of Flora'. Paris, Musée du Louvre*

(b)

15 (a) *Jan Steen, 'A Terrace Scene with Figures'. London, The National Gallery*

     (b) *Pieter de Hooch, 'Interior of a Dutch Home'. London, The National Gallery*

(b)

(a)

[*Giraudon*

16 *Rembrandt*

(a) *'Portrait of a Young Man'.*
    Paris, Musée du Louvre

(b) *'The Supper at Emmaus'.*
    Paris, Musée du Louvre

(b)

[SMN

17   Rubens, 'The Rape of the Daughters of Leucippus'. Munich, Alte Pinakothek

18   *Velasquez, 'The Surrender of Breda'. Madrid, Prado*

19 (a) *Giovanni B. Tiepolo, 'Pegasus and Fame'.   Venice, Palazzo Labia*

(b) *Francesco Guardi, 'The Lagoon of San Marco'.   Venice, The Accademia*

(a)

(b)

(a)

20 (a) *Van Dyck, 'George and Francis Villiers'. London, The National Gallery*

(b) *Thomas Gainsborough, 'The Morning Walk'. London, The National Gallery*

[NG

21   (a) *Thomas Gainsborough, 'The Watering Place'. London, The National Gallery*

   (b) *Joshua Reynolds, 'The Graces Decorating Hymen'. London, The National Gallery*

[NG

22   Antoine Watteau, 'L'Enseigne de Gersaint', Berlin Staatlichen Museen

(a)

23 (a) *William Hogarth, 'The Countess's Dressing Room'. London, The National Gallery*

(b) *Jean-Baptiste Greuze, 'The Village Betrothal'. Paris, Musée du Louvre*

(b)

(a)

(b)

24 *Busts of Royalty from the triforium of the Cathedral Saint Vittus in Prague:*

(a) *Charles IV of Luxemburg, King of Bohemia*

(b) *Blanche of Valois, Queen of Bohemia*

(c) *John the Blind, King of Bohemia*

(c)

[*Giraudon*

25   *Moses figure from the Calvary* ('*The Well of Moses*').
Abbey of Champol near Dijon. Early fifteenth century

[BFM]

(b)

[BFM]

(a)

26 (a) *Veit Stoss, 'The Annunciation'. Nuremberg, Church of Saint Lawrence*

(a) Nicola Pisano, 'The Adoration of the Magi'. Detail from the pulpit of the Baptistry, 1259, Pisa

(b) Lorenzo Ghiberti, 'The Birth of Eve'—'The Creation'. Detail from a panel of the 'Gates of Paradise'. Florence, bronze doors of the Baptistery

(a)

[Refot-Stockho

28 (a) *Bernt Notkes, 'Saint George and the Dragon'. Stockholm, Church of Saint Nicola*

(b) *Donatello, 'Saint George and the Dragon'. Florence, Church of Orsanmichele*

(b)

[Alino

(a)

(b)

29 (a) *Donatello, 'Saint George'. Florence, Museo Nazionale (Bargello)*
    (b) *Lorenzo Ghiberti, 'Saint Stephen'. Florence, Church of Orsanmichele*

(b)

(a)

30 (a) *Verrocchio, Monument of Colleoni, Venice*

(b) *Donatello, Monument of Erasmo Gattamelatta, Padua*

31 (a) *Verrocchio, 'David', c. 1473. Florence, Accademia*
   (b) *Donatello, 'David'. Florence, Accademia*
   (c) *Michelangelo, 'David'. Florence, Accademia*

(a)

[Brogi-Giraudon

32 (a) *Rossellino, 'Virgin and Child'.
Tomb of the Cardinal of Portugal,
Florence, S. Miniato. Detail*

      (b) *Luca della Robbia, 'Virgin and
Child'. Museo Nazionale (Bargello)*

(b)

[Alinari

33   (a) *Giovanni da Bologna (Giambologna), 'Venus'. Florence, Buontalenti Grotto, Boboli Gardens*

      (b) *Jean Goujon, 'Tritons et Néréides'*

(a)

[*Alinari*

[SMN

34 (a) *Martinez Montañes, 'Saint
          John the Baptist'. Seville,
          Museo Provincial*

    (b) *Gregorio Fernandez, 'Pieta'.
          Valladolid, Museo Provincial*

(a)

[Anderson-Giraudon

(b)

(b)

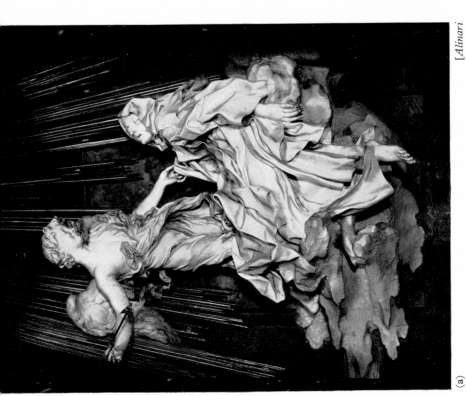

(a)

35 (a) Bernini, 'The Ecstasy of Saint Theresa'. Rome, Santa Maria della Vittoria

       (b) Egid Quirin Asam, 'The Assumption'. Rohr Abbey Church, The high altar

36　(a)　*A. Coysevox, 'Diana'*
　　　　(Marie-Adélaïde de Savoie,
　　　　duchesse de Bourgogne).
　　　　Paris, Musée du Louvre

　　(b)　*Houdon, Voltaire, Musée de*
　　　　Versailles

(a)　　　　　　　　　　　*Giraudon*

(b)　　　　　　　　　　　[SMN

(a)

(b)

37 (a) *Church of the Transfiguration, 1714. Kizhi*

(b) *Cathedral of Saint Basil the Blessed, 1555–60. Moscow*

(a)

(b)

38 Cologne, the cathedral (1248 onwards)

(a) General view

(b)

39   (a) *Marburg, Saint Elizabeth, c. 1257–83*

      (b) *Nuremberg, Saint Lawrence, the interior. 1439*

(a)

(a)

[C▸

40 (a) *Albi, the Cathedral*, 1282–1390

(b) *Seville, the Cathedral* (1402–1520), *from the south-east*

(b)

[B▸

[scu]

[scu]

41   *The Cathedral of Gerona*
   (a) *The façade*
   (b) *The nave, 1417–1598*

(a)

(b)

42 Cambridge, King's College
Chapel, 1446–1515

(a) *General view*

(b) *The interior, facing east*

[BI

43 (a) *Bourges, The House of Jacques Coeur,* 1442–53

(b) *Venice, Cà d'Oro. Detail of the façade,* 1424–36

[*Gisèle Freund*]

(b)

[BFM]

(a)

44 (a) *Granada, The Cathedral,*
         'Portal of the Pardon'.

    (b) *Quito, The Cathedral.*

(a)

45 *Mexico City*

   (a) *The Cathedral,* 1563–1667

   (b) *Metropolitan Sanctuary,*
      eighteenth century

(b)

(a)

46 *Filippo Brunelleschi*

  (a) *Florence, Church of San
      Lorenzo, 1421–60: the
      interior*

  (b) *Florence, dome of the
      Cathedral, 1420–34. In the
      background the Campanile
      by Giotto, 1334–59*

(b)

47 (a) *Florence, Palazzo
    Strozzi: the façade,
    1489–1539*
    (b) *Paris, Hotel (now
    museum) Carnavalet,
    c. 1545*

(b)

[Alinar

48 (a) *Venice, Palazzo Vendramin-Calergi,* 1481

(b) *Baldassare Peruzzi, Rome, Palazzo Pietro Massimi,* 1532–36

(b)

[Anderson-Giraudo

(a)

49   *Andrea Palladio*

(a) *Villa Capra (the Rotonda),*
    Vicenza, 1550

(b) *Il Redentore, Venice,*
    façade, 1570

(b)

(a)

[Alina

50 (a) *Rome: The Capitol (Campidoglio), planned by Michelangelo, c.* 1538

(b) *Rome: Villa Giulia (Villa of Pope Julius III), c.* 1555

(b)

[Alina

51   (a) *Louis Levau and André Le Nôtre, Château of Vaux-le-Vicomte, 1657–1661.
          Aerial view*

     (b) *Versailles, the Palace, 1661–1756. Aerial view*

(a)

52 (a) *J. H. Mansart, Saint Louis des Invalides, Paris, 1680–91*

(b) *Christopher Wren, Saint Paul's Cathedral, London, 1675–1710*

(b)

53 *The Gesù Church, Rome,* 1568–84
   (a) *The façade* (G. della Porta)
   (b) *the interior* (G. B. Vignola)

(a)

[*Alinari*

54 *Francesco Borromini*

(a) *Rome, San Carlo
    alle Quatro
    Fontane, 1665–67.
    The façade*

(b) *Rome, the dome of
    San Ivo della
    Sapienza,
    1642–59. The
    interior*

(b)

[BFM

55 (a) *Balthasar Neumann,*
          Vierzehnheiligen Church,
          1744–72: the nave
    (b) *Die Wies, Bavaria,*
          1745–54: the main altar

(b)

[GSM

(a)

56 (a) *Paris, Hôtel de Rohan, 1705–08*

(b) *Versailles, Le Petit Trianon, 1762–68*

(b)

(a)

(b)

57 (a) *Ornamental motif in the Chinese style (Chinoiserie), Paris, Hôtel de Rohan*
    (b) *The Library in Rococo style, Potsdam, Palace of Sans Souci*

(a)

58   (a) *N. Bataille, 'The Apocalypse', detail of the tapestry designed by Jean Bandol,*
          c. 1375. Angers, Musée des Tapisseries

      (b) *Gobelins tapestry, 'The Visit of Louis XIV to the Gobelins Factory', seventeenth*
          century. Paris, Musée du Louvre

(b)

(a)   [*Giraudon*

59 (a) *Italian Majolica work: plate
        from Faenza, fifteenth
        century. Paris, Musée Cluny*

    (b) *Bohemian glass,* 1592

(b)

(a)   (b)   (c)

[BNM]   BNM   [MKF]

60   *Figures from the 'Commedia dell' Arte'*

(a) *'Pantalone', Munich, the Nymphenburg, c. 1740. Bayerisches Nationalmuseum, Munich*

(b) *'Isabella', Munich, the Nymphenburg, c. 1740. Bayerisches Nationalmuseum, Munich*

(c) *'Capitano', Vienna, c. 1760. Museum für Kunsthandwerk, Frankfurt*

(a)

(b)

61 (a) *Granada, The Alhambra, Court of the Lions*

(b) *Samarkand, The Gur Amir, Mausoleum of Timur, early fifteenth century*

(a)

62 (a) *Riza 'Abbasi,
painting divided in
two parts. Seattle,
Seattle Art
Museum, gift of the
late Mrs. Donald
E. Frederick*

(b) *Muhammad Jafar
Kashani, tomb cover
for Iman Riza,
silkwork of the
sixteenth century.
Cincinnati Art
Museum*

(b)

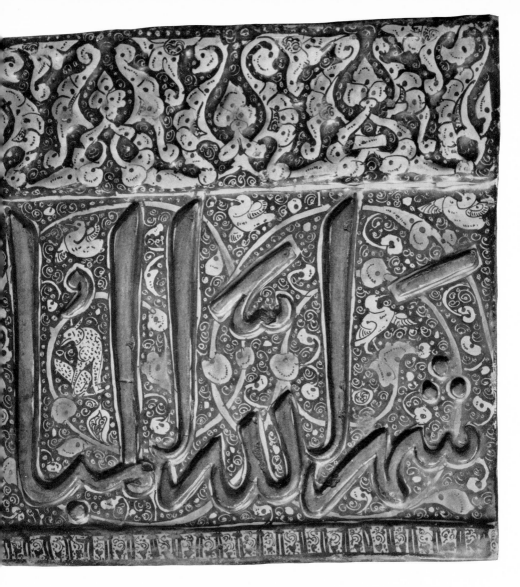

63 (a) *Ceramic tile, Seattle Art Museum, Eugene Fuller Memorial Collection*
   (b) *Kufic inscription on the Taj-Mahal*

(a)

64 (a) *Delhi, The Great Mosque, The 'Alāi Darwāza,* 1310
    (b) *Bijapur, The Ibrahīm Rawda,* 1626–33 (*Ibrahim's II tomb and mosque*)

(b)

65 (a) *Ahmadabad,*
The Jāmi' Mosque,
main gate

(b) *Agra, Jāhāngīrī's*
Palace, detail of the
colonnade

(a)

(a)

(b)

66 (a) *Fathpūr-Sīkrī,
The Panch
Mahal*

(b) *Fathpūr-Sīkrī,
The Buland
Darwāza,* 1601–
02

[*Photo Josephine Powell*

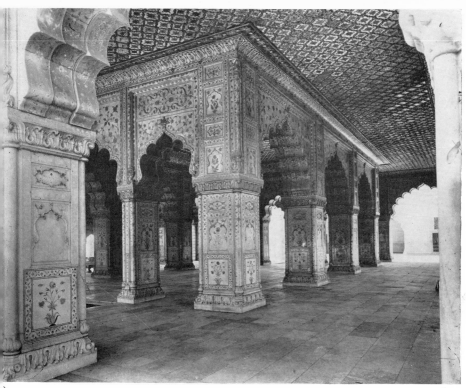

67   (a) *Delhi, The Palace, the interior of the Diwān-i-Khās*
       (b) *Agra, The Tāj Mahal,* 1631–53

(b)

(a)

68 (a) *Alwar, Darbar of Jāhāngīr*
     (b) *Basavān, Darbar Scene*

[ASI

69 (a) *Trichinapalli, the interior of the Mandapa*

     (b) *Shrīrāngam, Ranganātha Temple, columns in the 'Horse Court'*

(b)

[*Photo André Petit*

(a)

70 (a) *Hampi, Vitthala
        (Vinshu) Temple,
        the mandapa*

    (b) *Trichinapalli,
        Shrīrāngam Temple,
        the southern Gopuram*

(b)

71 (a) *Chao Meng-fu, detail from 'Autumn Colours in the Ch'iao and Hua Mountains'. Taipei, National Palace Museum*

(b) *Ni Tsan, 'Jung-hsi Studio', dated* 1372. *Taipei, National Palace Museum*

(b)

(a)

72 (a) *Lü Chi, 'Birds in Snowy Landscape'. Taipei,*
         National Palace Museum

     (b) *Shen Chou, 'Night Vigil'. Taipei, National*
          Palace Museum

(b)

73 (a) *Wang Hui, detail from a landscape, 'Mount Fu-ch'un'. Washington, Freer Gallery of Art, Smithsonian Institution*

(b) *Ch'en Hung-shou, detail from 'Episodes in the Life of T'ao Yüan-ming', dated 1650. Purchase 1954 (Acc. No. 1912.1) Honolulu, Hawaii, Honolulu Academy of Arts*

(a)

(b)

74 (a) *Tao Tchi, after the story 'The Peach Blossom Spring'. Washington, The Freer Gallery of Art, Smithsonian Institution*

(b) *G. Castiglione (Lang Shih-Ning), 'Ladies-in-Waiting in the Yüan-Ming-Yüan'. Hamburg, Museum für Völkerkunde und Vorgeschichte*

(a)

(b)

75 (a) *Kon-do (main hall)
of Kwanshin-ji
Temple, Osaka
Prefecture. Early
fourteenth century*

(b) *Kyaku-den (guest
hall) of Kōjō-in
Temple, Shiga
Prefecture*

(c) *Kinkaken (Golden
Pavilion) of Roknon-
ji Temple, Kyoto
(c. 1397)*

(c)

(a) [JC

76   (a) *The main donjon of Himeji Castle, Hyōgo Prefecture*

      (b) *Hai-den (hall of worship) of Osaki Hachiman Jinja (Shinto shrine), Miyagi Prefecture*

(b) [JC

77 Takashina Takakane, 'The Miracle Record of Kasuga Shinto Shrine', detail from the scroll painting

[JCU]

(a)

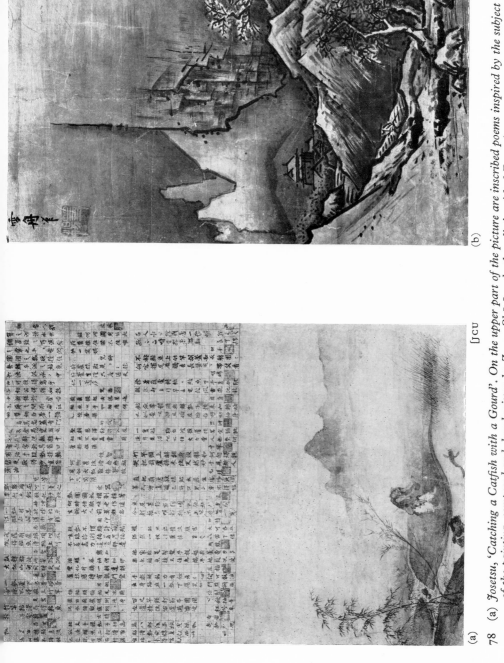

[JCU]

(b)

78 (a) *Josetsu, 'Catching a Catfish with a Gourd'. On the upper part of the picture are inscribed poems inspired by the subject of the painting, composed and handwritten by Zengu Shūsō and other distinguished Zen priests*

   (b) *Seshū, 'Winter Landscape'*

79 (a) *Kanō Eitoku, 'Kara-shishi' (an imaginary lion-like animal), six-fold screen*

(b) *Ogata Kōrin, 'Red Plum Tree' (screen)*

(b)

鈴木春信画

[JCU

80   *Suzuki Harunobu, 'Women on the veranda'* (ukiyoe *print*)

81   *Head of a court official of Benin (sixteenth–eighteenth century) (Collection P. Vérité)*

(a)

82 (a) *The Feathered Serpent, Quetzalcoatl,*
          fourteenth–sixteenth century, Mexico,
          Museo Nacional de Antropologia

     (b) *Chichen-Itza, Yucatan, Mexico. Chao-mool, god of rain*

(b)

[INAH

83   *Cholula, México, in 1581, showing pre-Conquest shrines within the colonial grid*

84 (a) *Simple microscope, silver instrument by Leeuwenhoek, c. 1673, which magnified about ×275*
     (b) *Simple microscope with six lenses and various implements for mounting different objects, made by Johan van Musschenbroek, c. 1700*
     (c) *Tripod microscope by Edmund Culpeper, c. 1730*
     (d) *Compound microscope by Cuff, c. 1743*   *Leyden, Royal Museum of the History of Science*

(a) and (b) were the best instruments for scientific work, (c) was suitable for amateur work; (d) was one of the best compound microscopes of the period, but optically it was slightly inferior to (a) and (b)

(a)

(b)

85   (a) *First illustration of cells (texture of cork) by Robert Hooke, who called them 'cells or pores', from* Micrographia, 1665

    (b) *Gnat, from Jan Swammerdam,* Biblia Naturae, 1737–38. *Posthumously published.* University Library, Leyden

    (c) *Fresh water micro-organisms on the roots of a duckweed (Hydra Vorticeldia); diatoms and rotaria, observed by Leeuwenhoek, December 25, 1702*

    (d) *Leeuwenhoek-Huygens, spermatozoa of man and dog, sketch made after a drawing of Leeuwenhoek, now lost, March 1678*

Leyden, Royal Museum of the History of Science

(c)

(d)

(a) i   *[Photo Edmark*

(a) ii   *[Photo Edmark*

86 (a) *English middle Gothic (Y-type) astro-labe, 'The Painswick Astrolabe',*
        c. 1370–
        i. *Front view*   ii. *Back view*

     (b) *Eastern Islamic spherical astrolabe, 885 AH (1480/1 AD). Signed 'Work of Músà. Year 885'. Brass and silver work*

     Oxford, Museum of the History of Science

(b)   *[Photo Edmark*

87 (a) *Model of one of Galileo's telescopes, c. 1610, Oxford, Museum of the History of Science*

(b) *English 9-foot refracting telescope, c. 1700, Oxford, Museum of the History of Science*

(c) *Reflecting telescope, after Newton, 1734. Made in London by George Hearne for W.J.'s Gravesande (length of the tube 2.50 m.).*

Leyden, Royal Museum of the History of Science

[*Photos Edmark*]

(a)

(b)

(c)

88 (a) *Paris, Louis XIV visits the Academy of Sciences. Around the king the courtiers and the academicians. On the horizon can be seen the building of the Royal Observatory*

(b) *Greenwich, the Royal Observatory in Flamsteed's time showing observers with quadrant and telescope*

(a)

[BN

(b)

[SM

(a)

89 *The Pendulum clock. Christian Huygens type clock dating from the year of the patent, 1657, made by Salomon Coster*

    (a) *The dial*

    (b) *The mechanism and the pendulum*

Leyden, Royal Museum of the History of Science

(b)

(a)

(b)

90 *Calculating machine
of Blaise Pascal, 1642:
Paris, Arts et Métiers*

(a) *The machine*

(b) *The mechanism*

[*Robert Laffont*

(a)

(b)

91 *Giovanni Borelli, De motu animalium, Rome, 1680. Plates XIII and XIV. On plate (b) can be seen one of the earliest equipments for underwater exploration*

(a)

(b)

92 (a) *An eighteenth-*
century laboratory
c. 1750

(b) *Jean-Jacques*
Durameau,
'Saltpetre Factory
in Rome', drawing,
1766. Paris, Musé
du Louvre, Cabinet
des dessins

(b)

93   (a) *The anatomy lesson, from John of Ketham,* Fasciculus Medicinae, *Venice,* 1500

     (b) *Leonardo da Vinci, Anatomical drawings*

     (c) *Vesalius, Anatomical plate from* De Humani Corporis Fabrica, 1543

(a)

94 (a) *The main ward in a hospital in the fifteenth century. From a miniature. Paris, Archives de l'Assistance Publique*

(b) *A ward in the Hôpital de la Charité in the seventeenth century. Engraving by Abraham Bosse. Paris, Bibliothèque nationale*

(b)

(a)

(b)

(c)

95   *Eighteenth-century electricity experiments*
      (a) *J. Desaguliers,* De Natuurkunde . . . (*Amsterdam,* 1746)
      (b) *Conductivity experiment from W. Watson,* Expériences et observations . . . de
          l'électricité (*Paris,* 1748)
      (c) *Late eighteenth-century electrical machine with electrical chimes and gunner. (Powder
          was put in the gun which was then closed with a cork. When spark was sent through
          the powder, the cork came off with a bang and the bells chimed)*
                                        Leyden, Royal Museum of the History of Science

(a) Corn-mill driven by horizontal water-wheel, drawing from Agostino Ramelli, Le Diverse et Artificiose Machine, 1588

(b) Grinding-mill with horizontal water-turbine, drawing from G. H. Boeklev, 1662

[SML]

[SML]

(a)

(b)

(a)　　　　　　　　　　　　　　　　　　　[SML]　　　　　　　　　　　　　　　　　　(b)　　　　　　　[SML]

97　WIND POWER

(a) *Tower mill for grinding corn, from Agostino Ramelli, Le Diverse et Artificiose Machine*, 1588

(b) *Wind-driven water pump, c.* 1560

98   (a) *Early wooden bed lathe,*
         early eighteenth century

    (b) *Rose engine, German, c. 1750*

99 THE STEAM-ENGINE

(a) *Explanatory drawing of Denis Papin's steam cylinder apparatus*, 1690

(b) *Engraving of Newcomen's atmospheric engine, by Sutton Nicholls*, 1725

(a)

(b)

100 Road building: C. J. Vernet, 'Paysage', Paris, Musée du Louvre

In this painting of the 1760's can be seen road-building activities: in the foreground the workmen are paving the road; levelling and grading can be

101 Coalbrookdale cast iron bridge of 1779. Upstream view. This is the first cast iron bridge built by Abraham Darby and John Wilkinson. Photograph made in 1904

(a)

102 TECHNOLOGY

(a) *Lifting appliance, from Agricola,* De Re Metallica, 1556

(b) *Horse-powered bellows for ventilating a mine, from Agricola,* De Re Metallica, 1556

(b)

(a)

(b)

103   CANALS AND PORTS

    (a) *Naval yards at*
       St. Petersburg in the
       eighteenth century

    (b) *Machinery for*
       operating lock-gates,
       c. 1600

(a)

104   EARLY WORLD CARTOGRAPHY

    (a) *Henricus Martellus, Europe, Africa, Asia and Japan*

    (b) *The Waldseemüller Globe Map of* 1507

(b)

(a)

[*Yale*

105 (a) *J. D. Cassini,
World Map,
Paris,* 1696

(b) *J. B. B.
D'Anville,
World Map,
Paris,* 1761

(b)

[*Yale*

(a)

(c)

106 (a) *Model of a Mediterranean sailing ship of the fourteenth century*

(b) *Model of the Santa Maria, Christopher Columbus caravel,* 1492

(c) *Model of a Dutch herring bus,* c. 1584

London, Science Museum

(b)

(b)

(a)

107   (a) *Model of the St. Michael, 1669. Courtesy of Robert Spence*
     (b) *Model of Captain Cook's 'Endeavour Bark', 1768. Courtesy of C. W. Whitaker*
                                 London, Science Museum

[SML]

[Giraudon]

(a)

(b)

[Giraudon]

(c)

108

(a) *A medieval peasant using a carruca (wheeled plough), from a miniature by Pol de Limbourg, Chantilly, Musée Condé*

(b) *A medieval peasant harrowing a field, from a miniature by Pol de Limbourg ('October', The Book of Hours of the Duke of Berri)*

(c) *Cultivation in France, middle eighteenth century. From Diderot's Encyclopédie. The engraving shows a seeder, a plough, a roller and a harrow*